Nuclear Structure

CONTENTS OF VOLUMES I, II, AND III

NUCLEAR STRUCTURE

VOLUME I *Single-Particle Motion*

AAGE BOHR
The Niels Bohr Institute, University of Copenhagen

BEN R. MOTTELSON
NORDITA, Copenhagen

W. A. BENJAMIN, INC. / 1969 / *New York, Amsterdam*

NUCLEAR STRUCTURE

VOLUME I: *Single-Particle Motion*

Library of Congress Catalog Card Number 68-57860
Manufactured in the United States of America
12345K321098

The Publisher is pleased to acknowledge the assistance of Sophie Adler, who designed the text, and Wladislaw Finne, who designed the cover.

W.A. BENJAMIN, INC.
New York, New York 10016

PREFACE

The plan for the present treatise originated about a decade ago at the time of major developments relating collective nuclear properties to the motion of the individual nucleons. In trying to describe these developments, we gradually came to appreciate that their proper exploitation required a broader discussion starting from the more phenomenological analysis of nuclear properties. We thus eventually became involved (without appreciating the time that would be required) in a more systematic attempt to evaluate the present status in our understanding of nuclear structure.

Some of our colleagues have argued that a proper presentation of the subject should start with the Schrödinger equation for the nuclear many-body system and proceed by appropriate approximations to derive the observed nuclear properties. We view the subject, however, in a rather different way. In the study of a many-body system such as the nucleus with its rich variety of structural facets, the central problem appears to be the identification of the appropriate concepts and degrees of freedom that are suitable for describing the phenomena encountered. Progress in this direction has been achieved by a combination of approaches based partly on clues provided by experimental data, partly on the theoretical study of model systems, and partly on the exploration of general relations following from considerations of symmetry.

In the presentation of the subject matter, we have found it convenient to exploit a threefold division at several different levels of organization. Thus, the exterior form is physically divided into three volumes with three chapters in each. Single-particle motion is the main topic of Volume I, but we have chosen to precede the discussion with a summary of the important symmetry features of nuclear systems, which represent a continuing theme throughout the whole book. Volume II is devoted to the phenomenological analysis of the consequences of nuclear deformations. Volume III deals with the microscopic theory of collective phenomena, starting from the analysis of few particle configurations.

The many dimensional relations between theory and experiment have led us to a further threefold division of the material into text, illustrative examples, and appendices. The text represents an attempt at a systematic development of the subject, in which each section builds only on the concepts explained in previous sections. While the main conclusions, which can be drawn from comparison with the experiments, are given in the text, the one-dimensional presentation is inappropriate in the discussion of the actual information provided by the experiments. In fact, any real experiment involves a whole nucleus, and the analysis may often require the full arsenal of available tools and a broad body of information concerning the nucleus under study. For this reason we have placed most of the discussion of empirical data in sections labeled "Illustrative Examples," in which we have felt free to employ results from any section of the book. The theory of nuclear structure and the analysis of experiments involve general tools that are more conveniently presented as separate topics, since they apply to phenomena within wide domains of quantal physics. In the appendices, we have included brief discussions of a number of such topics with a view to making the book as self-contained as possible. For example, the formulation of electromagnetic, β-decay, and nuclear reaction theory is treated in this manner with the emphasis on defining the matrix elements measured by these different processes. Angular momentum algebra and other symmetry problems, elements of statistical mechanics, and a number of simple models are also treated in appendices.

The division into text, illustrative examples, and appendixes is clearly indicated by the typography. To further help the reader, each page has been labeled by one of the familiar Chinese characters 文 (wen = text), 圖 (t'u = illustration), and 附 (f'u = appendix), which so graphically convey the distinction between the three divisions.

In the long labors involved in preparing this book we have received invaluable support and stimulation from a large number of colleagues. The material of each chapter has been the special province of a Chapterman who has helped with the collection and organization of the material as well as with critical comments on the presentation. For this important contribution we wish to thank Hans Lütken (Chapters 1 and 4), Jakob Peter Bondorf (Chapter 2), Jørgen Damgaard (Chapter 3), Bertel Lohmann Andersen (Chapter 5), Carl Jørgen Veje (Chapter 6), Peter Winge (Chapter 7), Jens Bang (Chapter 8), and Bent Sørensen (Chapter 9). The presentation has greatly benefited from the critical comments of Peter Axel, J. P. Elliott, and John Rasmussen, who undertook to read the entire manuscript. We would also like to thank Norman Austern,

John Blair, G. E. Brown, K.-Y. Chan, George Ewan, James Hamilton, J. D. Jackson, A. K. Kerman, Thomas Lauritsen, John Nagel, Ove Nathan, S. G. Nilsson, John Rogers, Léon Rosenfeld, Lev Sliv, W. J. Swiatecki, Takeshi Udagawa, Aage Winther, and Toshimitsu Yamazaki, whose advice we have sought in connection with special sections. It is impossible for us to mention all those among the members and visitors to the Institute who have contributed with suggestions and help in the preparation of the material. As will be apparent from the acknowledgements in figure captions, such help has played an important role in the preparation of a large fraction of all the figures.

It is hard to imagine how we could have coped with the immense organizational problem of bringing all the material together, and processing it through the numerous stages from preliminary version to completed proofs, if Sophie Hellmann had retired at the normal age of 70. We wish to express our admiration and gratitude for her eminent generalship of the entire campaign. The many versions of the manuscript were typed and retyped by Lise Madsen, whose endurance and devotion to the cause have been a major support. The illustrations have been skillfully and imaginatively drawn by Henry Olsen. In Sinological questions we have benefited from the advice of Søren Egerod.

Aage Bohr
Ben Mottelson

Copenhagen
August 1968

CONTENTS

CHAPTER 1

Symmetries and Conservation Laws

1-1 NUCLEAR CONSTITUTION

Nuclei are aggregates consisting of two types of particles, protons and neutrons, together referred to as the nucleons. The main properties of free nucleons are summarized in Table 1-1, p. 4.

The forces responsible for binding nuclear systems belong to the category of "strong interactions," which comprises the interactions among nucleons, mesons, and hyperons, collectively referred to as hadrons. It is in the nature of the strong interactions that the structure of each of these particles and the forces between any two of them involve to a greater or lesser extent the interplay of all the hadrons. The complexity of these phenomena is especially revealed in collisions with energies large compared to the rest masses of the particles. Thus, a collision between two nucleons with energies in the giga-electron volt range has appreciable probability for producing a great variety of strongly interacting particles. Although a number of the general features characterizing the strong interactions are understood, the basic character of these phenomena and the relationship to other known interactions remain a challenging field of investigation.

In the structure of nuclei, however, the full complexity of the strong interactions does not usually come into play, owing to the fact that nuclei are relatively weakly bound systems. The energy required to remove a nucleon from a nucleus is about 5–10 MeV, and the average kinetic energy of the nucleons in the nucleus is of the order of 25 MeV. These energies are small compared with the rest energies not only of the nucleons themselves ($Mc^2 \approx 1000$ MeV), but also of the lightest of the hadrons, the π mesons ($m_\pi c^2 \approx 137$ MeV). In the analysis of nuclear bound states and reactions at not too high energies, it is therefore a good first approximation to regard the nucleus as composed of a definite number of nucleons with properties similar to those of free nucleons, and moving with nonrelativistic velocities ($v^2/c^2 \lesssim 0.1$). The virtual presence of other particles may then be approximately taken into account in terms of forces acting between the nucleons. It appears that the main features of the nuclear binding can be attributed to two-body forces, which can be most directly studied in two-nucleon scattering experiments at the appropriate energies and in the properties of the deuteron ground state. The available data make possible a rather detailed characterization of these forces, which turn out to be of quite complicated character. (See the discussion in Sec. 2-5.) At the present time, hardly anything is known about the many-body forces between nucleons; this problem might be studied most directly in the scattering and bound state properties of the three- and four-nucleon systems.

In addition to the strong interactions, the nucleons produce electromagnetic effects and the still weaker type of interactions that manifest themselves in the β-decay processes, and belong to the category of "weak interactions." Although these additional weaker interactions play a relatively minor role in the nuclear structure itself, they are of decisive importance for the study of nuclear phenomena. Thus, they determine the degree of stability of the bound nuclear states, the states that cannot emit nucleons and which therefore would be completely stationary if only the strong interactions were present. Moreover, the study of nuclear transmutation by electromagnetic processes is an especially important tool for probing nuclear structure, because this interaction is relatively simple and has well-established properties. It may also be remarked that our contact with the nuclear phenomena ultimately arises entirely from the electromagnetic signals produced by the nuclear particles.

Because of the complexity of the nuclear forces and the difficulties inherent in a detailed description of systems with large numbers of degrees of freedom, the characterization of nuclear states in terms of symmetry properties and the application of conservation laws play a prominent role in the analysis of nuclear phenomena. The symmetry laws of nuclear physics stem partly from the invariance of the interactions with respect to transformations of the space-time coordinate system. While the invariance under the continuous transformations (translations, rotations, and Lorentz transformations) appears to have universal validity, the reflection symmetries have been found to be only partially valid. The study of nuclear phenomena has contributed in an important manner to the elucidation of the degree of validity of these symmetries.

The nuclear processes are governed by additional symmetries for which there is no apparent connection with invariance under space-time transformations. Thus, the stability of nuclei is attributed to the conservation of baryon number (see Table 1-1), which appears as a counterpart to the law of conservation of the electric charge number. The study of β processes has revealed an analogous conservation law for lepton number (see Sec. 3D-1).

Another type of symmetry is associated with the existence of the two states of the nucleon (neutron and proton) with intimately related properties (see Table 1-1). This degeneracy reflects invariance properties of the strong interactions, referred to as isobaric symmetry. The generalization of this symmetry to include the additional, approximate, degeneracies discovered in the hadronic spectrum is at the present time a central topic in particle physics.

The nucleons are fermions and therefore obey the exclusion principle, which requires the wave function to be antisymmetric with respect to exchange of identical particles. The consequence of isobaric symmetry for the nuclear structure is closely connected with permutation symmetry imposed by the exclusion principle.

Property	Proton		Neutron	
	Value	Method of measurement	Value	Method of measurement
Mass, Mc^2	938.26 MeV	Mass spectroscopy	939.55 MeV	$n - p$ difference from nuclear reactions
Spin, I	1/2	Atomic and molecular hyperfine structure (1)	1/2	Neutron beam magnetic resonance (2)
Statistics	Fermi-Dirac	H_2 rotational spectrum	Fermi-Dirac	Nuclear structure
Mean life, τ_m	$>10^{21}$ years (3)	Counting (4)	17.0 ± 0.4 min ($n \rightarrow p + e^- + \bar{\nu}_e$)	Counting protons in a neutron beam (5)
Electric charge	$1 \pm 10^{-15}e$	Molecular beam electric deflection (6)	$0 \pm 6 \times 10^{-12}e$	Electric deflection (7)
Radius of charge distribution, $(\langle r_E^2 \rangle)^{1/2}$	0.805 ± 0.011 fm	Electron-proton scattering (8)	0.36 ± 0.01 fm (0 ± 0.08 fm) (9)	Neutron-electron scattering in atoms (8)
Magnetic dipole moment, μ, in units of $e\hbar/2M_pc$	$2.79274 \pm 6 \times 10^{-5}$	Atomic and molecular beams; nuclear induction (1)	$-1.91314 \pm 4 \times 10^{-5}$	Neutron beam magnetic resonance (1)
Radius of magnetic moment, $(\langle r_M^2 \rangle)^{1/2}$	0.80 ± 0.03 fm	Electron-proton scattering (8)	0.79 ± 0.15 fm	Electron-deuteron scattering (8)
Coupling to π mesons, $f^2/\hbar c$	0.081 ± 0.003	$\pi - p$ scattering; $p - p$ scattering (10)	0.08	$\pi^- + p \rightarrow \pi^0 + n$; $n - p$ scattering (10)

▼ **Table 1-1**

1 See, for example, N. F. Ramsey, *Molecular Beams*, Clarendon Press, Oxford (1956). Still more accurate later determinations can be found in G. H. Fuller and V. W. Cohen, *Nuclear Moments*, Appendix 1 to Nuclear Data Sheets (1965).

2 C. P. Stanford, T. E. Stephenson, and S. Bernstein, *Phys. Rev.* **96**, 983 (1954).

3 The stability of the proton seems to imply the existence of a new conservation law, the conservation of nucleons. In high-energy collisions, one does observe processes in which nucleons are transformed into other kinds of particles. Thus, the conservation law must be generalized; one speaks of the conservation of baryons (see Fig. 1-11 for the baryon spectrum). There is no evidence of any violations of this generalized conservation law.

4 F. Reines, C. L. Cowan, and M. Goldhaber, *Phys. Rev.* **96**, 1157 (1954); F. Reines, C. L. Cowan, and H. W. Kruse, *Phys. Rev.* **109**, 609 (1957).

5 A. N. Sosnovsky, P. E. Spivak, Yu. A. Prokofiev, I. E. Kutikov, and Yu. P. Dobrinin, *Nuclear Phys.* **10**, 395 (1959). A recent measurement has given a neutron mean life of $\tau_m = 15.60 \pm 0.23$ min.; C. J. Christensen, A. Nielsen, A. Bahnsen, W. K. Brown, and B. M. Rustad, *Phys. Letters* **26B**, 11 (1967). See Appendix 3C for a summary of the various evidence which determines the nuclear β-decay coupling constants. Similar but less detailed information is available on the other "weak couplings" involving nucleons, such as $\mu^- + p \rightarrow n + \nu_\mu$, $\Lambda \rightarrow p + \pi^-$, etc.

6 A discussion of the present status of the experimental evidence on the neutrality of atoms has been given by V. W. Hughes, Chapter 13 in *Gravitation and Relativity*, edited by H.-Y. Chiu and W. F. Hoffmann, Benjamin, New York (1964). From experiments attempting to measure a change in potential associated with the effusion of a macroscopic amount of H_2 gas, it seems that one may set the much smaller limit of about $10^{-20}e$ for the charge of the molecule.

7 I. S. Shapiro and I. V. Estulin, *Soviet Phys. JETP* **3**, 626 (1956).

8 The radii of the electric charge and magnetic moment distributions are defined in terms of the form factors discussed in Sec. 3C-4. For a review of the experimental determinations of the form factors, see L. N. Hand *et al.*, *Rev. Mod. Phys.* **35**, 335 (1963).

9 The value in parenthesis is the mean square radius for the Dirac electric form factor. This form factor, together with the Pauli anomalous moment form factor, provides an alternative description of the electromagnetic structure of the nucleons. (See L. L. Foldy, *Rev. Mod. Phys.* **30**, 471, 1958; L. N. Hand, *et al.*, *loc. cit.*)

10 The π-nucleon coupling constant, f, characterizes the strength of the π-meson field surrounding the nucleon, similarly to the manner in which the electric charge characterizes the strength of the electric field (see Sec. 2-5a). The most accurate determination of f is obtained from an analysis of the dispersion relations for forward scattering of π^+ and π^- by protons; the coupling constant gives the strength of the "pole term" associated with the resonance process $\pi^- + p \rightarrow n \rightarrow \pi^- + p$ (occurring for negative kinetic energy of the incident π). Evidence on the coupling constant for $n \rightarrow n + \pi^0$ comes from the charge exchange scattering $\pi^- + p \rightarrow \pi^0 + n$ and is consistent with isobaric symmetry of the π-nucleon interaction. A review of the analysis has been given by J. Hamilton and W. S. Woolcock, *Rev. Mod. Phys.* **35**, 737 (1963). (For a discussion of the π-nucleon dispersion relations based on a correspondence treatment of the causality condition, see A. Bohr, 1961.) The π-nucleon coupling constant can also be determined from the analysis of peripheral nucleon-nucleon collisions (see Cziffra *et al.*, 1959; MacGregor *et al.*, 1959; see also Sec. 2-5a). ▲

The present chapter brings together discussions of the various symmetries that provide important tools for the description of the nuclear phenomena. This subject is in itself one of great scope as a part of the study of the elementary interactions. The systematic treatment of nuclear structure starts with Chapter 2, and some readers may prefer to give Chapter 1 only a short perusal and to return to this material when it is needed in connection with the later applications.

▼

ILLUSTRATIVE EXAMPLES TO SECTION 1-1

Properties of nucleons (*Table 1-1*)

The kinematic properties of a particle are characterized by the mass and the spin. These two relativistic invariants specify the transformation properties of the one-particle states with respect to space-time translations, rotations, and Lorentz transformations. (The mass and spin may be referred to as the quantum numbers labeling the representations of the Lorentz group.) States involving several identical particles are further characterized by the statistics which are manifest even when the particles are outside the range of mutual interaction. (The statistics label the representations of the permutation group; see Appendix 1C.) For the proton and neutron, the mass, spin, and statistics are listed in Table 1-1, p. 4.

The next item in Table 1-1 is the lifetime. An unstable particle is, strictly speaking, a transient stage in a collision process. However, when the lifetime τ is so long that $\Gamma = \hbar/\tau$ is small compared with the mass and other energies characteristic of the intrinsic structure, the decaying particle can be approximately treated as an entity whose properties are independent of the mode of formation. (The decay constant Γ may be regarded as an imaginary component of the mass; see Appendix 3F.)

The additional items in Table 1-1 involve the interaction of nucleons with the various force fields. The charge and magnetic moment occupy a special position in the sense that these coupling constants can be determined from classical experiments, employing macroscopic electromagnetic fields. If the wavelength of the electromagnetic field becomes sufficiently small, the interaction depends on the distribution of charge and magnetic moment inside the nucleons (the electromagnetic form factors). The leading moments of these distributions are included in the table.

The last item in Table 1-1 gives the coupling constant of the nucleons to the π-mesic field. This coupling constant is one of many characterizing the strong interaction between nucleons and other hadrons. It is, however, one that acquires

▲

▼ special significance in low-energy nuclear physics, since it determines the nucleonic potential at large distances (see Sec. 2-5a). The coupling parameters ▲ associated with the weak interaction of nucleons are considered in Appendix 3D.

1-2 NUCLEAR SYMMETRY PROPERTIES ASSOCIATED WITH SPACE-TIME INVARIANCE[1]

1-2a Continuous Transformations

If no external fields act on a system, the Hamiltonian is invariant with respect to translations of the coordinate system, in space and time, as well as with respect to rotations of the coordinate axes. In addition, the equations of motion are unaffected by a uniform motion of the system (Galilean, or Lorentz, invariance).

Spatial translations

The general connection between invariance and conservation laws is illustrated most simply by the spatial translations, by which the coordinate system $\mathcal{K}$ is displaced to a new set of axes $\mathcal{K}'$. This symmetry is of basic significance for physical processes, since it implies the conservation of momentum. In the discussion of the intrinsic nuclear structure, the translation invariance plays only a minor role, but we consider it here as a prototype for the formulation of symmetries in quantal systems.

The translational invariance can be expressed by the statement that to every quantum state $|A\rangle$ there corresponds a translated state $|A'\rangle$ whose properties, described by an observer in $\mathcal{K}'$, are identical with those of $|A\rangle$, as seen from $\mathcal{K}$.

The relation between the equivalent sets of states $|A\rangle, |B\rangle, \ldots$ and $|A'\rangle, |B'\rangle, \ldots$ is such that corresponding scalar products are equal

$$\langle B' \,|\, A'\rangle = \langle B \,|\, A\rangle \tag{1-1}$$

The transformation from $|A\rangle$ to $|A'\rangle$ is therefore unitary,

$$|A'\rangle = \mathcal{U}\,|A\rangle = \sum_B |B\rangle\,\langle B|\,\mathcal{U}\,|A\rangle \tag{1-2}$$

where $\langle B \,|\, \mathcal{U}\,|A\rangle$ is an element of a unitary matrix ($\mathcal{U}\mathcal{U}^\dagger = \mathcal{U}^\dagger\mathcal{U} = 1$).

[1] The far-reaching significance of the space-time symmetries for the description of atomic and subatomic phenomena was emphasized at an early stage in the development of quantum theory by E. Wigner (see, for instance, Wigner, 1959).

Because the consequences of the formalism are expressed in terms of probabilities (absolute squares of amplitudes), the equivalence between the states $|A\rangle$ and $|A'\rangle$ requires only the equality of scalar products to within a phase factor, $|\langle B' \,|\, A'\rangle| = |\langle B \,|\, A\rangle|$. However, by a suitable choice of phases for the states $|A'\rangle$, it is always possible to achieve either the relation (1-1) or the relation $\langle B' \,|\, A'\rangle^* = \langle B \,|\, A\rangle$ corresponding to an antiunitary transformation. An example of an antiunitary transformation is provided by the time reversal operation discussed below. Continuous transformations, such as translations, can be associated only with unitary transformations. (For a proof that the unitary and antiunitary transformations exhaust all possibilities, see Wigner, 1959, p. 233; Messiah, 1962, p. 633.)

The above formulation of the translational invariance is equivalent to the relation

$$\langle B' |\, T' \,| A'\rangle = \langle B |\, T \,| A\rangle \tag{1-3}$$

for all matrix elements. In this relation, T is an arbitrary operator expressed in terms of the variables in $\mathscr{K}$, while T' is the corresponding operator in $\mathscr{K}'$. If we view the change of coordinate system in terms of a transformation of the operators, it follows from Eqs. (1-2) and (1-3) that

$$T' = \mathscr{U} T \mathscr{U}^{-1} \tag{1-4}$$

Thus, the transformation of the position $\mathbf{r}_k$, momentum $\mathbf{p}_k$, and spin $\mathbf{s}_k$ of a particle, labeled k, is given by

$$\begin{aligned} \mathbf{r}'_k &= \mathbf{r}_k - \mathbf{a} = \mathscr{U}\mathbf{r}_k\mathscr{U}^{-1} \\ \mathbf{p}'_k &= \mathbf{p}_k \qquad = \mathscr{U}\mathbf{p}_k\mathscr{U}^{-1} \\ \mathbf{s}'_k &= \mathbf{s}_k \qquad = \mathscr{U}\mathbf{s}_k\mathscr{U}^{-1} \end{aligned} \tag{1-5}$$

where $\mathbf{a}$ represents the displacement of $\mathscr{K}'$ with respect to $\mathscr{K}$. If T is a function of $\mathbf{r}_k$, $\mathbf{p}_k$, $\mathbf{s}_k$, the transformed operator T' is the same function of $\mathbf{r}_k'$, $\mathbf{p}_k'$, $\mathbf{s}_k'$. Note that, if $T = \rho(\mathbf{r})$ is the particle density at the space point $\mathbf{r}$, a displacement of all the particles has the same effect on T as the inverse displacement of $\mathbf{r}$, and thus $T' = \rho(\mathbf{r} + \mathbf{a})$. (Examples of transformations of field operators, such as $\rho(\mathbf{r})$, are considered in Sec. 1A-7.)

The transformation operator $\mathscr{U}$ can be expressed in the form

$$\mathscr{U}(\mathbf{a}) = \exp\left\{-\frac{i}{\hbar}\,\mathbf{a}\cdot\mathbf{P}\right\} \tag{1-6}$$

where $\mathbf{P}$ is the total momentum, that is, the sum of the nucleon momenta with additional contributions from photons, leptons, mesons, etc., that may be present in the system. The transformation (1-5) follows from Eq. (1-6) and the canonical commutation relations for the coordinates and momenta of a particle.

A finite translation of the coordinate system may be generated by a series of infinitesimal steps

$$\mathscr{U}(\delta\mathbf{a}) = 1 - \frac{i}{\hbar}\,\delta\mathbf{a}\cdot\mathbf{P} \tag{1-7}$$

and **P** is referred to as the generator of infinitesimal translations.

The conservation law associated with translational symmetry expresses the invariance of the Hamiltonian (the energy) with respect to a translation of the coordinate system. The Hamiltonian therefore commutes with $\mathscr{U}(\mathbf{a})$, and hence with **P**, implying the law of conservation of linear momentum.

In the formulation of the basic laws of quantum mechanics, one may take the invariance arguments as a starting point. Thus, we may define the momentum **P** as the Hermitian operator associated with infinitesimal translations through Eq. (1-7). The canonical commutation relations for position and momentum operators then follow from the geometrical relation $\mathbf{r}_k' = \mathbf{r}_k - \mathbf{a}$ (see Eq. (1-5)).

Time displacements

A displacement in time by the amount t_0 takes us from the original system $\mathscr{K}$ to a system $\mathscr{K}'$, such that clocks in $\mathscr{K}'$ register the time $t' = t - t_0$ when those in $\mathscr{K}$ show the time t. The state $|A'\rangle$ is thus characterized by the fact that events taking place in $|A\rangle$ at $t = t_1$ take place in $|A'\rangle$ at $t' = t_1$, that is, for $t = t_1 + t_0$.

The unitary transformation from $|A\rangle$ to $|A'\rangle$ is generated by the operator

$$\mathscr{U}(t_0) = \exp\left\{\frac{i}{\hbar}Ht_0\right\} \tag{1-8}$$

where H is the total energy. Using this transformation, we obtain for the time dependence of operators (see the corresponding relation (1-4))

$$T' = T(t) = \exp\left\{\frac{i}{\hbar}Ht\right\}\,T(t=0)\exp\left\{-\frac{i}{\hbar}Ht\right\} \tag{1-9}$$

We can thus also view the conservation of total momentum as an expression of the commutability of spatial translations and time displacements, which implies that the translations are time-independent operations.

Rotations

Rotational invariance plays a decisive role in the analysis of nuclear phenomena. Partly, one may exploit the infinitesimal rotations, which define the angular momentum and spherical tensor properties of nuclear states and operators; and partly one may employ the finite rotations to define an intrinsic coordinate frame, as in the theory of nuclear rotations and in the helicity description of single-particle wave functions. The systematic formulation of the rotational transformations is considered in Appendix 1A; in the present section, we indicate the relation of this analysis to the description of translational invariance as considered above.

The unitary operator associated with a rotation $\boldsymbol{\chi}$ (specified by the direction of the axis of rotation and the magnitude χ of the rotation angle) can be written, in analogy to Eq. (1-6),

$$\mathscr{R}(\boldsymbol{\chi}) = \exp\{-i\boldsymbol{\chi} \cdot \mathbf{I}\} \tag{1-10}$$

where $\mathbf{I}$ is the total angular momentum in units of $\hbar$. The law of conservation of angular momentum reflects the invariance of the Hamiltonian with respect to rotations or, equivalently, the fact that spatial rotations and displacements in time are commutable operations.

While translations of the coordinate system in different directions are commutable operations (and therefore the components of $\mathbf{P}$ commuting operators), rotations with respect to different axes do not commute. The commutation relations for the components of $\mathbf{I}$

$$[I_x, I_y] = iI_z \quad \text{and cyclic permutations} \tag{1-11}$$

can be obtained from the relation (1-10) by considering the effect of two infinitesimal rotations taken in different orders.

The rotational invariance implies the possibility of labeling the stationary states by the total angular momentum quantum numbers IM representing the eigenvalues of $(\mathbf{I})^2$ $(=I(I+1))$ and I_z $(=M)$. These quantum numbers characterize the transformation of the states under rotation of the coordinate system. A similar characterization of operators leads to a classification in terms of spherical tensors, labeled by the symmetry numbers $\lambda\mu$. Thus, a tensor component $T_{\lambda\mu}$ transfers an angular momentum λ with component μ to the state on which it acts.

The commutation relations for angular and linear momenta may be obtained from geometrical arguments, similar to those leading to Eq. (1-11), by considering the effect of successive infinitesimal translations and rotations taken in different orders

$$\begin{aligned}
&[I_x, P_x] = 0 \\
&[I_x, P_y] = iP_z \\
&\text{and cyclic permutations}
\end{aligned} \tag{1-12}$$

Thus, in order to form states that are simultaneously eigenstates of total momentum and angular momentum, we must go to the rest frame in which $\mathbf{P} = 0$.

Galilean transformations

The properties of systems with $\mathbf{P} \neq 0$ follow from those in the rest system by Galilean (or Lorentz) invariance, which expresses the invariance of the interactions with respect to a transformation to a coordinate system $\mathscr{K}'$ moving with uniform velocity with respect to $\mathscr{K}$. This invariance applies to the nucleus as a whole, but is not immediately applicable to the description of individual nucleons moving in the nucleus, since the rest system of the remaining nucleons defines a preferred coordinate system. Thus, in the discussion of nuclear structure, we shall have little occasion to exploit this important general symmetry.

In the nonrelativistic approximation, a transformation to a uniformly moving system $\mathscr{K}'$ coinciding momentarily with the fixed system $\mathscr{K}$ is expressed by the relations (Galilean transformation)

$$\begin{aligned} \mathbf{r}'_k &= \mathbf{r}_k \\ \mathbf{v}'_k &= \mathbf{v}_k - \mathbf{u} \\ \mathbf{s}'_k &= \mathbf{s}_k \end{aligned} \tag{1-13}$$

where $\mathbf{u}$ is the velocity of $\mathscr{K}'$ with respect to $\mathscr{K}$, while $\mathbf{v}_k$ is the velocity of the kth particle, that is, the time derivative of $\mathbf{r}_k$.

If the interactions between the particles are velocity dependent, we must distinguish between the velocity and momentum operators, which are related to each other by

$$\mathbf{v}_k = \frac{i}{\hbar}[H, \mathbf{r}_k] = \frac{\mathbf{p}_k}{M_k} + \frac{i}{\hbar}[W, \mathbf{r}_k] \tag{1-14}$$

The Hamiltonian has been expressed in the form

$$H = \sum_k \frac{(\mathbf{p}_k)^2}{2M_k} + W \tag{1-15}$$

where the mass of the kth particle is denoted by M_k, while W represents the interactions. The Galilean invariance implies that W depends only on relative velocities of the particles and is thus invariant under the transformation (1-13), that is, $W' = W$. From Eq. (1-14) and the corresponding relation for the variables referred to the moving system, we obtain the transformation of the momenta (see also Eq. (1-13))

$$\mathbf{p}'_k = \mathbf{p}_k - M_k \mathbf{u} \tag{1-16}$$

The transformation of the coordinates and momenta given by Eqs. (1-13) and (1-16) can be accomplished by the unitary operator

$$\mathscr{U}(\mathbf{u}) = \exp\left\{\frac{i}{\hbar}\mathscr{M}\mathbf{u}\cdot\mathbf{R}_{\text{cm}}\right\} \tag{1-17}$$

where $\mathscr{M}$ and $\mathbf{R}_{\text{cm}}$ represent the total mass and the center-of-mass coordinate

$$\begin{aligned} \mathscr{M} &= \sum_k M_k \\ \mathbf{R}_{\text{cm}} &= \frac{1}{\mathscr{M}}\sum_k M_k \mathbf{r}_k \end{aligned} \tag{1-18}$$

The center-of-mass coordinate is therefore the generator of infinitesimal Galilean transformations. (A Galilean transformation is formally similar to a translation, with the roles of coordinates and momenta interchanged.)

For Galilean invariant interactions, the Hamiltonian (1-15) can be written in the form

$$H = H_{\text{intr}} + \frac{(\mathbf{P})^2}{2\mathscr{M}} \tag{1-19}$$

where the Galilean invariant intrinsic Hamiltonian H_{intr} depends only on the relative velocities (and relative coordinates, assuming translational invariance). Thus, the dynamics of the system can be separated into a Galilean invariant intrinsic motion and a center-of-mass motion of the system as a whole. The invariance properties of the Hamiltonian can also be expressed by the relation

$$\frac{i}{\hbar}[H, \mathbf{R}_{\text{cm}}] = \frac{1}{\mathscr{M}}\mathbf{P} \tag{1-20}$$

for the commutator of H with the generator of Galilean transformations.

The Galilean invariance is a property of the interactions and of the equations of motion. The kinetic energy, however, and the total Hamiltonian are not invariant (see Eqs. (1-16) and (1-20)). Thus, in contrast to the case of translational and rotational invariance, we obtain no new conservation law nor new quantum numbers.

The relativistic generalization of relation (1-19), expressing the Lorentz invariance, is given by

$$H = (H_{\text{intr}}^2 + c^2(\mathbf{P})^2)^{1/2} \tag{1-21}$$

where H_{intr} and H now also include the rest masses of the particles. The relation (1-21) differs from (1-19) not only in the higher-order terms in $\mathbf{P}$, but also because the total rest mass, H_{intr}, now includes the binding energy and thus depends on the intrinsic motion.

The unitary transformation generating Lorentz transformations cannot be expressed in a form corresponding to Eq. (1-17), since the center-of-mass coordinate (or the coordinate of a particle) cannot be defined in a relativistically covariant manner. The generator of Lorentz transformations can be expressed in terms of the derivative operator in momentum space and involves an additional part acting on the spin variables. (The resultant rotation of the spin vector is referred to as the Thomas precession.)

Rotating coordinate frames

While the dependence of the energy on the linear momentum follows from Galilean invariance (see Eq. (1-19)), there is no general relation for the dependence of the energy on the angular momentum since, in a rotating coordinate system, the equations of motion are modified by the occurrence of Coriolis and centrifugal forces. In some situations, these forces produce only a small perturbation on the intrinsic structure, and the energy can then be approximately expressed as a simple function of the total angular momentum, I, similar to the relation (1-19). Under such conditions, the spectrum of the system exhibits a rotational band structure. In other situations, the centrifugal effects become large, even for a single quantum of rotational motion, and there may be no simple physical relation between different quantum states with successive values of I. The conditions under which rotational structure occurs in the nuclear spectra will be an important topic in following chapters.

The energy as a function of the angular momentum, considered formally as a continuous variable by an analytic continuation of the equations of motion, is often referred to as a Regge trajectory. An exact analysis of such trajectories is possible for certain simple models, such as that of a nonrelativistic two-particle system, for which a complete separation between rotational and intrinsic motion can be performed. (See de Alfaro and Regge, 1965. For a review of relativistic extensions of the Regge analysis and its application in scattering theory, see, for example, Oehme, 1963.) An example of the ambiguities that may arise in the definition of trajectories for many-particle systems is discussed in Sec. 4-5.

1-2b Space Reflection

We begin the discussion of the reflection symmetries by considering the space inversion, which has especially simple properties of far-reaching significance for the discussion of nuclear structure. The discovery of the violation of parity in the β processes has led to extensive exploration of the degree of validity of the various reflection symmetries and to deeper insight into the relationship between these symmetries.

A reflection of the three spatial coordinate axes, which transforms a right-handed into a left-handed system, can be associated with a unitary transformation, $\mathscr{P}$, which inverts all spatial coordinates. The degrees of freedom of a particle are thus transformed according to

$$\begin{aligned} \mathbf{r}'_k &= -\mathbf{r}_k = \mathscr{P}\mathbf{r}_k\mathscr{P}^{-1} \\ \mathbf{p}'_k &= -\mathbf{p}_k = \mathscr{P}\mathbf{p}_k\mathscr{P}^{-1} \\ \mathbf{s}'_k &= \mathbf{s}_k = \mathscr{P}\mathbf{s}_k\mathscr{P}^{-1} \end{aligned} \tag{1-22}$$

The transformation of momenta and spins follows from geometrical considerations concerning the commutation of a spatial reflection with translations and rotations

$$\begin{aligned} \mathscr{P}\mathscr{U}(\mathbf{a}) &= \mathscr{U}(-\mathbf{a})\mathscr{P} \\ \mathscr{P}\mathscr{R}(\chi) &= \mathscr{R}(\chi)\mathscr{P} \end{aligned} \tag{1-23}$$

The geometrical interpretation of the reflection operation does not determine the effect of $\mathscr{P}$ on other quantum numbers such as the electric charge or baryon number, for which there is no established connection with the space-time description. We shall define $\mathscr{P}$ to be a space reflection operator that leaves these quantities invariant. It is well known that, for systems of particles governed by electromagnetic forces (atoms, molecules, etc.), the Hamiltonian commutes with such a reflection operator, as a consequence of the $\mathscr{P}$ invariance of the electromagnetic interactions. By testing the assumption of $\mathscr{P}$ invariance for nuclear systems, we can determine the extent to which the nuclear interactions possess this symmetry.

If the interactions commute with $\mathscr{P}$, we can simultaneously diagonalize the Hamiltonian and $\mathscr{P}$, and label the stationary state $|A\rangle$ by the corresponding eigenvalue π_A of $\mathscr{P}$

$$\mathscr{P}|A\rangle = \pi_A|A\rangle \tag{1-24}$$

The state of a nucleon (neutron or proton) at rest must be an eigenstate of $\mathscr{P}$, since there exist no other states with the same mass and the same charge and baryon number. Because of the conservation of baryon number A and electric charge Ze, the relative parity of states with different A or Z is arbitrary, and we are free to fix it by assigning an intrinsic parity of $+1$ for the neutron and for the proton. The parity of a nuclear state is thus a property of the relative motion of the nucleons. Acting twice with $\mathscr{P}$ on a nuclear wave function expressed in terms of coordinates (or momenta) and spin variables is an identity, and hence

$$\pi_A = \pm 1 \tag{1-25}$$

(The interaction between nucleons may lead to the production (real or virtual) of other particles (mesons, photons, etc.), but the total parity is not affected, provided the interactions are $\mathscr{P}$ invariant.)

We can characterize the various operators by their transformation under $\mathscr{P}$. For operators T which transform into themselves, apart from a phase factor, we have

$$\mathscr{P}T\mathscr{P}^{-1} = \pi_T T \qquad \pi_T = \begin{matrix} +1 \text{ even} \\ -1 \text{ odd} \end{matrix} \tag{1-26}$$

Any operator can be divided into two parts which are, respectively, even and odd under the parity transformation. For an operator T satisfying Eq. (1-26), the matrix elements between eigenstates of $\mathscr{P}$ obey the relation

$$\begin{aligned} \langle B|T|A\rangle &= \langle B|\mathscr{P}^{-1}\mathscr{P}T\mathscr{P}^{-1}\mathscr{P}|A\rangle \\ &= \pi_A\pi_B\pi_T\langle B|T|A\rangle \end{aligned} \tag{1-27}$$

which leads to the selection rule

$$\pi_A\pi_B\pi_T = 1 \tag{1-28}$$

For example, the electric dipole moment, which is a linear expression in the coordinates of the particles, has $\pi(E1) = -1$, while the magnetic dipole moment is proportional to the angular momenta in the system, and thus has $\pi(M1) = +1$.

More generally, electric moments of multipole order λ have $\pi(E\lambda)=(-1)^\lambda$, while $\pi(M\lambda)=(-1)^{\lambda+1}$ for magnetic multipole operators (see Appendix 3C). Thus, between states of the same parity we have only even electric and odd magnetic multipole transitions, and between states of different parity the only multipoles are odd electric and even magnetic. The vanishing of the expectation value of all odd electric and even magnetic multipoles in a state of definite parity is a special case of these rules.

In an effort to test one of these rules in a very sensitive way, a careful search was made for an electric dipole moment of the neutron. The experiments (Miller *et al.*, 1967; Shull and Nathans, 1967) set an upper limit of $D \lesssim 10^{-22}e$ cm on the value of the neutron dipole moment. Despite the electric neutrality of the neutron, the magnetic moment reveals the existence of electric currents comparable to those in the proton (see Table 1-1); hence, in the absence of special symmetries one might expect $D \sim 10^{-13}e$ cm, since the internal structure of the neutron has a spatial extent of about 10^{-13} cm. The above experimental limit on D might thus be interpreted as setting a limit, $F \lesssim 10^{-9}$, on the amplitude of odd parity admixture in the neutron state. This conclusion is, however, weakened by the fact that time reversal invariance would also imply the vanishing of D (see p. 20), and therefore it is not clear whether it is $\mathscr{P}$ or $\mathscr{T}$ invariance that is being tested in this experiment.

We can also express the consequences of reflection invariance by observing that, if the Hamiltonian commutes with $\mathscr{P}$, the parity quantum number must be a constant of the motion, and thus we may speak of the conservation of parity. The selection rules governing the emission of multipole radiation may also be viewed as following from the conservation of parity. We have only to recognize that the emitted photon has a parity $(-1)^\lambda$ for electric multipoles and $(-1)^{\lambda+1}$ for magnetic multipoles, and hence Eq. (1-28) may be read as an equation demanding that the total parity of the system be the same both before and after the transition. In nuclear scattering or reaction processes, we can label the different channels with their appropriate parity quantum number, and the conservation of parity tells us that only channels of the same parity can be coupled.

Experimental evidence testing the parity selection rules in an α-decay process is shown in Fig. 1-1, p. 22; the selection rules in a γ-decay process are tested by the experiment discussed in connection with Fig. 1-2, p. 24. This, and many similar experiments, establish the fact that, in processes involving nuclear and electromagnetic interactions, the parity selection rules are obeyed to a high degree of accuracy. In contrast to the nuclear and electromagnetic interactions, the weak interactions are found to violate the space reflection symmetry (Lee and Yang, 1956; Wu *et al.*, 1957). The manner in which parity violation is exhibited by the β-decay processes is illustrated in Fig. 1-3, p. 26.

The interactions responsible for β decay are expected to give rise to weak parity-violating forces acting between the nucleons, and thus to a small violation of the parity selection rules in nuclear processes (see Sec. 3D-1). Evidence for such an effect, which is of considerable significance for the exploration of the weak interactions, is discussed in connection with Fig. 1-2.

The $\mathscr{P}$ invariance discussed above involves the additional assumption that space reflection does not affect dynamical properties such as the electric charge. A space-reflection symmetry of considerably expanded validity is obtained by combining $\mathscr{P}$ with the operation $\mathscr{C}$, which interchanges particles and antiparticles (charge conjugation; see the text adjoining Fig. 1-3, p. 26). However, it has been found that even the combined $\mathscr{PC}$ symmetry is violated in the K^0 decay (Christensen *et al.*, 1964); the scope and nature of these symmetries are thus an area of continuing and exciting investigation.

1-2c Time Reversal

The appreciation of the broad implications of time reversal symmetry in nuclear systems has only developed gradually during the past decades. The main concepts and results are summarized in the present section, but since this symmetry has a different form from that of the other symmetries considered above, the subject is somewhat further elaborated in Appendix 1B. Recent discoveries have brought into focus the question of the validity of time reversal for the various fundamental interactions, and this problem is one of considerable current interest.

The classical equations of motion governing a system of interacting particles are invariant with respect to the direction of time, that is, with respect to a transformation that reverses the motion of all the components of the system. For a quantal system, such a transformation is characterized by

$$\begin{aligned} \mathbf{r}_k' &= \mathbf{r}_k = \mathscr{T}\mathbf{r}_k\mathscr{T}^{-1} \\ \mathbf{p}_k' &= -\mathbf{p}_k = \mathscr{T}\mathbf{p}_k\mathscr{T}^{-1} \\ \mathbf{s}_k' &= -\mathbf{s}_k = \mathscr{T}\mathbf{s}_k\mathscr{T}^{-1} \end{aligned} \qquad (1\text{-}29)$$

for the position, momentum, and spin variables of a particle.

As in the case of the space reflection, the effect of time reversal on properties such as the electric charge does not follow from the geometrical significance of $\mathscr{T}$. We shall pursue the consequences of an assumed invariance with respect to a $\mathscr{T}$ operation, that affects only the kinematical properties of the components of the system, in the manner given by Eq. (1-29). Such an invariance applies, for example, to the equations of quantum electrodynamics, which are known to have a wide range of validity.

A transformation with the properties (1-29) cannot be accomplished by an operation of the usual, unitary, type. In fact, a unitary transformation preserves algebraic relations between operators, while time reversal changes the sign of the commutation relations, such as

$$\begin{aligned} [p_x, x] &= -i\hbar \to [p'_x, x'] = i\hbar \\ [s_x, s_y] &= is_z \to [s'_x, s'_y] = -is'_z \end{aligned} \tag{1-30}$$

Thus, a unitary transformation inverting the direction of **p** must also invert **r** (as for the parity operation), and cannot change the sign of all three components of **s**.

It is possible, however, to express $\mathscr{T}$ as a product of a unitary operator, $\mathscr{U}_{\mathscr{T}}$, and an operator, K, which implies taking the complex conjugate of all c numbers

$$\mathscr{T} = \mathscr{U}_{\mathscr{T}} K \tag{1-31}$$

Such a transformation, which is called antiunitary, produces the necessary extra change of sign in the transformation of the commutation relations (1-30).

The effect of the operator K depends on the representation considered. Thus, if $|\alpha\rangle$ denotes the basis vectors specifying a representation, complex conjugation transforms a state $|A\rangle$ into the state with complex conjugate components in the representation $|\alpha\rangle$,

$$\begin{aligned} |A\rangle &= \sum_\alpha |\alpha\rangle\langle\alpha|A\rangle \\ K|A\rangle &= \sum_\alpha |\alpha\rangle\langle\alpha|A\rangle^* \end{aligned} \tag{1-32}$$

If we choose a new basis set $|\alpha'\rangle$ for which $\langle\alpha|\alpha'\rangle$ is not real for all α and α', the effect of K changes. For example, in a representation containing the state $|A\rangle$ among the basis vectors, we have $K|A\rangle = |A\rangle$.

Time reversal, however, is an operation with a definite physical significance, and therefore independent of the representation in which its properties are evaluated. The dependence of K on representation is therefore compensated by a corresponding dependence of the unitary operator in Eq. (1-31). Examples are given in Appendix 1B.

For an antiunitary transformation, we have

$$\begin{aligned} |A'\rangle &= \mathscr{U}K|A\rangle \\ \langle B|A\rangle &= \langle B|K\mathscr{U}^{-1}\mathscr{U}K|A\rangle \\ &= \langle KB|\mathscr{U}^{-1}|A'\rangle^* \\ &= \langle B'|A'\rangle^* \end{aligned} \tag{1-33}$$

The transfer of the operator K from its position in front of $\mathscr{U}^{-1}$, where it complex conjugates all the following operators as well as the ket, $|A\rangle$, to the position in front of B, where K acts only on the bra, $\langle B|$, is equivalent to a complex conjugation of the entire matrix element. The relations (1-33) between scalar products imply a complete equivalence between the sets of states $|A\rangle$ and $|A'\rangle$, since the physical consequences of the formalism are expressed in terms of the absolute values of matrix elements. (See the comments on p. 8.)

By an argument similar to that employed in Eq. (1-33), it is seen that the general relation (1-3) between matrix elements referring to the reference systems $\mathscr{K}$ and $\mathscr{K}'$ is replaced by

$$\begin{aligned}\langle B'|\,T'\,|A'\rangle &= \langle\mathscr{T}B|\,\mathscr{T}T\mathscr{T}^{-1}\,|\mathscr{T}A\rangle\\ &= \langle B|\,T\,|A\rangle^* \end{aligned}\tag{1-34}$$

The commutation relations assumed in Eq. (1-29) can also be interpreted in terms of the commutability of time reversal with spatial translations and rotations. In fact, since $\mathscr{T}$ changes the sign of i, the commutation with $\mathscr{U}(\mathbf{a})$ and $\mathscr{R}(\chi)$ implies that $\mathscr{T}$ anticommutes with linear and angular momenta, as in Eq. (1-29). For the time displacement operator (1-8), we have

$$\mathscr{T}\mathscr{U}(t) = \mathscr{U}(-t)\mathscr{T}\tag{1-35}$$

and thus $\mathscr{T}$ transforms an operator $T(t)$ into $T'(-t)$, where $T'(t=0)$ is the time reverse of $T(t=0)$.

It is not possible to associate a quantum number with $\mathscr{T}$ that plays a role corresponding to that of parity. In fact, if A is an eigenstate of $\mathscr{T}$, the eigenvalue depends on the phase of $|A\rangle$. Thus, if

$$\mathscr{T}\,|A\rangle = \exp(i\varphi_A)\,|A\rangle\tag{1-36}$$

a suitable change of phase leads to a state with eigenvalue unity,

$$\mathscr{T}\,\exp\left(i\,\frac{\varphi_A}{2}\right)|A\rangle = \exp\left(-i\,\frac{\varphi_A}{2}\right)\mathscr{T}\,|A\rangle = \exp\left(i\,\frac{\varphi_A}{2}\right)|A\rangle\tag{1-37}$$

The effect of the time reversal operation is therefore intimately connected with the phase of the state.

The consequences of $\mathscr{T}$ invariance may be exhibited by employing a set of basis states with phases specified in terms of their transformation under $\mathscr{T}$. We shall construct such a set in the angular momentum representation.

Since $\mathscr{T}$ anticommutes with the total angular momentum, it is convenient to combine $\mathscr{T}$ with a rotation $\mathscr{R}$ through the angle π about an axis perpendicular to the z axis (the axis of space quantization). Such a rotation also inverts I_z and thus

$$\begin{aligned}[\mathscr{R}\mathscr{T}, I_z] &= 0\\ [\mathscr{R}\mathscr{T}, (\mathbf{I})^2] &= 0\end{aligned}\tag{1-38}$$

It is therefore possible to construct a set of basis states with quantum numbers

IM, which are also eigenvectors of $\mathscr{R}\mathscr{T}$. By suitably choosing the phases of these states, the eigenvalues of $\mathscr{R}\mathscr{T}$ may be set equal to unity,

$$\mathscr{R}\mathscr{T}\,|\alpha IM\rangle = |\alpha IM\rangle \tag{1-39}$$

where α represents a set of additional quantum numbers specifying the internal structure of the states. The conventional phasing corresponds to choosing the rotation axis of $\mathscr{R}$ to be the y axis; from the expression for $\mathscr{R}_y(\pi)$ (see Eq. (1A-47)), one then obtains from Eq. (1-39)

$$|\overline{\alpha IM}\rangle \equiv \mathscr{T}\,|\alpha IM\rangle = (-1)^{I+M}\,|\alpha I\,-M\rangle \tag{1-40}$$

We have here introduced a notation, to be frequently employed in the following, by which a bar over a set of quantum numbers (such as $\overline{\alpha IM}$) designates the time-reversed state. (In the phase convention (1-39), the $\mathscr{T}$ invariance has been linked to the $\mathscr{R}$ invariance. For systems that are $\mathscr{T}$ invariant but not $\mathscr{R}$ invariant, a convenient choice of basis states and the associated reality properties of matrix elements is considered in Sec. 1B-2.)

The operator $\mathscr{T}^2$ is again a unitary operator and commutes with all the particle coordinates (see Eq. (1-29)). By acting with $\mathscr{R}\mathscr{T}$ on both sides of Eq. (1-39), and employing the fact (see Eq. (1A-47)) that a rotation $\mathscr{R}^2$ of 360° gives $+1$ for integer spins (corresponding to even number of nucleons, n) and -1 for half-integer spin (corresponding to odd n), one finds

$$\mathscr{T}^2 = (-1)^n \tag{1-41}$$

From Eq. (1-41) we may conclude that, for odd n, there are no eigenstates of $\mathscr{T}$, since according to Eq. (1-37) any eigenstate of $\mathscr{T}$ has $\mathscr{T}^2 = +1$.

If $|A\rangle$ is an eigenstate of a $\mathscr{T}$-invariant Hamiltonian, with energy E_A, the state $\mathscr{T}|A\rangle$ is also an eigenstate of H with the energy E_A. Since $\mathscr{T}|A\rangle$ cannot be proportional to $|A\rangle$ for n odd, it follows that the stationary states of an odd-n system are pairwise degenerate. (This result is referred to as Kramers' theorem and was first obtained in connection with the study of electron orbits in crystals (Kramers, 1930).) In systems possessing rotational invariance, this degeneracy appears as a special case of the $(2I+1)$-fold degeneracy associated with a state of angular momentum I (since $2I+1$ is even for odd n). In a deformed nucleus, the individual nucleon orbits retain a twofold degeneracy as a result of Kramers' theorem.

In the basis set (1-39), the relation (1-34) can be written

$$\begin{aligned}\langle\alpha_2 I_2 M_2|T|\alpha_1 I_1 M_1\rangle \\ = \langle\alpha_2 I_2 M_2|\mathscr{R}\mathscr{T}\,T(\mathscr{R}\mathscr{T})^{-1}|\alpha_1 I_1 M_1\rangle^*\end{aligned} \tag{1-42}$$

Thus, if the operator T is invariant under $\mathscr{R}\mathscr{T}$, all its matrix elements are real;

if T changes sign, its matrix elements are purely imaginary. In this manner, the transformation of operators under time reversal characterizes the phase of their matrix elements. The corresponding relations for $\mathscr{P}$, which do not involve a complex conjugation, lead instead to selection rules in the matrix elements (see Eq. (1-27)).

For a time reversal and rotationally invariant system, the Hamiltonian H commutes with $\mathscr{T}$ and $\mathscr{R}$; all the matrix elements of H are thus real, and the stationary states of the system are real vectors in the representation (1-39).

As a further example of phase relations implied by Eq. (1-42), we consider the z component of the electric dipole moment, which is invariant under $\mathscr{T}$ but changes sign under $\mathscr{R}$. Its matrix elements are, therefore, purely imaginary. In contrast, the z component of the magnetic dipole operator, which is odd under $\mathscr{T}$ and $\mathscr{R}$ separately and therefore commutes with $\mathscr{R}\mathscr{T}$, has real matrix elements. More generally, the matrix elements have the phase i^{λ} for electric multipole moments and $i^{\lambda+1}$ for magnetic multipoles (see Eqs. (1A-75) and (3C-10)).

Time reversal invariance of the electromagnetic coupling implies real relative phases for the amplitude of different multipole components in a γ transition of mixed multipolarity. In fact, these amplitudes are proportional to the matrix elements of the electromagnetic coupling between the initial nuclear state and the final state containing the γ quantum, and these matrix elements are real as a consequence of the relation (1-42). For an example of this phase rule, see p. 24.

The transformation properties of operators under $\mathscr{R}\mathscr{T}$ can be used to obtain selection rules for expectation values. Because the expectation value of a Hermitian operator must be real, Eq. (1-42) implies that expectation values of Hermitian operators that are odd under $\mathscr{R}\mathscr{T}$ must vanish. An example is provided by the electric dipole moment D, which is the expectation value of the z component of the dipole operator, in the magnetic substate $M = I$. The very small upper limit that can be set experimentally on the dipole moment of the neutron (see p. 15) must therefore be taken as a measure of the amplitude in the neutron state associated with the violation of both $\mathscr{P}$ and $\mathscr{T}$.

There are also important consequences of $\mathscr{T}$ invariance for nuclear scattering and reaction processes. The states describing such processes, although they may have a definite energy, are quasistationary, since they are associated with a direction in time (a difference between final and initial conditions). The time reversal operator therefore inverts not only the momenta and spins of the particles involved in the reaction, but also the direction of the processes themselves. Thus, $\mathscr{T}$ symmetry relates a reaction to its inverse (see Sec. 1B-3).

Tests of $\mathscr{T}$ invariance in scattering and reaction processes are illustrated in Figs. 1-4 and 1-6. The experimental evidence is consistent with time reversal invariance for the nuclear interactions, but is much less precise than in the case of space reflection invariance (see above); it is possible to conclude that, if there is a part of the nuclear interaction that changes sign under $\mathscr{T}$, it must be at least two orders of magnitude weaker than the invariant part of the interaction. The $\mathscr{T}$ invariance of the electromagnetic and weak interaction processes in the nucleus have been tested with a similar accuracy. (See, for example, the test of the phase rule for electromagnetic transitions of mixed multipolarity by Kistner, 1967, and the evidence on correlations in β decay quoted in connection with Fig. 1-3. For a further discussion of tests of time reversal in nuclear processes, see Henley and Jacobsohn, 1959.)

The combined reflection symmetry $\mathscr{PCT}$, where $\mathscr{C}$ is the charge conjugation (see p. 16), can be shown to follow from relativistic invariance together with certain rather general assumptions regarding the locality of interactions. (See, for example, Kemmer *et al.*, 1959; Streater and Wightman, 1964, give a discussion involving only Memorable Concepts.) If one accepts these assumptions, the validity of $\mathscr{T}$ invariance becomes equivalent to the validity of $\mathscr{PC}$ invariance. The evidence for $\mathscr{PC}$ violation in K° decay (see p. 16) thus implies a corresponding breakdown of $\mathscr{T}$ invariance. For a discussion of experiments testing $\mathscr{PCT}$ invariance, see Lee and Wu (1965 and 1966).

▼

ILLUSTRATIVE EXAMPLES TO SECTION 1-2

Test of parity conservation in α decay (Fig. 1-1)

An α-decay process leading to a daughter nucleus in a $0+$ state (for example, the ground state of an even-even nucleus) is governed by a simple parity selection rule. The final state of the process associated with two particles, each with spin zero (the α particle and the daughter nucleus), has a total angular momentum equal to the orbital angular momentum of relative motion ($I = L$) and a total parity given by the parity of this relative motion $(\pi = (-1)^L = (-1)^I)$. The law of conservation of parity thus forbids the α decay for states in the parent nucleus with $\pi = -(-1)^I$ (that is, with $I\pi = 0-, 1+, 2-, \ldots$).

This selection rule accounts for the stability against α emission observed for a number of states in ^{16}O with energies above the threshold for α decay to the ^{12}C ground state (see Fig. 1-1). Among these states is the 8.88 MeV level, which can be populated by allowed β decay of ^{16}N. Since the ground state of ^{16}N has $I\pi = 2-$, as follows from the shape of the β spectrum for the branch leading to the ^{16}O ground state, the 8.88 MeV level in ^{16}O must have negative parity and $I = 1, 2$, or 3. Its α stability thus suggests a $2-$ assignment, and this is confirmed by the observed angular correlations exhibited by the γ decay.

▲ A very careful search for an α-decay branch from the 8.88 MeV level has

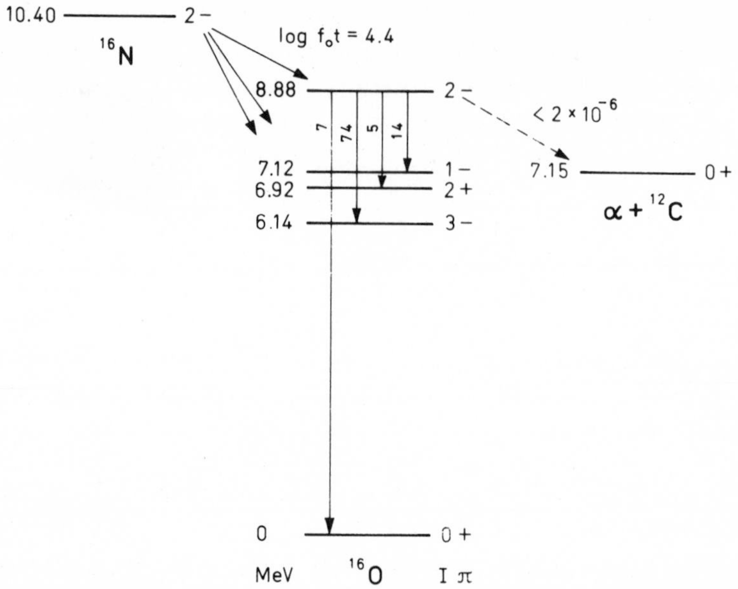

Figure 1-1 The upper limit for the α branch from the 8.8 MeV state in ^{16}O has been established by R. E. Segel, J. W. Olness, and E. L. Sprenkel, *Phil. Mag.* **6**, 163 (1961) and *Phys. Rev.* **123**, 1382 (1961). The additional information in the figure is taken from the compilation by F. Ajzenberg-Selove and T. Lauritsen, *Nuclear Phys.* **11**, 1 (1959). All energies are measured from the ground state of ^{16}O.

established the upper limit of 2×10^{-6} for the ratio of α- and γ-decay probabilities (see Fig. 1-1).

The rate of γ emission has not been measured experimentally, but can be estimated if one assumes the 8.88 MeV level to be approximately described in terms of the particle-hole configuration $(p_{1/2}^{-1}d_{5/2})$; $I = 2$, $T = 0$. (See the discussion of the ^{16}O spectrum in Chapter 7.) For the $M2$ transition to the ground state, we then obtain (using Eqs. (3B-25) and (3C-37) and the fact that the $T = 0$ excitation involves a symmetric combination of neutron and proton excitations) the transition probability $B(M2; 2- \rightarrow 0+) \approx 1.2 \times 10^{-26}(e\hbar/2Mc)^2$ cm^2, corresponding to a partial width of $(\Gamma_\gamma)_{2- \rightarrow 0+} \approx 6 \times 10^{-4}$ eV (see Eq. (3C-18)). The decay to the ground state accounts for 7% of the total decay, and the above estimate of the partial width implies $(\Gamma_\gamma)_{\text{total}} \approx 10^{-2}$ eV.

The rate of the γ transition, $2- \rightarrow 0+$, however, is very sensitive to configuration mixtures, and estimates indicate that such correlations lead to a reduction of the partial width by a factor of about 10 (Elliott and Flowers, 1957). The observation that the 8.88 MeV level is not strongly excited in inelastic proton scattering also indicates that the transition is weaker than the pure single-particle picture would imply. In view of the uncertainties in the detailed interpretation of the ^{16}O excitation spectrum, we take the above estimate of Γ_γ as a conservative upper limit, which implies $\Gamma_\alpha < 2 \times 10^{-8}$ eV. In contrast, a

▼ 2+ level at the same energy, with unit reduced width (see Eq. (3F-65)), would have $\Gamma_\alpha \approx (\Gamma_\alpha)_{sp} \approx 60$ keV. The experimental data thus imply a retardation factor of the order of 3×10^{12} or more.

In the presence of small amounts of parity-violating forces, the α decay could take place by an admixture of a small component of a 2+ state into the wave function for the ^{16}O level, or by an admixture of a 0− state into the ^{12}C or α wave functions. The order of magnitude, ε, of such admixtures roughly corresponds to the ratio of parity-violating to parity-conserving forces. Since the α width is proportional to ε^2, the experiment indicates that ε does not greatly exceed 10^{-6}. A quantitative conclusion, however, would require a more detailed analysis of the effects of parity-violating forces on the wave functions for the initial and final states of the process as well as of the mechanism by which the α emission takes place.

Search for parity admixtures of nuclear states by analysis of circular polarization of γ radiation (Fig. 1-2)

The assumption of $\mathscr{P}$ invariance implies that the properties of γ rays emitted by a nucleus in a state of definite parity are invariant with respect to a reflection in the origin. Such a reflection inverts the direction of propagation of the γ rays without affecting their angular momenta. The circular polarization represents the component of angular momentum along the direction of propagation (the helicity) and thus changes sign under the reflection. Hence, it follows from $\mathscr{P}$ symmetry that the number of right-hand polarized γ rays emitted in any given direction equals the number of left-handed quanta emitted in the opposite direction. If the radiating nuclei are randomly oriented, the radiation is isotropic and the circular polarization vanishes in all directions.

An especially careful search for a violation of this parity rule has been made for the 482 keV transition in ^{181}Ta, shown in Fig. 1-2. The excited state is populated in the β decay of ^{181}Hf and, since the β rays are not detected, we are dealing with γ radiation from randomly oriented nuclei. The circular polarization of the radiation is analyzed by the scattering on magnetized iron.

The 482 keV radiation is predominantly of mixed $M1 + E2$ character, and a presence of circular polarization thus requires a small admixture of $E1$ or $M2$ radiation. Since $M2$ radiation is intrinsically much weaker than $E1$ radiation, the main contribution is expected from $E1$ admixture. With such an admixture, a circular polarization arises from the interference between the $E1$ and $M1$ components of the radiation. (For randomly oriented nuclei, there can be no interference between radiations of different multipole order λ.) A fully circularly polarized photon ($h = \pm 1$) is a superposition of equal amounts of states with opposite parities

$$|\lambda h = \pm 1\rangle = \frac{1}{\sqrt{2}}(|E\lambda\rangle \pm |M\lambda\rangle)$$

▲ as follows from the fact that the states with opposite helicity transform into each

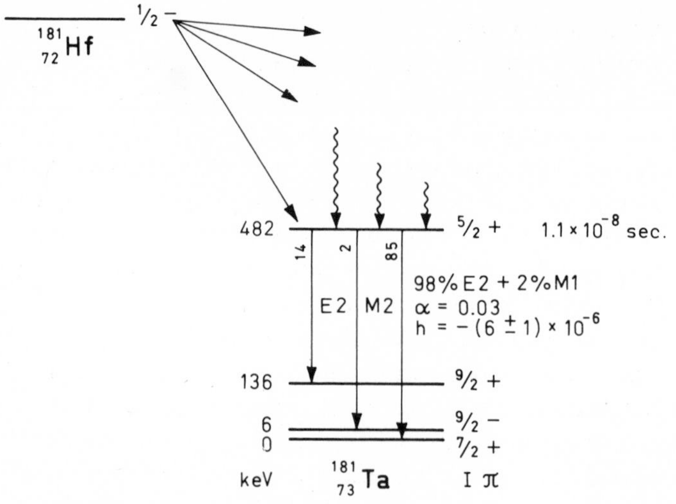

Figure 1-2 The circular polarization h of the 482 keV γ ray in ^{181}Ta has been measured by V. M. Lobashov, V. A. Nazarenko, L. F. Saenko, L. M. Smotritsky, and G. I. Kharkevitch, *Phys. Letters*, **25B**, 104 (1967). The additional information in the figure is taken from *Table of Isotopes* by Lederer *et al.* (1967).

▼ other under the parity transformation. (The transformation coefficients are real if the states λh, $E\lambda$, and $M\lambda$ have the standard phasing ($\mathscr{R}\mathscr{T} = 1$; see Eq. (1-39)).) Hence $\langle h \rangle = 2c(E1)\, c(M1)$, where $c(E1)$ and $c(M1)$ are the amplitudes of the $E1$ and $M1$ radiation, normalized to a total strength of unity $\left(c^2(E2) + c^2(M1) + c^2(E1) \approx c^2(E2) + c^2(M1) = 1\right)$. This assumes real relative amplitudes for the different multipole components, as required by time reversal invariance (see p. 20). If $\mathscr{T}$ invariance is also violated, the value of $\langle h \rangle$ is reduced ($\langle h \rangle = 2\,\mathrm{Re}\{c(E1)c(M1)\}$) and vanishes if $c(E1)$ and $c(M1)$ are 90° out of phase (maximal $\mathscr{T}$ violation). The experiment thus provides a test for interactions violating parity, but conserving time reversal.

Since the $M1$ admixture is $c^2(M1) = 2 \times 10^{-2}$, a circular polarization of -6×10^{-6} (see Fig. 1-2) implies $c^2(E1) \approx 4 \times 10^{-10}$. From the measured half-life of the 482 keV level and the observation that $85\%(1 - 0.03) = 82\%$ of the decays are associated with the 482 keV γ transition, we obtain a total γ-decay rate $T_\gamma(482) \approx 5 \times 10^7\ \mathrm{sec}^{-1}$. Thus, the partial $E1$ decay rate becomes $T(E1) \approx 2 \times 10^{-2}\ \mathrm{sec}^{-1}$, corresponding to a reduced transition probability $B(E1;\, 5/2 \rightarrow 7/2) \approx 10^{-42} e^2\ \mathrm{cm}^2$ (see Eq. (3C-18)).

The ground state and the 482 keV level in ^{181}Ta can be described in terms of different single-particle states for the last proton moving in a spheroidal potential, and we may therefore compare the observed $B(E1)$ value with that expected for a single-particle $E1$ transition in such a nucleus. The 482 keV level has the quantum numbers [402 5/2] (see Chapter 5) and is connected by an

▲ unhindered $E1$ transition to the level [503 7/2], $I = 7/2$, having the same K, I

▼ values as the ground state. For harmonic oscillator wave functions, the strength of this transition is (see Chapters 4 and 5) $B(E1; [402\ 5/2], I = 5/2 \rightarrow [503\ 7/2], I = 7/2) \approx 10^{-26} e^2\ \text{cm}^2$. A $B(E1)$ value for the 482 keV decay of the magnitude indicated thus corresponds to a retardation factor of the order of 10^{-16}.

One may attempt to describe the effect of parity-violating interactions in terms of an average pseudoscalar field. If we require time reversal invariance, such a one-particle field must be velocity dependent (since $\boldsymbol{\sigma} \cdot \mathbf{r}$ is odd with respect to $\mathscr{T}$), and if we restrict ourselves to first order in the velocity, the field is of the form $(Mc)^{-1}\{\boldsymbol{\sigma} \cdot \mathbf{p} V_{\text{odd}}(\mathbf{r}) + V_{\text{odd}}(\mathbf{r}) \boldsymbol{\sigma} \cdot \mathbf{p}\}$. The presence of a pseudoscalar component in the field implies that the predominantly positive parity single-particle states will contain small components of negative parity. The negative parity states associated with large $E1$ transition matrix elements (such as the [503 7/2] state considered above) occur at excitation energies of 5–10 MeV, and a $B(E1)$ value of the magnitude considered thus indicates a parity-violating coupling matrix element of the order of 10^{-1} eV, corresponding to a pseudoscalar potential V_{odd} of order 10^{-8} as compared with the scalar potential.

Parity-violating interactions of such an order of magnitude can be interpreted within the framework of the theory of weak interactions. If these interactions are assumed to operate not only between nucleons and leptons, but also among the nucleons themselves, they produce parity-violating nuclear forces of strength 10^{-6} to 10^{-7} as compared with the strong interactions. (See Sec. 3D-1b; the nucleon-lepton coupling acting in second order also produces parity-violating nuclear forces, but of much smaller magnitude ($\sim 10^{-12}$).)

An attempt at a quantitative analysis of the parity-violating effect implied by the weak interactions involves a critical examination of a number of points.

(a) An estimate of the effective nuclear two-body forces implied by the weak interactions. These forces may be expected to have considerable complexity resulting from the interplay between the strong and weak interactions.

(b) A derivation of the average parity-violating field implied by these forces and an estimate of the possible significance of more specific two-particle interaction effects. (Some aspects of the problems (a) and (b) have been considered by Blin-Stoyle, 1960, and by Michel, 1964.)

(c) A detailed analysis of the effect of the parity-violating field on the one-particle motion. (Aspects of this problem have been considered by Wahlborn, 1965.)

Parity violation in β decay. Test of time reversal invariance (Fig. 1-3)

The violation of parity in weak interaction processes has been established by the observation of a number of correlation effects showing a departure from mirror symmetry.

Figure 1-3 gives a schematic illustration of such a correlation, between the
▲ orientation, $\mathbf{I}$, of the parent nucleus and the direction, $\mathbf{p}_\beta$, of the emitted β

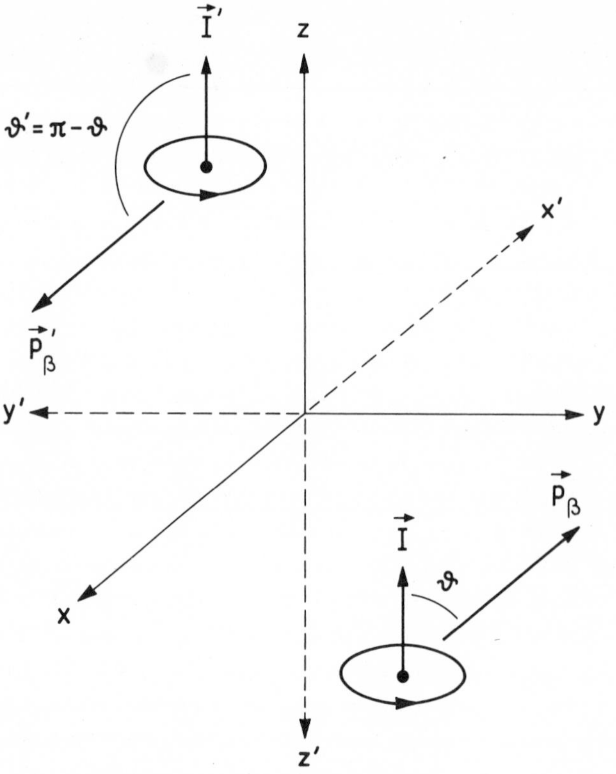

Figure 1-3 Violation of reflection symmetry in β decay.

particle. If the decaying system possesses a definite parity which is conserved during the process, the system is identical to its mirror image obtained by a reflection in the origin. (The states $|A\rangle$ and $|A'\rangle = \mathscr{P}|A\rangle = \pi_A|A\rangle$ differ only by a phase factor.) Space inversion symmetry would thus imply that the number of β particles emitted at an angle ϑ with respect to the direction of orientation is equal to the number emitted at an angle $\pi - \vartheta$. In fact, however, one observes large forward-backward asymmetries in these processes. The first discovery of parity violation was based on an experiment of this type, involving a polarized source of ^{60}Co nuclei (Wu *et al.*, 1957).

One can also express the observed departure from reflection symmetry in terms of the nonvanishing expectation value of the quantity $\mathbf{I} \cdot \mathbf{p}_\beta$. This product is a pseudoscalar (a rotational invariant that changes sign under reflections) and its expectation value thus vanishes for a state of definite parity. Examples of other pseudoscalar correlations observed in β-decay processes are $\langle \mathbf{s}_\beta \cdot \mathbf{p}_\beta \rangle$ (helicity of β particles emitted by randomly oriented nuclei) and $\langle (\mathbf{p}_\beta \cdot \mathbf{p}_\gamma)(\mathbf{s}_\gamma \cdot \mathbf{p}_\gamma) \rangle$ (circular polarization of γ rays following β emission from randomly oriented nuclei).

The parity selection rules that can be formulated in terms of the vanishing of expectation values for pseudoscalar quantities have a semiclassical

▼ significance, since they directly express the internal reflection symmetry of the system. Further selection rules, with no classical analogs, involve the parity quantum numbers; thus, for example, in a two-particle decay process ($A \rightarrow B + C$), the conservation of parity implies $\pi_A = \pi_B \pi_C(-1)^L$, where L is the angular momentum in the relative motion of B and C; an example of this selection rule is discussed in Fig. 1-1.

The assumption of $\mathscr{PC}$ invariance implies that a decaying antiparticle is the mirror image of a decaying particle (with the same polarization), and thus pseudoscalar correlations are of equal magnitude and opposite sign for the decay of particle and antiparticle. It has not so far been possible to test this symmetry directly for the decay of nuclei or nucleons, but $\mathscr{PC}$ invariance has been established for the decay of π and μ mesons. Thus, the helicities of the μ particles in π decay are found to be opposite for π^+ and π^- and the μ^- decay is also observed to be the mirror of the μ^+ decay (see, for example, Alikhanov *et al.*, 1960). Evidence for a small violation of $\mathscr{PC}$ in K^0 decay is mentioned on p. 16.

The $\mathscr{T}$ transformation directly relates a decay process to the inverse process of formation, which, in the case of β decay, would involve the experimentally difficult reaction by which an electron-neutrino pair is captured by the daughter nucleus. The final state of the decay and the initial state in the formation process differ not only in the direction of motion (and spins) of the particles, but also in the phase shift caused by the interaction between the particles (which is of opposite sign for the two states). By compensating for this phase shift (the Coulomb phase shift in the case of β decay), one can obtain relationships among the decay amplitudes themselves, expressing the consequence of $\mathscr{T}$ invariance (see Eq. (1B-39)).

The situation is especially simple if the final state interaction can be neglected, as in the case of γ decay and, approximately, for β decay of light nuclei. The consequences of $\mathscr{T}$ invariance then become quite analogous to those of $\mathscr{P}$ invariance, and imply the vanishing of expectation values of quantities that are odd under $\mathscr{T}$.

Whereas the correlations considered above, such as $\mathbf{I} \cdot \mathbf{p}_\beta$ and $\mathbf{s}_\beta \cdot \mathbf{p}_\beta$, are even under $\mathscr{T}$, an example of a correlation which changes sign under $\mathscr{T}$ is provided by $\mathbf{I} \cdot \mathbf{p}_\beta \times \mathbf{p}_R$, where $\mathbf{p}_R$ is the momentum of the recoiling nucleus. The quantity $\langle \mathbf{I} \cdot \mathbf{p}_\beta \times \mathbf{p}_R \rangle$ has been measured in the neutron decay and is found to be less than about 10% of its maximum value $I p_\beta p_R$ (see Wu and Moszkowski, 1966, p. 180). For the β decay of ^{19}Ne, the validity of the time reversal relations has been established to an accuracy of a few percent (Calaprice *et al.*, 1967).

Comparison of cross sections for inverse reactions (Fig. 1-4)

The time reversal symmetry relates the cross sections of the inverse reactions $a_1 + a_2 \rightleftarrows b_1 + b_2$. The symmetry of the scattering amplitude associated ▲

▼ with $\mathscr{T}$ invariance is discussed in Sec. 1B-3. From the relation (1B-29) for the S-matrix element, together with the expressions (1B-31) and (1B-34) for the scattering amplitudes and cross sections, it follows that cross sections for inverse reactions satisfy the condition

$$\frac{d\sigma(a_1 + a_2 \to b_1 + b_2)}{d\sigma(b_1 + b_2 \to a_1 + a_2)} = \frac{p_b^2(2b_1 + 1)(2b_2 + 1)}{p_a^2(2a_1 + 1)(2a_2 + 1)} \tag{1-43}$$

The differential cross sections for the inverse processes refer to the same total energy and scattering angle, in the center-of-mass system, and the spins of the particles are denoted by a_1, and so on. The cross sections in Eq. (1-43) refer to unpolarized particles and thus represent averages over the initial polarizations ▲ and sums over final polarizations.

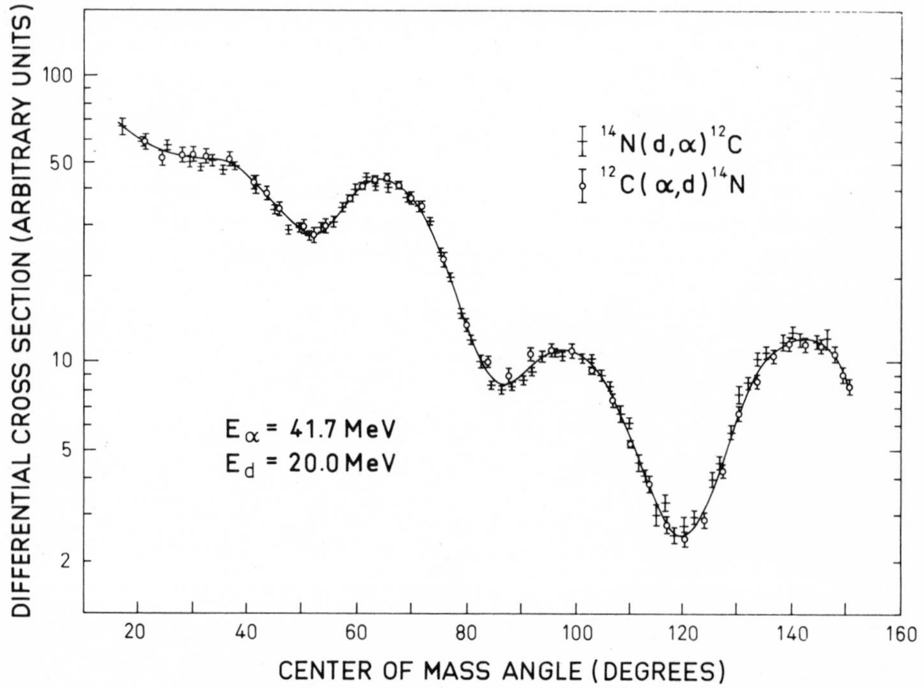

Figure 1-4 The figure shows cross sections for inverse reactions as given by D. Bodansky, S. F. Eccles, G. W. Farwell, M. E. Rickey, and P. C. Robinson, *Phys. Rev. Letters* **2**, 101 (1959).

▼ The right-hand side of the above relation (1-43) is independent of the scattering angle, and this independence has been tested in the reactions $\alpha + {}^{12}C \rightleftarrows d + {}^{14}N$ as illustrated in Fig. 1-4. No absolute determination of ▲ cross sections was made. The relative cross sections for the reactions are very similar; the deviations amount on the average to about 5%, which is also the estimated experimental uncertainty.

Recent studies of the inverse reactions $^{24}Mg + d \rightleftarrows {}^{25}Mg + p$ (Bodansky *et al.*, 1966) and $^{24}Mg + \alpha \rightleftarrows {}^{27}Al + p$ (von Witsch *et al.*, 1967) have tested the reciprocity relation (1-43) to an accuracy of a fraction of a percent.

Polarization asymmetry relation in elastic scattering (*Figs. 1-5 and 1-6*)

The time reversal symmetry relates the polarization of a final particle in a reaction $a_1 + a_2 \rightarrow b_1 + b_2$ to the azimuthal asymmetry in the inverse process with polarized particles.

As an example we consider the elastic nuclear scattering of an incident particle of spin 1/2 (for example, n, p, or ^{3}H). We denote by $\sigma(R; m_s \rightarrow m_s')$ the cross section for the scattering process R (right-handed deflection) with m_s and m_s' specifying the polarization of the incident and the scattered particle in a direction normal to the collision plane (see Fig. 1-5). The cross section represents

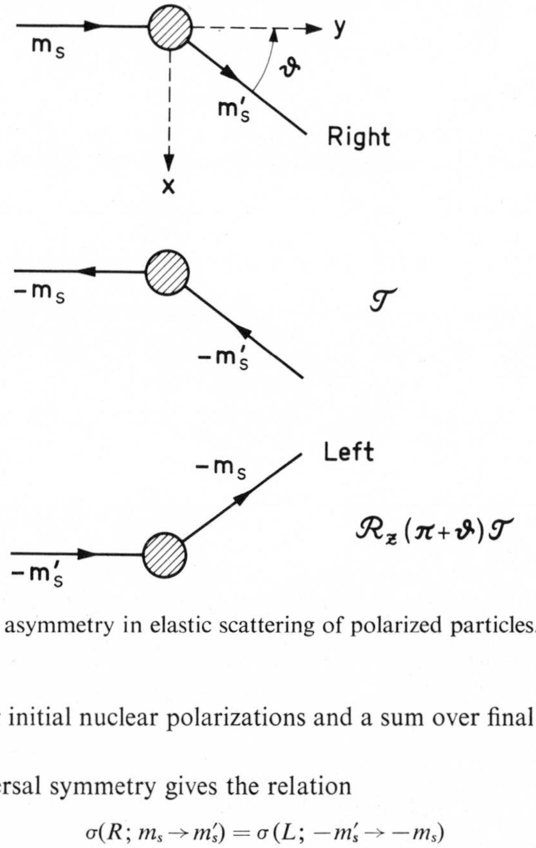

Figure 1-5 Right-left asymmetry in elastic scattering of polarized particles.

an average over initial nuclear polarizations and a sum over final nuclear polarizations.

Time reversal symmetry gives the relation

$$\sigma(R; m_s \rightarrow m_s') = \sigma(L; -m_s' \rightarrow -m_s) \tag{1-44}$$

since, after a rotation about the z axis by the angle $\pi + \vartheta$, the inverse process goes into the scattering process L, with left-handed deflection (see Fig. 1-5). In

▼ addition, the processes R and L are related by a rotation of π about the y axis

$$\sigma(R; m_s \to m') = \sigma(L; -m_s \to -m'_s) \tag{1-45}$$

The polarization of the scattered particle, for unpolarized incident beam, is

$$P = \frac{\sum_{m_s} \sigma(R; m_s \to 1/2) - \sum_{m_s} \sigma(R; m_s \to -1/2)}{\sum_{m_s} \sigma(R; m_s \to 1/2) + \sum_{m_s} \sigma(R; m_s \to -1/2)} \tag{1-46}$$

which is seen to be equal to the azimuthal asymmetry defined by

$$A = \frac{\sum_{m_s} \sigma(R; 1/2 \to m_s) - \sum_{m_s} \sigma(L; 1/2 \to m_s)}{\sum_{m_s} \sigma(R; 1/2 \to m_s) + \sum_{m_s} \sigma(L; 1/2 \to m_s)} \tag{1-47}$$

▲ as a consequence of the relations (1-44) and (1-45).

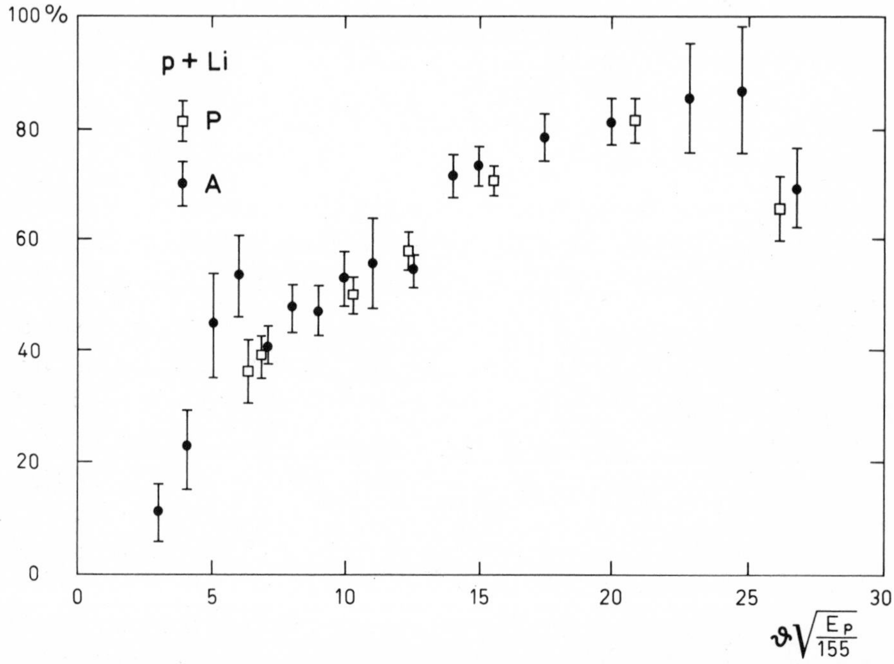

Figure 1-6 The figure shows the polarization (P) and azimuthal asymmetry (A) as given by P. Hillman, A. Johansson, and G. Tibell, *Phys. Rev.* **110**, 1218 (1958).

▼ Figure 1-6 shows measured values of P and A for the scattering of high-energy protons on Li. The polarization measurements refer to an average energy of $E_p = 180$ MeV, while the asymmetry determination, which requires a polarized beam obtained by first scattering the protons on a carbon target, refers to the energy 155 MeV. The angular scale in the figure is chosen so as to correct approximately for this energy difference and it is seen that the two measurements agree ▲ within the experimental error of about 8 %.

▼ In order to obtain an unambiguous test of $\mathscr{T}$ symmetry, the target nucleus must have a finite spin, since for spin zero, the relation $P = A$ can also be obtained from $\mathscr{P}$ conservation. In fact, a reflection in the collision plane gives a phase $(-1)^{m_s}$ for each particle in a reaction; hence, for target spin 0, $\mathscr{P}$ conservation implies $(-1)^{m_s - m'_s} = +1$, which for $s = \frac{1}{2}$ allows only the nonflip processes $m_s = m'_s$. With this restriction, the above relation (1-44) follows from the relation (1-45) and is therefore a consequence of rotational symmetry.

Thus, for ^{7}Li, in which the spin angular momentum is mainly concentrated on a single proton, only the contribution of this particle to the scattering provides a test of $\mathscr{T}$ symmetry, if $\mathscr{P}$ symmetry is assumed. The data in Fig. 1-6 therefore only provide weak limits on the ratio of the $\mathscr{T}$ violating to $\mathscr{T}$ invariant nuclear fields. The polarization-asymmetry relation has also been tested in other scattering processes, including $p-p$ scattering (see, for instance, Hillman *et al.*,
▲ *loc. cit.*, Fig. 1-6).

1-3 ISOBARIC INVARIANCE

1-3a Isospin Symmetry

Isospin of nucleons

A fundamental feature of nuclear structure is associated with the presence of two kinds of nucleons, the neutron and the proton. The near equality of the mass of these two particles ($\Delta M/M = 1.4 \times 10^{-3}$; see Table 1-1, p. 4) immediately suggests a deep similarity between them (Heisenberg, 1932), and the more detailed study of their role in nuclear processes has revealed a basic symmetry between neutron and proton in all nuclear interactions. The symmetry in the interaction was first recognized as a result of the analysis of the low-energy *np* and *pp* scattering (Breit *et al.*, 1936). At low energies ($E < 5$ MeV), the *np* system interacts mainly in the ^1S and ^3S channels, but the exclusion principle restricts the *pp* system to the ^1S channel. A detailed analysis of the observed scattering reveals that the *np* interaction in the ^1S channel is equal to the *pp* interaction (with the Coulomb force subtracted) to within a few percent. (For references, see the discussion in Sec. 2-5a.) The existence of a general symmetry between *np*, *nn*, and *pp* interactions is strikingly borne out by the comparison of the spectra of different isobars (nuclei having the same total number of nucleons, but different numbers of neutrons and protons). Examples will be discussed at the end of the present section.

Thus, we are led to consider the hypothesis that the nuclear forces are independent of the charge of the nucleon. Because of the exclusion principle, the charge independence symmetry refers only to the channels with antisymmetric space-spin wave functions, that is, singlet spin ($S = 0$) and even orbital angular momentum (^1S, ^1D, ...), or triplet spin ($S = 1$) and odd orbital symmetry (^3P, ^3F, ...). In these channels, the interaction is assumed to be the same for *nn*, *np*, and *pp* systems. The symmetric channels ^3S, ^1P, ^3D, ... are permitted only for the *np* system.

The consequences of charge independence are most conveniently obtained in a formalism that regards the neutron and proton as two different states of a single particle. Thus, the wave function for a nucleon will depend partly on the usual space and spin variables ($\mathbf{r}$ and $\sigma_z (= 2s_z = \pm 1)$) and partly on an isobaric variable τ_z, which distinguishes between a neutron ($\tau_z = 1$) and a proton ($\tau_z = -1$). For a neutron in the state $\psi(\mathbf{r}, \sigma_z)$, we write

$$\psi_n(\mathbf{r}, \sigma_z) = \psi(\mathbf{r}, \sigma_z, \tau_z = 1) = \psi(\mathbf{r}, \sigma_z)\begin{pmatrix}1\\0\end{pmatrix} \tag{1-48}$$

while, for a proton in the same state, we have

$$\psi_p(\mathbf{r}, \sigma_z) = \psi(\mathbf{r}, \sigma_z)\begin{pmatrix}0\\1\end{pmatrix} \tag{1-49}$$

The protons and neutrons are known to obey the exclusion principle, which requires the wave function to be antisymmetric under the exchange of all coordinates of two protons or two neutrons. In order to obtain a treatment exploiting the relationship of the two types of nucleons, we impose a generalized exclusion principle, which requires the wave function to be antisymmetric with respect to the interchange of all the coordinates (space, spin, and isospin) of any two nucleons.

The generalized exclusion principle is not an extra assumption, but rather a part of a convenient formalism. In fact, the isobaric notation introduces a redundance in the enumeration of the states, since the configuration involving a proton and a neutron with the coordinates $\mathbf{r}_p$, $\sigma_z(p)$ and $\mathbf{r}_n$, $\sigma_z(n)$ can be described either by the set of variables ($\mathbf{r}_1 = \mathbf{r}_p$, $\sigma_z(1) = \sigma_z(p)$, $\tau_z(1) = -1$, $\mathbf{r}_2 = \mathbf{r}_n$, $\sigma_z(2) = \sigma_z(n)$, $\tau_z(2) = +1$) or by the set involving an interchange of 1 and 2 for all the coordinates (space, spin, and isospin coordinates). The antisymmetry condition thus serves to remove this extra degree of freedom. It is also possible to treat the consequences of charge independence without the introduction of isobaric variables or of a generalized exclusion principle (see Bayman, 1966).

In the isobaric formalism, the operators become matrices in the isobaric coordinates of the particles. For example, the interaction between two neutrons may be written

$$V_{nn}(1, 2) = \begin{pmatrix}1 & 0\\0 & 0\end{pmatrix}_1 \begin{pmatrix}1 & 0\\0 & 0\end{pmatrix}_2 V(1, 2) \tag{1-50}$$

where the subscripts indicate that the matrices act in the isobaric space of particle 1 and particle 2, respectively.

As is well known from the quantal description of the spin, any 2×2 matrix can be expressed in terms of linear combinations of the unit matrix and the three Pauli matrices. It is therefore possible to express the operators in isobaric space in terms of the isospin matrices

$$\tau_x = \begin{pmatrix} 0 & 1 \\ 1 & 0 \end{pmatrix}$$
$$\tau_y = \begin{pmatrix} 0 & -i \\ i & 0 \end{pmatrix} \tag{1-51}$$
$$\tau_z = \begin{pmatrix} 1 & 0 \\ 0 & -1 \end{pmatrix}$$

for the individual nucleons. The matrices are regarded as the components of a vector $\boldsymbol{\tau}$ in a three-dimensional isospace, with axes labeled x, y, and z. The z component, which is diagonal, corresponds to the isobaric variable introduced above.

From the matrices (1-51) we obtain the isobaric spin operators

$$\mathbf{t} = \tfrac{1}{2}\boldsymbol{\tau} \tag{1-52}$$

whose components obey the commutation relations for components of an angular momentum vector (see Eq. (1-11)). Since $(\mathbf{t})^2 = 3/4$, the nucleon has the total isospin $t = 1/2$, and the z components $m_t = t_z = +1/2$ (for neutron) and $-1/2$ (for the proton).[2]

Rotational invariance in isospace

For systems with two or more nucleons, the isospins may be coupled to a total

$$\mathbf{T} = \sum_k \mathbf{t}_k \tag{1-53}$$

with the z component

$$M_T = T_z = \tfrac{1}{2}(N - Z) \tag{1-54}$$

Since the components of $\mathbf{T}$ again satisfy the commutation relations of an angular momentum vector, the eigenvalues of $(\mathbf{T})^2$ are $T(T+1)$ with $T = 0, 1, 2, \ldots$ for systems with an even number of nucleons and $T = 1/2, 3/2, \ldots$ for odd numbers of nucleons. The operator $\mathbf{T}$ can be associated with rotations in isospace in

---

[2] The isospin assignment for neutron and proton, which is here adopted, is conventional in nuclear physics problems and has the advantage that the heavy nuclei with large neutron excess have their isospins aligned in the direction of the positive z axis ($M_T > 0$). In elementary particle physics, the convention $m_t = +1/2$ for the proton and $m_t = -1/2$ for the neutron is usually employed.

the same manner as the angular momentum **I** generates rotations in ordinary space.

The assumption of charge independence implies that the interaction, and the total Hamiltonian, can be written in a form that does not explicitly involve the isospin variables of the nucleons. We must remember, however, that, as part of the isobaric formalism, we have introduced a generalized exclusion principle, which can be expressed by the relation

$$P(ik) = P^r(ik)P^\sigma(ik)P^\tau(ik) = -1 \tag{1-55}$$

for each pair of particles (ik). The operators P^r, P^σ, and P^τ exchange the space, spin, and isospin variables of the two particles, and P is thus the total exchange operator.

The relation (1-55) implies a connection between the isospin and the space-spin degrees of freedom. Thus, for example, a two-particle interaction depending on the symmetry of the two-particle state in spin-orbital space can be written in either of the two forms

$$\begin{aligned} V(ik) &= \tfrac{1}{2}(V^{(s)} + V^{(a)}) + \tfrac{1}{2}(V^{(s)} - V^{(a)})P^r P^\sigma \\ &= \tfrac{1}{2}(V^{(s)} + V^{(a)}) - \tfrac{1}{2}(V^{(s)} - V^{(a)})P^\tau \end{aligned} \tag{1-56}$$

where $V^{(s)}$ and $V^{(a)}$ are functions of the space and spin variables of the interacting nucleons. The interaction in the channels ${}^3S, {}^1P, \ldots$, which are symmetric in spin-orbital space, is denoted by $V^{(s)}$, while $V^{(a)}$ is the interaction in the antisymmetric channels ${}^1S, {}^3P, \ldots$. (Charge independence implies no relationship between $V^{(s)}$ and $V^{(a)}$, which are in fact rather different.) The component of $V(ik)$ involving P^τ is referred to as a charge exchange interaction and may be associated with an exchange of charged quanta, such as π mesons, between the two nucleons.

The charge exchange operator can be expressed in terms of the nucleonic isospins

$$P^\tau = \tfrac{1}{2}(1 + \boldsymbol{\tau}_i \cdot \boldsymbol{\tau}_k) = \begin{cases} +1, & T = 1 \\ -1, & T = 0 \end{cases} \tag{1-57}$$

as can be seen by direct evaluation of the effect of P^τ on a two-particle state, or from the relation

$$\begin{aligned} (\mathbf{T})^2 = T(T+1) &= (\mathbf{t}_i + \mathbf{t}_k)^2 \\ &= \tfrac{3}{2} + \tfrac{1}{2}\,\boldsymbol{\tau}_i \cdot \boldsymbol{\tau}_k \end{aligned} \tag{1-58}$$

where the total isospin T for the two particles equals 1 for isospin symmetric states ($P^\tau = +1$) and 0 for antisymmetric states ($P^\tau = -1$).

We can thus express the dependence of the relations (1-55) and (1-56) on the nucleonic isospins in terms of the products $(\boldsymbol{\tau}_i \cdot \boldsymbol{\tau}_k)$ for the different pairs of particles. Since these products are isoscalars, it follows that the entire description is invariant with respect to rotations in isospace.

Conversely, rotational invariance in isospace implies charge independence, so that the two symmetries are synonymous for a system of nucleons. In fact, it can be seen that the most general function of the isospins, which is an isoscalar, can be expressed as a function of the products $(\boldsymbol{\tau}_i \cdot \boldsymbol{\tau}_k)$ and thus of the charge exchange operators $P^{\tau}(ik)$. A rotationally invariant Hamiltonian can therefore be written, by means of the relation (1-55), without explicit reference to the isobaric variables.

The rotational invariance in isospace implies that the Hamiltonian commutes with the total isospin **T**. The stationary states can thus be labeled with the quantum number T, and the states form degenerate multiplets consisting of $2T+1$ components with different $M_T = T_z$. Isobaric multiplet structure is found to be a general feature of the nuclear spectra, thus providing abundant experimental evidence for the charge independence of nuclear interactions. The degeneracy between the multiplet components with different M_T (isobaric analog states) is lifted by the Coulomb forces (see below). Examples of isobaric multiplet structure are illustrated in Figs. 1-7, p. 43, and 1-9, p. 47, as well as in Figs. 3-2a to 3-2f.

The isobaric invariance also has important consequences for nuclear reaction processes giving selection rules and intensity relations associated with the conservation of isospin (see examples discussed on p. 46). Similarly, certain transition operators take a very simple form in the isobaric spin formalism, and thereby give rise to selection rules in the corresponding transitions. (Examples are discussed in connection with Fig. 1-8, p. 44, Fig. 1-10, p. 52, and Table 1-3, p. 53.)

Charge symmetry

Some of the relations following from charge independence can also be obtained from the weaker assumption of charge symmetry, based on the equality of the *pp* and *nn* interactions. This symmetry can be expressed as an invariance with respect to the operation $\mathscr{R}_\tau$, which replaces all neutrons by protons, and *vice versa*. For nuclei with $N = Z$, the charge symmetry implies that the stationary states are either even ($r_\tau = +1$) or odd ($r_\tau = -1$) with respect to $\mathscr{R}_\tau$.

In the isospin formalism, the charge symmetry operation corresponds to a rotation in isospin of 180° about an axis perpendicular to the z axis, and may be taken to be

$$\mathcal{R}_\tau = \exp\{-i\pi T_y\} \tag{1-59}$$

For states with $N = Z$ (that is, $M_T = 0$), we thus have

$$r_\tau = (-1)^T \tag{1-60}$$

Examples of selection rules that can be associated with the charge symmetry quantum number are discussed on p. 46.

Violation of isobaric symmetry

The isobaric invariance is violated by the electromagnetic interaction. The symmetry-breaking effects in the nuclear structure are partly associated with the Coulomb force (and magnetic forces) between nucleons. Additional effects arise from the neutron-proton mass difference and small charge-dependent components in the strong nucleonic interactions, which appear to be associated with the electromagnetic structure of the nucleons.

For the lightest nuclei, these effects are relatively small and can be rather accurately treated as perturbations, which mainly act to give small energy splittings between the isobaric multiplets (see, for instance, Fig. 1-7). In heavier nuclei, the Coulomb field may become very strong, reaching values of the order of 20 MeV inside the heaviest nuclei. Thus, for a long time, it was expected that the isobaric symmetry might be of little significance in heavy nuclei. The discovery of well-defined isobaric multiplet structure (Anderson and Wong, 1961) has revealed, however, that the strong Coulomb interactions are rather ineffective in breaking the isobaric symmetry. Examples of isobaric analog states in medium heavy nuclei are illustrated in Fig. 1-9.

The validity of the T quantum number in heavy nuclei may be understood from the fact that the Coulomb field varies rather slowly over the nuclear volume. Thus, the wave functions of the individual protons are only little affected and the main result of the Coulomb field is to add to the nuclear energy a term depending on the number of protons (that is, on M_T) without violating the T quantum number. An estimate of the purity of the T quantum number for low-lying nuclear states is given in Fig. 2-6. For highly excited states, appreciable T mixing must be expected, since states of different isospin but same spin and parity occur close together and can be coupled by even relatively weak perturbations. Such coupling effects are discussed in connection with Fig. 1-9, p. 51. In general, reactions proceeding through the formation of long-lived intermediate states may thus involve appreciable isospin mixing, but in direct reactions the short duration of the collision leads to a much greater range of validity for the isospin quantum number.

The problem of broken symmetry is one of general significance in nuclear and elementary particle physics. The approximate validity of the isobaric invariance in heavy nuclei provides an example of the persistence of symmetries, even in the presence of strong symmetry-breaking perturbations.

Isobaric invariance and permutation symmetry

In the above we have formulated the isobaric symmetry in terms of invariance with respect to rotations in isospace. One can also view this symmetry in terms of the transformation of the Hamiltonian and its eigenstates under permutation of the isospin variables of the particles. Such an approach is in some ways more directly related to the physical phenomena that motivated the introduction of the symmetric description of nucleons.

In the isobaric formalism, the Hamiltonian is automatically invariant with respect to permutations involving all the coordinates of two particles (space, spin, and isospin). A charge-independent Hamiltonian, however, can be written in a form that does not involve the isospin variables and is therefore also invariant with respect to permutations of the isobaric variables separately, and hence also with respect to permutations of space-spin coordinates separately. One can thus classify the eigenstates of the Hamiltonian in terms of symmetry quantum numbers characterizing the transformation of the wave function under permutations in isospace and in spin-orbital space. The general tools for such a classification of states in terms of permutation symmetry are discussed in Appendix 1C.

For a two-particle system, the wave functions are either symmetric in isospace ($T=1$) and antisymmetric in spin-orbital space, or antisymmetric ($T=0$) in isospace and symmetric in spin-orbital space. For any number of nucleons, one can classify the totally antisymmetric states in terms of the permutation symmetry in isospace, labeled by the partition $[f]$, and the conjugate symmetry $[\tilde{f}]$ in spin-orbital space (see Sec. 1C-1f). Since the isospin variable of a nucleon can take only two values, only partitions $[f]=[f_1 f_2]$ can occur, and the symmetry quantum numbers f_1 and f_2 are equivalent to the total number of particles ($A=f_1+f_2$) and the total isospin $\left(T=\frac{1}{2}(f_1-f_2)\right)$; see Sec. 1C-2c.

For a system of particles, each of which can occur in g different states, the classification in terms of permutation symmetry is equivalent to a classification in terms of the transformation properties with respect to g-dimensional unitary transformations (U_g) acting on the single-particle wave functions (see Sec. 1C-3). For $g=2$, the unitary transformations are, as we have seen, equivalent to rotations in a three-dimensional space (R_3), corresponding to the fact that the Pauli matrices, which generate U_2 transformations, have the commutation relations characteristic of an angular momentum vector.

The possibility of formulating the isobaric invariance in terms of a rotation symmetry is thus contingent on the fact that we are dealing with the equivalence between two states of a particle (proton and neutron). One may also consider the possibility of more extensive symmetries. Thus, if the nuclear interactions were independent of the spins as well as the isospins of the nucleons, for a given spatial configuration, we would be dealing with an equivalence between four states of the nucleon ($\sigma_z = \pm 1, \tau_z = \pm 1$). In such a situation the states can be classified in terms of "super-multiplets" labeled by the quantum numbers characterizing the representations of the U_4 group (Wigner, 1937; Hund, 1937). Although this supermultiplet symmetry is violated by important components in the nuclear forces that couple spin and orbit, it represents a useful approximation in the study of certain light nuclei (see Chapter 7).

1-3b Extension of Isobaric Symmetry

Since the nuclear forces are interwoven with the properties of all the strongly interacting particles, the isobaric symmetry is expected to be a general property of all the strong interaction phenomena. The experimental data confirm this view; the mesons and the excited states of the nucleons (the baryon spectrum) can be grouped into isobaric multiplets (see Figs. 1-11, p. 57 and 1-12, p. 63), and in scattering and reaction processes one observes the expected intensity rules corresponding to the conservation of the total isobaric spin.

The study of the nucleonic interactions in the GeV range has revealed a great richness of phenomena, associated with the occurrence of metastable states representing excitations of mesons and nucleons (that is, states with baryon numbers $A = 0$ and $A = 1$). The properties and reactions involving these new "particles" are found to be governed by symmetry principles and conservation laws in addition to those already considered for the nucleons. In the following, we shall briefly discuss these extended symmetries, which give a generalized framework for viewing the isobaric symmetry of the nucleons.

In the hadronic spectra, one also finds families of states with the same generalized isobaric symmetry quantum numbers, but with increasing values of the angular momentum. (Examples are illustrated in Fig. 1-13, p. 65.) There is so far little evidence concerning the dynamical relationship between the states belonging to such a family, or trajectory.

Strangeness

Among the excited states in the meson and baryon spectrum (see Figs. 1-11 and 1-12), some are found to have lifetimes many orders of magnitude longer than the natural unit for strongly interacting systems (the time it takes for a particle to cover a distance comparable with the range of the interactions). The existence of these approximately discrete states may be attributed to selection rules associated with another quantum number, the strangeness, which is found to be closely connected with the isospin (Gell-Mann, 1953; Nishijima, 1954).

The possibility of such an additional quantum number might be suggested by the puzzling constant 1/2 in the relation between the charge Z (in units of e)

and the z component of the isospin of a nucleon

$$Z = -T_z + 1/2 \tag{1-61}$$

Indeed the semistable excited states of the nucleon are characterized by different values for this constant.

The strangeness quantum number S may be defined by the relation

$$\begin{aligned} Z &= -T_z + \left(\frac{S+A}{2}\right) \\ &= -T_z + \frac{Y}{2} \end{aligned} \tag{1-62}$$

where A is the baryon number ($+1$ for a single baryon, -1 for an antibaryon, and 0 for a meson). As an alternative to S one may introduce the hypercharge $Y = S + A$.

The pronounced stability of some of the meson and baryon states can be interpreted in terms of the law of conservation of strangeness (or hypercharge). It is also found that all scattering and reaction processes are characterized by $\Delta S = 0$, where S is the sum of the strangeness quantum numbers of the particles.

According to Eq. (1-62), the conservation of S is equivalent to the conservation of T_z, if we assume the conservation laws for charge and baryon number, both of which appear to have universal validity. The conservation of S (and T_z) is a feature not only of the strong interactions but also of the electromagnetic forces. The weak interactions responsible for the decay of hyperons and heavy mesons, which violate the conservation of S and T_z, appear to be closely related to those giving rise to the β processes (see Sec. 3D-1).

The stability of the particles with $S \neq 0$, and the fact that they interact with nucleons with forces comparable to those acting between nucleons, makes possible the formation of nuclei with $S \neq 0$. A number of such "hypernuclei" involving a bound Λ particle have indeed been observed. (The Λ particle has the quantum numbers $A = 1, Z = 0, S = -1, T = 0$.) In spite of the rather difficult experimental conditions for the study of these systems, a considerable body of evidence has been accumulated, especially regarding the binding energies (and in some cases also spin values) for ground states of hypernuclei (see Table 1-4, p. 55). These data provide information on the Λ-nucleon interaction. (See especially the evidence for charge independence and for rather strong spin dependence provided by the data in Table 1-4.) Although the present information concerning hypernuclei is extremely primitive compared with that on nuclei with $S = 0$, the study of the properties and reactions involving hypernuclei is potentially an important part of the subject of nuclear structure.

Systems with $S = +1$ formed by adding a K^+ particle to nuclei do not appear to form bound states, owing to the predominantly repulsive character of the K^+ nucleon force. (See also the absence of baryonic resonance states with $S = +1$ (Fig. 1-11).)

Unitary symmetry

The existence of a higher symmetry encompassing isospin and strangeness was first suggested (Gell-Mann, 1961; Ne'eman, 1961) by the observation that the baryonic and mesonic states can be grouped into multiplets with related properties. Thus, the semistable baryons ($n, p, \Lambda, \Sigma^+, \Sigma^0, \Sigma^-, \Xi^0, \Xi^-$) all have spin 1/2. Similarly, the lightest mesons ($\pi^+, \pi^0, \pi^-, K^+, K^-, K^0, \bar{K}^0, \rho$) form a multiplet of pseudoscalar (0−) particles.

The pattern of this multiplet structure can be interpreted in terms of an invariance with respect to unitary transformations in three dimensions (SU_3 invariance). The representations of this symmetry group can be labeled by the quantum numbers λ and μ, connected with the partition numbers by $\lambda = f_1 - f_2$, $\mu = f_2 - f_3$ (see Sec. 1C-3b). In elementary particle physics, the representations are usually labeled simply by the dimensionality $h = \frac{1}{2}(\lambda + 1)(\mu + 1)(\lambda + \mu + 2)$ (see Eq. (1C-27)). The states of a given multiplet can be specified by the isospin and strangeness, that is, by the three quantum numbers T, M_T, and S (see Sec. 1C-3b). For example, the nucleon isobaric doublet (neutron and proton) belongs to an octuplet $((\lambda\mu) = (11))$ comprising also $\Lambda(T = 0, S = -1)$, $\Sigma(T = 1, S = -1)$, and $\Xi(T = 1/2, S = -2)$. (See further examples of SU_3 multiplets in Figs. 1-11 and 1-12.) The relationship between the states belonging to the same SU_3 representation is expressed in terms of intensity rules in production and decay processes, ratios between moments, etc. (See, for example, the discussion of nucleon electromagnetic moments and form factors (Sec. 3C-4) and of the weak interaction current (Sec. 3D-2e).)

The SU_3 multiplets, which would be degenerate if the interactions were SU_3 invariant, exhibit mass separations amounting to several hundred MeV (see Figs. 1-11 and 1-12). These splittings must be attributed to the presence of rather large components in the strong interactions, which violate SU_3 symmetry but preserve the isospin (or SU_2) symmetry. The pattern of the mass splittings is rather well accounted for by assuming the symmetry-violating mass term to transform under SU_3 as a member of the octuplet representation (see the discussion in connection with Fig. 1-11).

The SU_3 symmetry is also violated by the electromagnetic interactions which, indeed, are known to violate the isospin invariance. The available evidence appears to be compatible with the assumption that the electromagnetic interactions are invariant with respect to all the SU_3 transformations that conserve the electric charge (Coleman and Glashow, 1961). These transformations comprise those generated by the electric charge itself (expressing charge conservation) and an additional SU_2 subgroup, the generators of which are referred to as the U spin (Levinson *et al.*, 1963). (The similar invariance with respect to all SU_3 transformations conserving hypercharge is a property of the strong interactions and is equivalent to the conservation of hypercharge and of T spin.) The electromagnetic mass differences of the baryons are discussed on p. 61 as an example of the consequences following from the assumption that the electromagnetic interaction is a scalar in U space.

A striking feature of the SU_3 classification is the absence of multiplets transforming as the fundamental three-dimensional representation (in contrast to the existence of the nucleon doublet in the SU_2 scheme). One has, therefore, considered the possibility that the strongly interacting particles are bound states composed of subunits (the quarks) which comprise a triplet (Gell-Mann, 1964; Zweig, 1964). The triplet $((\lambda\mu) = (10))$ consists of an isospin doublet with $S = 0$ and an isospin singlet with $S = -1$. In such a model, the baryon number of the quark must be taken to be $A = 1/3$, which implies noninteger values of the charge number (see Eq. (1-62)). In this interpretation the SU_3 symmetry is a consequence of the equivalence of the three quark states in the same manner as the isospin symmetry in nuclei can be traced back to the equivalence of the neutron and proton. One can thus also view the partition quantum numbers labeling the SU_3 representations in terms of permutation symmetry, referring to the transformation of the states under permutation of the quark variables in spin-orbital space, or in isobaric space. (See Sec. 1C-3; the quarks are fermions, and the states thus totally antisymmetric under permutations in both spaces.) Thus, for example, the baryon octuplet with $(\lambda\mu) = (11)$ and $(I\pi) = (1/2+)$ can be formed by three quarks with the mixed permutation symmetry $[f] = [21]$. The baryon states may contain additional quark-antiquark pairs, which may be included by incorporating the quarks in the Dirac sea into the description. The baryon octuplet is thus labeled $[f] = [N+2, N+1, N]$, where $3N$ is the number of quarks in the filled Dirac sea. The meson octuplet, however, is formed from one (or more) baryon-antibaryon pairs and has the partition $[f] = [N+1, N, N-1]$. The two partitions are associated with the same SU_3 symmetry $((\lambda\mu) = (f_1 - f_2, f_2 - f_3) = (11))$, but are distinguished by the total quark number n $(= f_1 + f_2 + f_3 - 3N)$ or, equivalently, by the baryon number $A = n/3$.

There is so far no evidence for the existence of quarks as separate entities. They are not produced with detectable cross sections by present accelerators, and their mass would thus have to be large.

One can further extend the unitary symmetry by combining the transformations in isobaric space (SU_3) with transformations in spin space, to obtain an SU_6 symmetry. In the analysis in terms of quarks, one assumes invariance of the interactions with respect to the six states of the quarks (two spin states for each quark). The extension of SU_3 to SU_6 symmetry is thus analogous to the extension of nuclear isospin symmetry (SU_2) to the spin-isospin (or orbital) symmetry (SU_4) (see p. 37).

The SU_6 symmetry makes it possible to bring together the lowest observed SU_3 multiplets into SU_6 supermultiplets (see pp. 62 and 64) and provides an interpretation of various observed intensity relations. It is also remarkable that the observed ratio of the magnetic moments of neutron and proton finds a simple interpretation within the SU_6 symmetry scheme (see Sec. 3C-4). However, the application of SU_6 symmetry is restricted by the coupling between spin and orbit, which in some situations completely violates the symmetry. The proper domain of validity of SU_6 symmetry is a problem of great current interest.[3]

---

[3] For a review of the development of the SU_3 symmetry classification for the strongly interacting particles, see the reprint volume by Gell-Mann and Ne'eman, *The Eightfold Way*, 1964. The development of SU_6 symmetry is summarized by Dyson, *Symmetry Groups in Nuclear and Particle Physics*, 1966. A presentation of the unitary symmetry classification, involving only elementary mathematical tools, has been given by Lipkin, *Lie Groups for Pedestrians*, 1965.

It may be added that many of the consequences which follow from the higher symmetries (SU_3 and SU_6) can be obtained on the basis of the "independent quark model," without assuming the higher symmetries. In this model, the baryons are regarded as consisting of three quarks, while the mesons are quark-antiquark bound states, and the scattering and reaction amplitudes for processes involving the different particles are obtained as a simple superposition of the amplitudes for scattering processes involving the constituent quarks and antiquarks. (See, for example, Lipkin, 1967.)

▼

ILLUSTRATIVE EXAMPLES TO SECTION 1-3

Isobaric triplets and singlets in $A = 14$ (Figs. 1-7 and 1-8)

The known levels of the nuclei with $A = 14$ are shown in Fig. 1-7. The most strongly bound state is the ground state of ^{14}N with $I\pi = 1+$. This level has no analog in the spectra of ^{14}C and ^{14}O and is therefore an isobaric singlet ($T = 0$). The ground state of ^{14}C, the 2.312 MeV state of ^{14}N, and the ground state of ^{14}O, which all have $I\pi = 0+$, form an isobaric triplet with $M_T = +1$, 0, and -1, respectively. After correction for the neutron-proton mass difference of 0.78 MeV, the differences in binding energy between the members of the triplet become $\mathscr{E}(^{14}\text{O}) - \mathscr{E}(^{14}\text{N}^*) = 3.62$ MeV and $\mathscr{E}(^{14}\text{N}^*) - \mathscr{E}(^{14}\text{C}) = 2.94$ MeV. A simple estimate of the Coulomb energy differences can be obtained from the expression (2-19), which yields 3.8 MeV and 3.2 MeV for the binding energy differences ($^{14}\text{O} - {}^{14}\text{N}^*$) and ($^{14}\text{N}^* - {}^{14}\text{C}$), respectively. (The consistency of the nuclear size determinations as obtained from Coulomb energies and electron scattering data has been discussed by Wilkinson and Mafethe, 1966, for the nuclei with $4 < A < 16$.)

The ^{14}O and ^{14}C nuclei have no low-lying excited states; thus, all the low-energy levels in ^{14}N, with the exception of the 2.3 MeV state, must be assigned $T = 0$. Starting at about 5 MeV in ^{14}O and 6 MeV in ^{14}C, a number of excited levels have been found, which can be correlated with corresponding ($T = 1$, $M_T = 0$) members in the ^{14}N spectrum. For the $T = 1$ states, the figure shows the excitation energies relative to the lowest $T = 1$ state (the $0+$ level) in the same nucleus. It is seen that the corresponding levels (characterized by the same spin and parity) have approximately the same excitation energies. There are significant shifts, however, typically amounting to several hundred keV, which reflect differences in the Coulomb energy associated with the intrinsic structure of the states.

It appears probable that the largest of the level shifts are associated with the fact that the average value of the Coulomb repulsion is somewhat different

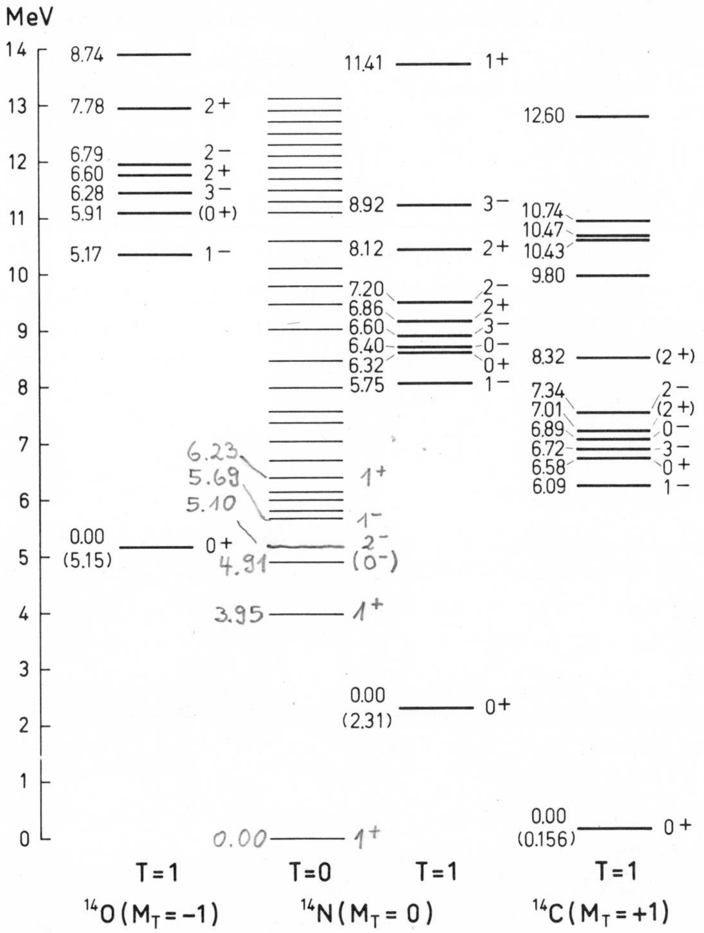

Figure 1-7 The level schemes for the nuclei with $A = 14$ are based on the compilation by F. Ajzenberg-Selove and T. Lauritsen, *Nuclear Phys.* **11**, 1 (1959), on the results given by D. E. Alburger, A. Gallmann, J. B. Nelson, J. T. Sample, and E. K. Warburton, *Phys. Rev.* **148**, 1050 (1966), and on a private communication by G. Ball and J. Cerny (August, 1966). The relative energies represent atomic masses.

▼ for particle orbits with different quantum numbers and that, in particular, the Coulomb energy is somewhat reduced for the loosely bound orbits and for the unbound resonance states (Thomas-Ehrman shift; Ehrman, 1951; Thomas, 1952). Thus, the levels with the greatest downward shifts are expected to have $I\pi = 0-$ or $1-$ and to have a large parentage of ^{13}C($I\pi = 1/2-$) combined with s-wave protons. This expectation is confirmed by the observed large reduced widths for proton emission. A similar effect is discussed in connection with the weakly bound single-particle states of the $A = 17$ system (see Fig. 3-2b).

▲ The assignment of isospin to the levels leads to important consequences for various nuclear processes. Thus, the $E1$ radiative transition strength depends on the matrix element of the electric dipole operator

$$D = \sum_k e_k z_k = e \sum_k \tfrac{1}{2}(1 - \tau_z(k)) z_k$$

$$= \tfrac{1}{2} e \sum_k z_k - \tfrac{1}{2} e \sum_k \tau_z(k) z_k \qquad (1\text{-}63)$$

The first term depends only on the position of the center of mass of the whole nucleus and thus cannot cause transitions between different nuclear states; it is this term that gives the Thompson scattering of photons by the nucleus. The second term is the z component of a vector in isospace and thus implies the selection rules

$$|T_i - T_f| \leqslant 1 \leqslant T_i + T_f \qquad (1\text{-}64)$$

for the isospin quantum numbers of the combining levels.

In self-conjugate nuclei ($N = Z$, $M_T = 0$), all transitions with $T_f = T_i$ are forbidden, since the transition matrix element is proportional to $\langle T_i M_T 1 0 | T_f M_T \rangle$ (see Eq. (1A-132)), which vanishes for $T_i = T_f$ and $M_T = 0$. The isospin selection rules for $E1$ radiation were formulated by Trainer (1952) and by Gamba *et al.* (1952).

The selection rule forbidding $E1$ transitions between two $T = 0$ states can be tested by the decay of the 5.69 MeV, $T = 0$ level in ^{14}N (see Fig. 1-8); it is

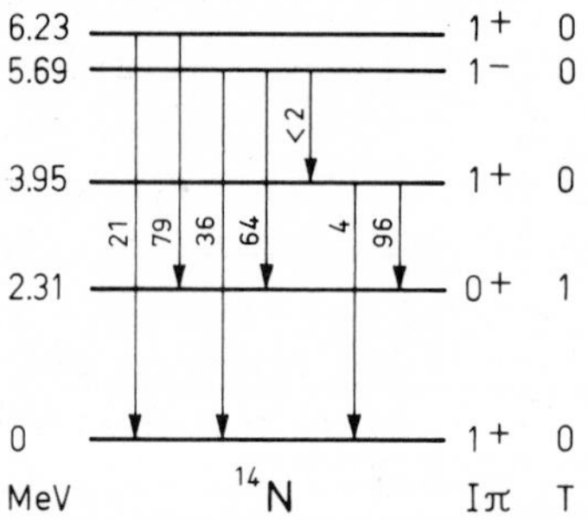

Figure 1-8 Dipole transitions in ^{14}N. The numbers on the arrows represent relative γ intensities as determined by S. Gorodetzky, R. M. Freeman, A. Gallmann, and F. Haas, *Phys. Rev.* **149**, 801 (1966).

found that the transitions to the ground state and the 3.95 MeV, $T = 0$ level are weaker by an order of magnitude than the allowed transition to the 2.31 MeV, $T = 1$ level. (Note that, for the same nuclear matrix element, the transition rate for an $E1$ transition varies as the cube of the transition energy; see Eq. (3C-18).)

The $M1$ transition operator is also predominantly an isovector, since the

▼ magnetic moment (in units of nuclear magnetons) can be expressed in the form

$$\begin{aligned}\boldsymbol{\mu} &= \sum_k (g_s(k)\mathbf{s}_k + g_l(k)\mathbf{l}_k) \\ &= \sum_k \{\tfrac{1}{2}(1-\tau_z(k))(g_p\mathbf{s}_k + \mathbf{l}_k) + \tfrac{1}{2}(1+\tau_z(k))g_n\mathbf{s}_k\} \\ &= \tfrac{1}{2}\mathbf{I} + 0.38\sum_k \mathbf{s}_k - \sum_k \tau_z(k)(4.71\ \mathbf{s}_k + \tfrac{1}{2}\mathbf{l}_k) \qquad (1\text{-}65)\end{aligned}$$

where we have inserted the values $g_p = 5.59$ and $g_n = -3.83$ for the spin g factors for proton and neutron.

The first term in Eq. (1-65) is proportional to the total angular momentum **I** and does not contribute to transitions between different states. The second term is a scalar in isospace, but has a coefficient that is an order of magnitude smaller than that for the last term (the isovector part). Thus we expect the isospin selection rules discussed above for $E1$ radiation to be also approximately valid for $M1$ radiation (Morpurgo, 1958). This is confirmed in the examples shown in Fig. 1-8, where the $T=0 \rightarrow T=1$ $M1$ transitions are seen to be considerably stronger than the $T=0 \rightarrow T=0$ transitions.

In nuclear reaction processes, the conservation of isospin can lead to important selection rules. Thus, in the process

$$^{16}\mathrm{O} + {}^{2}\mathrm{H} \rightarrow {}^{14}\mathrm{N}^* + {}^{4}\mathrm{He}$$

the ^{16}O target, as well as ^{2}H and ^{4}He, has $T=0$; therefore we only expect to populate $T=0$ states in ^{14}N. Indeed it is found that the $T=1$ (2.31 MeV) state is very weakly populated in comparison with the other low-lying states in ^{14}N. For example, for a bombarding energy $E_d = 24$ MeV, the yield of the 2.31 MeV state is $0.7 \pm 0.6\%$ of the yield of the ground state (Cerny *et al.*, 1963).

The conclusions regarding the validity of isospin conservation that can be drawn from the observed small yield of the 2.31 MeV level are somewhat weakened by the fact that specific features of the reaction mechanism may also contribute to the reduction of the yield. In fact, the strong (d, α) reactions appear to take place as two-particle pickup processes in which the picked up *n-p* pair is in a relative *s* state with unit spin ($S = 1$). Such a process cannot populate a $0+$ state in ^{14}N.

As another example, the conservation of isobaric spin implies that the reaction

$$^{14}\mathrm{N} + {}^{12}\mathrm{C} \rightarrow {}^{14}\mathrm{N}^* + {}^{12}\mathrm{C}^*$$

should not excite the 2.31 ($T=1$) state of ^{14}N as long as ^{12}C is not at the same time excited to a $T=1$ state (such states do not occur in ^{12}C below 15.1 MeV). Indeed, all the low-lying states of ^{12}C and ^{14}N are observed in this reaction, except ^{14}N* (2.31 MeV). The experiments employing an incident ^{14}N beam of 27 MeV set a limit of $\sim 1/15$ on the intensity of ^{14}N* (2.31 MeV) as compared to
▲ ^{14}N* (3.95 MeV, $T=0$) produced in this reaction (Halbert and Zucker, 1961).

▼ The selection rules for the transitions and reactions involving the states of ^{14}N could also have been discussed in terms of the charge symmetry quantum number. For this nucleus with $N = Z$, the states can be classified by the eigenvalue $r_\tau = \pm 1$ of the charge symmetry operator $\mathscr{R}_\tau$ given by Eq. (1-59). Since the electric dipole transition operator is odd under $\mathscr{R}_\tau$ and the magnetic dipole transition operator approximately odd, $E1$ and $M1$ transitions between states of equal r_τ are forbidden. Moreover, we have the conservation law for r_τ in reaction processes. The observed selection rules can thus be accounted for by assigning $r_\tau = +1$ to the $T = 0$ states and $r_\tau = -1$ to the $T = 1$ states.

The similarity between the states in ^{14}C and ^{14}O can also be attributed to charge symmetry, but their relationship to the isobaric analog states in ^{14}N can only be understood in terms of the full charge independence. An example of reactions testing charge independence rather than charge symmetry is provided by the processes $^{12}C(^3He, p)^{14}N$ and $^{12}C(^3He, n)^{14}O$. The yields of the two reactions populating the first excited state of ^{14}N and its isobaric analog state, the ground state of ^{14}O, have been measured for bombarding energies from 6.5 to 11 MeV (Fulbright *et al.*, 1965). The cross sections at a fixed angle exhibit large variations with energy, but are found over the whole energy range to be approximately in the ratio 1 : 2, as implied by isospin conservation. In fact, the system $^{12}C + {}^3He$ has $T = 1/2$, $M_T = -1/2$, and the ratio of the two cross sections is thus

$$\langle 1 0 \tfrac{1}{2} - \tfrac{1}{2} | \tfrac{1}{2} - \tfrac{1}{2} \rangle^2 : \langle 1 -1 \tfrac{1}{2} \tfrac{1}{2} | \tfrac{1}{2} - \tfrac{1}{2} \rangle^2 = 1 : 2$$

Further tests of the charge independence relations have been obtained from a study of the reactions $^{16}O(p, t)$ and $^{16}O(p, {}^3He)$ leading respectively to the ground state of ^{14}O and to the 2.31 MeV isobaric analog state in ^{14}N (Cerny and Pehl, 1964). The cross sections for the two reactions induced by 44 MeV protons exhibit very similar angular distributions and the ratio of the yields was found to be 2.1 with an accuracy of a few percent. Charge independence implies a ratio of 2.

Isobaric analog states observed in proton-induced resonance reactions (Fig. 1-9 and Table 1-2)

In medium heavy and heavy nuclei, the strong Coulomb interaction implies that the most stable nuclei with given A have a large neutron excess, and thus $M_T = \frac{1}{2}(N - Z) \gg 1$. The quantum number T must be equal to or greater than M_T, and all the low-lying energy levels are found to have minimum isospin, $T = T_0 = M_T$. This feature of the spectra reflects the important systematic effects in the nuclear binding that favor low values of T (see the discussion in Sec. 2-1f).

The lowest states with $T = T_0 + 1$ occur at excitation energies well above the threshold for proton emission and have been found to give rise to well-defined sharp resonances in proton scattering (Fox *et al.*, 1964). The study of such resonances has provided an extensive body of evidence regarding the validity of isospin symmetry in heavier nuclei. ▲

Figure 1-9 shows the level spectrum of ^{117}Sb ($M_T = 15/2$). The $T = 17/2$ states have been observed as resonances in the $^{116}_{50}$Sn(p, p) and $^{116}_{50}$Sn(p, n) processes. The interpretation of the observed resonances as $T = 17/2$ states implies that these levels are isobaric analogs of low-lying levels in ^{117}Sn ($M_T = 17/2$). The data in Fig. 1-9 as well as in Table 1-2 show that there is indeed a striking

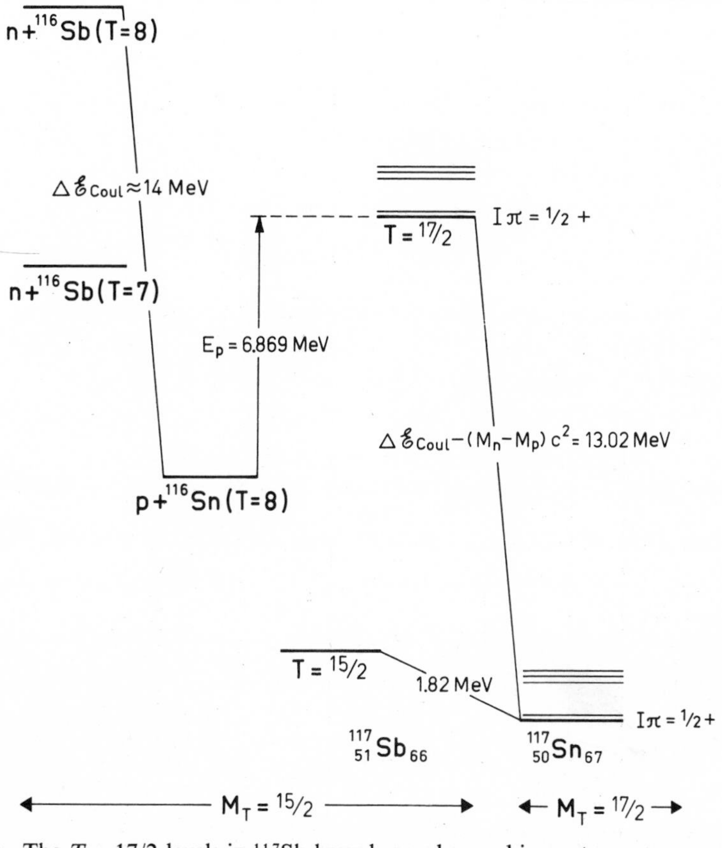

Figure 1-9 The $T = 17/2$ levels in ^{117}Sb have been observed in proton resonance reactions on ^{116}Sn by P. Richard, C. F. Moore, J. A. Becker, and J. D. Fox, *Phys. Rev.* **145**, 971 (1966). The additional information on energy levels and binding energies has been obtained from *Table of Isotopes* by Lederer *et al.* (1967).

correspondence as regards energy spacing and spin-parity quantum numbers for the $T = 17/2$ levels in the two nuclei. The difference in binding energy between the $M_T = 15/2$ and $M_T = 17/2$ members of the $T = 17/2$ multiplets amounts to 13.8 MeV, and may be compared with the estimate (2-19) for the Coulomb energy, which yields

$$\Delta\mathscr{E}_{\text{Coul}} = \mathscr{E}_{\text{Coul}}(Z = 51, A = 117) - \mathscr{E}_{\text{Coul}}(Z = 50, A = 117) = 13.8 \text{ MeV}$$

One expects small variations in the Coulomb energy shift for the different $T = 17/2$ states, depending on the intrinsic structure of the levels. The observed

$^{116}Sn(p,p)^{116}Sn$							$^{116}Sn(d,p)^{117}Sn$			
E_p(c.m.) (MeV)	$E - E_0$ (MeV)	l_p	$I\pi$	Γ_p (keV)	Γ (keV)	$\Gamma_p/(\Gamma_p)_{sp}$	E (MeV)	l_n	$I\pi$	σ/σ_{sp}
6.869	0.000	0	1/2+	16.5	42	0.38	0.0	0	1/2+	0.65
7.022	0.153	2	(3/2 5/2)+	8.3	37	0.52	0.16	2	3/2+	0.55
7.873	1.004	2	(3/2 5/2)+	1.8	42	0.051	1.03	2	5/2+	0.061
8.038	1.169	2	(3/2 5/2)+	1.4	35	0.035	1.19	2	5/2+	0.033

Table 1-2 Comparison between $T = 17/2$ states in $^{117}_{51}Sb$ and $^{117}_{50}Sn$. The table compares the properties of the isobaric analog states observed in proton scattering on ^{116}Sn (Richard *et al.*, *loc. cit.*, Fig. 1-9) and (d, p) reactions on the same target (E. J. Schneid, A. Prakash, and B. L. Cohen, *Phys. Rev.* **156**, 1316, 1967). Column one gives the proton energy in the center-of-mass system. The energy in column two measures the excitation of the resonance state from the energy E_0 of the lowest $T = 17/2$ state in ^{117}Sb. Column eight gives the excitation energy of the corresponding states in ^{117}Sn. The single-particle proton widths $(\Gamma_p)_{sp}$ employed in column seven have been calculated by J. P. Bondorf and H. Lütken (private communication, 1967). The results of the coupled channel calculation are rather similar to those obtained by considering the scattering of a single proton in the nuclear potential and multiplying the width (as given by Eq. (3F-65)) by the factor $(2T_0 + 1)^{-1}$, which represents the probability of the proton channel in the state (1-66).

▼ variations are quite small ($\lesssim$20 keV), and this may be understood from the fact that the Coulomb energy difference represents the average Coulomb energy for the proton states obtained by replacing one of the 17 different excess neutrons in ^{117}Sn by a proton. Since the different levels in ^{117}Sn differ primarily in the orbits of a single or a few neutrons, the energy shift is expected to vary only little from level to level.

The excitation energy of the lowest $T = 17/2$ level in ^{117}Sb is 11.2 MeV (see Fig. 1-9) and may be compared to the estimate (2-18), which yields

$$\mathscr{E}(A = 117, T = 17/2, M_T = 15/2) - \mathscr{E}(A = 117, T = 15/2, M_T = 15/2) \approx 13.5 \text{ MeV}$$

assuming $b_{\text{sym}} \approx 50$ MeV (see Eq. (2-15)). The estimated energy difference must be somewhat reduced on account of shell structure effects, which give an added stability to the $Z = 50$ proton configuration in the Sn isotopes and their isobaric analog states in the Sb isotopes.

The resonance structure in the elastic proton scattering can be represented by a scattering amplitude consisting of a smoothly varying part (direct amplitude) and resonance amplitudes of Breit–Wigner form (see Eqs. (3F-10) and (3F-12)). Since the proton energies are several MeV below the Coulomb barrier, the direct amplitude is approximately equal to the amplitude for Coulomb scattering. The elastic proton widths Γ_p and the total widths Γ obtained from the resonance analysis are listed in Table 1-2. The angular distribution of the resonance scattering determines the orbital angular momentum l_p of the resonating proton, but is rather insensitive to the value of j_p. The extracted proton widths somewhat depend on the value of j_p; the quoted values of Γ_p are obtained by assuming j_p equal to the observed spin of the analog state in ^{117}Sn.

The observed values of Γ_p may be compared with the single-particle widths $(\Gamma_p)_{\text{sp}}$ that would be expected if the resonances could be described in terms of single-particle motion. The states in ^{117}Sn would then correspond to a single neutron moving in the potential of the ^{116}Sn nucleus in its ground state, while the isobaric analog state in ^{117}Sb would be represented by (see, for example, Eq. (3-19c))

$$|T = T_0 + 1/2, M_T = T_0 - 1/2\rangle$$
$$= \left(\frac{1}{2T_0 + 1}\right)^{1/2} |p; T_0, M_T = T_0\rangle + \left(\frac{2T_0}{2T_0 + 1}\right)^{1/2} |n; T_0, M_T = T_0 - 1\rangle \quad (1\text{-}66)$$

This state is a linear combination of proton + target (^{116}Sn) and neutron + target analog (lowest $T = 8$ state in ^{116}Sb).

The Coulomb field implies that the state (1-66) is coupled to the $T = T_0 - 1/2$ state with the same single-particle configuration

$$|T = T_0 - 1/2, M_T = T_0 - 1/2\rangle$$
$$= \left(\frac{2T_0}{2T_0 + 1}\right)^{1/2} |p; T_0, M_T = T_0\rangle - \left(\frac{1}{2T_0 + 1}\right)^{1/2} |n; T_0, M_T = T_0 - 1\rangle \quad (1\text{-}67)$$

▲ A striking consequence of the Coulomb interaction is the fact that the proton channel is open while the neutron channel is closed. (The proton energy is below the threshold for a (p, n) reaction exciting the analog state of the target, as can be seen from Fig. 1-9.) This asymmetry between proton and neutron channels implies a major coupling of the states (1-66) and (1-67) when the nucleon is outside the nucleus (Robson, 1965). The single-particle proton widths in Table 1-2 have been obtained from a calculation taking into account the coupling between the two channels (1-66) and (1-67) and based on the potential

$$V = V_0(r) + \frac{V_1(r)}{A}(\mathbf{t}\cdot\mathbf{T}_0) + V_{\text{Coul}}(r)(\tfrac{1}{2} - t_z) + \Delta\mathscr{E}_{\text{Coul}}(\tfrac{1}{2} + t_z) \tag{1-68}$$

The first two terms represent the isoscalar and isovector nuclear potentials (see Eq. (2-29)), and $V_{\text{Coul}}(r)$ is the Coulomb potential.

The ratio between the observed Γ_p and the single-particle value provides a measure of the single-particle parentage factor (see Sec. 3-5b and Appendix 3F) and can be compared with the parentage factor observed in the neutron transfer reactions (^{116}Sn$(d, p)^{117}$Sn) populating the $M_T = 17/2$ components of the $T = 17/2$ states (see Sec. 3-5a and Appendix 3E). The correspondence exhibited in Table 1-2 between the ratios of Γ_p to $(\Gamma_p)_{\text{sp}}$ for the proton reactions and the ratios σ_{dp} to $(\sigma_{dp})_{\text{sp}}$ for the stripping reactions provides further tests of the interpretation of the states as members of a T multiplet. The agreement is good, except for the 1/2+ state. A discrepancy of the magnitude indicated for the 1/2+ state would be surprising in view of the additional evidence confirming the interpretation of the states as isobaric analogs. The discrepancy, however, is hardly beyond the uncertainties in the present analysis of the reaction cross sections.

The total width of the observed resonances in (p, p) scattering and (p, n) reactions considerably exceeds the proton width for elastic scattering (see Table 1-2). Additional small contributions to the width are associated with inelastic proton scattering, but the main part of the width must be attributed to the coupling of the $T_0 + 1/2$ resonances with the neighboring $T_0 - 1/2$ levels.

The spacing of $T_0 - 1/2$ levels of given I and π may be estimated from Eq. (2-57). Employing the value $a = (\pi^2/6)g_0 = 17\ \text{MeV}^{-1}$ for the parameter a related to the single-particle level density g_0 (obtained from the analysis of nuclear reactions, see Fig. 2-12), one may estimate the total density of levels with $I\pi = 1/2+$

$$\rho(A = 117, E = 11.2\ \text{MeV}, I = \tfrac{1}{2}, \pi) \approx 4\ (\text{eV})^{-1}$$

The dense spectrum of $T_0 - 1/2$ levels is expected to have great complexity and one may describe the T-violating coupling as a decay of the $T_0 + 1/2$ levels with the formation of a compound nucleus in the $T_0 - 1/2$ channel. Because of the Coulomb barrier, the compound nucleus decays primarily by neutron emission and the observed resonance (p, n) reactions may be interpreted in this manner.

A significant contribution to the compound nucleus formation is expected to be associated with the coupling via the $T = 15/2$ state (1-67); one may attempt

▼ to describe the further coupling of this state to the compound nucleus by means of an imaginary component in the potential for the $T = 15/2$ channel. (Auerbach *et al.*, 1966; Bondorf *et al.*, 1966; Tamura, 1966). The term $\Delta\mathscr{E}_{\text{Coul}}$ should also contain an imaginary part associated with the decay width of the isobaric analog of the target (A. Kerman, private communication).

Since the resonance state decays primarily via compound nucleus formation ($\Gamma_{\text{comp}} > \Gamma_p$), the $T = 17/2$ state is strongly coupled to the $T = 15/2$ levels in the resonance region, and we are dealing with a typical strength function phenomenon (see Secs. 2-4b and 3F-1c). Thus, the true eigenstates of the scattering process are $T = 15/2$ levels, each of which has received a small component of the $T = 17/2$ level. In this sense, the isospin quantum number is completely violated.

The widths Γ of the $T = 17/2$ strength functions, though very large compared with level spacings in the $T = 15/2$ spectrum, are small compared with the spacing of $T = 17/2$ states with same $I\pi$. In spite of the strong T mixing for the individual scattering states, the properties of the isobaric analog levels therefore retain a well-defined meaning in terms of integrated values for the narrow strength functions. Interpreted in this manner, the above analysis of energies, spin parity quantum numbers, and partial widths for isobaric analog states is only little affected by the T mixing.

Test of isobaric symmetry in β transitions of $0^+ \rightarrow 0^+$ type (Fig. 1-10 and Table 1-3)

Isospin allowed transitions. The allowed β transitions of Fermi type provide a direct test of the isobaric symmetry, since the transition operator, apart from a normalization factor, equals a component

$$T_{\pm} = T_x \pm iT_y = \sum_k t_x(k) \pm it_y(k) \tag{1-69}$$

of the total isospin. (This structure of the transition operator is a consequence of the assumed general relationship between the vector β current and the electromagnetic current (the "conserved vector current" theory) and thus also includes the contributions of virtual mesons in the nucleus (see Eqs. (3D-11) and (3D-40)).

The operator (1-69) vanishes except for transitions between members of an isobaric multiplet, for which we have

$$\langle T, M_T \pm 1 \,|T_{\pm}|\, TM_T\rangle = ((T \mp M_T)(T \pm M_T + 1))^{1/2} \tag{1-70}$$

independently of other properties of the nuclear states. This result can be directly tested for transitions where initial as well as final states have $I\pi = 0+$, since such transitions are of pure Fermi type (the Gamow–Teller matrix element vanishes).

▲ An example of such a transition is provided by the decay of ^{14}O going to the

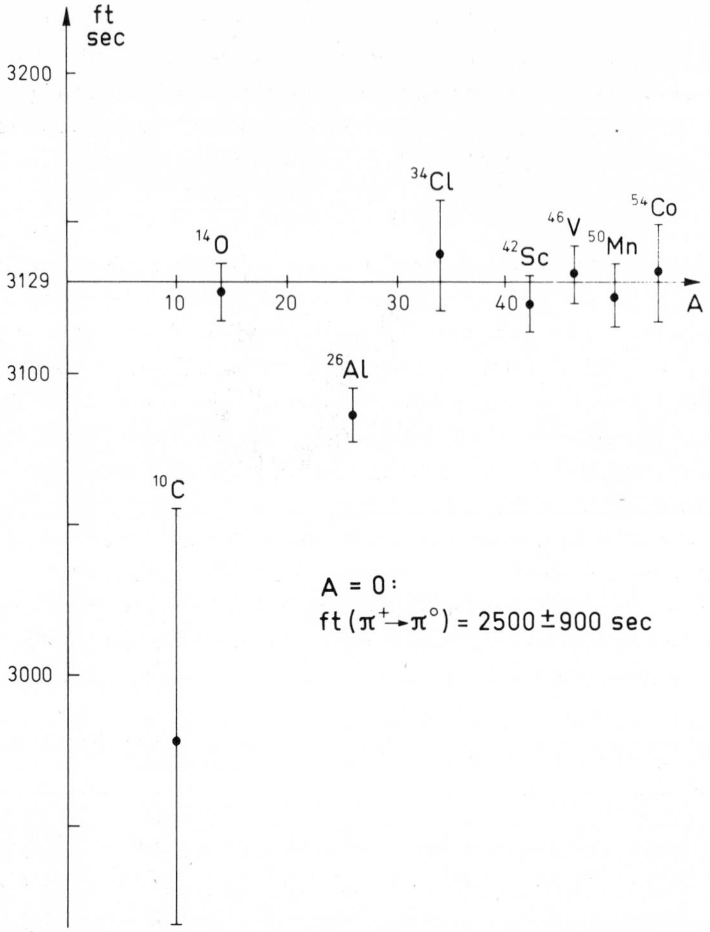

Figure 1-10 The figure shows the experimental *ft* values given by J. M. Freeman, J. G. Jenkin, G. Murray, and W. E. Burcham, *Phys. Rev. Letters* **16**, 959 (1966); see also the references quoted in this article. The *ft* values include radiative corrections and effects of the finite nuclear size, as well as corrections for the screening of the nuclear Coulomb field by the atomic electrons. The *ft* value of the $\pi^+ \rightarrow \pi^0$ decay is taken from A. F. Dunaitsev, V. I. Petrukhin, Yu. D. Prokoshkin, and V. I. Rykalin, *Int. Conf. on Fundamental Aspects of Weak Interactions*, BNL 837(C-39), p. 344, Brookhaven (1963). A more recent measurement has given $ft(\pi^+ \rightarrow \pi^0) = 3190 \pm 320$ sec (Depommier *et al.*, 1968).

▼ 2.31 MeV state of ^{14}N (see Fig. 1-7). Figure 1-10 shows the available evidence on this type of transition. All the examples refer to $T = 1$ states, and the constancy of the observed *ft* values thus provides evidence for the isobaric purity of the corresponding states. The most accurately determined *ft* values are seen to be constant to within the accuracy of the measurement, which is better than $\frac{1}{2}\%$ (the only exception is the *ft* value for the decay of ^{26}Al, which shows a deviation of $1\frac{1}{2}\%$). ▲

▼ An estimate of the isospin impurity caused by the Coulomb field is given in Fig. 2-6. Such an estimate yields admixtures of components with $T = 2$ into the predominantly $T = 1$ states, with intensities $P(T = 2)$ increasing rapidly with Z and reaching values of a few tenths of a percent for the heaviest nuclei in Fig. 1-10. (The value of $P(T = 2)$ for nuclei with $T_0 = 1$ is obtained by multiplying the value of $P(T = 1)$ for nuclei with $N = Z$ (which is the quantity plotted in Fig. 2-6) by the factor $\langle T_0 M_T 10 \,|\, T M_T \rangle^2$.) However, as discussed in connection with Fig. 2-6, these isospin impurities have only little effect on the β-transition matrix element, since they represent a cumulative effect associated with all the protons in the nucleus and are therefore approximately the same for parent and daughter nuclei. The transition matrix element is affected only by the coupling between the Coulomb distortion effect and the few nucleons carrying the unit isospin. The estimate (2-109) indicates that this coupling leads to a reduction of the ft values, which for $A < 50$ is an order of magnitude smaller than the isospin impurities shown in Fig. 2-6.

Isospin forbidden transitions. The forbiddenness of Fermi transitions with $\Delta T \neq 0$ has also been observed. Table 1-3 contains the known $0^+ \rightarrow 0^+$ transitions between states of different isobaric spin ($\Delta T = 1$). Comparing the ft values with those in Fig. 1-10 we see that the $\Delta T = 1$ transitions are hindered by factors ▲ of the order of 10^4 to 10^8, as compared to the $\Delta T = 0$ transitions.

	T_i	T_f	ft (sec)	c^2
$^{66}Ge \rightarrow {}^{66}Ga$	1	2	6×10^6	3×10^{-4}
$^{66}Ga \rightarrow {}^{66}Zn$	2	3	8×10^7	1×10^{-5}
$^{156}Eu \rightarrow {}^{156}Gd$	15	14	5.8×10^9	3.6×10^{-8}
$^{156}Eu \rightarrow {}^{156}Gd(1.05)$	15	14	1.5×10^{10}	1.4×10^{-8}
$^{170}Lu \rightarrow {}^{170}Yb$	14	15	5.7×10^9	3.7×10^{-8}
$^{234}Np \rightarrow {}^{234}U$	24	25	1.8×10^8	7×10^{-7}
$^{234}Np \rightarrow {}^{234}U(0.81)$	24	25	1.5×10^9	8×10^{-8}
$^{234}Np \rightarrow {}^{234}U(1.04)$	24	25	1.4×10^9	9×10^{-8}

Table 1-3 For the β transitions to excited states in the daughter nucleus, the excitation energy in MeV is given in parenthesis. The decay of ^{64}Ga to ^{64}Zn (log ft = 6.6) may also belong to the group of $\Delta T = 1$ Fermi transitions, but the spin 0+ for ^{64}Ga is not well established. The experimental data for ^{66}Ge are taken from R. A. Ricci, R. K. Girgis, and R. van Lieshout, *Nuclear Phys.* **21**, 177 (1960); for ^{66}Ga, from D. C. Camp and L. M. Langer, *Phys Rev.* **129**, 1782 (1963); for ^{156}Eu, ^{170}Lu, and ^{234}Np, from P. G. Hansen, H. L. Nielsen, K. Wilsky, and J. G. Cuninghame, *Phys. Letters* **24B**, 95 (1967) and the references quoted herein.

▼ Small contributions to the transition strength for the $\Delta T = 1$ decays arise from higher-order corrections to the Fermi matrix element (for instance, the ▲ multipole moment $\mathcal{M}(j_V, \kappa = 1, \lambda = 0)$ and the radial dependence of the Fermi

▼ operator itself; see Appendix 3D). An estimate of these effects indicates, however, that they are insignificant in the cases considered. The transition strength is therefore ascribed to isobaric spin impurities in the nuclear states caused by the electromagnetic interaction or by possible other interaction components violating charge independence. (For a discussion of the effect of charge-dependent nucleonic interactions on β-decay matrix elements, see the review by Blin-Stoyle (1964, pp. 213 ff.).)

The main effect can be described in terms of a small admixture of the analog state of the parent into the daughter state, or of the analog of the daughter into the parent. (For $T_i = T_f + 1$, where T_i and T_f represent the isospins of parent and daughter states, respectively, the $T = T_i$, $M_T = T_i - 1$ analog of the parent may be admixed into the daughter state, while for $T_i = T_f - 1$, the $T = T_f$, $M_T = T_f - 1$ analog of the daughter may be admixed into the parent.) In the last column of Table 1-3, we list the square of the amplitude c for the admixture, determined from the observed ft values. The normalization factor in the transition operator (the Fermi coupling constant g_V) is obtained from the $\Delta T = 0$ transitions in Fig. 1-10, and thus

$$2T_{\max} c^2 = \frac{6260}{ft\ (\text{sec})} \tag{1-71}$$

where $T_{\max}$ is the larger of T_i and T_f.

For three of the decays (^{156}Eu $\rightarrow$ ^{156}Gd(gr.st.), ^{170}Lu $\rightarrow$ ^{170}Yb, and ^{234}Np $\rightarrow$ ^{234}U), a rather detailed analysis is possible in terms of the transition of a single particle moving in a spheroidal potential. Estimates of the effects of the Coulomb field in causing a T admixture are found to account approximately for the observed transition intensities (Damgaard, 1966).

The $\Delta T = 1$ Fermi transitions can also be studied in mixed Fermi and Gamow–Teller decays (allowed decays with $\Delta I = 0$, excluding $0 \rightarrow 0$). The ft value gives the sum of the Fermi and Gamow–Teller transition strength, and the ratio between them can be obtained by several methods. The most frequently used is the measurement of the circular polarization of γ quanta as a function of the angle between the β and γ radiation. The Fermi matrix elements for all the $\Delta T = 1$ transitions are found to be very small. For a compilation of Fermi matrix elements in mixed transitions, see Daniel and Schmitt (1965).

Binding energies and spin of hypernuclei (Table 1-4)

The mass of the Λ particle is considerably smaller than the mass of any other state with strangeness $S = -1$ and baryon number $A = 1$ (see Fig. 1-11). The next higher state with these quantum numbers is the Σ particle, whose mass is 80 MeV greater than that of the Λ particle. The nuclei with $S = -1$ can therefore be approximately described as systems composed of nucleons and a Λ particle. ▲

▼ The binding energy B_Λ of a Λ particle in a hypernucleus (also referred to as the separation energy S_Λ) is given by

$$-B_\Lambda = M({}^A_\Lambda Z) - M({}^{A-1}Z) - M_\Lambda \tag{1-72}$$

and is determined by measuring the kinetic energies of all the disintegration products when the hypernucleus decays by one of the two modes

$$\begin{aligned} {}^A_\Lambda Z &\to {}^A Z + 176.0 \text{ MeV} - B_\Lambda \\ {}^A_\Lambda Z &\to {}^A(Z+1) + \pi^- + 37.7 \text{ MeV} - B_\Lambda \end{aligned} \tag{1-73}$$

The available evidence on Λ-binding energies in hypernuclei is given in ▲ Table 1-4. One sees that the binding energies for Λ particles are of similar

Nucleus	T	M_T	B_Λ(MeV)	$I\pi$
${}^3_\Lambda H$	0	0	0.32 ± 0.17	1/2+
${}^4_\Lambda H$	1/2	1/2	1.95 ± 0.14	0+
${}^4_\Lambda He$	1/2	−1/2	2.07 ± 0.09	0+
${}^5_\Lambda He$	0	0	3.04 ± 0.03	
${}^7_\Lambda He$	1	1	4.4 ± 0.7	
${}^7_\Lambda Li$	0	0	5.42 ± 0.11	
${}^7_\Lambda Be$	1	−1	5.9 ± 0.8	
${}^8_\Lambda Li$	1/2	1/2	6.60 ± 0.13	1−
${}^8_\Lambda Be$	1/2	−1/2	6.57 ± 0.20	
${}^9_\Lambda Li$	1	1	8.24 ± 0.28	
${}^9_\Lambda Be$	0	0	6.24 ± 0.25	
${}^{10}_\Lambda Be$	1/2	1/2	8.9 ± 0.5	
${}^{10}_\Lambda B$	1/2	−1/2	8.8 ± 0.5	
${}^{11}_\Lambda B$	0	0	10.0 ± 0.3	
${}^{12}_\Lambda B$	1/2	1/2	11.09 ± 0.21	
${}^{13}_\Lambda C$	0	0	10.6 ± 0.4	
${}^{14}_\Lambda C$	1/2	1/2	13.2 ± 0.7	
${}^{14}_\Lambda N$	1/2	−1/2	11.7 ± 0.5	

Table 1-4 The experimental data are taken from the compilation by R. Levi-Setti, *Proc. Int. Conf. on Hyperfragments, St. Cergue*, March, 1963 (CERN 64-1) and from C. Mayeur, J. Sacton, P. Vilain, G. Wilquet, D. Stanley, P. Allen, D. H. Davis, E. R. Fletcher, D. A. Garbutt, M. A. Shaukat, J. E. Allen, V. A. Bull, A. P. Conway, and P. V. March, Université Libre de Bruxelles, Bulletin No. 24, December 1965.

In the notation ${}^A_\Lambda Z$ for hypernuclei, Z gives the atomic species (the total nuclear charge Z) in the usual chemical notation, and A is the total number of baryons. The subscript Λ indicates that the strangeness quantum number is $S=-1$. The assumed T quantum numbers are the lowest values consistent with the observed $M_T = \frac{1}{2}(N-Z)$.

magnitude as the binding energies for nucleons in $S = 0$ systems (nuclei with strangeness zero; see, for example, Fig. 2-4). However, the Λ-binding energy continues to increase with A, while the nucleon binding energy does not, corresponding to the fact that the bound Λ particle does not have to satisfy the exclusion principle with respect to the nucleons of the systems. The lowest Λ orbit is the $1s_{1/2}$ state, for which the kinetic energy is approximately

$$E_{\mathrm{kin}} \approx \frac{\pi^2 \hbar^2}{2M_\Lambda R^2} = 118 A^{-2/3} \text{ MeV} \tag{1-74}$$

assuming $A \gg 1$ and $R = 1.2A^{1/3}$ fm. For ^{13}C (the heaviest hyperfragment in Table 1-4 with even Z and even N), we have $E_{\mathrm{kin}} \approx 20$ MeV, and from the observed B_Λ we obtain the rough estimate $V = B_\Lambda + E_{\mathrm{kin}} \approx 30$ MeV for the potential acting on the Λ particle. This value for the binding potential is consistent with evidence on the decay of heavy hyperfragments formed by capture of K^- mesons in the Ag and Br nuclei of photographic emulsions (see, for example, Lemonne *et al.*, 1965). The estimated value of 30 MeV for the potential energy of Λ particles in nuclei is approximately half of the average potential acting on a nucleon at the Fermi surface (see Sec. 2-1g).

One can see from Table 1-4 some evidence for charge independence of the interaction of Λ particles with nucleons. There are several pairs forming isobaric doublets, such as ($^4_\Lambda$H, $^4_\Lambda$He) and ($^8_\Lambda$Li, $^8_\Lambda$Be), while $^7_\Lambda$He and $^7_\Lambda$Be belong to an isobaric triplet. The isobaric analog states are found to have approximately the same binding energies. (The apparently smaller binding in $^7_\Lambda$He as compared with that of the isobaric analog $^7_\Lambda$Be may possibly be ascribed to the presence of excited states of $^7_\Lambda$He in the hypernuclei decays on which the B_Λ determinations have been based (see Pniewsky and Danysz, 1962).)

The evidence on the spin and parity values in the table (Λ is assigned an intrinsic parity of $+1$) comes from angular correlation measurements as well as from the determination of branching ratios for different decay modes (see, for example, the survey by Levi-Setti, 1964.) From the spin values together with the variation of the binding energies in the lightest hypernuclei, one may conclude that the Λ-nucleon interaction has a rather strong spin dependence, favoring the singlet state (^1S). This is contrary to the nucleon-nucleon interaction for which the attraction is strongest in the triplet state (^3S); see Sec. 2-5. The spin dependence of the Λ-nucleon force also appears to be responsible for the fluctuations in B_Λ with respect to a smooth increase with A. Thus, the relatively small binding in $^9_\Lambda$Be and $^{13}_\Lambda$C seems to be connected with the fact that the neutrons and protons in these systems tend to form a state with $I = 0$, which allows no spin correlation with the Λ particle. (For a discussion of the evidence on the Λ-nucleon force obtained from hypernuclei studies, see Dalitz, 1963.)

A few cases of hypernuclei with two Λ particles have been identified: $^6_{\Lambda\Lambda}$He (Prowse, 1966) and $^{10}_{\Lambda\Lambda}$Be (Danysz *et al.*, 1963). The total binding energy of the two Λ particles is found, in both cases, to exceed twice the value of B_Λ (for $^5_\Lambda$He

▼ and $^{9}_{\Lambda}$Be, respectively) by the amount 4.5 ± 0.5 MeV, which thus represents the interaction energy of the Λ particles.

Multiplets in the baryon spectrum (Fig. 1-11 and Table 1-5)

Some of the well-established states in the low-energy excitation spectrum of the nucleon (states with baryon number $A = 1$) are shown in Fig. 1-11. The states are labeled by the angular momentum and parity $I\pi$, the strangeness S, and the isospin T. The T quantum number is expressed in terms of the multiplicity $2T + 1$ of the states. In many cases, the evidence for the assignments is ▲

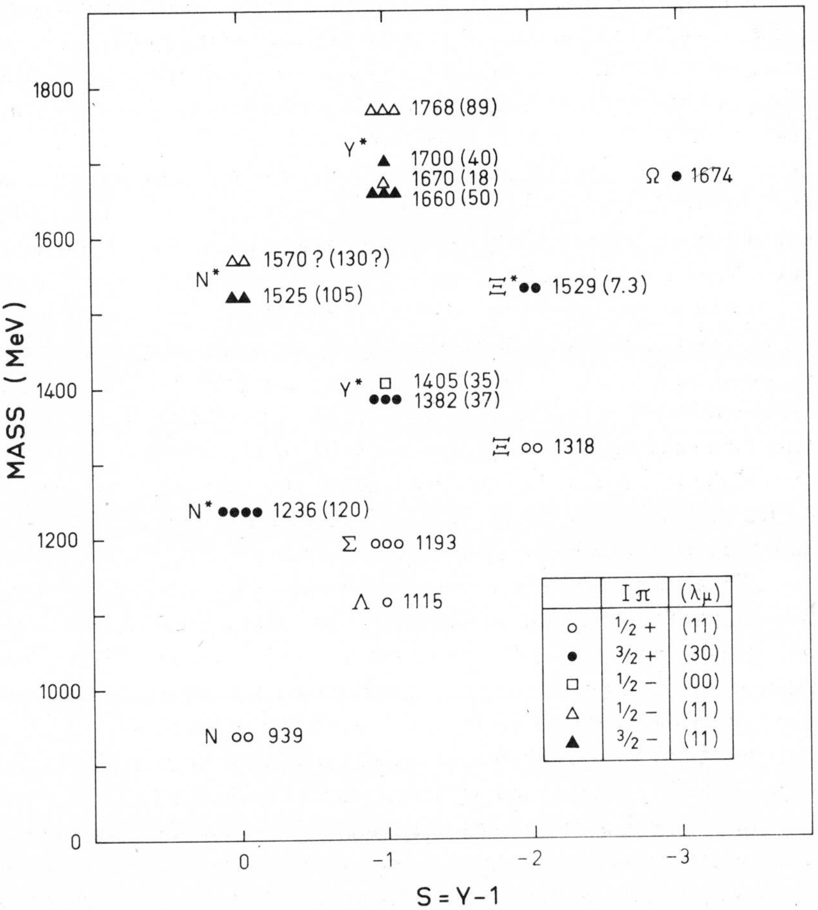

Figure 1-11 Excited states of the nucleon. The experimental data are taken from the survey by A. H. Rosenfeld, A. Barbaro-Galtieri, W. J. Podolsky, L. R. Price, P. Soding, C. G. Wohl, M. Roos, and W. J. Willis, *Rev. Mod. Phys.* **39**, 1 (1967). The numbers give the masses in MeV and the full width at half maximum is listed in parenthesis (for the states decaying by strong interactions). For T multiplets, the numbers give the average for the observed M_T components. The tentative ($I\pi$) assignment for the Y^* particle with mass 1768 MeV has been suggested (Dalitz, 1967) on the basis of a possible grouping into SU_3 multiplets.

incomplete and is partially based on the possibility of joining the states into SU_3 multiplets, as will be discussed below. It must also be emphasized that, in addition to the states in the figure, many more excited baryon states have been observed, but for most of these the assignments are very uncertain. (Some of the higher states are included in Fig. 1-13; for a comprehensive survey of the experimental data, see Rosenfeld *et al.*, *loc. cit.*, Fig. 1-11.)

The baryon levels in Fig. 1-11 are grouped into multiplets associated with a classification according to SU_3 symmetry. These multiplets are labeled by the quantum numbers $(\lambda\mu)$, and the (S, T) components contained in a given multiplet can be found by means of the general rules discussed in Secs. 1C-2 and 1C-3. It is convenient for this purpose to think of the baryons as composed of three quarks, each of which can be in three different states forming an isobaric doublet with strangeness zero and an isoscalar with strangeness -1. Thus, the $(\lambda\mu) = (11)$ and $(\lambda\mu) = (30)$ multiplets correspond to the diagrams

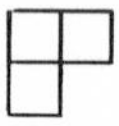 $(\lambda\mu) = (11)$ and 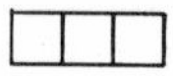 $(\lambda\mu) = (30)$

The different components are obtained by labeling each box with the set of quantum numbers of the quark states, with the restrictions given in Sec. 1C-2b. In this manner, one can directly enumerate the possible (S, M_T) values and hence the (S, T) components. For example, the (11) multiplet is an octuplet containing the (S, T) components $(0, 1/2)$, $(-1, 0)$, $(-1, 1)$, and $(-2, 1/2)$, while the (30) multiplet is a decuplet consisting of the (S, T) components $(0, 3/2)$, $(-1, 1)$, $(-2, 1/2)$, and $(-3, 0)$.

From Fig. 1-11 it is seen that the low-lying $I\pi = 1/2+$ levels form an octuplet, while the $3/2+$ levels can be grouped into a decuplet. The higher states shown in the figure appear to comprise a singlet with $I\pi = 1/2-$ and two octuplets with $I\pi = 1/2-$ and $3/2-$, respectively; however, the expected $S = -2$ components of these octuplets have not so far been observed.

The significance of the SU_3 symmetry quantum numbers, first suggested by the simple pattern of the observed baryon levels, is confirmed by an extensive body of evidence concerning matrix elements between the states (see Gell-Mann and Ne'eman, 1964). At the same time, it is apparent from Fig. 1-11 that there are rather large symmetry-violating interactions responsible for the mass splittings of several hundred MeV between the different states of the SU_3 multiplets. It is remarkable that these mass splittings are found to obey a simple rule that can be interpreted as a first-order perturbation effect of a symmetry-breaking interaction, transforming as the $T = 0$, $S = 0$ member of an octuplet representation with $A = 0$.

The mass formula is especially simple for the decuplet, since the representation product $(30) \otimes (11)$ contains the representation (30) only once (see Sec. 1C-1g). The mass splittings are therefore proportional to a Clebsch-Gordan coefficient in SU_3 space and can be immediately evaluated by noting that the

▼ hypercharge operator, Y, is an operator with the same transformation properties as the assumed symmetry-breaking interaction. The mass splittings are therefore proportional to Y,

$$\Delta M = aAY \tag{1-75}$$

(The argument is the same as that which implies that the diagonal matrix elements of the z component of a vector operator are proportional to those of $I_z(=M)$.) In Eq. (1-75), we have inserted the factor A to ensure that ΔM is the same for particles and antiparticles. The relation (1-75) is seen to be obeyed with an accuracy of a few MeV; indeed, on this basis the mass of the Ω particle was accurately predicted prior to its experimental discovery.

For more general representations $(\lambda\mu)$, the mass formula may involve two parameters (reduced matrix elements), since the product $(\lambda\mu) \otimes (11)$ in general contains the representation $(\lambda\mu)$ twice. We can construct the generalized mass formula by employing two combinations of the SU_3 generators that are isoscalars, strangeness conserving, and transform as members of an octuplet. As the first, we may take the linear operator Y used above, and, as the second, a quadratic expression which must be a linear combination of the isoscalars $(\mathbf{T})^2$, Y^2, and 1. The appropriate combination transforming as an octuplet member may be found by noting that, for the decuplet, the matrix elements must be proportional to Y. Omitting the constant term, the mass formula can be written (Gell-Mann, 1962; Okubo, 1962)

$$\Delta M = aAY + b(T(T+1) - \tfrac{1}{4}Y^2) \tag{1-76}$$

For the $I\pi = 1/2+$ octuplet, there are three observed mass differences, and one obtains the relation

$$\tfrac{1}{2}(M_N + M_\Xi) = \tfrac{1}{4}(3M_\Lambda + M_\Sigma) \tag{1-77}$$

A similar relation predicts the missing $S = -2$ components of the $I\pi = 1/2-$ and $I\pi = 3/2-$ octuplets to have $M \approx 1820$ MeV and $M \approx 1855$ MeV, respectively.

The above derivation of the mass relations is based on the assumption that the SU_3 violating interaction has the tensorial structure corresponding to a member of a $(\lambda\mu) = (11)$ representation. For a discussion of possible origins of this "octuplet dominance," see, for example, the reprint collection by Gell-Mann and Ne'eman (1964).

One may also attempt to discuss the mass splittings in terms of effective interactions between quarks in a model in which one takes quite literally the interpretation of the baryons as composed of three particles, which may be in any one of the three states with the quantum numbers given above. We use a notation where p, n are the two members of the isodoublet, and λ the isosinglet with strangeness. (Such a model for the mass splittings has been discussed, in the context of SU_6 symmetry, by Federman *et al.*, 1966.) ▲

▼ In the model considered, the mass splittings arise partly from a difference in the masses of the strange and nonstrange quarks, which contributes a term proportional to Y, and partly from the interactions. The two-body bonds can be classified into five types (assuming isobaric spin invariance and strangeness conservation):

$$\begin{aligned} &V_s(pp) = V_s(pn) = V_s(nn) \\ &V_s(p\lambda) = V_s(n\lambda) \\ &V_s(\lambda\lambda) \\ &V_a(pn) \\ &V_a(p\lambda) = V_a(n\lambda) \end{aligned} \tag{1-78}$$

The bonds labeled s are symmetric in the SU_3 variables and therefore, presumably, antisymmetric in the spin-orbital variables, while the bonds labeled a are antisymmetric in the SU_3 variables. If the interaction were SU_3 invariant, the bonds would be independent of the quarks involved, and thus would be described in terms of two parameters, one for the symmetric and one for the antisymmetric bonds. We are therefore left with two independent combinations of symmetric bonds and one combination of antisymmetric bonds, which can contribute to mass splittings within an SU_3 multiplet.

As the simplest application, we consider the splittings within the decuplet. This representation is completely symmetric in the SU_3 variables and therefore only symmetric bonds occur, and we have

$$\begin{aligned} V(N^*) &= 3V_s(pp) \\ V(Y^*) &= V_s(pp) + 2V_s(p\lambda) \\ V(\Xi^*) &= 2V_s(p\lambda) + V_s(\lambda\lambda) \\ V(\Omega) &= 3V_s(\lambda\lambda) \end{aligned} \tag{1-79}$$

Since there are three mass splittings and only two independent symmetric interactions, the assumption of two-body forces immediately implies one relation between the masses

$$M(\Omega) - M(N^*) = 3(M(\Xi^*) - M(Y^*)) \tag{1-80}$$

which is seen to be a weaker form of the mass equation (1-75). The full relation (1-75) requires the additional symmetry for the two-body interaction

$$V_s(pp) + V_s(\lambda\lambda) = 2V_s(p\lambda) \tag{1-81}$$

The general interaction (1-78) for the symmetric bonds, if expanded in terms of irreducible tensors in SU_3, contains one scalar, one tensor of rank $(\lambda\mu) = (11)$, and one belonging to the 27-dimensional representation $(\lambda\mu) = (22)$. The relation (1-81) implies the vanishing of the (22) component. ▲

In the octuplet, the antisymmetric bonds also contribute, and the total interaction becomes

$$\begin{aligned} V(N) &= \tfrac{3}{2}V_s(pp) + \tfrac{3}{2}V_a(np) \\ V(\Lambda) &= V_a(np) + \tfrac{3}{2}V_s(p\lambda) + \tfrac{1}{2}V_a(p\lambda) \\ V(\Sigma) &= V_s(pp) + \tfrac{1}{2}V_s(p\lambda) + \tfrac{3}{2}V_a(p\lambda) \\ V(\Xi) &= \tfrac{1}{2}V_s(p\lambda) + \tfrac{3}{2}V_a(p\lambda) + V_s(\lambda\lambda) \end{aligned} \tag{1-82}$$

Since the antisymmetric bonds have tensor structure in SU_3 corresponding to a scalar and an octuplet, the relation (1-81) is quite generally sufficient to ensure the mass formula (1-76) and, therefore, in particular that the $I\pi = 1/2+$ octuplet satisfies the relation (1-77).

The mass splittings within the isospin multiplets of the semistable baryon states (those decaying only by weak or electromagnetic interactions) are listed in Table 1-5. These splittings are attributed to the electromagnetic interactions,

Particle	M (MeV)
n	939.550 ± 0.005
p	938.256 ± 0.005
Σ^-	1197.4 ± 0.1
Σ^0	1192.6 ± 0.1
Σ^+	1189.5 ± 0.1
Ξ^-	1321.2 ± 0.2
Ξ^0	1314.7 ± 1.0
$\pi^\pm$	139.58 ± 0.02
π^0	134.97 ± 0.02
$K^\pm$	493.8 ± 0.1
K^0	497.9 ± 0.2

Table 1-5 Masses for isobaric multiplets in the baryon and meson spectra. The data are taken from the compilation by Rosenfeld *et al.*, *loc. cit.*, Fig. 1-11.

and their magnitude provides a measure of the violation of isospin symmetry. The pattern of the electromagnetic contributions to the masses provides guidance as to the tensorial structure of the electromagnetic interaction in terms of the SU_3 variables. In particular, the masses are found to be compatible with the assumption that the electromagnetic interaction is invariant under the SU_2 subgroup associated with the U spin (see p. 40). The U spin is analogous to the T spin and, thus, the nucleon octuplet can be decomposed into U-spin multiplets

▼ within each of which all the particles have the same charge. One thus obtains two U-spin doublets (N^+, Σ^+) and (Σ^-, Ξ^-), a singlet $((\frac{1}{2}\sqrt{3})\Sigma^0 - \frac{1}{2}\Lambda^0)$, and a triplet $(N^0, \frac{1}{2}\Sigma^0 + (\frac{1}{2}\sqrt{3})\Lambda^0, \Xi^0)$, where $N^+ =$ proton and $N^0 =$ neutron. The assumed U-spin invariance implies that the electromagnetic mass shifts are the same for the components in a multiplet. Combining these relations, we obtain one constraint on the splittings of the T multiplets in the octuplet

$$M(N^+) - M(N^0) = M(\Sigma^+) - M(\Sigma^-) + M(\Xi^-) - M(\Xi^0) \tag{1-83}$$

As seen from Table 1-5, this relation is satisfied within the accuracy of the measured masses. It may be noted that the validity of the relation (1-83) not only depends on the assumed U-spin invariance of the electromagnetic interaction, but also depends on the validity of the U-spin quantum numbers for the particles involved. This latter symmetry is violated by the stronger SU_3 symmetry-breaking interactions responsible for the large mass shifts.

In the SU_6 classification, the $I\pi = 1/2+$ octuplet and the $3/2+$ decuplet are viewed as belonging to a single representation with quantum numbers $[f] = [3]$, which is totally symmetric in the spin-isobaric variables of the quarks and totally antisymmetric in the space variables. The dimensionality of the representation in spin-isobaric space is $h = 56$ (see Eq. (1C-27)), corresponding to eight spin doublets and ten spin quadruplets, and the observed states can therefore be accounted for, if we assume the orbital motion to give a single preferred state with $L = 0$. One may attempt to classify the negative parity states in terms of a representation with $[f] = [21]$ associated with an orbital $L = 1$ state with conjugate symmetry. The dimensionality of this representation in spin-isobaric space is $h = 70$, and the total number of states is therefore $(2L + 1)h = 210$. If specified by the total angular momentum (and parity), these states comprise the following SU_3 multiplets: $I\pi = 1/2-$ (a singlet, two octuplets, and a decuplet), $I\pi = 3/2-$ (a singlet, two octuplets, and a decuplet), and $I\pi = 5/2-$ (an octuplet). Apart from the states shown in Fig. 1-11, there is preliminary evidence for the occurrence of a number of states with quantum numbers corresponding to the missing members of the 210-dimensional SU_6 multiplet. (See Dalitz, 1967, for a survey of experimental data and a discussion of the interpretation on the basis of a quark model.)

One may attempt to derive a mass formula for the splittings within the SU_6 multiplets by assuming the symmetry-violating interaction to have the simplest possible tensorial structure, as for the analysis of the mass splittings within the SU_3 multiplets. For SU_6, this assumption implies a mass operator transforming as a member of the 35-dimensional $[f] = [21111]$ representation. Such an operator has only a single reduced matrix element when acting between states belonging to the $[f] = [3]$ representation, and one therefore again obtains the mass formula (1-75), which does not account for the observed pattern. (For a tensorial decomposition of the empirical mass splittings, see Harari and Rashid, 1966.)

▲ The total spectrum of fermions (particles with half-integer spin) comprises, in addition to hadrons, also the family of leptons. The hadronic fermions have baryon number $A \neq 0$ (baryons ($A = 1$) and antibaryons ($A = -1$), as well as nuclei and antinuclei with $|A| = 3, 5, \ldots$), while the leptons have $A = 0$. The known leptons are the electron ($m_e = 0.51$ MeV), the muon ($m_\mu = 105.7$ MeV), and the two types of neutrinos (ν_e, ν_μ; zero mass). The leptons are associated with weak interactions and electromagnetic processes, but do not participate in the strong interactions. The leptonic processes appear to be governed by the conservation of lepton number ($L = 1$ for leptons ($e^-, \mu^-, \nu_e, \nu_\mu$) and $L = -1$ for antileptons ($e^+, \mu^+, \bar{\nu}_e, \bar{\nu}_\mu$); see Sec. 3D-1).

Multiplets in the meson spectrum (Fig. 1-12)

Some of the well-established states in the low-energy excitation spectrum of mesons (states with $A = 0$) are shown in Fig. 1-12. The quantum numbers

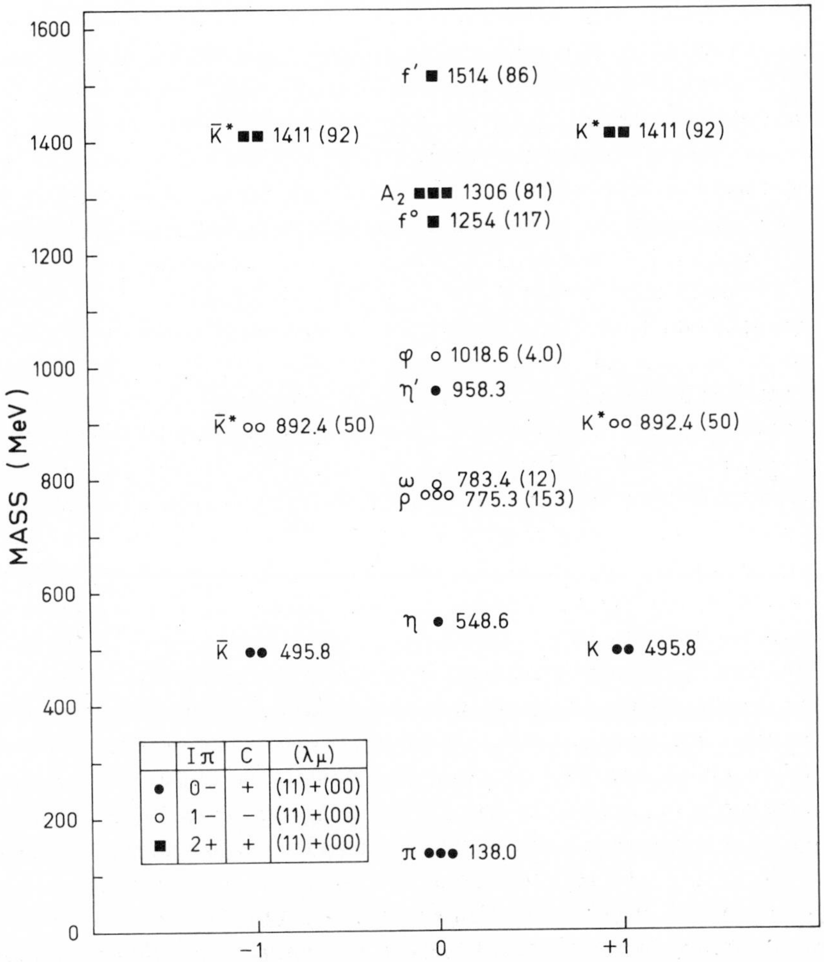

Figure 1-12 Spectrum of meson states. The experimental data are taken from the survey by Rosenfeld *et al.*, *loc. cit.*, Fig. 1-11. The abscissa is S ($= Y$).

▼ labeling the states are the same as in Fig. 1-11. In addition, the meson levels with $S=0$ and $M_T=0$ can be assigned a charge conjugation number, C. (All the meson states with $S=0$ can be assigned a G parity, with G representing the product of the charge conjugation operator and the charge symmetry operator; thus, for $M_T=0$, we have $G=C\,(-1)^T$.) For the long-lived states, the mass splittings within the T multiplets are listed in Table 1-5.

The meson levels in Fig. 1-12 can be grouped into three octuplets and three singlets with respect to SU_3 symmetry. However, it is found that the singlets and the $T=0$, $S=0$ octuplets with the same $I\pi$ are coupled to a significant extent so that the observed $T=0$, $S=0$ levels represent superpositions of singlet and octuplet components. Evidence on the mixing has been obtained from observed branching ratios in production and decay processes. Assuming the validity of a mass formula equivalent to Eq. (1-77), one can also estimate the masses of the unperturbed octuplet states with $T=0$, $S=0$, and in this manner determine the mixing ratios. It appears that a consistent interpretation of a variety of data can be obtained, although uncertainties remain, for example, as to whether the mass relation should be applied to the masses or to the square of the masses. (For a survey of the various estimates of the mixing amplitudes, see Goldhaber, 1967.)

In the quark model, the mesons are viewed as consisting of a quark and an antiquark. For a given spin-orbital configuration, there are nine isobaric states that comprise an SU_3 octuplet and a singlet.

In the SU_6 classification, the $I\pi=0-$ and $1-$ levels in Fig. 1-12 can be grouped into a singlet and a 35-dimensional representation with the quantum numbers $[f]=[0]$ and $[21111]$, respectively, both associated with orbital motion with $L=0$, $\pi=-1$. These 36 states have the symmetry quantum numbers implied by the quark model.

The spectrum of bosons (particles with integer spin) comprises, in addition to the hadrons with $A=0$ (mesons) and composite structures (nuclei, atoms, etc.), the photon and, if gravitational quanta occur, the graviton.

Families of baryon states with same isobaric symmetry (Fig. 1-13)

There is some evidence that hadronic states with the same isobaric symmetry (T, S, $(\lambda\mu)$, as well as A) can be grouped into families consisting of a series of states with the mass increasing smoothly with increasing values of I. Examples of such suggested families, or trajectories, in the baryon spectrum are shown in Fig. 1-13. The members of these families have the same parity and values of I differing by two ($I=1/2$, $5/2$, $9/2$, ... or $I=3/2$, $7/2$, $11/2$, ...). The states are observed as resonances in π-nucleon scattering, but for the higher resonances, the spin parity assignment is very uncertain and mainly based on the systematics suggested by the trajectories themselves.

Families of states, such as those considered in Fig. 1-13, may suggest a relationship similar to that governing the members of a rotational band, but there is so far little evidence concerning the dynamical degree of freedom involved ▲ in the excitations along the trajectory.

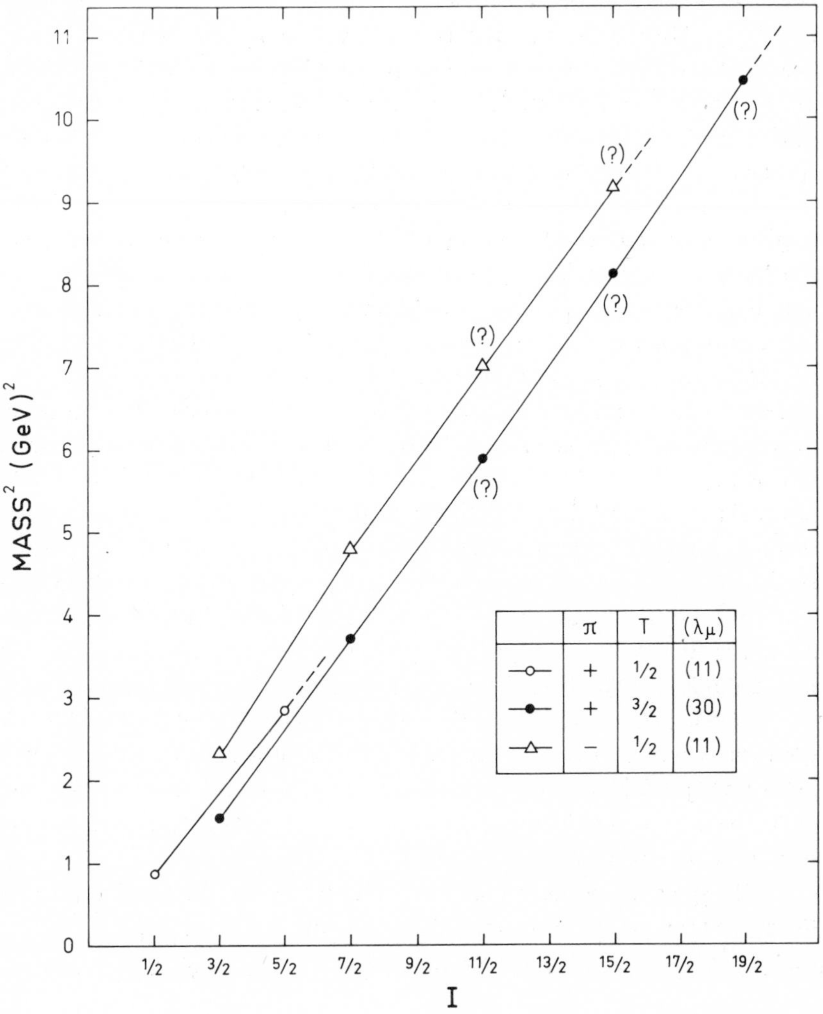

Figure 1-13 Baryon trajectories. The experimental data are taken from the survey by Rosenfeld *et al.*, *loc. cit.*, Fig. 1-11. A question mark indicates that the spin-parity assignment for the observed resonance state is not established. The quantum number *I* is the angular momentum. (This notation, which is standard in nuclear physics, differs from that conventionally employed in elementary particle physics, where *I* is used for isospin and *J* for total angular momentum.)

1-4 INVARIANCE CONDITIONS FOR NUCLEAR FORCES

The invariance laws considered in the previous sections of this chapter impose restrictions on the structure of the nuclear forces. In this section, we shall consider the most general dependence of these forces on the nucleonic variables. (Such an analysis was first given by Eisenbud and Wigner, 1941.)

1-4a Velocity-Independent Forces

Since the binding forces between nucleons result from the exchange of other particles (especially π mesons) with rest energies rather large compared to the kinetic energies of nucleons in nuclei, one may expect the forces to be approximately static. We therefore first consider forces independent of the nucleon velocities.

A static force acting between two nucleons may depend on the spin and isospin variables, and on the coordinates $\mathbf{r}_1$ and $\mathbf{r}_2$. Because of translational invariance, the force can involve only the relative distance $\mathbf{r} = \mathbf{r}_1 - \mathbf{r}_2$. One distinguishes between central forces (depending only on the magnitude, not the direction of $\mathbf{r}$) and noncentral forces (depending also on the direction of $\mathbf{r}$ with respect to the spin vectors).

The most general central static potential, which satisfies rotational invariance and isobaric symmetry, can be written

$$V_{\text{central}} = V_0(r) + (\boldsymbol{\sigma}_1 \cdot \boldsymbol{\sigma}_2)\, V_\sigma(r) + (\boldsymbol{\tau}_1 \cdot \boldsymbol{\tau}_2)\, V_\tau(r) + (\boldsymbol{\sigma}_1 \cdot \boldsymbol{\sigma}_2)(\boldsymbol{\tau}_1 \cdot \boldsymbol{\tau}_2) V_{\sigma\tau} \quad (1\text{-}84)$$

(We are here using the spin and isospin operators $\boldsymbol{\sigma} = 2\mathbf{s}$ and $\boldsymbol{\tau} = 2\mathbf{t}$, which are conventionally employed in the present context.)

The dependence of the interaction on the spin and isospin coordinates can also be expressed in other forms, which are sometimes more convenient. Using the space exchange operator P^r, the charge exchange operator P^τ given by Eq. (1-57), and the spin exchange operator

$$P^\sigma = \tfrac{1}{2}(1 + \boldsymbol{\sigma}_1 \cdot \boldsymbol{\sigma}_2) = \begin{cases} +1 & \text{for} \quad S = 1 \\ -1 & \text{for} \quad S = 0 \end{cases} \quad (1\text{-}85)$$

together with the relation (1-55), which expresses the generalized exclusion principle, the potential (1-84) can be written in terms of the three exchange operators. It is customary to use the notation

$$V_{\text{central}} = V_W(r) + V_M(r)P^r + V_B(r)P^\sigma - V_H(r)P^\tau \quad (1\text{-}86)$$

and to refer to Wigner, Majorana, Bartlett, and Heisenberg forces. One may also characterize the force in terms of projection operators that select particular channels of the two-nucleon system

$$\begin{aligned} V_{\text{central}} = {} & {}^{31}V(r)\, \mathscr{P}(T = 1, S = 0, L \text{ even}) \\ & + {}^{13}V(r)\, \mathscr{P}(T = 0, S = 1, L \text{ even}) \\ & + {}^{11}V(r)\, \mathscr{P}(T = 0, S = 0, L \text{ odd}) \\ & + {}^{33}V(r)\, \mathscr{P}(T = 1, S = 1, L \text{ odd}) \end{aligned} \quad (1\text{-}87)$$

where $\mathscr{P}(S = 0, T = 1, L \text{ even})$ is the projection operator for the spin singlet and angular momentum, L, even channel, and so on. The potentials used in Eqs. (1-84), (1-86), and (1-87) are linearly related,

$$\begin{aligned}
V_W &= V_o - V_\sigma - V_\tau + V_{\sigma\tau} \\
V_M &= -4V_{\sigma\tau} \\
V_B &= 2V_\sigma - 2V_{\sigma\tau} \\
V_H &= -2V_\tau + 2V_{\sigma\tau} \\
{}^{31}V &= V_W + V_M - V_B - V_H = V_o - 3V_\sigma + V_\tau - 3V_{\sigma\tau} \\
{}^{13}V &= V_W + V_M + V_B + V_H = V_o + V_\sigma - 3V_\tau - 3V_{\sigma\tau} \\
{}^{11}V &= V_W - V_M - V_B + V_H = V_o - 3V_\sigma - 3V_\tau + 9V_{\sigma\tau} \\
{}^{33}V &= V_W - V_M + V_B - V_H = V_o + V_\sigma + V_\tau + V_{\sigma\tau}
\end{aligned} \tag{1-88}$$

Noncentral forces may involve the additional scalars $(\mathbf{r} \cdot \sigma_1)$ and $(\mathbf{r} \cdot \sigma_2)$, but cannot depend on these linearly without violating $\mathscr{P}$ as well as $\mathscr{T}$ symmetry (see Eqs. (1-22) and (1-29)).[4] The only possible combination is the product $(\mathbf{r} \cdot \sigma_1)(\mathbf{r} \cdot \sigma_2)$, which is usually introduced in terms of the operator

$$S_{12} = \frac{3(\mathbf{r} \cdot \boldsymbol{\sigma}_1)(\mathbf{r} \cdot \boldsymbol{\sigma}_2)}{r^2} - \boldsymbol{\sigma}_1 \cdot \boldsymbol{\sigma}_2 \tag{1-89}$$

An interaction proportional to Eq. (1-89) is referred to as a tensor force, and is similar to the potential between two magnetic dipoles. The force acts only in triplet states ($S = 1$), and the general static tensor force thus involves two parts:

$$V_{\text{tensor}} = \{V_T^{(\text{even})}(r)\mathscr{P}(T = 0, L \text{ even}) + V_T^{(\text{odd})}(r)\mathscr{P}(T = 1, L \text{odd})\}S_{12} \tag{1-90}$$

referring to even and odd orbital motion.

The tensor operator (1-89) is the scalar product (see Eq. (1A-71)) of two second-rank tensors, of which the first is formed from the spin vectors σ_1 and σ_2 and the second from the unit vector $\hat{\mathbf{r}}$ in the direction of $\mathbf{r} = \mathbf{r}_1 - \mathbf{r}_2$,

$$S_{12} = (24\pi)^{1/2}\big((\sigma_1\sigma_2)_{\lambda=2} Y_{\lambda=2}(\hat{\mathbf{r}})\big)_{(22)0} \tag{1-91}$$

We here use an abbreviated notation for the coupling of tensors (and angular momenta) that will be extensively employed throughout the rest of the book (see p. 80).

[4] The general form of the $\mathscr{P}$-violating weak interaction potential between nucleons has been considered by Blin-Stoyle (1960) and by Herczeg (1963).

1-4b Velocity-Dependent Forces

Although the empirical data confirm the expectation that the interaction between nucleons at not too high energies can be expressed in terms of potentials of predominantly static type, there is also evidence for important velocity-dependent components.

The forces can depend only on the relative nucleonic momentum $\mathbf{p} = \mathbf{p}_1 - \mathbf{p}_2$ (Galilean invariance). To first order in $\mathbf{p}$, we can form the scalars $(\mathbf{r} \cdot \mathbf{p})$, $(\boldsymbol{\sigma} \cdot \mathbf{p})$, and $(\mathbf{r} \times \mathbf{p} \cdot \boldsymbol{\sigma})$, of which the first violates $\mathscr{T}$ symmetry and the second $\mathscr{P}$ symmetry. Hence, the only possibility is the spin-orbit coupling $(\mathbf{r} \times \mathbf{p} \cdot \boldsymbol{\sigma})$, and the associated two-body interaction has the form

$$V_{\text{spin-orbit}} = \{V_{LS}^{(\text{even})}(r)\mathscr{P}(T=0) + V_{LS}^{(\text{odd})}(r)\mathscr{P}(T=1)\}\mathbf{L} \cdot \mathbf{S} \tag{1-92}$$

where the spins enter symmetrically $(\mathbf{S} = \frac{1}{2}(\boldsymbol{\sigma}_1 + \boldsymbol{\sigma}_2)$. The symmetric choice is required, since the total potential must be symmetric with respect to interchange of all coordinates of particles 1 and 2. Charge-independent interactions are symmetric in the τ variables and thus also in the space-spin variables.

The symmetry in the spin variables $\boldsymbol{\sigma}_1$ and $\boldsymbol{\sigma}_2$, which characterizes the spin-orbit coupling (1-92) as well as the tensor force (1-90), implies that these non-central interactions commute with the total spin operator $(\mathbf{S})^2$ and, therefore, do not couple singlet and triplet states. Indeed, the conservation of the spin quantum number S for a two-nucleon state is a general consequence of charge independence and space reflection symmetry, since the antisymmetry condition (1-55) gives the relation

$$\pi(-1)^{S+T} = -1 \tag{1-93}$$

Thus, the conservation of π and T implies the conservation of S. (Isospin symmetry is essential for the conservation of S; in the hydrogen atom, for example, the spin-orbit coupling is asymmetric in the spins of the electron and proton and therefore mixes triplet and singlet states.)

If one considers potentials involving higher powers in $\mathbf{p}$, a large number of terms becomes possible. Certain terms of this type have been employed in the analysis of nucleon-nucleon scattering data (see the second-order spin-orbit interaction in Eq. (2-223)).

We have considered the interaction in a system consisting of only two nucleons. If additional particles are present, there may be interaction terms depending on the coordinates of three or more particles. The structure of these terms can be analyzed in a similar manner as followed above. On account of the relatively weak binding of nuclear systems, however, the two-body forces are expected to dominate.

In nuclear shell-model calculations, one employs effective two-body forces acting between the particles in unfilled shells (see Sec. 7-1). These effective forces include contributions from the virtual excitation of the rest of the nucleons (the nuclear core), and therefore have a lower symmetry than the forces between nucleons in free space. In fact, the nuclear core is neither translational nor Galilean invariant (nor rotationally invariant for deformed nuclei); in heavy nuclei with large neutron excess, the effective forces may also depend on the orientation of the nucleonic isospins with respect to the isospin of the nuclear core.

APPENDIX

1A

Rotational Invariance

This appendix gives a brief summary of some aspects of the quantum theory of angular momentum and rotational transformations, which are employed in the text. There are available a number of books that give a more detailed presentation of the theory of rotational invariance from various points of view. References to these texts as well as a historical survey of the subject may be found in Biedenharn and van Dam (1965).

1A-1 Angular Momentum Matrices

The components of an angular momentum vector **j** (which may represent orbital, spin, or total angular momentum of a particle, or of a group of particles or quanta) obey the commutation relations

$$[j_x, j_y] = ij_z \quad \text{and cyclic permutations} \tag{1A-1}$$

These relations may be interpreted in terms of the geometrical commutation rules for the rotations associated with the angular momentum components (see Eq. (1-11)) and also represent a special case of the commutation rules between an angular momentum and a vector quantity (see Eq. (1A-57)).

The algebraic relations (1A-1) imply that the square of **j** commutes with all the components of **j**, and if we assume that the matrices representing **j** are of finite dimension, the eigenvalues of $(\mathbf{j})^2$ can take on the values

$$(\mathbf{j})^2 = j(j+1) \qquad j = 0, \tfrac{1}{2}, 1, \ldots \tag{1A-2}$$

For given j, the eigenvalues of a component of **j** are

$$j_z = m \qquad m = -j, -j+1, \ldots, j \tag{1A-3}$$

In the representation in which j_z is diagonal, the nonvanishing matrix elements of the angular momentum operators are

$$\begin{aligned} \langle jm | j_z | jm \rangle &= m \\ \langle jm \pm 1 \,|\, j_x \pm ij_y \,|\, jm \rangle &= ((j \mp m)(j \pm m + 1))^{1/2} \end{aligned} \tag{1A-4}$$

The nondiagonal matrix elements in Eq. (1A-4) involve arbitrary phase factors associated with the choice of relative phases for the states with different m. The phase convention (1-39) implies that the matrix elements of j_x are real while those of j_y are purely imaginary, since j_x commutes with $\mathscr{R}\mathscr{T}$ while j_y anticommutes with $\mathscr{R}\mathscr{T}$ (see Eq. (1-42)). We are thus left with arbitrary real phase factors (± 1), which are conventionally fixed by the requirement that the matrix elements of $j_x \pm ij_y$ be positive (Condon and Shortley, 1935). (Note that this phase convention enters in the matrix elements of the rotation operator and is thus implied in the derivation of the relation (1-40) for time reversal.)

1A-2 Coupling of Angular Momenta

If two components in the system have angular momenta j_1 and j_2, the coupling of these two components may produce states with resultant angular momentum

$$J = |j_1 - j_2|, |j_1 - j_2| + 1, \ldots, j_1 + j_2 \tag{1A-5}$$

The coupled states JM can be written in the form

$$|(j_1 j_2)JM\rangle \equiv |j_1 j_2\rangle_{(j_1 j_2)JM} = \sum_{m_1 m_2} |j_1 m_1, j_2 m_2\rangle \langle j_1 m_1 j_2 m_2 | JM\rangle \tag{1A-6}$$

where the expansion coefficients are referred to as vector addition coefficients. (In the literature, these quantities are also referred to as Clebsch–Gordan coefficients or Wigner coefficients.)

The vector addition coefficients obey the orthogonality relations

$$\begin{gathered}\sum_{m_1 m_2} \langle j_1 m_1 j_2 m_2 | JM\rangle \langle j_1 m_1 j_2 m_2 | J'M'\rangle = \delta(J, J')\, \delta(M, M') \\ \sum_{JM} \langle j_1 m_1 j_2 m_2 | JM\rangle \langle j_1 m_1' j_2 m_2' | JM\rangle = \delta(m_1, m_1')\, \delta(m_2, m_2')\end{gathered} \tag{1A-7}$$

corresponding to the orthonormality of the basis sets $j_1 m_1, j_2 m_2$, and $(j_1 j_2)JM$. In Eq. (1A-7), we have assumed the vector addition coefficients to be real quantities, as is implied by the phase convention (1-39); in fact, the transformation connecting any two basis sets, both satisfying (1-39), has real coefficients. The sign of the vector addition coefficients depends on the choice of the real phases for the states JM relative to those for the states $j_1 m_1, j_2 m_2$. We follow the convention of Condon and Shortley (1935), based on the relations (1A-4) and the phase choices

$$\begin{gathered}\langle j_1 m_1 = j_1, j_2 m_2 = j_2 | J = j_1 + j_2, M = j_1 + j_2\rangle = 1 \\ \langle (j_1 j_2)J'M | j_{1z} | (j_1 j_2)JM\rangle \geq 0 \qquad (J' \neq J)\end{gathered} \tag{1A-8}$$

Since $J_z = j_{1z} + j_{2z}$ is diagonal in J, the last prescription is unsymmetrical in j_1 and j_2. Thus, the ordering of the coupled angular momenta is significant; an exchange of j_1 and j_2 gives

$$|j_1 j_2\rangle_{(j_2 j_1)JM} = (-1)^{j_1 + j_2 - J} |j_1 j_2\rangle_{(j_1 j_2)JM} \tag{1A-9}$$

The vector addition coefficients possess a number of important symmetry properties describing the effect of a reversal of the angular momenta

$$\langle j_1 m_1 j_2 m_2 | j_3 m_3 \rangle = (-1)^{j_1+j_2-j_3} \langle j_1 -m_1 j_2 -m_2 | j_3 -m_3 \rangle \tag{1A-10}$$

and

$$\begin{aligned} \langle j_1 m_1 j_2 m_2 | j_3 m_3 \rangle &= (-1)^{j_1+j_2-j_3} \langle j_2 m_2 j_1 m_1 | j_3 m_3 \rangle \\ &= (-1)^{j_1-m_1} \left(\frac{2j_3+1}{2j_2+1} \right)^{1/2} \langle j_1 m_1 j_3 -m_3 | j_2 -m_2 \rangle \\ &= (-1)^{j_2+m_2} \left(\frac{2j_3+1}{2j_1+1} \right)^{1/2} \langle j_3 -m_3 j_2 m_2 | j_1 -m_1 \rangle \end{aligned} \tag{1A-11}$$

for the effect of permutations of the angular moment.

In the special case of a coupling to a resultant $j_3 = 0$, we obtain

$$\begin{aligned} \langle j_1 m_1 j_2 m_2 | 00 \rangle &= (-1)^{j_1-m_1} (2j_2+1)^{-1/2} \langle j_1 m_1 00 | j_2 -m_2 \rangle \\ &= (-1)^{j_1-m_1} (2j_1+1)^{-1/2} \, \delta(j_1, j_2) \, \delta(m_1, -m_2) \end{aligned} \tag{1A-12}$$

One can also view the coupling $\mathbf{j}_1 + \mathbf{j}_2 = \mathbf{j}_3$ in terms of a coupling of the three vectors to a resultant $J = 0$,

$$\begin{aligned} &|(j_1 j_2) j_3, j_3 ; 00 \rangle \\ &\quad = \sum_{m_1 m_2 m_3} \langle j_1 m_1 j_2 m_2 | j_3 -m_3 \rangle (-1)^{j_3+m_3} (2j_3+1)^{-1/2} | j_1 m_1, j_2 m_2, j_3 m_3 \rangle \\ &\quad = (-1)^{j_1-j_2+j_3} \sum_{m_1 m_2 m_3} \begin{pmatrix} j_1 & j_2 & j_3 \\ m_1 & m_2 & m_3 \end{pmatrix} | j_1 m_1, j_2 m_2, j_3 m_3 \rangle \end{aligned} \tag{1A-13}$$

where

$$\begin{pmatrix} j_1 & j_2 & j_3 \\ m_1 & m_2 & m_3 \end{pmatrix} \equiv (-1)^{j_1-j_2-m_3} (2j_3+1)^{-1/2} \langle j_1 m_1 j_2 m_2 | j_3 -m_3 \rangle \tag{1A-14}$$

is referred to as a $3j$ symbol or a Wigner symbol.

The symmetry relations (1A-10) and (1A-11) take an especially simple form when expressed in terms of the $3j$ symbol. Thus, the $3j$ symbol is invariant under even permutations of the columns; under odd permutations or under the change of sign of all the m values, the $3j$ symbol is multiplied by the phase factor $(-1)^{j_1+j_2+j_3}$.

Closed expressions and recursion relations for the vector addition coefficients can be found in textbooks on the theory of angular momenta. Extensive tables are also available (see the directory by Way and Hurley, 1966) as well as computer programs for the numerical evaluation of these coefficients. In many applications, one of the j values is small ($j \leq 2$). In such cases, vector addition coefficients take a rather simple form and can be found in many textbooks discussing the application of the theory of angular momentum.

1A-3 Recoupling Coefficients

1A-3a Coupling of three angular momenta

Three angular momenta $\mathbf{j}_1$, $\mathbf{j}_2$, and $\mathbf{j}_3$ can be coupled in several ways to a resultant $\mathbf{J}$. Thus, we can first perform the coupling $\mathbf{j}_1 + \mathbf{j}_2 = \mathbf{J}_{12}$ and subsequently

$\mathbf{J}_{12} + \mathbf{j}_3 = \mathbf{J}$; another possibility is $\mathbf{j}_2 + \mathbf{j}_3 = \mathbf{J}_{23}$ followed by $\mathbf{j}_1 + \mathbf{J}_{23} = \mathbf{J}$. The transformation between these two coupling schemes

$$\begin{aligned} |j_1 j_2 j_3\rangle_{(j_1j_2)J_{12},j_3;\,JM} &\equiv \sum_{m_1m_2m_3M_{12}} \langle j_1m_1j_2m_2|J_{12}M_{12}\rangle\langle J_{12}M_{12}j_3m_3|JM\rangle|j_1m_1,j_2m_2,j_3m_3\rangle \\ &= \sum_{J_{23}} \langle j_1,(j_2j_3)J_{23};J|(j_1j_2)J_{12},j_3;J\rangle |j_1j_2j_3\rangle_{j_1,(j_2j_3)J_{23};\,JM} \end{aligned} \tag{1A-15}$$

involves a set of expansion coefficients referred to as recoupling coefficients or Racah coefficients. The transformation is independent of the orientation of the system as a whole and thus is diagonal in M, with coefficients independent of M.

The transformation to other possible coupling schemes, such as $(j_1j_3)J_{13},j_2;J$, may be obtained from Eq. (1A-15), using the recoupling coefficients (1A-9) for two angular momenta.[5]

The transformation (1A-15) corresponds to the relation for the vector addition coefficients

$$\begin{aligned} &\langle j_1m_1j_2m_2\,|\,J_{12}\,m_1+m_2\rangle\,\langle J_{12}\,m_1+m_2\,j_3m_3\,|\,JM\rangle \\ &\quad= \sum_{J_{23}} \langle j_1m_1J_{23}\,m_2+m_3\,|\,JM\rangle\,\langle j_2m_2j_3m_3\,|\,J_{23}\,m_2+m_3\rangle \\ &\qquad\times \langle j_1,(j_2j_3)J_{23};J\,|(j_1j_2)J_{12},j_3;J\rangle \end{aligned} \tag{1A-16}$$

Employing the orthogonality relations (1A-7) for these coefficients, one can also express the recoupling coefficient in Eq. (1A-16) as a sum over products of four vector addition coefficients.

The recoupling coefficients are real (see p. 71) and, as transformation coefficients between complete sets of states, they obey orthonormality and completeness relations such as

$$\begin{aligned} &\sum_{J_{12}} \langle j_1,(j_2j_3)J_{23};J\,|\,(j_1j_2)J_{12},j_3;J\rangle\,\langle j_1,(j_2j_3)J'_{23};J\,|\,(j_1j_2)J_{12},j_3;J\rangle \\ &\quad= \delta(J_{23},J'_{23}) \end{aligned} \tag{1A-17}$$

and

$$\begin{aligned} &\sum_{J_{23}} \langle (j_1j_3)J_{13},j_2;J\,|\,j_1,(j_2j_3)J_{23};J\rangle\,\langle j_1,(j_2j_3)J_{23};J\,|\,(j_1j_2)J_{12},j_3;J\rangle \\ &\quad= \langle (j_1j_3)J_{13},j_2;J\,|\,(j_1j_2)J_{12},j_3;J\rangle \end{aligned} \tag{1A-18}$$

The recoupling coefficients possess a number of symmetry properties, which are conveniently expressed in terms of the $6j$ symbol defined by

$$\begin{aligned} &\langle j_1,(j_2j_3)J_{23};J\,|\,(j_1j_2)J_{12},j_3;J\rangle \\ &\quad= (-1)^{j_1+j_2+j_3+J}((2J_{12}+1)(2J_{23}+1))^{1/2}\begin{Bmatrix} j_1 & j_2 & J_{12} \\ j_3 & J & J_{23} \end{Bmatrix} \end{aligned} \tag{1A-19}$$

---

[5] A coupling scheme that treats the three angular momenta symmetrically can be obtained by employing eigenstates of the operator $\mathbf{j}_1 \cdot (\mathbf{j}_2 \times \mathbf{j}_3)$ (see Chakrabarti, 1964; Dragt, 1965).

An equivalent definition of the $6j$ symbol is

$$\langle (j_1 j_3)J_{13}, j_2; J \,|\, (j_1 j_2)J_{12}, j_3; J\rangle$$
$$= (-1)^{j_2+j_3+J_{12}+J_{13}}(2J_{12}+1)^{1/2}(2J_{13}+1)^{1/2}\begin{Bmatrix} j_2 & j_1 & J_{12} \\ j_3 & J & J_{13} \end{Bmatrix} \quad \text{(1A-20)}$$

The $6j$ symbol is invariant under any permutation of the columns, or interchange of upper and lower arguments in each of any two columns.

If one of the six angular momenta vanishes, the $6j$ symbol reduces to

$$\begin{Bmatrix} j_1 & j_2 & j_3 \\ j_2 & j_1 & 0 \end{Bmatrix} = (-1)^{j_1+j_2+j_3}(2j_1+1)^{-1/2}(2j_2+1)^{-1/2} \quad \text{(1A-21)}$$

which is equivalent to the relation

$$\langle j_1, (j_2 j_3)J_{23} = j_1; J=0 \,|\, (j_1 j_2)J_{12} = j_3, j_3; J=0\rangle = 1 \quad \text{(1A-22)}$$

1A-3b Coupling of four angular momenta

Four angular momenta can be coupled in many different ways, such as

$$\begin{matrix} \mathbf{j}_1 + \mathbf{j}_2 = \mathbf{J}_{12} & \mathbf{j}_3 + \mathbf{j}_4 = \mathbf{J}_{34} & \mathbf{J}_{12} + \mathbf{J}_{34} = \mathbf{J} \\ \mathbf{j}_1 + \mathbf{j}_3 = \mathbf{J}_{13} & \mathbf{j}_2 + \mathbf{j}_4 = \mathbf{J}_{24} & \mathbf{J}_{13} + \mathbf{J}_{24} = \mathbf{J} \end{matrix} \quad \text{(1A-23)}$$

The transformation between these two coupling schemes involves recoupling coefficients depending on nine angular momenta

$$|j_1 j_2 j_3 j_4\rangle_{(j_1 j_2)J_{12},\,(j_3 j_4)J_{34};\,JM}$$
$$= \sum_{J_{13}J_{24}} \langle (j_1 j_3)J_{13}, (j_2 j_4)J_{24}; J \,|\, (j_1 j_2)J_{12}, (j_3 j_4)J_{34}; J\rangle \,|(j_1 j_2 j_3 j_4\rangle_{(j_1 j_3)J_{13},\,(j_2 j_4)J_{24};\,JM} \quad \text{(1A-24)}$$

Other coupling schemes can be obtained from Eq. (1A-24) by employing the recoupling coefficients for three of the angular momenta.

The coefficients in Eq. (1A-24) can be expressed as a sum of products involving six vector addition coefficients, and are real quantities obeying orthonormality and completeness relations analogous to Eqs. (1A-17) and (1A-18). One can also express the recoupling coefficients in Eq. (1A-24) as a sum of products of three $6j$ symbols, since the recoupling can be performed in three steps, each of which involves only three angular momenta.

It is often convenient to express the coefficients associated with the recoupling of four angular momenta in terms of the $9j$ symbol, defined by

$$\langle (j_1 j_2)J_{12}, (j_3 j_4)J_{34}; J \,|\, (j_1 j_3)J_{13}, (j_2 j_4)J_{24}; J\rangle$$
$$= ((2J_{12}+1)(2J_{34}+1)(2J_{13}+1)(2J_{24}+1))^{1/2}\begin{Bmatrix} j_1 & j_2 & J_{12} \\ j_3 & j_4 & J_{34} \\ J_{13} & J_{24} & J \end{Bmatrix} \quad \text{(1A-25)}$$

The $9j$ symbol has a simple permutation symmetry. Thus, any even permutation of rows or columns, or a transposition (replacement of rows by columns) leaves the $9j$

symbol invariant, while an odd permutation of rows or columns introduces a phase factor $(-1)^{\Sigma j}$, where Σj is the sum of all the nine angular momenta.

If one of the j values vanishes, the $9j$ symbol reduces to a $6j$ symbol,

$$\begin{Bmatrix} j_1 & j_2 & j_3 \\ j_4 & j_5 & j_3 \\ j_6 & j_6 & 0 \end{Bmatrix} = (-1)^{j_2+j_3+j_4+j_6}((2j_3+1)(2j_6+1))^{-1/2}\begin{Bmatrix} j_1 & j_2 & j_3 \\ j_5 & j_4 & j_6 \end{Bmatrix} \tag{1A-26}$$

corresponding to the recoupling relation (see Eqs. (1A-22) and (1A-20))

$$\begin{aligned} &\langle (j_1j_3)J', (j_2j_4)J'; 0 \,|\, (j_1j_2)J, (j_3j_4)J; 0\rangle \\ &= \langle (j_1j_3)J', j_2; j_4 \,|\, (j_1j_2)J, j_3; j_4\rangle \\ &= (-1)^{j_2+j_3+J+J'}((2J+1)(2J'+1))^{1/2}\begin{Bmatrix} j_1 & j_2 & J \\ j_4 & j_3 & J' \end{Bmatrix} \end{aligned} \tag{1A-27}$$

For systems involving more than four angular momenta, the recoupling coefficients can be expressed in terms of higher invariants ($12j$, $15j$ symbols, and so on). These have properties analogous to those of $6j$ and $9j$ symbols, and can be expressed in terms of sums of products of coefficients of lower order. The different invariants also obey various recursion relations, which may be exploited in the numerical evaluation. (For references to tables of $6j$ and $9j$ symbols, see the directory by Way and Hurley, 1966. The simplest coefficients, in which one of the j values is small, are given in many textbooks.)

1A-4 Rotation Matrices. $\mathscr{D}$ Functions

The angular momentum operator is associated with the transformation of states under rotations of the coordinate system, in the manner indicated in Sec. 1-2a. We label the states by the total angular momentum I, the projection $M(=I_z)$, and additional quantum numbers α describing properties that are independent of the orientation of the coordinate frame (scalars).

If we introduce a new coordiante system $\mathscr{K}'$ obtained from the original system $\mathscr{K}$ by a rotation about a given axis (specified by the rotation vector $\boldsymbol{\chi}$), the transformation of states is given by (see Eq. (1-10))

$$\begin{aligned} |\alpha IM'\rangle_{\mathscr{K}'} &= \mathscr{R}(\boldsymbol{\chi})|\alpha IM'\rangle_{\mathscr{K}} \\ &= \sum_{M} |\alpha IM\rangle_{\mathscr{K}} \;\langle IM|\exp\{-i\boldsymbol{\chi}\cdot\mathbf{I}\}|IM'\rangle \end{aligned} \tag{1A-28}$$

where $|\alpha IM'\rangle_{\mathscr{K}'}$ is the state with magnetic quantum number M', as viewed from $\mathscr{K}'$, that is, with $I_{z'} = M'$. For the states labeled $\mathscr{K}$, the magnetic quantum number refers to the eigenvalue of I_z. We have omitted the index $\mathscr{K}$ on the matrix element of $\mathscr{R}(\boldsymbol{\chi})$, since the value of the matrix element is independent of the coordinate system in which it is evaluated, as long as the M quantum numbers and the components of $\mathbf{I}$ in $\mathscr{R}(\boldsymbol{\chi})$ refer to the same set of axes. (The components of $\boldsymbol{\chi}$ are in this connection to be regarded as a fixed set of numbers, equal to the components of the rotation vector in $\mathscr{K}$ or $\mathscr{K}'$ (the components are the same in these two systems).)

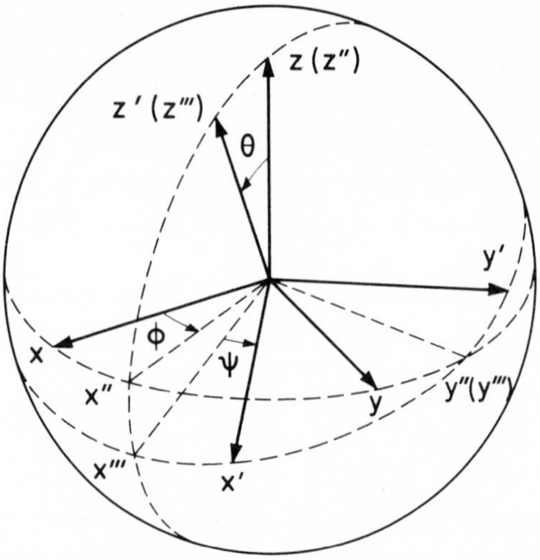

Figure 1A-1 Euler angles. The rotation from $\mathscr{K}(x, y, z)$ to $\mathscr{K}'(x', y', z')$ can be decomposed into three parts: a rotation by ϕ about the z axis to $\mathscr{K}''(x'', y'', z'')$, a rotation of θ about the new y axis (y'') to $\mathscr{K}'''(x''', y''', z''')$, and finally a rotation of ψ about the new z axis (z'''). It is seen that the Euler angles (ϕ, θ, ψ) are so defined that (θ, ϕ) are the polar angles of z' in $\mathscr{K}$, while $(\theta, \pi - \psi)$ are the polar angles of z in $\mathscr{K}'$. The Euler angles are, collectively, denoted by ω.

The transformation from $\mathscr{K}$ to $\mathscr{K}'$ can also be accomplished by a single rotation specified by the vector $\boldsymbol{\chi}$. The direction of $\boldsymbol{\chi}$ given by the polar angles $(\vartheta_\chi, \varphi_\chi)$ represents the axis of rotation, while the length χ is the angle of rotation, and we have the relationship

$$\cos\frac{\chi}{2} = \cos\frac{\theta}{2}\cos\frac{\phi+\psi}{2}$$

$$\sin\frac{\chi}{2}\sin\vartheta_x = \sin\frac{\theta}{2}$$

$$\varphi_x = \frac{\phi-\psi}{2} + \frac{\pi}{2}$$

between the parameters χ, ϑ_x, φ_x and the Euler angles φ, θ, ψ.

The transformation from $\mathscr{K}$ to a system $\mathscr{K}'$ with arbitrary orientation with respect to $\mathscr{K}$ can be decomposed into three rotations of the type (1A-28), each about a coordinate axis. The angles of rotation correspond to the three Euler angles $\omega = (\phi, \theta, \psi)$ needed to specify the orientation (see Fig. 1A-1)

$$\mathscr{K} \xrightarrow[\phi(z)]{} \mathscr{K}'' \xrightarrow[\theta(y'')]{} \mathscr{K}''' \xrightarrow[\psi(z''')]{} \mathscr{K}' \tag{1A-29}$$

Each step is characterized by the angle and (in parenthesis) the axis of rotation. We thus obtain

$$
\begin{aligned}
|IM'\rangle_{\mathscr{K}'} &= \sum_{M'''} |IM'''\rangle_{\mathscr{K}'''}\langle IM'''|\exp\{-i\psi I_z\}|IM'\rangle \\
|IM'''\rangle_{\mathscr{K}'''} &= \sum_{M''} |IM''\rangle_{\mathscr{K}''}\langle IM''|\exp\{-i\theta I_y\}|IM'''\rangle \\
|IM''\rangle_{\mathscr{K}''} &= \sum_{M} |IM\rangle_{\mathscr{K}}\langle IM|\exp\{-i\phi I_z\}|IM''\rangle
\end{aligned}
\tag{1A-30}
$$

and, for the total transformation,

$$|IM'\rangle_{\mathscr{K}'} = \sum_{M} |IM\rangle_{\mathscr{K}}\langle IM|\mathscr{R}|IM'\rangle \tag{1A-31}$$

with

$$\mathscr{R}(\omega) = \exp\{-i\phi I_z\}\exp\{-i\theta I_y\}\exp\{-i\psi I_z\} \tag{1A-32}$$

expressing the rotation operator in terms of the Euler angles.

The matrix elements of $\mathscr{R}$ occurring in Eq. (1A-31) define the $\mathscr{D}$ functions,[6]

$$
\begin{aligned}
\mathscr{D}^I_{MM'}(\omega) &\equiv \langle IM|\mathscr{R}(\omega)|IM'\rangle^* \\
&= \langle IM'|\exp\{i\psi I_z\}\exp\{i\theta I_y\}\exp\{i\phi I_z\}|IM\rangle
\end{aligned}
\tag{1A-33}
$$

Since $\mathscr{R}$ is a unitary operator, the relation (1A-31) can also be written

$$|\alpha IM\rangle_{\mathscr{K}} = \sum_{M'} \mathscr{D}^I_{MM'}(\omega)\,|\alpha IM'\rangle_{\mathscr{K}'} \tag{1A-34}$$

In the following we note some of the important properties of the $\mathscr{D}$ functions.

The matrix element in Eq. (1A-33) defining the $\mathscr{D}$ function is evaluated in the representation of the angular momentum matrices given in Sec. 1A-1. The dependence on the angles ϕ and ψ is especially simple

$$\mathscr{D}^I_{MM'}(\omega) = e^{iM\phi} d^I_{MM'}(\theta) e^{iM'\psi} \tag{1A-35}$$

and the θ dependence is given by

$$d^I_{MM'}(\theta) \equiv \langle IM'|\exp\{i\theta I_y\}|IM\rangle \tag{1A-36}$$

The d function is real, since I_y is a purely imaginary matrix, and has the symmetries

$$
\begin{aligned}
d^I_{MM'}(\theta) &= (-1)^{M-M'} d^I_{M'M}(\theta) \\
&= (-1)^{M-M'} d^I_{-M,-M'}(\theta) \\
&= d^I_{M'M}(-\theta)
\end{aligned}
\tag{1A-37}
$$

[6] We follow here a definition of the $\mathscr{D}$ functions that is extensively employed in nuclear physics problems, in particular in the description of rotational wave functions. The $\mathscr{D}$ function employed by Rose (1957) is the complex conjugate of that defined by Eq. (1A-33). The convention of Rose has been used, for example, by Jacob and Wick (1959) in their discussion of scattering theory based on the helicity representation, and has become customary in elementary particle physics. For the functions $d^I_{MM'}(\theta)$, which are real, the convention of Rose is the same as that employed here. The $d^I_{MM'}$ matrix employed by Edmonds (1957) is the transpose of that used here, and the $\mathscr{D}^I_{MM'}$ functions of Edmonds differ from Eq. (1A-33) by the phase factor $(-1)^{M-M'}$.

Thus, complex conjugation of a $\mathscr{D}$ function gives

$$\begin{aligned}\mathscr{D}^{I*}_{MM'}(\phi, \theta, \psi) &= (-1)^{M-M'}\mathscr{D}^{I}_{-M,-M'}(\phi, \theta, \psi) \\ &= (-1)^{M-M'}\mathscr{D}^{I}_{MM'}(-\phi, -\theta, -\psi)\end{aligned} \tag{1A-38}$$

Closed expressions for the $\mathscr{D}$ functions and their explicit form for small values of I can be found in many textbooks discussing rotational invariance.

For fixed I and ω, the $\mathscr{D}$ functions form a unitary matrix

$$\begin{aligned}\sum_{M} \mathscr{D}^{I*}_{MM_1}(\omega)\mathscr{D}^{I}_{MM_2}(\omega) &= \delta(M_1, M_2) \\ \sum_{M'} \mathscr{D}^{I*}_{M_1M'}(\omega)\mathscr{D}^{I}_{M_2M'}(\omega) &= \delta(M_1, M_2)\end{aligned} \tag{1A-39}$$

and for the inverse rotation ω^{-1}, characterizing the orientation of $\mathscr{K}$ with respect to $\mathscr{K}'$, we have

$$\begin{aligned}\mathscr{D}^{I}_{MM'}(\omega^{-1}) &= \mathscr{D}^{*}_{IM'M}(\omega) \\ (\phi, \theta, \psi)^{-1} &= (-\psi, -\theta, -\phi) = (\pi - \psi, \theta, -\pi - \phi)\end{aligned} \tag{1A-40}$$

The $\mathscr{D}$ functions form a complete orthogonal set of basis functions in ϕ, θ, ψ space, with the normalization

$$\begin{aligned}&\int_0^{\pi} \sin\theta\, d\theta \int_0^{2\pi} d\phi \int_0^{2\pi} d\psi \mathscr{D}^{I*}_{MM'}(\omega)\mathscr{D}^{I_1}_{M_1M'_1}(\omega) \\ &= \frac{8\pi^2}{2I+1}\, \delta(I, I_1)\, \delta(M, M_1)\, \delta(M', M'_1)\end{aligned} \tag{1A-41}$$

(The $\mathscr{D}$ functions with half-integer I change sign under rotations through 2π, and to obtain one-valued functions, one must therefore double the angular domain, for example by letting ϕ vary from 0 to 4π. Such an extension of the domain of integration in Eq. (1A-41) is necessary to obtain orthogonality if one of the angular momenta (I or I_1) is half-integer and the other integer. See also the comment on the double-valuedness of the representations of the rotation group in Sec. 1C-3b.)

The $\mathscr{D}$ functions represent generalizations of the spherical harmonics. (The spherical harmonics constitute a complete orthonormal set of functions on a sphere, that is, in θ, ϕ space or in θ, ψ space.) Thus, for $M' = 0$ (or $M = 0$), the $\mathscr{D}$ functions reduce to spherical harmonics

$$\begin{aligned}\mathscr{D}^{I}_{M0}(\omega) &= \left(\frac{4\pi}{2I+1}\right)^{1/2} Y_{IM}(\theta, \phi) \\ \mathscr{D}^{I}_{0M}(\omega) &= (-1)^{M}\left(\frac{4\pi}{2I+1}\right)^{1/2} Y_{IM}(\theta, \psi) \\ \mathscr{D}^{I}_{00}(\omega) &= P_I(\cos\theta)\end{aligned} \tag{1A-42}$$

By considering the relation (1A-34) for a coupled system $(I_1I_2)IM$, we obtain the coupling rule for $\mathscr{D}$ functions, which is extensively employed in the text,

$$\begin{aligned}&\sum_{M_1M_2} \langle I_1M_1I_2M_2 \mid IM\rangle \mathscr{D}^{I_1}_{M_1M'_1}(\omega)\mathscr{D}^{I_2}_{M_2M'_2}(\omega) \\ &= \langle I_1M'_1I_2M'_2 \mid IM'\rangle \mathscr{D}^{I}_{MM'}(\omega)\end{aligned} \tag{1A-43}$$

A similar relation can be obtained by coupling the $\mathscr{D}$ functions through their second index $(M'_1 M'_2)$. By an application of the orthogonality relation (1A-7) for the vector addition coefficients, the relation (1A-43) can also be written in the form

$$\mathscr{D}^{I_1}_{M_1 M'_1}(\omega)\mathscr{D}^{I_2}_{M_2 M'_2}(\omega) = \sum_{I=|I_1-I_2|}^{I=I_1+I_2} \langle I_1 M_1 I_2 M_2 | I M_1 + M_2\rangle \langle I_1 M'_1 I_2 M'_2 | I M'_1 + M'_2\rangle \mathscr{D}^{I}_{M_1+M_2,\, M'_1+M'_2}(\omega) \tag{1A-44}$$

If we introduce a coordinate system $\mathscr{K}_1$ with orientation ω_1 with respect to $\mathscr{K}$ and ω'_1 with respect to $\mathscr{K}'$, we obtain for the composition of rotations (by steps similar to those leading to Eq. (1A-31))

$$\begin{aligned} \mathscr{R}(\omega_1) &= \mathscr{R}(\omega)\mathscr{R}(\omega'_1) \\ \mathscr{D}^{I}_{MM'}(\omega_1) &= \sum_{M_1} \mathscr{D}^{I}_{MM_1}(\omega)\mathscr{D}^{I}_{M_1 M'}(\omega'_1) \end{aligned} \tag{1A-45}$$

For $M' = 0$, the relation (1A-45) gives the transformation of spherical harmonics under rotations of the coordinate system, and for $M = M' = 0$, we obtain the addition theorem for spherical harmonics,

$$\begin{aligned} Y_{IM}(\theta, \phi) &= \sum_{M'} \mathscr{D}^{I}_{MM'}(\omega)\, Y_{IM'}(\theta', \phi') \\ P_I(\cos\theta_{12}) &= \frac{4\pi}{2I+1}\sum_{M} Y^{*}_{IM}(\theta_1, \phi_1)\, Y_{IM}(\theta_2, \phi_2) \end{aligned} \tag{1A-46}$$

In the second expression, θ_{12} denotes the angle between the directions $\theta_2\phi_2$ and $\theta_1\phi_1$ corresponding, respectively, to ω'_1 and ω^{-1} in Eq. (1A-45); see also Eq. (1A-40).

The relation (1A-45) expresses the group property of the rotation operators and the $\mathscr{D}$ functions. The $\mathscr{D}$ functions are the irreducible representations of the rotation group (irreducible because it is not possible from the set of $(2I + 1)$ states IM with fixed I to construct subsets that transform separately under all rotations.)

In defining phase conventions for basis states in the angular momentum representation (see p. 19), it is convenient to employ the operator $\mathscr{R}_y(\pi)$ for rotations through an angle π about the y axis,

$$\begin{aligned} \mathscr{R}_y(\pi) &= \exp\{-i\pi I_y\} \\ \langle IM' | \mathscr{R}_y(\pi) | IM\rangle &= d^{I}_{M'M}(\pi) \\ &= (-1)^{I-M}\,\delta(M, -M') \end{aligned} \tag{1A-47}$$

Since the operation $\mathscr{R}_y(\pi)$ inverts the direction of the z axis, the state IM goes into $I\ {-M}$, and the phase factor may be obtained by first considering the state $M = I$. This state can be represented by the parallel coupling of $2I$ spin 1/2 systems, for each of which we have

$$\begin{aligned} \mathscr{R}_y(\pi) &= \exp\{-i\pi s_y\} = \exp\left\{-i\frac{\pi}{2}\sigma_y\right\} \\ &= \cos\frac{\pi}{2} - i\sigma_y \sin\frac{\pi}{2} = -i\sigma_y \end{aligned} \tag{1A-48}$$

where σ_y is the Pauli matrix. Thus, the phase factor for each spin, and for the total system, is $+1$. Since, moreover,

$$\mathscr{R}_y(\pi)(I_x + iI_y) = -(I_x - iI_y)\mathscr{R}_y(\pi) \tag{1A-49}$$

the phase factor in Eq. (1A-47) changes sign for each lowering of M by one unit.

1A-5 Spherical Tensors and Reduced Matrix Elements

1A-5a Definition of spherical tensors

One may characterize operators by the amount of angular momentum they transfer to the state on which they act. A spherical tensor of rank λ is a set of operators $T_{\lambda\mu}$ ($\mu = \lambda, \lambda - 1, \ldots, -\lambda$) transferring an angular momentum λ with the different components μ. For example, if the tensor operates on a state of angular momentum zero (specified by further quantum numbers α), we obtain

$$T_{\lambda\mu}|\alpha, I=0\rangle = \mathscr{N}\,|\gamma, I=\lambda, M=\mu\rangle \tag{1A-50}$$

where $\mathscr{N}$ is a normalization constant depending on the properties of the tensor and of the state α. The different μ components of the tensor are to have the same intrinsic properties and, thus, the states on the right-hand side of Eq. (1A-50) differ only in M, while they have the same specification γ and normalization $\mathscr{N}$.

If we generalize to the action of $T_{\lambda\mu}$ on states of arbitrary angular momentum I_1, we obtain

$$\begin{aligned} T_\lambda|\alpha, I_1\rangle_{(I_1\lambda)I_2M_2} &\equiv \sum_{\mu M_1} \langle I_1M_1\lambda\mu|I_2M_2\rangle T_{\lambda\mu}|\alpha, I_1M_1\rangle \\ &= \mathscr{N}\,|\gamma, I_2M_2\rangle \end{aligned} \tag{1A-51}$$

with $\mathscr{N}$ independent of M_2. We are here employing a notation, by which the operators and states are written without magnetic quantum numbers, while the coupling scheme is specified in a subscript. This notation has the flexibility of allowing a coupling of the angular momenta in arbitrary order (such as $(\lambda I_1)I_2M_2$ instead of $(I_1\lambda)I_2M_2$ as in Eq. (1A-51); see also Eq. (1A-15)).

The tensor property of an operator may also be expressed in terms of its transformation under a rotation of the coordinate system. By applying the relation (1A-34) to both sides of Eq. (1A-51), one obtains, by means of Eq. (1A-43),

$$T_{\lambda\mu} = \sum_{\mu'} \mathscr{D}^{\lambda}_{\mu\mu'}(\omega)T'_{\lambda\mu'} \tag{1A-52}$$

where T' is the tensor in the rotated coordinate system. Hence, $T'_{\lambda\mu} = T_{\lambda\mu}(x \to x')$ where x and $x' = x'(x, \omega)$ represent the dynamical variables, such as position and spin of a particle, referred to the coordinate systems $\mathscr{K}$ and $\mathscr{K}'$. Thus, from Eq. (1-4) together with Eq. (1A-52) follows

$$\mathscr{R}^{-1}(\omega)T_{\lambda\mu}\mathscr{R}(\omega) = \sum_{\mu'} \mathscr{D}^{\lambda}_{\mu\mu'}(\omega)T_{\lambda\mu'} \tag{1A-53}$$

(One expresses the property (1A-53) by saying that the operators $T_{\lambda\mu}$ transform as an irreducible representation of the rotation group.)

For infinitesimal rotations ($\mathscr{R} \approx 1 - i\delta\chi \cdot \mathbf{I}$; see Eq. (1-10)) we obtain from Eqs. (1A-33) and (1A-53)

$$[\mathbf{I}, T_{\lambda\mu}] = \sum_{\mu'} \langle \lambda\mu' | \mathbf{I} | \lambda\mu \rangle T_{\lambda\mu'} \tag{1A-54}$$

or, by means of Eq. (1A-4),

$$\begin{aligned} [I_x \pm iI_y, T_{\lambda\mu}] &= ((\lambda \mp \mu)(\lambda \pm \mu + 1))^{1/2} T_{\lambda\,\mu\pm1} \\ [I_z, T_{\lambda\mu}] &= \mu T_{\lambda\mu} \end{aligned} \tag{1A-55}$$

The relations (1A-51), (1A-53), and (1A-54) or (1A-55) are all equivalent and any one may be taken as the definition of a spherical tensor.

A tensor of rank $\lambda = 0$ is a rotational invariant (a scalar). A vector $\mathbf{V}$, expressed in terms of its spherical components

$$V_\mu = V_{\lambda=1,\mu} = \begin{cases} +\dfrac{1}{\sqrt{2}}(V_x - iV_y) & \mu = -1 \\ V_z & \mu = 0 \\ -\dfrac{1}{\sqrt{2}}(V_x + iV_y) & \mu = +1 \end{cases} \tag{1A-56}$$

is a spherical tensor of rank $\lambda = 1$. Thus, the commutation relation (1A-54) for $\lambda = 1$ can also be written in the form

$$[I_x, V_y] = iV_z \quad \text{and cyclic permutations} \tag{1A-57}$$

of which Eq. (1A-1) is a special case.

Further examples of tensors are the spherical harmonics $Y_{\lambda\mu}(\vartheta, \varphi)$ of the angular coordinates of a particle. Thus, if one multiplies an s state ($l = 0$) of a particle with $Y_{\lambda\mu}(\vartheta, \varphi)$, a state of angular momentum $\lambda\mu$ is formed. The tensor properties of $Y_{\lambda\mu}$ are expressed by Eq. (1A-46), which is of the form (1A-52). Similarly, the $\mathscr{D}^{\lambda}_{\mu\nu}(\omega)$ for fixed ν form a spherical tensor of rank λ, which may be integer or half-integer; the angles ω may represent the orientation of the dynamical system as a whole or of a single particle. The tensor properties of creation operators are considered below (Sec. 1A-5e).

Any operator can be expanded in a series of spherical tensors, corresponding to the different values of the angular momentum that it can transfer. For example, the electric multipole moments are the tensors resulting from the expansion of the electric charge density (see Sec. 1A-8).

1A-5b Reduced matrix elements

If we take the product of Eq. (1A-51) with an arbitrary state having angular momentum quantum numbers $I_2' M_2'$, we obtain

$$\begin{aligned} \langle \beta I_2' M_2' | T_\lambda | \alpha I_1 \rangle_{(I_1\lambda)I_2M_2} &= \sum_{\mu M_1} \langle I_1 M_1 \lambda\mu | I_2 M_2 \rangle \langle \beta I_2' M_2' | T_{\lambda\mu} | \alpha I_1 M_1 \rangle \\ &= \mathscr{N} \langle \beta I_2' M_2' | \gamma I_2 M_2 \rangle \\ &= \mathscr{N}' \,\delta(I_2, I_2')\, \delta(M_2, M_2') \end{aligned} \tag{1A-58}$$

where $\mathscr{N}'$ is independent of the magnetic quantum numbers. Multiplying both sides of

Eq. (1A-58) with $\langle I_1 M_1' \lambda\mu' \,|\, I_2 M_2\rangle$, summing over $I_2 M_2$, and exploiting the orthogonality properties of the vector addition coefficients lead to the following relation (in which all the primes have been dropped):

$$\langle \beta I_2 M_2 | T_{\lambda\mu} | \alpha I_1 M_1\rangle = \mathcal{N} \langle I_1 M_1 \lambda\mu \,|\, I_2 M_2\rangle \tag{1A-59}$$

This relation is known as the Wigner–Eckart theorem. Its essence is that the dependence of the matrix element on the "magnetic" quantum numbers μ, M_1, and M_2 is given by the vector addition coefficient; this dependence follows from the geometry of the problem.

The constant $\mathcal{N}$ in Eq. (1A-59) is usually expressed in terms of the reduced matrix element $\langle \beta I_2 \| T_\lambda \| \alpha I_1\rangle$ defined such that

$$\langle \beta I_2 M_2 \,|\, T_{\lambda\mu} | \alpha I_1 M_1\rangle = (2I_2 + 1)^{-1/2} \langle I_1 M_1 \lambda\mu \,|\, I_2 M_2\rangle \langle \beta I_2 \| T_\lambda \| \alpha I_1\rangle \tag{1A-60}$$

or

$$\langle \beta I_2 \| T_\lambda \| \alpha I_1\rangle = (2I_2 + 1)^{1/2} \langle \beta I_2 M_2 | T_\lambda | \alpha I_1 \rangle_{(I_1\lambda)I_2M_2} \tag{1A-61}$$

For example, the matrix elements (1A-4) of the angular momentum vector (which is a tensor of rank $\lambda = 1$) can be written

$$\langle IM' | (I)_{\lambda=1,\mu} | IM\rangle = (I(I+1))^{1/2} \langle IM1\mu \,|\, IM'\rangle \tag{1A-62}$$

corresponding to

$$\langle I \| (I)_{\lambda=1} \| I\rangle = (I(I+1)(2I+1))^{1/2} \tag{1A-63}$$

The commutation relations (1A-54) between **I** and an arbitrary tensor $T_{\lambda\mu}$ can thus also be expressed in the form

$$[I_\mu, T_{\lambda\mu'}] = (\lambda(\lambda+1))^{1/2} \langle \lambda\, \mu' 1 \mu \,|\, \lambda\, \mu + \mu'\rangle T_{\lambda\, \mu+\mu'} \tag{1A-64}$$

The relation (1A-61) expresses the reduced matrix element in the coupling scheme $\mathbf{I}_1 + \boldsymbol{\lambda} = \mathbf{I}_2$, but relations more symmetric in I_1 and I_2 are obtained by viewing the coupling as one in which the three angular momenta produce a resultant zero ($\mathbf{I}_1 + \boldsymbol{\lambda} - \mathbf{I}_2 = 0$). The inversion of the direction of $\mathbf{I}_2$ may be accomplished by a time reversal.

We first illustrate the procedure for the scalar product of state vectors

$$\begin{aligned}
\langle \beta\bar{I}_2 \,|\, \alpha I_1\rangle_{(I_1 I_2)0} &\equiv \sum_{M_1 M_2} \langle I_1 M_1 I_2 M_2 \,|\, 00\rangle \langle \overline{\beta I_2 M_2} \,|\, \alpha I_1 M_1\rangle \\
&= \sum_{M_1 M_2} (-1)^{I_1 - M_1} (2I_1 + 1)^{-1/2}\, \delta(I_1, I_2)\, \delta(M_2, -M_1) \\
&\qquad \times (-1)^{I_2 + M_2} \langle \beta I_2 \; -M_2 \,|\, \alpha I_1 M_1\rangle \\
&= (2I_2 + 1)^{1/2} \langle \beta I_2 M_2 \,|\, \alpha I_1 M_2\rangle\, \delta(I_1, I_2)
\end{aligned} \tag{1A-65}$$

where we have employed the relation (1A-12) and the notation $\bar{A}$ for the time-reversed state $\mathscr{T}A$. In a similar manner, the reduced matrix element can be written in the form (if we drop the indices α and β)

$$\begin{aligned}\langle I_2 \| T_\lambda \| I_1 \rangle &= (2I_2+1)^{1/2} \langle I_2 M_2 | T_\lambda | I_1 \rangle_{(I_1\lambda)I_2M_2} \\ &= \langle \overline{I_2} | T_\lambda | I_1 \rangle_{(I_1\lambda)I_2, I_2; 0}\end{aligned} \tag{1A-66}$$

The symmetry of the coupling scheme with respect to I_1 and I_2 (see Eq. (1A-22)) provides the motivation for the normalization chosen for the reduced matrix element (see also p. 85).

A nuclear transition $I_1 \to I_2$ involving the transfer of angular momentum λ can be described in terms of a transition operator $T_{\lambda\mu}$, such that the transition amplitudes are proportional to the matrix elements (1A-60). The total transition probability, summed over μ and over the polarization M_2 of the final state, is independent of M_1 and given by the reduced transition probability

$$\begin{aligned}B(T_\lambda; I_1 \to I_2) &\equiv \sum_{\mu M_2} |\langle I_2 M_2 | T_{\lambda\mu} | I_1 M_1 \rangle|^2 \\ &= (2I_1+1)^{-1} |\langle I_2 \| T_\lambda \| I_1 \rangle|^2\end{aligned} \tag{1A-67}$$

For the inverse transition, $I_2 \to I_1$, we have

$$B(T_\lambda; I_2 \to I_1) = \frac{2I_1+1}{2I_2+1} B(T_\lambda; I_1 \to I_2) \tag{1A-68}$$

since the absolute value of the reduced matrix element is invariant under the interchange of I_1 and I_2 (see Eq. (1A-79); for processes with transfer of charge or nucleon number, the left-hand side of Eq. (1A-68) involves the adjoint tensor T_2^H). The relation (1A-68) expresses detailed balance for reaction rates averaged over polarizations.

An advantage of using the quantity B (rather than the reduced matrix element) to express the total transition rate comes from the fact that many experiments directly determine B, while the determination of the reduced matrix element requires a knowledge of the spin of the initial state.

1A-5c Reduced matrix elements for coupled systems

If the dynamical system is composed of two parts 1 and 2 (two particles or groups of particles, spin and orbit of a particle, etc.), one can characterize the operators not only in terms of the total tensorial rank (associated with rotations of the total system), but also in terms of the tensorial properties with respect to the two separate parts of the system. Thus, one can expand operators depending on the variables x_1 and x_2 (referring to the two parts of the system) in components of the form

$$T_{\lambda\mu}(x_1, x_2) = (F_{\lambda_1}(x_1) G_{\lambda_2}(x_2))_{(\lambda_1\lambda_2)\lambda\mu} \tag{1A-69}$$

The reduced matrix element of this coupled tensor between states $(I_1I_2)I$ and $(I_1'I_2')I'$, where I_1 and I_1' refer to part 1, and I_2, I_2' to part 2 of the system with total angular momenta I and I', can be expressed in terms of the reduced matrix elements of F_{λ_1} and G_{λ_2} by means of a recoupling of the type (1A-24). The reduced matrix element is written in the form (1A-61), and after the recoupling, one employs Eq. (1A-58) and the orthogonality relations (1A-7) for the vector addition coefficients. Using again Eq. (1A-61) and expressing the recoupling coefficient in terms of a $9j$ symbol (see Eq. (1A-25)), one finally obtains

$$\begin{aligned}
&\langle (I_1'I_2')I' \| (F_{\lambda_1}(x_1)G_{\lambda_2}(x_2))_{(\lambda_1\lambda_2)\lambda} \| (I_1I_2)I\rangle \\
&= (2I'+1)^{1/2}\langle (I_1'I_2')I'M' | F_{\lambda_1}G_{\lambda_2} | I_1I_2\rangle_{(I_1I_2)I,\,(\lambda_1\lambda_2)\lambda;\,I'M'} \\
&= \sum_{I''_1I''_2} \langle (I_1I_2)I, (\lambda_1\lambda_2)\lambda; I' | (I_1\lambda_1)I_1'', (I_2\lambda_2)I_2''; I'\rangle \\
&\quad\times (2I'+1)^{1/2}\langle (I_1'I_2')I'M' | F_{\lambda_1}G_{\lambda_2} | I_1I_2\rangle_{(I_1\lambda_1)I''_1,\,(I_2\lambda_2)I''_2;\,I'M'} \\
&= (2I'+1)^{1/2} \sum_{I''_1I''_2} \langle (I_1I_2)I, (\lambda_1\lambda_2)\lambda; I' | (I_1\lambda_1)I_1'', (I_2\lambda_2)I_2''; I'\rangle \\
&\quad\times \sum_{\substack{M'_1M'_2\\ M''_1M''_2}} \langle I_1'M_1'I_2'M_2' | I'M'\rangle \langle I_1''M_1''I_2''M_2'' | I'M'\rangle \\
&\quad\times \langle I_1'M_1' | F_{\lambda_1} | I_1\rangle_{(I_1\lambda_1)I''_1M''_1} \langle I_2'M_2' | G_{\lambda_2} | I_2\rangle_{(I_2\lambda_2)I''_2M''_2} \\
&= (2I'+1)^{1/2}\langle (I_1I_2)I, (\lambda_1\lambda_2)\lambda; I' | (I_1\lambda_1)I_1', (I_2\lambda_2)I_2'; I'\rangle \\
&\quad\times \langle I_1'M_1' | F_{\lambda_1} | I_1\rangle_{(I_1\lambda_1)I'_1M'_1} \langle I_2'M_2' | G_{\lambda_2} | I_2\rangle_{(I_2\lambda_2)I'_2M'_2} \\
&= ((2\lambda+1)(2I+1)(2I'+1))^{1/2} \begin{Bmatrix} I_1 & I_2 & I \\ \lambda_1 & \lambda_2 & \lambda \\ I_1' & I_2' & I' \end{Bmatrix} \langle I_1' \| F_{\lambda_1} \| I_1\rangle \langle I_2' \| G_{\lambda_2} \| I_2\rangle
\end{aligned} \tag{1A-70}$$

In the special case of $\lambda = 0$, the tensor product in Eq. (1A-69) is a scalar

$$(F_\lambda(x_1)G_\lambda(x_2))_0 = (2\lambda+1)^{-1/2} \sum_\mu (-1)^{\lambda-\mu} F_{\lambda\mu}(x_1)G_{\lambda-\mu}(x_2) \tag{1A-71}$$

(The conventional definition of the scalar product of two tensors omits the factor $(-1)^\lambda(2\lambda+1)^{-1/2}$ in expression (1A-71).) For the scalar product, the $9j$ symbol in Eq. (1A-70) reduces to a $6j$ symbol (see Eq. (1A-26)), and we obtain

$$\begin{aligned}
&\langle (I_1'I_2')I \| (F_\lambda(x_1)G_\lambda(x_2))_0 \| (I_1I_2)I\rangle \\
&\qquad = (-1)^{\lambda+I+I_1+I'_2}(2\lambda+1)^{-1/2}(2I+1)^{1/2} \begin{Bmatrix} I_1 & I_2 & I \\ I_2' & I_1' & \lambda \end{Bmatrix} \\
&\qquad\quad \times \langle I_1' \| F_\lambda \| I_1\rangle \langle I_2' \| G_\lambda \| I_2\rangle
\end{aligned} \tag{1A-72}$$

As another application of the relation (1A-70), we consider the matrix element of a multipole operator F_λ receiving contributions from both parts of the coupled system

$$\begin{aligned}
&\langle \alpha_1'\alpha_2'(I_1'I_2')I' \| F_\lambda(x_1) + F_\lambda(x_2) \| \alpha_1\alpha_2(I_1I_2)I\rangle \\
&= ((2I+1)(2I'+1))^{1/2} \\
&\quad \times \Bigg\{ (-1)^{I'_1+I'_2+I+\lambda} \begin{Bmatrix} I_1 & I_2 & I \\ I' & \lambda & I_1' \end{Bmatrix} \langle \alpha_1'I_1' \| F_\lambda \| \alpha_1I_1\rangle\, \delta(I_2, I_2')\, \delta(\alpha_2, \alpha_2') \\
&\quad + (-1)^{I_1+I_2+I'+\lambda} \begin{Bmatrix} I_1 & I_2 & I \\ \lambda & I' & I_2' \end{Bmatrix} \langle \alpha_2'I_2' \| F_\lambda \| \alpha_2I_2\rangle\, \delta(I_1, I_1')\, \delta(\alpha_1, \alpha_1') \Bigg\}
\end{aligned} \tag{1A-72a}$$

The quantities α_1, α_2 and α_1', α_2' are additional quantum numbers labeling the states of the two parts of the system.

1A-5d Transformation under time reversal and Hermitian conjugation

The reduced matrix element is, in general, a complex number. Its phase is related to the transformation of $T_{\lambda\mu}$ under time reversal. Since the $\mathscr{T}$ transformation inverts angular momenta, it transforms $T_{\lambda\mu}$ into a tensor component of symmetry $\lambda, -\mu$. It is thus convenient to consider the combined transformation $\mathscr{R}\mathscr{T}$, where $\mathscr{R}$ is the rotation $\mathscr{R}_y(\pi)$ (see Sec. 1-2c, as well as Appendix 1B). Usually, the tensors encountered transform into themselves under $\mathscr{R}\mathscr{T}$, except for a phase factor

$$\mathscr{R}\mathscr{T}\,T_{\lambda\mu}(\mathscr{R}\mathscr{T})^{-1} = c_{\mathscr{T}}\,T_{\lambda\mu} \tag{1A-73}$$

(More generally, one can decompose $T_{\lambda\mu}$ into parts with the transformation property (1A-73).) From Eqs. (1A-53) and (1A-47) it is seen that the transformation (1A-73) is equivalent to

$$\mathscr{T}\,T_{\lambda\mu}\mathscr{T}^{-1} = c_{\mathscr{T}}(-1)^{\lambda+\mu}T_{\lambda-\mu} \tag{1A-74}$$

The phase factor $c_{\mathscr{T}}$ is not an intrinsic property of T_λ, since it depends on the phase of the operator. Thus, by multiplying T_λ with a suitable phase factor, we can always achieve $c_{\mathscr{T}} = +1$.

If we assume that the nuclear states are phased according to Eq. (1-39), we obtain from Eqs. (1-42) and (1A-73)

$$\langle I_2 \,\|T_\lambda\|\, I_1\rangle^* = c_{\mathscr{T}}\langle I_2 \,\|T_\lambda\|\, I_1\rangle \tag{1A-75}$$

Thus, the phase choice leading to $c_{\mathscr{T}} = +1$ implies that all matrix elements are real. (For example, in the case of the electromagnetic multipoles, $c_{\mathscr{T}} = +1$ is obtained by multiplying electric moments by i^λ and magnetic moments by $i^{\lambda-1}$; see Eq. (3C-10).)

The symmetry of the reduced matrix element with respect to the interchange of initial and final states is related to the behavior of $T_{\lambda\mu}$ under Hermitian conjugation. The Hermitian conjugate $T^\dagger_{\lambda\mu}$ of a spherical tensor removes the angular momentum $\lambda\mu$ from the state on which it acts, and the operator

$$T^H_{\lambda\mu} \equiv (-1)^{\lambda+\mu}(T_{\lambda-\mu})^\dagger \tag{1A-76}$$

is thus again a spherical tensor, as can be formally proved from Eq. (1A-53), using the symmetry relation (1A-38). From Eq. (1A-60) we therefore obtain, using Eqs. (1A-10) and (1A-11),

$$\langle I_1 \,\|T^H_\lambda\|\, I_2\rangle = (-1)^{I_1+\lambda-I_2}\langle I_2 \,\|T_\lambda\|\, I_1\rangle^* \tag{1A-77}$$

If $T_{\lambda\mu}$ is self-adjoint, that is, if

$$T_{\lambda\mu} = c_H\,T^H_{\lambda\mu} \tag{1A-78}$$

the relation (1A-77) can be written

$$\langle I_1 \,\|T_\lambda\|\, I_2\rangle = c_H(-1)^{I_1+\lambda-I_2}\langle I_2 \,\|T_\lambda\|\, I_1\rangle^* \tag{1A-79}$$

Combining Eq. (1A-79) with Eq. (1A-75), we obtain

$$\langle I_1 \,\|T_\lambda\|\, I_2\rangle = -c(-1)^{I_1+\lambda-I_2}\langle I_2 \,\|T_\lambda\|\, I_1\rangle \tag{1A-80}$$

where

$$c = -c_{\mathscr{T}}\,c_H \tag{1A-81}$$

While $c_{\mathscr{T}}$ and c_H depend on the phase of $T_{\lambda\mu}$ and may take complex values, the product

c is independent of the overall phase of $T_{\lambda\mu}$ and equals $+1$ or -1. The phase factor c also characterizes the particle-hole conjugation of the operator $T_{\lambda\mu}$ (see Eq. (3-13).) Values of c for one-particle operators are listed in Eq. (3-15).

1A-5e Tensor properties of creation operators

The operator $a^\dagger(jm)$, which creates a particle in the state jm, is the m component of a tensor of rank j, as follows directly from the definition of tensor operators. The formalism based on annihilation and creation operators is discussed in Appendix 2A. The transformation of $a^\dagger(jm)$ under time reversal is given by

$$\begin{aligned}\mathscr{T} a^\dagger(jm)\mathscr{T}^{-1} &= a^\dagger(\overline{jm}) \\ &= (-1)^{j+m} a^\dagger(j\,-m) \end{aligned} \tag{1A-82}$$

as can be seen, for example, by letting $\mathscr{T}$ act on the state $|jm\rangle = a^\dagger(jm)|0\rangle$. The phase factor $c_{\mathscr{T}}$ is therefore unity, and the matrix elements of $a^\dagger(jm)$ are real, in a representation with the phase convention (1-39).

The Hermitian conjugate of $a^\dagger(jm)$ is the annihilation operator $a(jm)$, from which we can construct the tensor (see Eq. (1A-76))

$$b^\dagger(jm) \equiv a(\overline{jm}) = (-1)^{j+m} a(j-m) \tag{1A-83}$$

The operator $b^\dagger(jm)$ may also be interpreted in terms of the creation of a hole state (see Sec. 3-1b). From Eq. (1A-77) we thus obtain

$$\begin{aligned}\langle I_2 \| a(\bar{j}) \| I_1\rangle &= \langle I_2 \| b^\dagger(j) \| I_1\rangle \\ &= (-1)^{I_2+j-I_1}\langle I_1 \| a^\dagger(j) \| I_2\rangle \end{aligned} \tag{1A-84}$$

From products of $a^\dagger$ and a operators, one can form the spherical tensors

$$\begin{aligned} E_{\lambda\mu} &= \left(a^\dagger(j_2)a(\bar{j}_1)\right)_{(j_1 j_2)\lambda\mu} \\ &= \left(a^\dagger(j_2)b^\dagger(j_1)\right)_{(j_1 j_2)\lambda\mu} \end{aligned} \tag{1A-85}$$

These are unit tensor operators from which arbitrary one-particle operators can be constructed. Thus, from Eqs. (2A-24), (1A-60), and (1A-11), we obtain

$$\begin{aligned} T_{\lambda\mu} &= \sum_{\substack{j_1 m_1 \\ j_2 m_2}} (2j_2+1)^{-1/2} \langle j_1 m_1 \lambda\mu | j_2 m_2\rangle \langle j_2 \| T_\lambda \| j_1\rangle a^\dagger(j_2 m_2) a(j_1 m_1) \\ &= \sum_{j_1 j_2} (-1)^{j_1+j_2-\lambda} (2\lambda+1)^{-1/2} \langle j_2 \| T_\lambda \| j_1 \rangle \left(a^\dagger(j_2) a(\bar{j}_1)\right)_{(j_1 j_2)\lambda\mu} \end{aligned} \tag{1A-86}$$

The operator $c^\dagger(\lambda\mu)$ creating vibrational quanta may be chosen with a phase rule corresponding to Eq. (1A-82),

$$\begin{aligned}\mathscr{T} c^\dagger(\lambda\mu)\mathscr{T}^{-1} &= c^\dagger(\overline{\lambda\mu}) \\ &= (-1)^{\lambda+\mu} c^\dagger(\lambda\,-\mu) \end{aligned} \tag{1A-87}$$

and thus also has $c_{\mathscr{T}} = 1$ and real matrix elements. The conjugate tensor $c(\lambda\mu)$ has matrix elements given by a relation similar to (1A-84).

1A-6 Transformation to Intrinsic Coordinate System

In the description of many-body systems having a shape deviating from spherical symmetry (nonspherical nuclei, molecules, etc.), it is convenient to employ an intrinsic (or "body-fixed") coordinate frame. The transformation of operators from the fixed frame (the laboratory system) to the intrinsic frame involves special features as a result of the fact that the orientation angles ($\omega = \phi, \theta, \psi$) of the intrinsic frame are to be regarded as dynamical variables. The states of orientation can be specified by the angular variables or by the associated angular momenta.

The transformation to an intrinsic coordinate system is also employed in the description of the spin polarization of a particle in terms of the helicity.

1A-6a Components of angular momentum with respect to intrinsic axes

We label the intrinsic axes by $\kappa = 1, 2, 3$, and the spherical angular momentum components I'_ν with respect to the intrinsic frame are thus

$$I'_{\nu=\pm 1} = \mp \frac{1}{\sqrt{2}}(I_1 \pm iI_2) \qquad I'_{\nu=0} = I_3 \tag{1A-88}$$

The relation between I'_ν and the components referring to the fixed axes can be expressed in the form (see Eqs. (1A-52) and (1A-40))

$$\begin{aligned} I_\mu &= \sum_\nu \mathscr{D}^1_{\mu\nu}(\omega) I'_\nu = \sum_\nu I'_\nu \mathscr{D}^1_{\mu\nu}(\omega) \\ I'_\nu &= \sum_\mu \mathscr{D}^{1\dagger}_{\mu\nu}(\omega) I_\mu = \sum_\mu I_\mu \mathscr{D}^{1\dagger}_{\mu\nu}(\omega) \end{aligned} \tag{1A-89}$$

The operators I_μ and I'_ν do not commute with the orientation angles, but the sums in Eq. (1A-89) are independent of the ordering of the $\mathscr{D}$ functions and I components, as can be seen from Eq. (1A-55) with $T_{\lambda\mu} = \mathscr{D}^\lambda_{\mu\nu}$.

Commutation relations involving the I'_ν can be found by applying Eq. (1A-64) to the spherical tensors $\mathscr{D}^\lambda_{\mu\nu}$ and I_μ,

$$\begin{aligned} &[I'_\nu, I_\mu] = 0 \\ &[I'_\nu, \mathscr{D}^\lambda_{\mu\nu'}(\omega)] = (-1)^\nu (\lambda(\lambda+1))^{1/2} \langle \lambda\nu' 1 -\nu \mid \lambda, \nu' - \nu\rangle \mathscr{D}^\lambda_{\mu,\nu'-\nu}(\omega) \\ &[I'_\nu, I'_{\nu'}] = \sqrt{2}\langle 1\nu 1\nu' \mid 1, \nu+\nu'\rangle I'_{\nu+\nu'} \end{aligned} \tag{1A-90}$$

In terms of the Cartesian components, I_κ, the two last relations in Eq. (1A-90) can be written

$$\begin{aligned} &[I_1, I_2] = -iI_3 \quad \text{and cyclic permutations} \\ &[I_1 \pm iI_2, \mathscr{D}^\lambda_{\mu\nu}(\omega)] = ((\lambda\pm\nu)(\lambda\mp\nu+1))^{1/2} \mathscr{D}^\lambda_{\mu,\nu\mp 1}(\omega) \\ &[I_3, \mathscr{D}^\lambda_{\mu\nu}(\omega)] = \nu \mathscr{D}^\lambda_{\mu\nu}(\omega) \end{aligned} \tag{1A-91}$$

The commutation of I'_ν with I_μ is a simple consequence of the fact that the I'_ν components are independent of the orientation of the external system, and thus scalars with respect to the rotations generated by the I_μ. The commutation relations of the

I'_ν among themselves (and with $\mathscr{D}^\lambda_{\mu\nu}$) can also be obtained from geometrical considerations by interpreting the I'_ν as the generators of infinitesimal rotations about the intrinsic axes. The operators I'_ν describe the change in the state vector when the coordinate system (the fixed system) is rotated about an axis of the intrinsic frame. From this point of view there is a dissymmetry between the I'_ν and the I_μ, since the latter give the effect of a rotation of the fixed system about one of its own axes. However, we can also view the rotation operators in a different way, which formally restores the symmetry between the two sets of angular momentum components. Thus, the effect on the state vector produced by a rotation of the fixed system is equivalent to the effect of the opposite rotation of the intrinsic system, that is, of the body itself. We can therefore regard the I'_ν as the generators of inverse rotations by which the intrinsic system is rotated about one of its own axes.

The commutation relations of the I'_ν can now be obtained as for the I_μ (see Eq. (1-11)). For inverse rotations, we have

$$[\mathscr{R}_1^{-1}, \mathscr{R}_2^{-1}] = -((\mathscr{R}_1 \mathscr{R}_2)^{-1} - (\mathscr{R}_2\mathscr{R}_1)^{-1}) \tag{1A-92}$$

which implies that the commutators for the I'_ν involve a change of sign with respect to those for I_μ, in accordance with Eqs. (1A-91).

Similarly, the commutation relations between I'_ν and the rotation matrix $\mathscr{D}^\lambda_{\mu\nu}(\omega)$ for finite rotations can be interpreted in terms of the relation (1A-64) applied to inverse rotations with respect to the intrinsic frame.

Since the intrinsic components of the angular momentum vector commute with the space-fixed components, we can choose a representation that is diagonal in I_3 as well as in I_z and $(\mathbf{I})^2$. The eigenvalues of I_3 are denoted by K and the states may thus be labeled by the quantum numbers IKM (and an additional set α representing operators commuting with $I_{1,2,3}$ as well as with $I_{x,y,z}$).

The change of sign in the commutation relations for $I_{1,2,3}$ as compared with those for $I_{x,y,z}$ can be taken into account by representing $I_{1,2,3}$ by a set of matrices that are the complex conjugates of those associated with $I_{x,y,z}$. In the standard representation (see Sec. 1A-1), the complex conjugation simply implies a reversal of sign for I_2 as compared with I_y. The eigenvalues of I_3 are therefore (as for I_z) $K = -I, -I+1, \ldots, I$, while raising and lowering operators are interchanged. The nonvanishing matrix elements of $I_{1,2,3}$ are

$$\begin{aligned} \langle \alpha IKM | I_3 | \alpha IKM \rangle &= K \\ \langle \alpha IK \mp 1 M | I_1 \pm iI_2 | \alpha IKM \rangle &= ((I \pm K)(I \mp K + 1))^{1/2} \end{aligned} \tag{1A-93}$$

1A-6b Wave functions describing orientation of intrinsic system

The state of orientation of the body-fixed system is completely specified by the three angular momentum quantum numbers IKM representing the conjugates of the three orientation angles $\omega = (\phi, \theta, \psi)$. The transformation from the basis set $|\omega\rangle$ with sharply defined orientation to the basis set $|IKM\rangle$ may be obtained by employing the transformation (1A-34), with $\alpha = K$, to a coordinate system $\mathscr{K}'$ with orientation ω with respect to $\mathscr{K}$

$$|IKM\rangle_{\mathscr{K}} = \sum_{M'} \mathscr{D}^I_{MM'}(\omega)\,|IKM'\rangle_{\mathscr{K}'} \tag{1A-94}$$

The state $|\omega\rangle$ with orientation ω with respect to $\mathscr{K}$ has the orientation $\omega = 0$ with respect to $\mathscr{K}'$,

$$|\omega\rangle_{\mathscr{K}} = |\omega = 0\rangle_{\mathscr{K}'} \tag{1A-95}$$

and the scalar product of the state vectors in Eqs. (1A-94) and (1A-95) gives the wave function

$$\begin{aligned}\Phi_{IKM}(\omega) &\equiv \langle\omega\,|\,IKM\rangle\\ &= \sum_{M'} \mathscr{D}^I_{MM'}(\omega)\langle\omega = 0\,|IKM'\rangle\\ &= \mathscr{D}^I_{MK}(\omega)\langle\omega = 0\,|\,IKM = K\rangle\end{aligned} \tag{1A-96}$$

In fact, $\langle\omega = 0\,|\,IKM'\rangle$ vanishes except for $M' = K$, since I_3 equals I_z when acting on the state $|\,\omega = 0\rangle$ (see Eq. (1A-89)). From Eq. (1A-41), it follows that the normalized wave function (1A-96) can be written, with a suitable choice of phase,

$$\Phi_{IKM}(\omega) = \left(\frac{2I+1}{8\pi^2}\right)^{1/2} \mathscr{D}^I_{MK}(\omega) \tag{1A-97}$$

(It may be noted that the states $|IKM\rangle$ are not eigenstates of $\mathscr{R}\mathscr{T}$, since I_3 as well as I_z change sign under time reversal. This point is further discussed for the wave functions of deformed nuclei (Sec. 4-2) and for the helicity states (Sec. 3A-1).)

The $\mathscr{D}$ functions can thus also be viewed as the wave functions describing the orientation of a dynamical system with specified angular momentum quantum numbers I, M, and K. In the special case of a single spin-zero particle in a potential (or the relative motion of two particles without spin), the intrinsic angular momentum K is constrained to have the value zero, and the orientation wave functions reduce to the more familiar spherical harmonics (see Eq. (1A-42)).

While $(\mathbf{I})^2$ and I_z are constants of the motion for any system with rotational invariance, the commutator of the Hamiltonian with I_3 depends on the intrinsic dynamics of the system, and the stationary states do not, in general, possess a definite K value. (The conditions under which I_3 is an approximate constant of the motion are discussed in Chapter 4.)

1A-6c Intrinsic components of tensor operators

For an arbitrary tensor operator $T_{\lambda\mu}$ we can define intrinsic components $T'_{\lambda\nu}$ in terms of the relations (see Eq. (1A-52))

$$\begin{aligned}T_{\lambda\mu} &= \sum_{\nu} \mathscr{D}^{\lambda}_{\mu\nu}(\omega)T'_{\lambda\nu}\\ T'_{\lambda\nu} &= \sum_{\mu} \mathscr{D}^{\lambda\dagger}_{\mu\nu}(\omega)T_{\lambda\mu}\end{aligned} \tag{1A-98}$$

If the T components and the $\mathscr{D}$ functions do not commute, the ordering in Eq. (1A-98) is significant. Instead of the products in Eq. (1A-98), we could have used symmetrized expressions in the definition of the intrinsic components.

The intrinsic components $T'_{\lambda\nu}$ are scalars with respect to rotations of the external system and thus commute with I_μ. (The sum over μ in Eq. (1A-98) is seen to be the scalar product of the two tensors $\mathscr{D}^\lambda_{\mu-\nu}$ and $T_{\lambda\mu}$; see Eqs. (1A-38) and (1A-71).)

The commutation relations of the tensor components with I'_ν depend on the tensor properties of $T_{\lambda\mu}$ with respect to intrinsic rotations, which are not in general related to those characterizing the behavior under external rotations. Two examples will illustrate this point.

For $T_{\lambda\mu} = \mathscr{D}^\lambda_{\mu\nu_0}(\omega)$, the intrinsic components are c numbers $\big(T'_{\lambda\nu} = \delta(\nu, \nu_0)\big)$ and thus scalars with respect to internal as well as external rotations, while $T_{\lambda\mu}$ is a tensor component of rank λ with respect to internal and external rotations.

If $T_{\lambda\mu}$ is a scalar with respect to internal rotations as for the angular momentum components I_μ, the intrinsic components $T'_{\lambda\nu}$ form a tensor of rank λ with respect to internal rotations.

1A-7 Transformation of Fields

A field $F(\mathbf{r})$ is an operator associated with the space point $\mathbf{r}$. For given $\mathbf{r}$, the field depends on the dynamical variables x of the system (such as positions, momenta, and spins of constituent particles), and the field operator may, therefore, be written as $F(\mathbf{r}, x)$. (Note that the components of $\mathbf{r}$ are c numbers while the variables x are q numbers.)

If we rotate the coordinate system from $\mathscr{K}$ to $\mathscr{K}'$, we have (in analogy to Eq. (1-4))

$$\mathscr{R}F(\mathbf{r})\mathscr{R}^{-1} = F'(\mathbf{r}) \tag{1A-99}$$

where $F'(\mathbf{r})$ is the same function of the dynamical variables x' (referred to $\mathscr{K}'$) as $F(\mathbf{r})$ is of x,

$$F'(\mathbf{r}) = F(\mathbf{r}, x') \tag{1A-100}$$

A scalar field $\rho(\mathbf{r})$ is characterized by its invariance with respect to rotations of the coordinate frame in the sense that its value, at a definite point in space, is the same whether described by an observer in $\mathscr{K}$ or in $\mathscr{K}'$,

$$\rho(\mathbf{r}, x) = \rho(\mathbf{r}', x') \tag{1A-101}$$

or

$$\rho(\mathbf{r}) = \rho'(\mathbf{r}') \tag{1A-102}$$

where $\mathbf{r}'$ and $\mathbf{r}$ are the coordinates, referred to $\mathscr{K}'$ and $\mathscr{K}$, of the same point in space.

Combining Eq. (1A-99) with Eq. (1A-102), we obtain

$$\mathscr{R}^{-1}\rho(\mathbf{r})\mathscr{R} = \rho(\mathbf{r}') \tag{1A-103}$$

as the formal expression for the scalar character of the field. (Note that Eq. (1A-103) involves the inverse transformation as compared with Eq. (1A-99), corresponding to the fact that a rotation of the particle coordinates has the same effect on ρ as has the inverse rotation of **r**.)

An example of a scalar field is the electric charge density, which for a system of point charges can be expressed in the form

$$\rho_{el}(\mathbf{r}) = \sum_k e_k \, \delta(\mathbf{r} - \mathbf{r}_k) \tag{1A-104}$$

where $\mathbf{r}_k$ is the position and e_k the charge of the kth particle.

A vector field, such as a current density $\mathbf{j}(\mathbf{r})$, transforms under rotations as a vector, that is, a tensor of rank $\lambda = 1$. If we employ spherical vector coordinates, we thus have (see Eq. (1A-52)), in place of Eq. (1A-102),

$$j_\mu(\mathbf{r}) = \sum_{\mu'} \mathscr{D}^1_{\mu\mu'}(\omega) j'_{\mu'}(\mathbf{r}') \tag{1A-105}$$

or, by means of Eq. (1A-99), which holds for each value of μ,

$$\mathscr{R}^{-1} j_\mu(\mathbf{r}) \mathscr{R} = \sum_{\mu'} \mathscr{D}^1_{\mu\mu'}(\omega) j_{\mu'}(\mathbf{r}') \tag{1A-106}$$

In a similar manner, one can express the transformation of tensor fields of higher rank.

The field $a^\dagger(\mathbf{r}, m_s)$, representing the creation of a nucleon (spin 1/2 particle) at the point **r** with polarization m_s (see Sec. 2A-6) is a spinor field of rank 1/2, and its transformation is given by

$$\mathscr{R}^{-1} a^\dagger(\mathbf{r}, m_s) \mathscr{R} = \sum_{m'_s} \mathscr{D}^{1/2}_{m_s m'_s}(\omega) a^\dagger(\mathbf{r}', m'_s) \tag{1A-107}$$

One can also characterize the fields by their transformation with respect to the parity operation

$$\begin{aligned} \mathscr{P} \rho(\mathbf{r}) \mathscr{P}^{-1} &= \pi_\rho \, \rho(-\mathbf{r}) \\ \mathscr{P} \mathbf{j}(\mathbf{r}) \mathscr{P}^{-1} &= \pi_j \mathbf{j}(-\mathbf{r}) \end{aligned} \tag{1A-108}$$

where

$$\begin{aligned} \pi_\rho &= \begin{matrix} +1 & \text{scalar field} \\ -1 & \text{pseudoscalar field} \end{matrix} \\ \pi_j &= \begin{matrix} +1 & \text{axial vector field} \\ -1 & \text{polar vector field} \end{matrix} \end{aligned} \tag{1A-109}$$

The spinor field satisfies the relation

$$\mathscr{P} a^\dagger(\mathbf{r}, m_s) \mathscr{P}^{-1} = a^\dagger(-\mathbf{r}, m_s) \tag{1A-110}$$

corresponding to the even intrinsic parity of the nucleons (see p. 14).

1A-8 Field Couplings and Expansion in Multipole Moments

The interaction of the nucleus with "external" systems, such as the electromagnetic or β fields, or the projectiles in direct nuclear reactions, is often expressed as a local field coupling, involving at each space point **r** the product of a density function (a field) depending on the nuclear variables and a density function involving the variables of the external system. The expansion of such an interaction in terms of spherical tensors expresses the coupling in terms of nuclear multipole moments.

1A-8a Scalar field

A scalar coupling has the form

$$H' = \int \rho(\mathbf{r})\varphi(\mathbf{r})\, d\tau \tag{1A-111}$$

where $\rho(\mathbf{r})$ is a scalar nuclear density, while $\varphi(\mathbf{r})$ is a scalar function depending on the external variables. The tensor structure of Eq. (1A-111) is obtained by expanding $\varphi(\mathbf{r})$ in spherical harmonics,

$$\varphi(\mathbf{r}) = \sum_{\lambda\mu} \varphi^{\dagger}_{\lambda\mu}(r)\, Y_{\lambda\mu}(\hat{\mathbf{r}}) \tag{1A-112}$$

giving

$$H' = \sum_{\lambda\mu} \int \rho(\mathbf{r})\varphi^{\dagger}_{\lambda\mu}(r)\, Y_{\lambda\mu}(\hat{\mathbf{r}})\, d\tau \tag{1A-113}$$

Each term in Eq. (1A-113) is the μ component of a spherical tensor of rank λ in the nuclear variables, as can be seen from Eq. (1A-103) together with Eqs. (1A-46) and (1A-53). Since H' conserves angular momentum (is a scalar for the combined systems), $\varphi_{\lambda\mu}$ is a spherical tensor component $\lambda\mu$ in the variables of the external system.

An example of a scalar coupling is provided by the Coulomb interaction between the nucleus and an impinging particle. The density $\rho(\mathbf{r})$ is then the electric charge density of the nucleus while $\varphi(\mathbf{r})$ is the electrostatic potential produced by the particle. Denoting the coordinates of this particle by $\mathbf{r}_p$ and its charge by $Z_p e$, we have

$$\begin{aligned} \varphi(\mathbf{r}) &= \frac{Z_p e}{|\mathbf{r} - \mathbf{r}_p|} \\ &= \sum_{\lambda\mu} \frac{4\pi Z_p e}{2\lambda + 1} Y^*_{\lambda\mu}(\hat{\mathbf{r}}_p)\, Y_{\lambda\mu}(\hat{\mathbf{r}}) \begin{cases} r_p^{-\lambda-1} r^{\lambda} & r_p > r \\ r_p^{\lambda} r^{-\lambda-1} & r_p < r \end{cases} \end{aligned} \tag{1A-114}$$

The $\varphi_{\lambda\mu}$, defined in Eq. (1A-112), are thus expressed in the form

$$\varphi_{\lambda\mu}(r) = \frac{4\pi Z_p e}{2\lambda + 1} Y_{\lambda\mu}(\hat{\mathbf{r}}_p) \begin{cases} r_p^{-\lambda-1} r^{\lambda} & r_p > r \\ r_p^{\lambda} r^{-\lambda-1} & r_p < r \end{cases} \tag{1A-115}$$

It is seen that $\varphi_{\lambda\mu}$ is indeed a tensor component with symmetry $\lambda\mu$ with respect to rotations of the external particle.

The dependence of the interaction on the nuclear variables is especially simple if the particle does not penetrate into the nucleus (Coulomb excitation), in which case the $\lambda\mu$ term in H' is proportional to the electric multipole moment

$$\mathscr{M}(E\lambda, \mu) = \int \rho(\mathbf{r}) r^{\lambda} Y_{\lambda\mu}(\hat{\mathbf{r}})\, d\tau \tag{1A-116}$$

If the particle penetrates into the nucleus, the interaction involves moments of the more general type

$$\mathscr{M}(\rho, \lambda\mu) = \int \rho(\mathbf{r}) f_{\lambda}(r)\, Y_{\lambda\mu}(\hat{\mathbf{r}})\, d\tau \tag{1A-117}$$

where the radial form factor $f_\lambda(r)$ is obtained by an integration of $\varphi_{\lambda\mu}(r)$ with respect to the particle variable. Thus, if the nuclear excitation can be treated by first-order perturbation theory, $f_\lambda(r)$ is proportional to the matrix element of $\varphi_{\lambda\mu}(r)$ between initial and final state of the particle (which may, for example, be represented by "distorted waves").

As in the example of the Coulomb interaction, one can always express a scalar coupling (1A-111) in terms of multipole moments of the form (1A-117). For small r, the field $\varphi(\mathbf{r})$ may be expanded in powers of $\mathbf{r}$, and the leading order term in $\varphi_{\lambda\mu}(r)$ is seen to be proportional to r^λ (see, for example, Eq. (1A-115)). Thus, $f_\lambda(r)$ in Eq. (1A-117) varies as r^λ for sufficiently small r, and often it is convenient to normalize $f_\lambda(r)$ in terms of the expansion

$$f_\lambda(r) = r^\lambda + c_\lambda r^{\lambda+2} + \cdots \tag{1A-118}$$

about $r = 0$. The rate of convergence of the expansion (1A-118) depends on the momentum transfer in the interaction. Thus, for example, if the external system, before and after the interaction, is in a state of definite momentum (plane wave approximation), the $\mathbf{r}$ dependence of the matrix element of $\varphi(\mathbf{r})$ is given by

$$\begin{aligned} \langle \mathbf{p}_2 \,|\, \varphi(\mathbf{r}) |\, \mathbf{p}_1 \rangle &= \exp\{i\mathbf{q}\cdot\mathbf{r}\}\langle \mathbf{p}_2 \,|\varphi(\mathbf{r}=0)|\, \mathbf{p}_1\rangle \\ \mathbf{q} &\equiv \frac{1}{\hbar}(\mathbf{p}_1 - \mathbf{p}_2) \end{aligned} \tag{1A-119}$$

as follows from translational invariance, using the transformation $\mathscr{U}(\mathbf{a} = -\mathbf{r})$ (see Eq. (1-6)). The exponential in Eq. (1A-119) may be expanded in spherical harmonics, and yields a radial form factor $f_\lambda(r)$ proportional to the spherical Bessel function $j_\lambda(qr)$.

1A-8b Vector field

A vector interaction can be written

$$H' = -\int \mathbf{j}(\mathbf{r}) \cdot \mathbf{A}(\mathbf{r})\, d\tau \tag{1A-120}$$

where $\mathbf{j}(\mathbf{r})$ is a nuclear vector density (such as the electric current or the spin density), while $\mathbf{A}(\mathbf{r})$ is a vector field produced by the external system.

Vector fields can be expanded in the form

$$\mathbf{A}(\mathbf{r}) = \sum_{\kappa\lambda\mu} A^\dagger_{\kappa,\lambda\mu}(r)\boldsymbol{\Phi}_{\kappa,\lambda\mu}(\hat{\mathbf{r}}) \tag{1A-121}$$

where

$$\boldsymbol{\Phi}_{\kappa,\lambda\mu}(\hat{\mathbf{r}}) = (Y_\kappa(\hat{\mathbf{r}})\,\mathbf{e})_{(\kappa 1)\lambda\mu} \tag{1A-122}$$

is a vector spherical harmonic. The quantity $\boldsymbol{\Phi}_{\kappa,\lambda\mu}$ is a tensor of rank λ and component μ, formed by coupling the tensor Y_κ with the first-rank tensor $\mathbf{e}$ with components $\mathbf{e}_\nu$, each of which is a vector. The components $\mathbf{e}_\nu$ have the property that

$$\mathbf{V}\cdot\mathbf{e}_\nu = V_\nu \tag{1A-123}$$

for an arbitrary vector $\mathbf{V}$. Thus,

$$\begin{aligned} \mathbf{e}_{\nu=\pm 1} &= \mp\frac{1}{\sqrt{2}}(\mathbf{e}_x \pm i\mathbf{e}_y) \\ \mathbf{e}_{\nu=0} &= \mathbf{e}_z \end{aligned} \tag{1A-124}$$

where $\mathbf{e}_x$, $\mathbf{e}_y$, and $\mathbf{e}_z$ are unit vectors in the direction of the coordinate axes.

The vector spherical harmonics form a complete set of orthonormal functions for describing vector functions on a sphere, and can also be written in the form

$$\boldsymbol{\Phi}_{\kappa,\lambda\mu} = \begin{cases} (\lambda(2\lambda+1))^{-1/2}(r\nabla + \lambda\hat{\mathbf{r}})\,Y_{\lambda\mu} & \kappa = \lambda - 1 \\ -i(\lambda(\lambda+1))^{-1/2}(\mathbf{r}\times\nabla)\,Y_{\lambda\mu} & \kappa = \lambda \\ ((\lambda+1)(2\lambda+1))^{-1/2}(r\nabla - (\lambda+1)\hat{\mathbf{r}})\,Y_{\lambda\mu} & \kappa = \lambda + 1 \end{cases} \tag{1A-125}$$

where $\hat{\mathbf{r}}$ is a unit vector in the direction of $\mathbf{r}$.

With the expansion (1A-121), the interaction (1A-120) becomes

$$H' = -\sum_{\kappa\lambda\mu}\int A^{\dagger}_{\kappa,\lambda\mu}(r)\boldsymbol{\Phi}_{\kappa,\lambda\mu}(\hat{\mathbf{r}})\cdot\mathbf{j}(\mathbf{r})\,d\tau$$

$$= -\sum_{\kappa\lambda\mu}\int A^{\dagger}_{\kappa,\lambda\mu}(r)\big(Y_{\kappa}(\hat{\mathbf{r}})\,j(\mathbf{r})\big)_{(\kappa 1)\lambda\mu}\,d\tau \tag{1A-126}$$

Each term in Eq. (1A-126) is a spherical tensor component $\lambda\mu$ in the nuclear variables (obtained by coupling the tensor Y_κ of rank κ with the first-rank tensor j), and $\overline{\lambda\mu}$ with respect to the external system. The dependence of the nuclear variables can be expressed in terms of the multipole moments

$$\mathcal{M}(j, \kappa\lambda\mu) = \int f_{\kappa\lambda}(r)\boldsymbol{\Phi}_{\kappa,\lambda\mu}(\hat{\mathbf{r}})\cdot\mathbf{j}(\mathbf{r})\,d\tau$$

$$= \int f_{\kappa\lambda}(r)\big(Y_{\kappa}(\hat{\mathbf{r}})\,j(\mathbf{r})\big)_{(\kappa 1)\lambda\mu}\,d\tau \tag{1A-127}$$

where the radial functions $f_{\kappa\lambda}(r)$ are obtained from matrix elements of $A_{\kappa,\lambda\mu}$ for the external system. If $\mathbf{A}(\mathbf{r})$ is expanded in powers of r, the leading-order term in $A_{\kappa,\lambda\mu}(r)$, and thus in $f_{\kappa\lambda}(r)$, is seen to be proportional to r^{κ}.

One can also characterize the vector structure of the fields in terms of their components in a coordinate system specified by the direction of $\mathbf{r}$ (helicity representation). Denoting the components of $\mathbf{e}$ in this system by e_η, we have

$$\mathbf{e}_\nu = \sum_{\eta}\mathscr{D}^{1}_{\nu\eta}(\hat{\mathbf{r}})\mathbf{e}_\eta \tag{1A-128}$$

and thus (see Eqs. (1A-42) and (1A-43))

$$\boldsymbol{\Phi}_{\kappa,\lambda\mu}(\hat{\mathbf{r}}) = \left(\frac{2\kappa+1}{4\pi}\right)^{1/2}\sum_{\eta}\langle\kappa 0 1\eta\,|\,\lambda\eta\rangle\mathscr{D}^{\lambda}_{\mu\eta}(\hat{\mathbf{r}})\mathbf{e}_\eta$$

$$= \sum_{\eta}\langle\lambda -\eta 1\eta\,|\,\kappa 0\rangle\boldsymbol{\Psi}_{\eta,\lambda\mu}(\hat{\mathbf{r}}) \tag{1A-129}$$

with

$$\boldsymbol{\Psi}_{\eta,\lambda\mu}(\hat{\mathbf{r}}) = (-1)^{1+\eta}\left(\frac{2\lambda+1}{4\pi}\right)^{1/2}\mathscr{D}^{\lambda}_{\mu\eta}(\hat{\mathbf{r}})\mathbf{e}_\eta \tag{1A-130}$$

The helicity representation Eq. (1A-130) forms an alternative complete orthonormal set for expanding the vector fields. The associated multipole moments $\mathcal{M}(j, \eta\lambda\mu)$ are obtained from Eq. (1A-127) by replacing $\boldsymbol{\Phi}$ with $\boldsymbol{\Psi}$.

1A-8c Spinor fields

In the case of reactions involving the transfer of a nucleon, the interaction can be expressed in terms of a spinor coupling involving the field $a^\dagger(\mathbf{r}, m_s)$ creating a nucleon at point **r** with polarization m_s and a corresponding spinor quantity associated with the incident projectile and outgoing particle. The multipole expansion of $a^\dagger(\mathbf{r}, m_s)$ corresponds to the transformation to the single-particle quantum numbers *nljm*,

$$a^\dagger(\mathbf{r}, m_s) = \sum_{nljm} \langle nljm \,|\, \mathbf{r}, m_s \rangle a^\dagger(nljm) \tag{1A-131}$$

where $a^\dagger(nljm)$ is a tensor component with $\lambda\mu = jm$ (see Sec. 1A-5e).

1A-9 Tensors in Isospace

The isospin dependence of operators can be characterized by their tensorial properties in isospace. The tensorial rank is denoted by τ and the component is specified by μ_τ; thus, a tensor $F_{\tau\mu_\tau}$ is defined in terms of its transformation properties with respect to rotations in isospace or, equivalently, by the property that it transfers the isospin $\tau\mu_\tau$ to the state on which it acts. For example, an operator that is independent of the isospin variables is an isoscalar ($\tau = 0$), while an operator proportional to the isospin of a nucleon is an isovector ($\tau = 1$). The reduced matrix element in isospace can be defined by

$$\langle T'M_T' \,|F_{\tau\mu_\tau}|\, TM_T \rangle = \langle TM_T\tau\mu_\tau \,|\, T'M_T' \rangle (2T'+1)^{-1/2} \langle T' \,\|F_\tau\|\, T \rangle \tag{1A-132}$$

corresponding to Eq. (1A-60).

For the extended time reversal operation $\mathscr{F}$, which is the product of $\mathscr{T}$ and a rotation of $-\pi$ about the y axis in isospace (see Eqs. (1B-15) and (1B-16)), we have, in analogy to Eq. (1A-74),

$$\mathscr{F} F_{\lambda\mu,\tau\mu_\tau} \mathscr{F}^{-1} = c_{\mathscr{F}} (-1)^{\lambda+\mu+\tau+\mu_\tau} F_{\lambda-\mu,\tau-\mu_\tau} \tag{1A-133}$$

The phase factor $c_{\mathscr{F}}$ gives the phase of the reduced matrix element

$$\langle I'T' \|| F_{\lambda\tau} \||\, IT \rangle^* = c_{\mathscr{F}} \langle I'T' \|| F_{\lambda\tau} \||\, IT \rangle \tag{1A-134}$$

We have used a triple bar to emphasize that the matrix element is reduced in spin-orbital space as well as in isospace.

APPENDIX

1B

Time Reversal

The general properties of the time reversal operation have been considered in the text (Sec. 1-2c). In this Appendix we give some further details, discuss a few simple examples, and extend the formalism to include states associated with scattering and decay processes.

1B-1 Single-Particle States

We first consider the effect of time reversal on the wave function $\varphi_A(\mathbf{r})$ of a single particle without spin. The time-reversed state $\bar{A} = \mathscr{T} A$ has the same spatial density distribution as A, while motions are reversed, and the wave function is simply obtained by complex conjugation of φ_A,

$$\varphi_{\bar{A}}(\mathbf{r}) = \varphi_A^*(\mathbf{r}) \tag{1B-1}$$

The reversal of the motion can be seen, for example, by expanding in the components with momentum $\mathbf{p}$,

$$\begin{aligned} \varphi_A(\mathbf{r}) &= \int d^3p\, c_A(\mathbf{p}) \exp\left\{\frac{i}{\hbar}\,\mathbf{p}\cdot\mathbf{r}\right\} \\ \varphi_{\bar{A}}(\mathbf{r}) &= \int d^3p\, c_A^*(\mathbf{p}) \exp\left\{-\frac{i}{\hbar}\,\mathbf{p}\cdot\mathbf{r}\right\} \end{aligned} \tag{1B-2}$$

If we consider time-dependent wave functions, the effect of $\mathscr{T}$ also reverses the development in time. In fact, by applying the time displacement operator (see Eq. (1-8)), we obtain

$$\begin{aligned} \varphi_A(\mathbf{r}, t) &= \exp\left\{-\frac{i}{\hbar}\,Ht\right\}\varphi_A(\mathbf{r}, t=0) \\ \varphi_{\bar{A}}(\mathbf{r}, t) &= \exp\left\{-\frac{i}{\hbar}\,Ht\right\}\varphi_{\bar{A}}(\mathbf{r}, t=0) \\ &= \left(\exp\left\{\frac{i}{\hbar}\,Ht\right\}\varphi_A(\mathbf{r}, t=0)\right)^* \\ &= \varphi_A^*(\mathbf{r}, -t) \end{aligned} \tag{1B-3}$$

The Hamiltonian H is assumed to be time reversal invariant and thus a real operator. (For $H(\mathbf{r}, \mathbf{p}) = H(\mathbf{r}, -i\hbar\nabla_r)$, this assumption implies $H(\mathbf{r}, \mathbf{p}) = H(\mathbf{r}, -\mathbf{p})$.)

The wave function $\varphi_A(\mathbf{r})$ is the component of $|A\rangle$ in the coordinate representation $|\mathbf{r}\rangle$,

$$\varphi_A(\mathbf{r}) = \langle \mathbf{r} | A \rangle \tag{1B-4}$$

The simplicity of the time reversal operation in this representation arises from the invariance of the states $|\mathbf{r}\rangle$,

$$\mathcal{T} | \mathbf{r} \rangle = | \mathbf{r} \rangle \tag{1B-5}$$

Thus, we obtain (see Eq. (1-33))

$$\begin{aligned} \langle \mathbf{r} | A \rangle &= \langle \mathcal{T}\mathbf{r} | \mathcal{T} A \rangle^* \\ &= \langle \mathbf{r} | \mathcal{T} A \rangle^* \end{aligned} \tag{1B-6}$$

as the formal derivation of Eq. (1B-1).

The time reversal operator can be written as a product of a unitary operator $\mathcal{U}_{\mathcal{T}}$ and the complex conjugation operator K (see Eqs. (1-31) and (1-32)). The relation (1B-6) implies that, in the coordinate representation, the unitary operator $\mathcal{U}_{\mathcal{T}}$ is the indentity operator.

In the momentum representation, we may determine the effect of $\mathcal{T}$ by employing Eq. (1B-5) and the transformation from $|\mathbf{r}\rangle$ to $|\mathbf{p}\rangle$,

$$\begin{aligned} |\mathbf{p}\rangle &= (2\pi\hbar)^{-3/2} \int d^3r \exp\left\{\frac{i}{\hbar}\mathbf{p}\cdot\mathbf{r}\right\} |\mathbf{r}\rangle \\ \mathcal{T}|\mathbf{p}\rangle &= (2\pi\hbar)^{-3/2} \int d^3r \exp\left\{-\frac{i}{\hbar}\mathbf{p}\cdot\mathbf{r}\right\} |\mathbf{r}\rangle \end{aligned} \tag{1B-7}$$

In this representation, therefore, $\mathcal{U}_{\mathcal{T}}$ is an operator that transforms $\mathbf{p}$ to $-\mathbf{p}$, and is equivalent to the parity, $\mathcal{P}$.

In the angular momentum representation, the basis states, specified by r and the orbital angular momentum lm, are chosen such that

$$\langle \mathbf{r} | rlm \rangle = i^l Y_{lm}(\vartheta, \varphi) \tag{1B-8}$$

The phase factor i^l makes it possible to express $\mathcal{T}$ in terms of a rotation $\mathcal{R}$ of 180° about the y axis ($\vartheta \to \pi - \vartheta$; $\varphi \to \pi - \varphi$). In fact, as can be seen from Eq. (1B-6),

$$\begin{aligned} \mathcal{T} |rlm\rangle &= (-1)^{l+m} | rl\, -m\rangle \\ &= \mathcal{R}^{-1} |rlm\rangle \end{aligned} \tag{1B-9}$$

Thus, in the basis $|rlm\rangle$, the unitary operator $\mathcal{U}_{\mathcal{T}}$ equals $\mathcal{R}^{-1}$. (We have chosen to write $\mathcal{R}^{-1}$ rather than $\mathcal{R}$ in Eq. (1B-9); the two operations are identical for integer values of the angular momentum.)

In momentum space, the basis $|plm\rangle$ is defined by a relation corresponding to Eq. (1B-8), but without the phase factor i^l. The time reverse of $|plm\rangle$ is equal to $(-1)^{l+m}|pl-m\rangle$, where the factor $(-1)^l$ arises from the fact that $\mathcal{T}$ inverts the direction of $\mathbf{p}$. We thus again obtain $\mathcal{U}_{\mathcal{T}} = \mathcal{R}^{-1}$.

The relation $\mathcal{U}_{\mathcal{T}} = \mathcal{R}^{-1}$ also applies to the description of the spin. The conventional representation of the Pauli spin matrices

$$\sigma_x = 2s_x = \begin{pmatrix} 0 & 1 \\ 1 & 0 \end{pmatrix} \qquad \sigma_y = 2s_y = \begin{pmatrix} 0 & -i \\ i & 0 \end{pmatrix}$$
$$\sigma_z = 2s_z = \begin{pmatrix} 1 & 0 \\ 0 & -1 \end{pmatrix} \tag{1B-10}$$

is characterized by σ_x and σ_z being real matrices, and σ_y purely imaginary, that is,

$$K(s_x, s_y, s_z)K = (s_x, -s_y, s_z) \tag{1B-11}$$

Since $\mathscr{T}$ inverts all components of **s**, we have

$$\mathscr{U}_{\mathscr{T}}(s_x, s_y, s_z)\mathscr{U}_{\mathscr{T}}^{-1} = (-s_x, s_y, -s_z) \tag{1B-12}$$

which is satisfied for

$$\mathscr{U}_{\mathscr{T}} = \mathscr{R}^{-1} = \exp\{i\pi s_y\} = i\sigma_y \tag{1B-13}$$

1B-2 Many-Particle States (Bound Systems)

For a many-particle system we can choose basis states specified by radial variables together with orbital and spin angular momenta of the individual particles. In this basis, the unitary operator $\mathscr{U}_{\mathscr{T}}$ associated with time reversal equals the rotation $\mathscr{R}^{-1}$ acting on all the particles,

$$\mathscr{U}_{\mathscr{T}} = \mathscr{R}^{-1} = \exp(i\pi I_y) \tag{1B-14}$$

Thus, the operation $\mathscr{R}\mathscr{T}$ is simply the complex conjugation K. This relation is not affected by couplings of the individual angular momenta, since the vector addition coefficients are real in the standard representation (see Sec. 1A-2).

If the Hamiltonian H is invariant with respect to $\mathscr{R}\mathscr{T}$, we can choose a set of eigenstates of H that are also eigenstates of $\mathscr{R}\mathscr{T} = K$. Since the eigenvalue of K depends on the overall phase of the eigenstate, we can always choose the phases such that $K = \mathscr{R}\mathscr{T} = +1$. Such a state is characterized by real wave functions in the radial variables. The phase convention $\mathscr{R}\mathscr{T} = +1$ leads to the relation (1-40) and is adopted throughout the book in the description of bound states (except where explicitly stated). States describing collision processes do not have the time reversal invariance of the bound states, and will be considered in the following section.

For isospin-dependent operators, it is sometimes useful to employ an extended time reversal operation

$$\mathscr{F} \equiv \exp\{i\pi T_y\}\mathscr{T} \tag{1B-15}$$

which reverses not only velocities and spins, but also the direction of isospins (inversion of the "motion" in isospace). The action of $\mathscr{F}$ on a state with the standard phasing is given by

$$\mathscr{F}|IMTM_T\rangle = (-1)^{I+M+T+M_T}|I-MT-M_T\rangle \tag{1B-16}$$

as follows from Eqs. (1-40) and (1A-47).

In the above discussion we have linked the $\mathscr{T}$ transformation to the rotational invariance. For $\mathscr{T}$-invariant systems that are not invariant with respect to $\mathscr{R}$, we may employ basis states that are eigenstates of $\mathscr{T}$ itself, provided the number of particles, n, is even. One may obtain such an orthogonal basis by starting from an arbitrary state $|A\rangle$.

If this state is an eigenstate of $\mathscr{T}$, we can choose its phase such that the eigenvalue of $\mathscr{T}$ is $+1$ (see Eq. (1–37)). If $|A\rangle$ is not an eigenstate of $\mathscr{T}$, we construct

$$|A'\rangle = c_A(1+\mathscr{T})|A\rangle \tag{1B-17}$$

where the normalization factor c_A is taken to be real. Since $\mathscr{T}^2 = +1$, when operating on a state of even n (see Eq. (1–41)), it follows that $\mathscr{T}|A'\rangle = |A'\rangle$. Next, select a state B orthogonal to A' and (if B is not an eigenstate of $\mathscr{T}$) construct

$$|B'\rangle = c_B(1+\mathscr{T})|B\rangle \tag{1B-18}$$

which is seen to be orthogonal to $|A'\rangle$ and to satisfy $\mathscr{T}|B'\rangle = |B'\rangle$. Proceeding in this manner, one may obtain a complete orthonormal basis of eigenstates of $\mathscr{T}$ with eigenvalue $+1$. In this basis the matrix elements of a $\mathscr{T}$-invariant operator, such as the Hamiltonian, are real, as follows from Eq. (1–34).

For a system with an odd number of fermions, there are no eigenstates of $\mathscr{T}$ (see the discussion following Eq. (1-41)), but one can construct an orthogonal basis in which the states are pairwise $\mathscr{T}$ conjugate. Thus, starting from a state $|A\rangle$, we form $\mathscr{T}|A\rangle$, which is orthogonal to $|A\rangle$ as a consequence of the relation $\mathscr{T}^2 = -1$ (see Eq. (1-41)),

$$\begin{aligned}\langle \mathscr{T}A|A\rangle &= -\langle A|\mathscr{T}A\rangle^* \\ &= -\langle \mathscr{T}A|A\rangle = 0\end{aligned} \tag{1B-19}$$

Next, we select a state $|B\rangle$ that is orthogonal to $|A\rangle$ as well as to $\mathscr{T}|A\rangle$ and form $\mathscr{T}|B\rangle$, which is readily seen to be also orthogonal to $|A\rangle$ and $|\mathscr{T}A\rangle$. In this manner one may continue to form a complete basis.

For such a basis, it is convenient to use the notation $|\alpha\rho\rangle$, where ρ takes the values $+1$ and -1, such that

$$\begin{aligned}\mathscr{T}|\alpha\rho=1\rangle &= -|\alpha\rho=-1\rangle \\ \mathscr{T}|\alpha\rho=-1\rangle &= +|\alpha\rho=1\rangle\end{aligned} \tag{1B-20}$$

The total vector space is thus regarded as the product of an α space and a ρ space. In ρ space the operators are 2×2 matrices and can be expressed as linear combinations of the unit matrix ρ_0 together with the three Pauli matrices $\boldsymbol{\rho} = (\rho_1, \rho_2, \rho_3)$ (see Eq. (1B-10)). A general operator T can thus be written

$$\begin{aligned}T &= T_0\rho_0 + i\mathbf{T}\cdot\boldsymbol{\rho} \\ &= T_0\rho_0 + i\sum_{j=1}^{3} T_j\rho_j\end{aligned} \tag{1B-21}$$

where T_0, T_1, T_2, and T_3 are matrices in α space.

For the basis states (1B-20), the time reversal operation is represented by

$$\mathscr{U}_{\mathscr{T}} = \begin{pmatrix} 0 & 1 \\ -1 & 0\end{pmatrix} = i\rho_2 \tag{1B-22}$$

in analogy to the relation (1B-13) for time reversal in spin space. Hence, we have

$$\mathscr{T}\rho_0\mathscr{T}^{-1} = \rho_0 \qquad \mathscr{T}\boldsymbol{\rho}\mathscr{T}^{-1} = -\boldsymbol{\rho} \tag{1B-23}$$

and

$$\mathscr{T}T\mathscr{T}^{-1} = T_0^*\rho_0 + i\mathbf{T}^*\cdot\boldsymbol{\rho} \tag{1B-24}$$

A time reversal invariant operator T is therefore characterized by having real matrices

$$T_0^* = T_0 \qquad \mathbf{T}^* = \mathbf{T} \tag{1B-25}$$

In Eqs. (1B-24) and (1B-25), the operator $\mathbf{T}^*$ is obtained by a complex conjugation of the Cartesian components T_j.

Since the matrices ρ_0, $\boldsymbol{\rho}$ are Hermitian, we obtain the further relations

$$T_0^\dagger = T_0 \qquad \mathbf{T}^\dagger = -\mathbf{T} \tag{1B-26}$$

for a Hermitian operator T. An operator of the form (1B-21) satisfying Eqs. (1B-25) and (1B-26) is referred to as a real quaternion operator (the elements of the quaternion are defined in terms of four basic matrices ρ_0 and $-i\boldsymbol{\rho}$). The transformations that preserve the relationship (1B-20) among the basis states form a symplectic group. For a discussion of the quaternion representation and the symplectic transformations, see, for example, Dyson (1962b).

1B-3 Collision Processes

While the stationary bound states, for a time reversal invariant Hamiltonian, are invariant under $\mathscr{T}$, apart from the change of orientation (see Eq. (1-39)), the states describing a collision process are unsymmetric with respect to $\mathscr{T}$, since such a process has a definite direction in time. Thus, a collision state is characterized by a set of incident particles (or nuclei), which may scatter or produce new particles. We denote such a state by $|A \text{ in}\rangle$, where the quantum numbers A specify the momenta, spin polarization, and internal structure of the incident particles. For $t \to -\infty$, the state $|A \text{ in}\rangle$ represents the freely propagating incident particles, which can be described by wave packets with dimensions so large that the indeterminacy in momentum and energy can be neglected. If we analyze the collision state in terms of spherical waves describing the relative motion of the colliding systems and products formed in the collision, the state $|A \text{ in}\rangle$ may also be characterized by the asymptotic boundary condition that incoming spherical waves are present only in the incident channels specified by A.

The analysis of a collision process involves a conjugate set of states $|B \text{ out}\rangle$ with the property that, for $t \to \infty$, they develop into large wave packets associated with outgoing collision products B. In fact, the detection of products B corresponds to the determination of components $|B \text{ out}\rangle$ in the collision state $|A \text{ in}\rangle$. The transition amplitude for the reaction $A \to B$ is, therefore,

$$\langle B|S|A\rangle = \langle B \text{ out}|A \text{ in}\rangle \tag{1B-27}$$

which is referred to as the S-matrix element.

If the Hamiltonian is time reversal invariant, the operator $\mathscr{T}$ transforms an in-state into an out-state

$$\begin{aligned} \mathscr{T}|A \text{ in}\rangle &= |\bar{A} \text{ out}\rangle \\ \mathscr{T}|A \text{ out}\rangle &= |\bar{A} \text{ in}\rangle \end{aligned} \tag{1B-28}$$

where $\bar{A}$ is obtained from A by reversing momenta and transforming spins and angular momenta in accordance with the relations given above ($|\overline{\mathbf{p}m_s}\rangle = (-1)^{s+m_s}|-\mathbf{p}\,-m_s\rangle$, etc.). From Eq. (1B-28) we obtain (see Eq. (1-33))

$$\begin{aligned}\langle B|S|A\rangle &= \langle B\,\text{out}|A\,\text{in}\rangle \\ &= \langle \bar{B}\,\text{in}|\bar{A}\,\text{out}\rangle^* \\ &= \langle \bar{A}\,\text{out}|\bar{B}\,\text{in}\rangle \\ &= \langle \bar{A}|S|\bar{B}\rangle \end{aligned} \tag{1B-29}$$

as an expression for the time reversal invariance of the S matrix. The equality (1B-29) implies the reciprocity relation for the cross sections for inverse reactions (see the discussion in connection with Fig. 1-4, p. 28). In the case of elastic scattering, the amplitudes $\langle B|S|A\rangle$ and $\langle A|S|B\rangle$ are related by rotational invariance, and Eq. (1B-29) may thus restrict the possible form of the angular distribution and polarization (see the discussion in connection with Fig. 1-6, p. 30).

The relationship between the elements of the S matrix and the scattering cross sections can be obtained by evaluating the number of transitions per unit time and dividing by the flux of particles in the incident channel. We shall give the relation for reactions involving two incident and two outgoing particles (each of which may be a composite system).

The two-particle states may be specified by the total momentum $\mathbf{P}$, the total energy E in the center-of-mass system, the direction of the momentum $\mathbf{p}$ of one of the particles in the center-of-mass frame, and additional quantum numbers α specifying the intrinsic structure and polarization of the two particles. Since the collision conserves $\mathbf{P}$ and E, the S-matrix element can be written

$$\langle \mathbf{P}_B E_B \hat{\mathbf{p}}_B \beta|S|\mathbf{P}_A E_A \hat{\mathbf{p}}_A \alpha\rangle = \langle \mathbf{p}_B \beta|S|\mathbf{p}_A \alpha\rangle\, \delta(\mathbf{P}_A - \mathbf{P}_B)\, \delta(E_A - E_B) \tag{1B-30}$$

where the factor multiplying the δ functions may be referred to as the reduced S-matrix element. Assuming the two-particle states to be normalized per unit total momentum, total energy, and solid angle in relative motion, we can write the reduced S-matrix element in the form

$$\langle \mathbf{p}_B \beta|S|\mathbf{p}_A \alpha\rangle = \delta(\hat{\mathbf{p}}_A - \hat{\mathbf{p}}_B)\, \delta(\alpha, \beta) + \frac{i}{2\pi\hbar}(p_A p_B)^{1/2} f(\mathbf{p}_A \alpha \to \mathbf{p}_B \beta) \tag{1B-31}$$

The first term in Eq. (1B-31) is the value of S in the absence of interactions, while the second term is the transition amplitude. The scattering amplitude f introduced in Eq. (1B-31) may be regarded as defined by this relation.

The number of transitions per unit time and unit solid angle is

$$\frac{d^2N(\mathbf{p}_A \alpha \to \mathbf{p}_B \beta)}{dt\, d\Omega} = \frac{1}{2\pi\hbar} |\langle \mathbf{p}_B \beta|S|\mathbf{p}_A \alpha\rangle - \delta(\hat{\mathbf{p}}_A - \hat{\mathbf{p}}_B)\, \delta(\alpha, \beta)|^2 \tag{1B-32}$$

and since the flux of incident particles associated with waves normalized per unit energy is

$$(\rho v)_A = \frac{p_A^2}{(2\pi\hbar)^3} \tag{1B-33}$$

we obtain the differential cross section

$$d\sigma(\mathbf{p}_A \alpha \to \mathbf{p}_B \beta) = \frac{p_B}{p_A} |f(\mathbf{p}_A \alpha \to \mathbf{p}_B \beta)|^2\, d\Omega \tag{1B-34}$$

(In the helicity representation, we employ wave functions normalized to the total solid angle

$8\pi^2$ as in Eq, (3F-5). The scattering amplitude f is still defined by Eq. (1B-31) and is therefore reduced by a factor 2π. The flux (1B-33) is reduced by the same factor, and the expression (1B-34) for the cross section therefore contains an extra factor 2π; moreover, the element of solid angle is $2\pi \sin \vartheta \, d\vartheta \, d\varphi$.)

The scattering amplitude, defined by (1B-31), involves the momenta $\mathbf{p}_A$ and $\mathbf{p}_B$ in a symmetrical way. The time reversal relation (1B-29) thus implies

$$f(\mathbf{p}_A \alpha \rightarrow \mathbf{p}_B \beta) = f(\overline{\mathbf{p}_B \beta} \rightarrow \overline{\mathbf{p}_A \alpha}) \tag{1B-35}$$

1B-4 Decay Processes

The decay $A \rightarrow B$ of an unstable particle or of a nuclear state, A, into two or more particles represented by the state B is related by time reversal to the inverse process $\bar{B} \rightarrow \bar{A}$, by which incident particles in the state $\bar{B}$ form the system $\bar{A}$.

If the decaying state has a lifetime long compared to the periods of internal motion, one can describe the decay as a perturbation caused by some small part H' of the total Hamiltonian. For example, H' may represent the part of the interaction that violates the symmetry responsible for the stability of A (weak or electromagnetic interactions, etc.). To leading order in H', the decay is determined by the matrix element $\langle B \text{ out} | H' | A \rangle$ where the final state $|B \text{ out}\rangle$ represents the motion of the decay products in the absence of H'.

If the total Hamiltonian including H' is time reversal invariant, we obtain the relation (see Eqs. (1-34) and (1B-28))

$$\langle B \text{ out} | H' | A \rangle = \langle A | H' | \bar{B} \text{ in} \rangle \tag{1B-36}$$

connecting the decay matrix element to that of the formation process.

We can obtain an additional relation between formation and decay matrix elements in terms of the scattering matrix for the channels B representing the final states of the decay process. The scattering consists of a resonant part associated with the formation of the intermediate state A and a nonresonant part describing the scattering in the absence of the interaction H'. Since we consider only leading order effects in H', we may neglect the resonant part of the scattering. In evaluating the formation matrix element, we insert a complete set of outgoing states $|B' \text{ out}\rangle$ and employ Eq. (1B-27) for the scattering amplitude,

$$\begin{aligned} \langle A | H' | B \text{ in} \rangle &= \sum_{B'} \langle A | H' | B' \text{ out} \rangle \langle B' \text{ out} | B \text{ in} \rangle \\ &= \sum_{B'} \langle B' | S_0 | B \rangle \langle B' \text{ out} | H' | A \rangle^* \end{aligned} \tag{1B-37}$$

where S_0 is the scattering matrix in the absence of H', Thus, by combining Eqs. (1B-36) and (1B-37), we obtain restrictions on the decay amplitude itself, as a consequence of $\mathscr{T}$ invariance.

These relations take an especially simple form if we employ a set of scattering states B that are eigenstates of S_0

$$\langle B' | S_0 | B \rangle = \delta(B, B') \exp\{2i\delta_B\} \tag{1B-38}$$

where the phase shift δ_B in the channel B is a real number. (The possibility of transforming the S_0 matrix to the diagonal form (1B-38) with real phases δ_B expresses the unitarity of S_0, that is, the completeness and orthonormality of each of the sets of states $|B \text{ in}\rangle$ and $|B \text{ out}\rangle$). From Eqs. (1B-36) and (1B-38) we then obtain

$$\langle B \text{ out}|H'|A\rangle = \exp\{2i\delta_B\}\langle \bar{B} \text{ out}|H'|\bar{A}\rangle^* \tag{1B-39}$$

(The phase shift is the same in channels $\bar{B}$ and B, as a consequence of Eq. (1B-29).) The phase shifts δ_B in Eq. (1B-39) can be determined experimentally from the non-resonant scattering. If the structure of the final state interaction is known, the phase shifts can be computed theoretically. For example, in a β-decay process, the phase shifts result from the effect of the nuclear Coulomb field on the motion of the emitted electron.

In the case of γ decay (or β decay of light nuclei), the final state B can be approximately described in terms of freely moving particles ($\delta_B \ll 1$). We then have $|B \text{ in}\rangle \approx |B \text{ out}\rangle$ and it follows from Eq. (1B-36) that the decay amplitude for the process $A \rightarrow B$, where B specifies the direction and polarization of the decay products, is the complex conjugate of the amplitude for $\bar{A} \rightarrow \bar{B}$; in particular the rates of the two decays are equal.

The relationships discussed above can also be viewed in terms of the resonance scattering analysis (see Appendix 3F).

APPENDIX

1C

Permutation Symmetry

The identity of the nucleons implies that the nuclear Hamiltonian is invariant with respect to the permutations P_{jk} that exchange all the coordinates of the two particles j and k. These transposition operators are therefore constants of the motion, and we can classify the eigenstates of the Hamiltonian in terms of the quantum numbers that describe the permutation symmetry. The Fermi statistics of the nucleons only permits physical states that are completely antisymmetric and, thus, in the absence of any additional degeneracy or invariance, the consequences of the permutation symmetry (though very far reaching) would be fairly trivial.[7]

In many nuclear physics problems, the Hamiltonian not only is invariant with respect to permutations involving the complete set of coordinates, but, in addition, is approximately invariant with respect to permutation operators that act on a partial set of coordinates for each nucleon. For example, the charge independence of the nuclear forces implies that the Hamiltonian (with neglect of electromagnetic and weak interaction effects) can be written in a form in which the isobaric variables of the nucleons do not explicitly appear (see p. 34). Such a Hamiltonian is obviously invariant with respect to permutations P^{τ}_{jk} that act only on the isobaric coordinates of the nucleons, and is thus also invariant with respect to permutations that act on the space-spin coordinates, $P^{r}_{jk}P^{\sigma}_{jk}$. In some cases, it is of interest to study Hamiltonians that are invariant separately under the permutations P^{τ}_{jk}, P^{σ}_{jk}, and P^{r}_{jk}.

The occurrence of these additional symmetries implies that the eigenstates can be characterized by additional quantum numbers describing the symmetry of the state with respect to the permutation operators that act only on the partial set of coordinates of the nucleons.

The above remarks refer to particles obeying Fermi statistics, but very similar problems arise for systems of bosons. In the description of nuclear properties, one encounters boson systems, for example, in the treatment of excitations in terms of vibrational quanta (see especially Chapter 6), and in the treatment of the harmonic oscillator shell structure in terms of the oscillation quanta (Appendix 7B). The wave function for such a system must be totally symmetric with respect to permutations

[7] The treatment of antisymmetric many-particle states in terms of particle creation operators is discussed in Appendix 2A.

involving all the coordinates of each boson, but additional symmetry quantum numbers play a role if the Hamiltonian is approximately invariant with respect to permutations acting on only a partial set of coordinates of each boson.

The transpositions P_{jk} can be multiplied together to yield a quite general permutation P. For an n-particle system, there are $n!$ different permutations P, and the set of these operators forms a group called the symmetric group of n objects, S_n. Thus, the systematic discussion of the permutation symmetry of functions depending on n variables amounts to a study of the representations of the group S_n. In the present appendix (Sec. 1C-1), we shall introduce the main concepts that are needed in this study, derive the results for the simple cases of $n = 2$ and $n = 3$, and attempt to make plausible the results for general n; these results can always be obtained by straightforward extensions of the elementary methods employed for $n = 2$ and $n = 3$, though usually the extensions are tedious and the powerful mathematics of abstract group theory may be exploited to advantage in demonstrating general results appropriate to an n-body wave function.[8]

In all the examples mentioned above, the particle variables in one (or more) of the spaces are limited to a finite number of discrete values; thus, the isospin variable of a nucleon may take only two values, the quanta of the harmonic oscillator motion can have three directions, and so on. In this situation, it is convenient to build the wave functions from appropriately symmetrized product states (Sec. 1C-2).

The relationship between the different possible product states, belonging to a given permutation symmetry, can be studied in terms of the unitary transformations between the different states of the single-particle basis; these transformations are therefore intimately related to the permutation symmetry, and we shall consider some aspects of this relation in the last section of this appendix.

1C-1 Symmetry Quantum Numbers (Partitions)

1C-1a $n = 2$

Any function depending on the coordinates of two particles may be thought of as the sum of a symmetric function $\Phi_s(1, 2)$ and an antisymmetric function $\Phi_a(1, 2)$. The permutation operator P_{12}, which interchanges the coordinates of particle 1 and particle 2, yields

$$\begin{aligned} P_{12}\Phi_s(1, 2) &= \Phi_s(1, 2) \\ P_{12}\Phi_a(1, 2) &= -\Phi_a(1, 2) \end{aligned} \tag{1C-1}$$

Hence, the functions Φ_s and Φ_a go into themselves under the action of P_{12}, which can also be expressed by saying that these functions each carry a one-dimensional representation of the symmetric group S_2.

---

[8] For a more systematic treatment of these questions employing the methods of group theory, see, for example, Bayman (1957), Hamermesh (1962), and Littlewood (1950).

With a view to the more systematic notation applicable for general n, we may associate each of the representations of S_2 with a Young diagram consisting of $2 (=n)$ boxes. Two boxes placed in a row, ☐☐, label the symmetric functions, while two boxes placed in a column, ⊟, label the antisymmetric functions. The diagram may also be characterized by giving the number of boxes in each row; thus, $s = $ ☐☐ $= [2]$, while $a = $ ⊟ $= [11]$. The symbols $[2]$ and $[11]$ are referred to as partitions of the number $n = 2$.

1C-1b   n = 3

There are six $(=3!)$ permutation operations that can be performed on a three-particle function; the identity operation, the three transpositions, and the two cyclic permutations of all three coordinates

$$e \qquad\qquad e\Phi(1, 2, 3) = \Phi(1, 2, 3)$$

$$P_{12}, P_{13}, P_{23} \qquad P_{12}\Phi(1, 2, 3) = \Phi(2, 1, 3), \text{ etc.} \qquad (1\text{C-}2)$$

$$P_{123}, P_{132} \qquad P_{123}\Phi(1, 2, 3) = \Phi(2, 3, 1), \text{ etc.}$$

For any n, one can distinguish between even and odd permutations, depending on whether they involve an even or odd number of transpositions. Thus, for $n = 3$, the even permutations are e, P_{123}, P_{132}, while the odd permutations are P_{12}, P_{23}, P_{13}. Denoting the number of transpositions in a given permutation P by the symbol p, we have $(-1)^p = +1$ for the even permutations and $(-1)^p = -1$ for the odd permutations.

Functions depending on the coordinates of three particles can be divided into three symmetry types under the action of the operators (1C-2):

(a) Completely symmetric functions, for which

$$P_{jk}\Phi_s(1, 2, 3) = \Phi_s(1, 2, 3) \qquad (1\text{C-}3)$$

for any transposition P_{jk}. Such functions are also invariant under the cyclic permutation operators P_{123} and P_{132}, which can be written as products of two transpositions. The symmetric representation of S_3 is labeled by a Young diagram with three boxes in a row, ☐☐☐, or by the partition $[3]$. The projection operator $\mathscr{S}$, which picks out the symmetric part of any three-particle function, can be written

$$\mathscr{S} = \frac{1}{6}\sum_P P \qquad (1\text{C-}4)$$

where the sum is over all six permutations in S_3. The normalization in Eq. (1C-4) is chosen so that the projection operator is idempotent, $\mathscr{S}^2 = \mathscr{S}$.

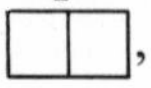

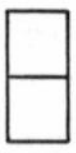

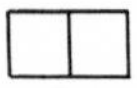

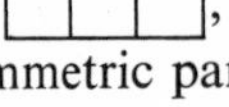

(b) Completely antisymmetric functions, for which

$$P_{jk}\Phi_a(1, 2, 3) = -\Phi_a(1, 2, 3) \tag{1C-5}$$

for any transposition P_{jk}. Functions with this property are invariant under cyclic permutations. The antisymmetric representation of S_3 is labeled by a diagram with three boxes in a column, , or by the partition [111]. The projection operator, $\mathscr{A}$, that picks out the antisymmetric part of a general three-particle function may be written

$$\mathscr{A} = \frac{1}{6}\sum_P (-1)^p P \tag{1C-6}$$

where $(-1)^p$ is the parity of the permutation defined above.

(c) Functions of mixed symmetry. These functions are characterized by the fact that they give zero when acted on by the symmetrizing operator, $\mathscr{S}$, and when acted on by the antisymmetrizing operator, $\mathscr{A}$. Examples of functions of mixed symmetry are

$$\begin{aligned} \Phi^{(1)} &= x_1 + x_2 - 2x_3 \\ \Phi^{(2)} &= x_1 - x_2 \end{aligned} \tag{1C-7}$$

where x_1 is any variable associated with particle 1. Since $\Phi^{(2)} = -\frac{1}{3}(1 + 2P_{13})\,\Phi^{(1)}$, it is seen that $\Phi^{(1)}$ and $\Phi^{(2)}$ go into each other under appropriate linear combinations of the permutation operators. Moreover, it can easily be verified that the result of any of the six permutation operators (1C-2) acting on $\Phi^{(1)}$ or $\Phi^{(2)}$ can be expressed again as a linear combination of $\Phi^{(1)}$ and $\Phi^{(2)}$. The two functions (1C-7), therefore, carry a two-dimensional representation of S_3.

As an alternative to the basis function (1C-7) we could, of course, have used any pair of independent linear combinations of $\Phi^{(1)}$ and $\Phi^{(2)}$. The particular choice (1C-7) is characterized by having definite permutation symmetry with respect to the coordinates of particles 1 and 2 (that is, $P_{12}\,\Phi^{(1)} = \Phi^{(1)}$ and $P_{12}\,\Phi^{(2)} = -\Phi^{(2)}$).

The functions (1C-7) are examples of a more general class of functions carrying the mixed symmetry

$$\begin{aligned} \Phi^{(1)} &= \frac{1}{\sqrt{6}}\left(\varphi_1(x_1)\varphi_2(x_2)\varphi_2(x_3) + \varphi_2(x_1)\varphi_1(x_2)\varphi_2(x_3) - 2\varphi_2(x_1)\varphi_2(x_2)\varphi_1(x_3)\right) \\ \Phi^{(2)} &= \frac{1}{\sqrt{2}}\left(\varphi_1(x_1)\varphi_2(x_2)\varphi_2(x_3) - \varphi_2(x_1)\varphi_1(x_2)\varphi_2(x_3)\right) \end{aligned} \tag{1C-8}$$

For $\varphi_1(x) = x$ and $\varphi_2(x) = \text{const.}$, these functions reduce to the form (1C-7), apart from the normalization. If $\varphi_1(x)$ and $\varphi_2(x)$ are orthogonal and normalized single-particle functions, then also the functions Φ given by Eq. (1C-8) form an orthonormal set. The permutation operators acting in this space are represented by the following matrices:

$$
e = \begin{pmatrix} 1 & 0 \\ 0 & 1 \end{pmatrix} \qquad P_{12} = \begin{pmatrix} 1 & 0 \\ 0 & -1 \end{pmatrix} \qquad P_{23} = \begin{pmatrix} -\frac{1}{2} & \frac{\sqrt{3}}{2} \\ \frac{\sqrt{3}}{2} & \frac{1}{2} \end{pmatrix}
$$

$$
P_{13} = \begin{pmatrix} -\frac{1}{2} & -\frac{\sqrt{3}}{2} \\ -\frac{\sqrt{3}}{2} & \frac{1}{2} \end{pmatrix} \qquad P_{132} = \begin{pmatrix} -\frac{1}{2} & -\frac{\sqrt{3}}{2} \\ \frac{\sqrt{3}}{2} & -\frac{1}{2} \end{pmatrix} \qquad P_{123} = \begin{pmatrix} -\frac{1}{2} & \frac{\sqrt{3}}{2} \\ -\frac{\sqrt{3}}{2} & -\frac{1}{2} \end{pmatrix} \tag{1C-9}
$$

which are seen to be unitary (and real orthogonal on account of the phase choice in Eq. (1C-8)). Equivalent unitary representations are obtained by unitary transformations of the basis set (1C-8).

The two-dimensional mixed symmetry representation is irreducible. A representation is referred to as irreducible if it is not possible to divide the total vector space spanned by the basis states into subspaces that are invariant under all the permutations of the group. If such subspaces existed, it would be possible by a linear transformation of the basis states to transform the matrices representing the permutation operators into a form consisting of quadratic blocks along the diagonal with zero matrix elements outside the blocks. A representation of this type would thus be reducible into representations of smaller dimensions (which might or might not themselves be irreducible). In the special case of a two-dimensional representation, reducibility would imply that all the permutation matrices could be simultaneously diagonalized, and this is clearly not the case for the matrices (1C-9). It may be noted that the irreducibility of a representation of the permutation group can be tested by considering only the transpositions between adjacent particles (P_{12} and P_{23} in the case of S_3). These permutation elements are referred to as generators of the permutation group, since all the permutations can be expressed as products of the adjacent transpositions.

The mixed symmetry representation of S_3 is labeled by the diagram  or by the partition [21]. The particular set of basis states (1C-8) can be further specified by their symmetry with respect to permutations acting on the first two particles; thus, $\Phi^{(1)}$ belongs to the symmetric and $\Phi^{(2)}$ to the antisymmetric representation of the subgroup S_2 consisting of e and P_{12}. We can therefore label the function $\Phi^{(1)}$ by the two diagrams 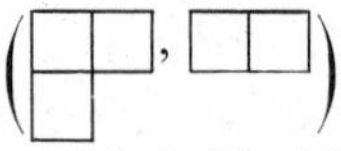 and $\Phi^{(2)}$ by the diagrams 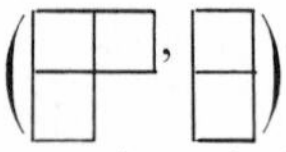. Alternatively, the functions are labeled by Young tableaux, in which the numbers 1, 2, and 3 are placed in the boxes of the diagram in such a manner that the removal of the box with the last number, 3, leads to the diagram specifying the representation of S_2 to which the function belongs. Thus, $\Phi^{(1)}$ is labeled by the tableau 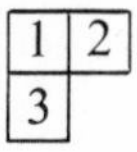

, and $\Phi^{(2)}$ by the tableau

$\begin{array}{|c|c|}\hline 1 & 3 \\ \hline 2 \\ \cline{1-1}\end{array}$. (For the one-dimensional representations, the tableaux are $\begin{array}{|c|c|c|}\hline 1 & 2 & 3 \\ \hline\end{array}$ for Φ_s and $\begin{array}{|c|}\hline 1 \\ \hline 2 \\ \hline 3 \\ \hline\end{array}$ for Φ_a, but in these cases the functions are already fully specified by the diagrams, since a totally symmetric (antisymmetric) function is necessarily symmetric (antisymmetric) with respect to particles 1 and 2.)

Besides the definition of the symmetry type [21] given above, it is possible to define this symmetry in other, but equivalent ways. For example, a function of type [21] can be characterized by the following two properties: (a) the function vanishes when acted upon by the symmetrizing operator, $\mathscr{S}$; (b) it is possible to find linear combinations of the permutation operators that, when acting on the function, yield a state that is symmetric with respect to interchange of particles 1 and 2 (see, for example, $\Phi^{(1)}$ above). Still another definition of [21] is a function that gives zero when acted on by the antisymmetrizing operator, $\mathscr{A}$, while the action of appropriate linear combinations of the permutation operators can yield a function that is antisymmetric with respect to interchange of particles 1 and 2 (see, for example, $\Phi^{(2)}$ above).

The possibility of these alternative definitions results from the fact that, if it is impossible to make a function symmetric in all three coordinates, this must imply that there is effectively at least one antisymmetric bond, and by acting with appropriate linear combinations of the permutation operators, we can bring the function to a form that explicitly exhibits this antisymmetry. Similarly, if it is impossible to antisymmetrize in all three particles, this must imply that there is effectively a symmetric bond in the wave function.

The two projection operators that pick out the [21] parts of a general function are

$$\begin{aligned} \mathscr{P}_1 &= \tfrac{1}{6}\,[2e + 2P_{12} - P_{13} - P_{23} - P_{123} - P_{132}] \\ \mathscr{P}_2 &= \tfrac{1}{6}\,[2e - 2P_{12} + P_{13} + P_{23} - P_{123} - P_{132}] \end{aligned} \qquad \text{(1C-10)}$$

where $\mathscr{P}_1$ projects onto functions of type $\Phi^{(1)}$, while $\mathscr{P}_2$ projects onto functions of type $\Phi^{(2)}$.

The three types of symmetry found above exhaust the possibilities for $n = 3$, as can be verified by noticing that

$$e = \mathscr{A} + \mathscr{S} + \mathscr{P}_1 + \mathscr{P}_2 \qquad \text{(1C-11)}$$

Thus, any function can be broken into parts having the three symmetries described above, and there are no parts left over, after these symmetries have been accounted for. Using the results of formal group theory, we could have concluded immediately that our enumeration of the irreducible representations of S_3 was complete, since the number of such representations is equal to the number of classes ($=3$ for S_3) or, equivalently, by employing the fact that the sum of the squares of the dimensions of the irreducible representations is equal to the number of operators in the group ($=6$ for S_3). For a discussion of these theorems, see, for example, Hamermesh (1962, pp. 68 ff.)

The above discussion has illustrated the simple relationship between the permutation symmetries for $n = 2$ and $n = 3$, which can be summarized in the following results:

(a) The diagrams labeling the irreducible representations of S_3 are obtained by adding a block to the diagrams for S_2, subject to the constraint that the length of a row (and a column) must not exceed that of preceding rows (and columns).

(b) The dimensionality of a representation of S_3 is equal to the number of ways in which the representation can be obtained from representations of S_2 in the manner stated above. Thus, the representations [3] and [111] can only be derived from [2] and [11], respectively, and are one dimensional, while the representation [21] can be derived from [2] as well as from [11] and is two dimensional.

(c) For a multidimensional representation of S_3, one can construct a basis (the standard basis) in which each member transforms irreducibly with respect to the S_2 subgroup consisting of the permutations acting on the first two particles.

It is found that these results can be simply generalized to give the relationship between the irreducible representations of S_n and S_{n-1} for arbitrary n. Thus, the symmetry types for functions depending on the coordinates of n particles can be obtained by successively adding particles, starting from $n = 2$ and $n = 3$.

1C-1c Partitions for general n

For functions involving the coordinates of n particles, the symmetry "quantum numbers" labeling the irreducible representations of S_n are written $[f_1 f_2 \cdots f_k]$ (sometimes shortened to $[f]$), where the f_i are integers obeying $f_1 \geq f_2 \geq \cdots \geq f_k$ and $f_1 + f_2 + \cdots + f_k = n$. The set of numbers $[f]$ represents a partition of n into k parts and is also expressed by a Young diagram consisting of n boxes arranged with f_1 boxes in the first row, f_2 boxes in the second row, and so on.

A function labeled by the partition $[f]$ is characterized by the following symmetry properties:

(a) By acting on the function with appropriate linear combinations of the permutation operators, we can generate a function that is symmetric in the coordinates of the first f_1 particles (that is, invariant with respect to any permutation of these coordinates) and is at the same time symmetric in the coordinates of the next f_2 particles, and so on.

(b) No linear combination of the permutation operators acting on the given function can generate a function that is symmetric in the coordinates of the first $f_1 + 1$ particles. Moreover, if the function has been symmetrized with respect to the first f_1 coordinates, it is impossible to symmetrize simultaneously in the next $f_2 + 1$ particles, and so on.

As in the definition of the three-particle symmetries, there are alternative and equivalent definitions of the symmetry properties, which result from the fact that the possibilities for symmetrization stated in (a) imply limitations on the possible degree of antisymmetrization. Similarly, the limitations on the degree of symmetrization stated in (b) can only result from the presence of antisymmetric bonds between some of the particles.

These relations can be expressed by considering, together with a given partition $[f]$, the conjugate partition $[\tilde{f}]$ obtained by interchanging rows and columns in the Young diagram. Thus, $\tilde{f}_1, \tilde{f}_2, \ldots$ give the length of the columns in the original diagram. We can now get an alternative definition of the symmetry $[f]$ by replacing the word "symmetric" in the above definition by "antisymmetric" and at the same time replacing the numbers $f_1, f_2, \ldots$ with the numbers $\tilde{f}_1, \tilde{f}_2, \ldots$; in this way, we get a characterization of the symmetry in terms of the maximal amount of antisymmetrization permitted by the partition $[f]$.

These different characterizations of the symmetry types, that is, of the irreducible representations of S_n, correspond to those given above for $n = 3$ and may be further tested on the illustrative four-particle functions shown in Table 1C-1, p. 128. In particular, these definitions imply that functions of the type $[n]$ $(\equiv [f_1 = n, f_2 = f_3 \cdots = 0])$, are completely symmetric in all n coordinates, while functions with symmetry $[111 \cdots 1]$ are completely antisymmetric in all n coordinates. All other partitions imply functions of mixed symmetry.

The dimension $h[f]$ of a given representation $[f]$ of S_n is equal to the number of ways in which the representation can be obtained by successively adding particles, starting from $n = 1$. This number is equivalent to the number of different Young tableaux that are possible, subject to the constraint that, at each stage in filling the diagram with numbers (for example, after filling in the first m integers), the part of the tableau that is filled corresponds to an allowed Young diagram (with $f_1 \geq f_2 \geq \cdots \geq f_k$). The constraint can also be expressed by saying that we only count the tableaux in which the numbers increase as we read from left to right in each row and also increase as we read down in each column (see the examples in Table 1C-1).

A systematic analysis of this counting procedure leads to the general dimensionality formula

$$h[f] \equiv h(S_n;\, [f_1 f_2 \cdots f_k])$$

$$= \frac{n!}{\prod_{i=1}^{k} (f_i + k - i)!} \prod_{i<j\leq k} (f_i - f_j + j - i) \qquad \text{(1C-12)}$$

(The number $h[f]$ may also be recognized as the trace of the identity element in the representation $[f]$ and thus may be deduced from the general formulas for the characters of the representations of the permutation group (see Hamermesh, 1962, p. 213).)

The only one-dimensional representations are the totally symmetric $(P = 1)$ and the totally antisymmetric $(P = (-1)^p)$. For the multidimensional representations, the basis functions are labeled by an index r. A particular set of basis states can be specified in terms of its transformation properties with respect to the subgroups

S_{n-1}, S_{n-2}, ..., S_2 of permutations acting on the first $n-1, n-2, \ldots, 2$ particles.

Any set of n-particle functions carrying an irreducible representation $[f]$ of S_n also carries representations of the subgroups S_{n-1}, S_{n-2}, ... but, in general, these representations will be reducible. By suitable linear transformations of the basis states, however, one can reduce the representations with respect to S_{n-1}, S_{n-2}, ... and thus obtain a basis, each member of which belongs to irreducible representations of the entire chain of subgroups. This basis defines the standard representation of the permutation operators. The functions belonging to this basis can be labeled by the set of partitions, or diagrams, specifying the transformation under S_n, S_{n-1}, ..., S_2, or by a Young tableau, in which the numbers from 1 to n are written into the Young diagram associated with the partition $[f]$. The diagram for S_m is thus obtained by removing the blocks containing the numbers $m+1, m+2, \ldots, n$.

In many applications, it is not necessary (or desirable) to explicitly write out the functions of the indicated symmetries $[f]r$ or the representation of the permutation operators, just as it is usually an advantage to avoid explicitly writing out the angular momentum matrices or vector couplings. However, we give in the fine print below a description of the permutation operators in the standard representation (Yamanouchi, 1937), since it may help to make the notation and the physical significance of these operators and the associated basis states somewhat more concrete.

We first consider the matrices of the transpositions between adjacent particles $P_{k-1,k}$ acting in the standard representation. The diagonal matrix elements are

$$\langle [f]r\,|P_{k-1,k}|\,[f]r\rangle = (\tau_{k-1,k}(r))^{-1} \tag{1C-13}$$

The integer $\tau_{k-1,k}(r)$ is the "axial distance" of k and $k-1$ in the tableau r, and is defined as

$$\tau_{k-1,k}(r) \equiv \text{col}(k) - \text{col}(k-1) - (\text{row}(k) - \text{row}(k-1))$$

where col(k) and row(k) are the column and row numbers of the kth particle in the tableau r. Thus, for example, $\tau_{k-1,k}(r) = +1$ if k and $k-1$ are in the same row and $\tau_{k-1,k}(r) = -1$ if they are in the same column. The nondiagonal matrix elements of $P_{k-1,k}$ between two states r and s have a nonvanishing value only if the positions of k and $k-1$ are interchanged in going from the tableau r to the tableau s, in which case

$$\langle [f]s\,|P_{k-1,k}|\,[f]r\rangle = (1 - (\tau_{k-1,k}(r))^{-2})^{1/2} \tag{1C-14}$$

The most general permutation, P, can be written as a product of transpositions of adjacent elements and thus we can construct the matrices of these more general operators in terms of those given above. Since, in the standard representation, $P_{k-1,k}$ is a real orthogonal matrix, it follows that all the permutation operators have this property,

$$P^{-1} = P^{\dagger} = \tilde{P} \tag{1C-15}$$

where the tilde denotes transposition.

It is seen that functions with tableaux r, in which $k-1$ and k are adjacent (in the same row or in the same column), are eigenfunctions of $P_{k-1,k}$ with eigenvalues $+1$ or -1, that is, symmetric or antisymmetric in these particles. For $[f] = [21]$, the standard representation is the same as that derived above (see Eq. (1C-9)).

The irreducibility of the representations $[f]$ implies that the matrices of the permutation operators obey orthogonality relations similar to those of the $\mathscr{D}$ functions of the rotation group. Thus, in analogy to Eq. (1A-41), we have

$$\frac{h([f^{(1)}])}{n!} \sum_P \langle [f^{(1)}]r_1 |P| [f^{(1)}]s_1 \rangle \langle [f^{(2)}]r_2 |P| [f^{(2)}]s_2 \rangle$$
$$= \delta([f^{(1)}], [f^{(2)}])\, \delta(r_1, r_2)\, \delta(s_1, s_2) \tag{1C-16}$$

The factor ($n!$) in Eq. (1C-16) corresponds to the factor $8\pi^2$ in Eq. (1A-41) and represents the number of elements in the group (for a continuous group, the sum over the group elements is replaced by an integration and the factor $8\pi^2$ is the total "volume" obtained by integrating over all Euler angles (ϕ, θ, ψ)); the factor $h([f^{(1)}])$ represents the dimension of the representation, as does the corresponding factor $(2I+1)$ in Eq. (1A-41).

The relation (1C-16) implies that we can use the matrices of the permutations to construct projection operators that pick out of a general function the component with specified symmetry $[f]r$ under the permutation operators (compare the analogous construction of projection operators in the rotation group as employed, for example, in Sec. 5-5). The projection operator can be expressed in the form

$$\mathscr{P}([f]r) = \frac{h([f])}{n!} \sum_P \langle [f]r |P| [f]r \rangle P \tag{1C-17}$$

In fact, from Eq. (1C-16) it follows that, when $\mathscr{P}$ acts on a general function

$$|\alpha\rangle = \sum_{[f^{(1)}]r_1} \langle [f^{(1)}]r_1 | \alpha \rangle \, |[f^{(1)}]r_1\rangle \tag{1C-18}$$

we obtain

$$\mathscr{P}([f]r)\,|\alpha\rangle = \langle [f]r | \alpha \rangle \, |[f]r\rangle \tag{1C-19}$$

One can verify that the operators defined in Eq. (1C-10) are special cases of this general construction. The projection operators obey the completeness relation

$$\sum_{[f]r} \mathscr{P}([f]r) = e \tag{1C-19a}$$

It is also possible to define generalized projection operators (Young operators)

$$\mathscr{P}([f]r \to s) = \frac{h([f])}{n!} \sum_P \langle [f]s |P| [f]r \rangle P \tag{1C-20}$$

which produce a state of symmetry $[f]s$ out of the $[f]r$ component of the state on which it acts. Thus, for a general function $|\alpha\rangle$, expanded in the form (1C-18), the orthogonality relation (1C-16) implies

$$\mathscr{P}([f]r \to s)\,|\alpha\rangle = \langle [f]r | \alpha \rangle \, |[f]s\rangle \tag{1C-21}$$

1C-1d Average value of the transposition operator

The difference between the number of symmetric pairs, n_s, and the number of antisymmetric pairs, n_a, in a wave function with permutation symmetry $[f]$ is given by

$$n_s - n_a = \langle [f]r | \sum_{j<k} P_{jk} | [f]r \rangle$$
$$= \tfrac{1}{2} \sum_{i=1}^{k} f_i(f_i - 2i + 1) \tag{1C-22}$$

This quantity is proportional to the trace of the class of the transpositions and may be obtained from the general formulas for the character of the representations of the symmetric group (see Hamermesh, 1962, p. 214).

The formula (1C-22) is also obtained if one ascribes symmetric bonds to all the particles in the same row of a Young tableau and antisymmetric bonds to particles in the same column, while particles that are in neither the same row nor the same column are counted as half symmetric and half antisymmetric and therefore do not contribute to (1C-22). While this interpretation of the Young tableau yields the correct result (1C-22) and is often a useful guide in thinking about the different symmetry types, such a description of a particular function $([f]r)$ is not strictly correct, as can be seen from the examples exhibited in Eq. (1C-7) and Table 1C-1. Indeed, for any of the multidimensional representations, it is impossible to construct a state that is simultaneously symmetric with respect to coordinates of particles in the same row and antisymmetric with respect to particles in the same column.

1C-1e Conjugate representations

The symmetry characterized by the conjugate partition, $[\tilde{f}]$, corresponds to an interchange between symmetry and antisymmetry as compared with the partition $[f]$ (see p. 111). From the above discussion it is clear that the dimension of the representation $[\tilde{f}]$ is the same as that of $[f]$ and, with each tableau r of $[f]$, we can associate a conjugate tableau $\tilde{r}$ of $[\tilde{f}]$, which is characterized by the interchange of symmetric and antisymmetric bonds.

In the explicit construction given above for the projection operators and permutation matrices in the standard representation, the choice of the phase of the nondiagonal matrix elements (1C-14) was arbitrary. However, in order that the conjugate diagram exactly correspond to an interchange of symmetric and antisymmetric pairs, it is necessary that we use one sign for the representation $[f]$ and then use the opposite sign in defining the states of the conjugate representation $[\tilde{f}]$. With this choice we have, for any permutation P,

$$\langle [f]r\,|P|\,[f]s\rangle = (-1)^p \langle [\tilde{f}]\tilde{r}\,|P|\,[\tilde{f}]\tilde{s}\rangle \tag{1C-23}$$

where $(-1)^p = +1$ and -1 for even and odd permutations, respectively.

1C-1f Inner products. Totally antisymmetric states

If a space wave function of symmetry $[f^{(1)}]$ is multiplied by a spin-isospin wave function with symmetry $[f^{(2)}]$, the product will in general contain many different symmetries $[f]$ with respect to permutations acting simultaneously on all the coordinates of the particles. Such a product of functions referring to different coordinates of the same particles is called an inner (or Kronecker) product and is labeled $[f^{(1)}] \times [f^{(2)}]$. The decomposition of inner products for $n = 3$ is given in Table 1C-2, p. 129. The general enumeration of symmetries resulting from inner products is discussed by Hamermesh (1962, pp. 254 ff.); for tables, see Itzykson and Nauenberg (1966).

The expansion of the inner product $[f^{(1)}] \times [f^{(2)}]$ in terms of irreducible representations $[f]$ is referred to as the Clebsch-Gordan series for the symmetric group S_n. For the rotation group, the corresponding series gives the enumeration of the different total angular momenta I formed by coupling two angular momenta I_1 and I_2. In this case, each representation $I\,(=I_1+I_2, \cdots, |I_1-I_2|)$ is formed only once, while in the product $[f^{(1)}] \times [f^{(2)}]$, a representation $[f]$ may occur several times.

By taking linear combinations of the inner products of the different states belonging to $[f^{(1)}]$ and $[f^{(2)}]$, one can form functions that transform according to a single definite symmetry $[f]$,

$$\Psi(x_k\,\xi_k\,;[f]r) = \sum_{r_1,\,r_2} \Phi(x_k\,;[f^{(1)}]r_1) X(\xi_k\,;[f^{(2)}]r_2) \langle [f^{(1)}]r_1, [f^{(2)}]r_2 \,|\, [f]r \rangle \quad \text{(1C-24)}$$

In this expression, $\Phi(x_k)$ and $X(\xi_k)$ are the two different parts of the n-particle wave function (referring to space and spin-isospin variables, respectively, or to space-spin and isospin variables, etc.) and the coupling coefficients $\langle [f^{(1)}]r_1, [f^{(2)}]r_2 \,|\, [f]r\rangle$ play the same role as the Clebsch-Gordan coefficients in the coupling of angular momenta. (In cases where the representation $[f]$ occurs several times in the product $[f^{(1)}] \times [f^{(2)}]$, the state Ψ as well as the coupling coefficients must be specified by further quantum numbers, in addition to $[f]$ and r.)

We are especially interested in totally antisymmetric wave functions, $[f] = [111 \cdots 1]$. In these, symmetric bonds in the x variables must be combined with antisymmetric bonds in the ξ variables, and the states must therefore be constructed as a product of conjugate representations. The coupling coefficient has the simple form

$$\langle [f^{(1)}]r_1, [f^{(2)}]r_2 \,|\, [1111 \cdots 1] \rangle = \delta([f^{(2)}], [\tilde{f}^{(1)}])\; \delta(r_2, \tilde{r}_1)(h[f^{(1)}])^{-1/2} \quad \text{(1C-25)}$$

where the normalization constant $h[f^{(1)}]$ is the dimension of the representation $[f^{(1)}]$. (In Eq. (1C-25) we have assumed a phase for the states $[f^{(2)}]r$ corresponding to that of a conjugate representation (1C-23) rather than of a standard representation.) The simplicity of the coupling coefficients (1C-25) is related to the fact that $[f] = [1111 \cdots 1]$ is a one-dimensional representation and is similar to the simplicity of the vector addition coefficients that couple L and $S\,(=L)$ to form a total $J = 0$.

For particles obeying Bose statistics, the states are completely symmetric, $[n]$, with respect to permutations acting on all the coordinates of the particles. To obtain such symmetric states, we must combine identical symmetries, $[f^{(1)}]r_1 = [f^{(2)}]r_2$, and the coupling coefficient is again a constant,

$$\langle [f^{(1)}]r_1, [f^{(2)}]r_2 \,|\, [n] \rangle = \delta([f^{(1)}], [f^{(2)}])\; \delta(r_1, r_2)(h[f^{(1)}])^{-1/2} \quad \text{(1C-26)}$$

1C-1g Outer product of wave functions with definite symmetry

Sometimes one is faced with a situation in which the wave function of the first n_1 particles has a permutation symmetry $[f^{(1)}]$ and this wave function is multiplied by a wave function of the next n_2 particles having symmetry $[f^{(2)}]$. One then needs to be able to enumerate the different possible symmetries $[f]$ of the $n = n_1 + n_2$ particle system constructed in this manner. Such products involving functions depending on the coordinates of different particles are called outer products (denoted $[f^{(1)}] \otimes [f^{(2)}]$).

It is fairly easy to recognize the symmetries resulting from the addition of a single particle ($[f^{(2)}] = [1]$). In the product $[f^{(1)}] \otimes [1]$, one obtains the Young diagrams that result from adding the extra block to the Young diagram of $[f^{(1)}]$ in all possible ways. Indeed, in counting the dimensions of the different representations (see p. 111), we have already implicitly employed this result.

When more general representations are multiplied, the result is restricted by the fact that the functions belonging to the partition $[f^{(2)}]$ have definite permutation symmetry with respect to interchanges of the n_2 particles, and thus they cannot be added to $[f^{(1)}]$ in all possible ways. These restrictions can be formulated in the following general prescriptions (see Littlewood, 1950) for enumerating the symmetries contained in the product $[f^{(1)}] \otimes [f^{(2)}]$:

(a) label the blocks of the first row of the Young diagram of $[f^{(2)}]$ by α, those of the second row by β, and so on;

(b) add the α blocks to the Young diagram of $[f^{(1)}]$ in all possible ways, subject to the restrictions that the resulting diagrams must all be regular (have a number of blocks in the second row that is less than or equal to that in the first row, and so on) and that no two α blocks may be placed vertically over each other;

(c) add the β blocks to the resulting diagram in all possible ways, subject to the same restrictions as above and to the further restrictions that, in reading from the upper right-hand corner from right to left with each row taken in order going down, the number of β blocks passed at any stage must not exceed the number of α's;

(d) continue in the same manner for the $\gamma, \delta, \ldots$ blocks.

The diagrams obtained in this manner give the decomposition of the product $[f^{(1)}] \otimes [f^{(2)}]$ into irreducible representations $[f]$, each of which may occur several times. These rules are exploited in the analysis of the symmetries of product wave functions (see p. 117). More generally, the decomposition of the outer product $[f^{(1)}] \otimes [f^{(2)}]$ gives the Clebsch-Gordan series for the unitary groups (see p. 123).

1C-2 Symmetry Classification of Wave Functions in Occupation Number Space

1C-2a Product states

The above discussion of the permutation symmetries is applicable to any wave function. Many problems of quantal physics deal with wave functions that can be expressed in terms of products of one-particle states or linear combinations of such products. The one-particle states may, for example, be orbital states of a single particle in a potential, the wave functions in isospace characterizing the orientation of the individual isospins, or the states of the individual quanta out of which the vibrational wave function may be built.

In many cases, the one-particle spectrum contains degeneracies (as, for example, the $(2l+1)$-fold degeneracy of the orbital functions in the configuration l^n, or the two-fold degeneracy of the isobaric spin states in the absence of the Coulomb interaction). The occurrence of these degeneracies raises new questions in connection with the symmetry classification of the wave functions. Thus, we may ask the following questions: Starting from all the n-particle product wave functions that can be formed out of a g-fold degenerate one-particle orbital, how can we construct linear combinations with specified permutation symmetry $[f]$? How many different states are there of given symmetry, and what additional quantum numbers can be used to label these different states? How can we further characterize the relationship between the states having the same permutation symmetry?

1C-2b *Permutation symmetry for product states*

Assuming some convenient basis for the one-particle states, we label these states by the quantum number m_a with $a = 1, 2, \ldots, g$.

First, we note that the product state in which all particles occupy a single one-particle state, m_a, obviously is totally symmetric ($[f] = [n]$). States with antisymmetric pairs can only be constructed from configurations containing different single-particle states. Thus, as is well known, a totally antisymmetric wave function ($[f] = [11 \cdots 1]$) requires n different m values, and for each such configuration, there is one totally antisymmetric state, the Slater determinant (see Appendix 2A). More generally, the possibility of antisymmetrizing between particles in the same column of a Young diagram implies that we can only construct the symmetry $[f_1 \cdots f_k]$ from configurations with at least k different m values.

For example, the isospin wave function is built from one-particle functions with $g = 2$ ($m_t = \pm 1/2$), which implies that the permutation symmetry can have at most two rows $[f] = [f_1 f_2]$, and since the space-spin function must have the conjugate symmetry, its partition quantum numbers $f_i'(=\tilde{f}_i)$ are restricted to $f_i' \leq 2$. Similarly, the one-particle spin-isospin functions have four quantum states, and thus the permutation symmetry in this part of the wave function is limited to partitions of the type $[f_1 f_2 f_3 f_4]$, which in turn implies the limitation $f_i'(=\tilde{f}_i) \leq 4$ for the space wave function.

The complete enumeration of the permutation symmetries associated with a configuration $\mathscr{C}(m) \equiv (m_1)^{n_1} (m_2)^{n_2} \cdots (m_g)^{n_g}$ can be obtained by noting that such a state may be thought of as built from an outer product of states of the type $(m_a)^{n_a}$, which are totally symmetric in n_a particles. Thus, the list of possible symmetries occurring for the configuration $\mathscr{C}(m)$ is obtained from an analysis of the symmetries contained in the product $[n_1] \otimes [n_2] \otimes \cdots \otimes [n_g]$.

From the rules given above for constructing these outer products, we can see that the number of times that the symmetry $[f]$ appears in the product is equal to the number of different tableaux that can be constructed by writing the occupied m values in the boxes of the Young diagram corresponding to $[f]$. The symmetry of the groups $[n_a]$ implies that the tableaux are restricted by the conditions that

(a) the same m value may not appear twice in any single column,

(b) the m values must read in increasing order (first all the m_1's, then m_2's, and so on) as we read from left to right in any row and as we read from top to bottom in any column.

Illustrations of these rules are given in Table 1C-3, p. 129, which considers configurations of the type p^3, and in Table 1C-5, p. 134, which considers product functions in spin-isospin space.

The tableaux obtained by filling the Young diagrams with the m values according to the above rules may be used to label the different states that have the same permutation symmetry. Such a tableau will be denoted by ρ_m, where the notation is intended to emphasize the distinction from the tableau r containing the particle numbers $k = 1 \cdots n$. A complete set of quantum numbers specifying the states based on product wave functions is thus $[f]r\rho_m$. (See the examples in Table 1C-3.)

The particular states associated with the tableau in which all the boxes of the first row are labeled by m_1, those in the second row by $m_2, \ldots,$ are referred to as states of maximal weight ($\rho_m^{\max}$). One may also describe these states as fully aligned in m space, since they contain the maximum number of particles in the state m_1, the maximum number of particles that can subsequently be accommodated in the state m_2, and so on.

The label ρ_m is equivalent to a set of $\frac{1}{2}g(g-1)$ quantum numbers which may, for example, be chosen as the set of partitions $[f'_1, \ldots, f'_{g-1}]$, $[f''_1, \ldots, f''_{g-2}]$, ... obtained by successively removing the boxes with $m_g, m_{g-1}, \ldots$ from the tableau ρ_m. The total number of states ρ_m (with fixed $[f]r$) can be expressed in the form (see Hamermesh, 1962, Chapter 10)

$$h(U_g\,;[f]) = \prod_{1 \leq i < j \leq g} \frac{(f_i - i - f_j + j)}{(j-i)} \tag{1C-27}$$

(The notation U_g refers to the fact that the set of states ρ_m carries an irreducible representation of the group of unitary transformations in g dimensions (see Sec. 1C-3). Thus, the expression (1C-27) gives the dimension of the representation $[f]$ of U_g. The above-mentioned set of $\frac{1}{2}g(g-1)$ quantum numbers characterizes a particular state ρ_m belonging to the representation $[f]$ of U_g in terms of its transformation under the chain of subgroups $U_{g-1}, U_{g-2}, \ldots$.)

In order to construct the state $[f]r\rho_m$ associated with the configuration $\mathscr{C}(m)$, we may start with the simple product wave function

$$\Phi_0 = \prod_{k=1}^{n} \varphi_{m(k)}(x_k) \tag{1C-28}$$

where $m(k)$ takes on the value m_1 for n_1 different values of k, and so on. For example, we may choose the following set of $m(k)$:

$$\begin{aligned} m(k) &= m_1 \qquad & k &= 1, 2, \ldots, n_1 \\ m(k) &= m_2 \qquad & k &= n_1 + 1, \ldots, n_1 + n_2 \\ &\;\;\vdots & &\;\;\vdots \\ m(k) &= m_g \qquad & k &= n - n_g + 1, \ldots, n \end{aligned} \tag{1C-29}$$

The product state (1C-28) may be regarded as a function of the variables x_k and $m(k)$.

Interpreted in this manner, it is a totally symmetric function with respect to permutations in k acting on the m variables as well as on the x variables,

$$P^m P^x \Phi_0 = P^x P^m \Phi_0 = \Phi_0 \tag{1C-30}$$

The desired state is to be constructed from linear combinations of permuted product functions $P^x\Phi_0$ $(=(P^m)^{-1}\Phi_0)$ and is characterized by having the symmetry $[f]r_x$ with respect to permutations acting on the x variables only, and $[f]r_m$ with respect to permutations acting on the m variables only. The particle number tableau r_m associated with the given quantum number tableau ρ_m is obtained by replacing the m values by k values according to the chosen ordering (1C-29). For example,

$$\rho_m = \begin{array}{|c|c|c|}\hline m_1 & m_2 & m_3 \\ \hline m_2 & \multicolumn{2}{c}{} \\ \cline{1-1}\end{array} \rightarrow \left\{ \begin{array}{l} r_m = \begin{array}{|c|c|c|}\hline 1 & 2 & 4 \\ \hline 3 & \multicolumn{2}{c}{} \\ \cline{1-1}\end{array} \\ \\ r_m = \begin{array}{|c|c|c|}\hline 1 & 3 & 4 \\ \hline 2 & \multicolumn{2}{c}{} \\ \cline{1-1}\end{array} \end{array} \right.$$

In general, several different r_m represent the same ρ_m, as in the example considered. The different choices, however, give rise to the same state, since Φ_0 is symmetric with respect to permutations P^m involving only k values belonging to the same m_a.

The function Φ_0 can be written as a sum of terms with specified symmetry $[f]r$ with respect to the permutations P^x. Since Φ_0 is totally symmetric when regarded as a function of x_k and $m(k)$, the individual terms possess the same symmetry $[f]r$ with respect to the permutations P^m (see Eq. (1C-26)). The state with symmetry $[f]r_x r_m$ can thus be obtained by acting on Φ_0 with an operator in x_k space of the form (1C-20), projecting from $[f]r_m$ to $[f]r_x$, or with an operator in $m(k)$ space, projecting from $[f]r_x$ to $[f]r_m$,

$$\begin{aligned} \Phi(x_k;[f]r_x\rho_m) &= \text{const} \sum_P \langle r_x|P|r_m\rangle P^x\Phi_0 \\ &= \text{const} \sum_P \langle r_m|P|r_x\rangle P^m\Phi_0 \end{aligned} \tag{1C-31}$$

(Since the tableaux r specify the pattern $[f]$, we have for brevity dropped the label $[f]$ in the matrix elements of P.) The equivalence of the two forms in Eq. (1C-31) follows from Eq. (1C-30) and the relation

$$\langle r_x|P|r_m\rangle = \langle r_m|P^{-1}|r_x\rangle \tag{1C-32}$$

which expresses the unitarity and reality of the matrices P. (See Eq. (1C-15).)

We can proceed to construct totally antisymmetric (or symmetric) wave functions in the particle variables (x, ξ) (as in Eqs. (1C-24) and (1C-25)) by combining Eq. (1C-31) with the corresponding functions

$$X(\xi_k;[\tilde f]\tilde r_\xi\tilde\rho_\mu) = \text{const}\sum_P \langle\tilde r_\xi|P|\tilde r_\mu\rangle P^\xi \prod_{k=1}^{n}\chi_{\mu(k)}(\xi_k) \tag{1C-33}$$

with conjugate symmetry in ξ space. From Eq. (1C-25) we then obtain

$$\begin{aligned} &\Psi(x_k\xi_k;[f]\rho_m\rho_\mu)_{\text{antisym}} \\ &\quad = (h[f])^{-1/2}\sum_{r_x}\Phi(x_k;[f]r_x\rho_m)X(\xi_k;[\tilde f]\tilde r_\xi=\tilde r_x\tilde\rho_\mu) \\ &\quad = \text{const}\sum_P\langle r_m|P|r_\mu\rangle P^m\sum_{P_2}(-1)^{p_2}P_2^x P_2^\xi\prod_{k=1}^{n}\varphi_{m(k)}(x_k)\chi_{\mu(k)}(\xi_k) \end{aligned} \tag{1C-34}$$

where we have employed the relation (see Eqs. (1C-23) and (1C-32))

$$\sum_{r_x} \langle r_x | P_1 | r_m \rangle \langle \tilde{r}_x | P_2 | \tilde{r}_\mu \rangle$$

$$= (-1)^{p_2} \langle r_\mu | P_2^{-1} P_1 | r_m \rangle = (-1)^{p_2} \langle r_m | P_1^{-1} P_2 | r_\mu \rangle \tag{1C-35}$$

Moreover, in Eq. (1C-34), the sum over P_1 and P_2 has been replaced by the equivalent sum over $P \equiv P_1^{-1} P_2$ and P_2, and we have expressed P_1^x in the form $P_2^x (P^{-1})^x = P_2^x P^m = P^m P_2^x$.

In Eq. (1C-34), the sum over P_2 is seen to be a Slater determinant based on one-particle wave functions with quantum numbers $m(k)$ and $\mu(k)$, and we can thus also write Eq. (1C-34) in terms of the fermion creation operators for these one-particle states (see Appendix 2A).

$$|[f]\rho_m \rho_\mu\rangle_{\text{antisym}}$$

$$= \text{const} \sum_P \langle r_m | P | r_\mu \rangle P^m \prod_{k=1}^{n} a^\dagger(m(k), \mu(k)) |0\rangle$$

$$= \text{const} \sum_P \langle \tilde{r}_\mu | P | \tilde{r}_m \rangle P^\mu \prod_{k=1}^{n} a^\dagger(m(k), \mu(k)) |0\rangle \tag{1C-36}$$

where $|0\rangle$ is the vacuum state. The second form of Eq. (1C-36) follows from Eq. (1C-23) and the fact that $P^m P^\mu$ acting on the totally antisymmetric state equals $(-1)^p$.

1C-2c Angular momenta of states with definite $[f]$

In general, the g-fold degeneracy of the one-particle states is a reflection of some symmetry of the one-particle Hamiltonian, and states based on the n-particle product wave function can be labeled by the quantum numbers of these additional symmetry operators. For example, if the one-particle Hamiltonian is rotationally invariant, the product states may be characterized by a total angular momentum, and it is useful to be able to enumerate the different angular momenta that can occur with any given symmetry $[f]$. There is not any simple and general solution to this problem, but it is possible to obtain the answer for any particular configuration by elementary counting in the m representation.

An especially simple example is provided by the question of the possible values of the total isospin T of isospin wave functions with definite permutation symmetry. In this case, $g = 2$ ($m_1 = +1/2$ and $m_2 = -1/2$) and the permutation symmetry is characterized by a partition with at most two numbers $[f_1 f_2]$. We consider first the completely symmetric states $[n]$. For given M, representing the sum of the individual m values, there is just one configuration, $(+1/2)^{n/2+M}(-1/2)^{n/2-M}$, and each M value from $M = n/2$ to $M = -n/2$ gives rise to a single m tableau by the rules given above. Thus, for the symmetric representation $[n]$, we have a single isospin $T = n/2$. For partitions with two rows $[f_1 f_2]$, we must have $m_1 = +1/2$ in the first f_2 boxes of the first row and $m_2 = -1/2$ in all the boxes of the second row in order to fulfil the requirements (a) and (b) above. Hence, these first f_2 columns do not contribute to the total M. The remaining $f_1 - f_2$ boxes of the first row can be filled in exactly the same ways as the symmetric representation $[n = f_1 - f_2]$. Thus, the permutation symmetry $[f_1 f_2]$ gives rise to the single isospin $T = (f_1 - f_2)/2$.

The fact that there is only a single isospin for a given permutation symmetry means that the quantum numbers (n, T) are equivalent to the symmetry quantum numbers $[f_1 f_2]$. It is also seen that the rules for coupling angular momenta can be obtained from the decomposition of outer products described on p. 116. The equivalence of angular momentum and permutation symmetry is special to a system with $g = 2$ (see Sec. 1C-3b).

The pairs of boxes in the same column in the above example may be recognized as forming the unique antisymmetric state $(T = M = 0)$ that is possible for two particles in a shell with $g = 2$ (closed shell configuration). The representation $[f_2 f_2]$ is made entirely of such closed shells and has a total $T = 0$.

Quite generally, a column in the Young diagram with the maximum number, g, of boxes corresponds to a completed shell and does not contribute to the total angular momentum. It may also be convenient to discuss a given symmetry in terms of the "holes" in completed shells; thus, for example, the angular momenta contained in $[f_1 \cdots f_g]$ are the same as those associated with the symmetry $[f_1 - f_g, \ldots, f_1 - f_2, 0]$.

Tables 1C-4 and 1C-5 (pp. 132 and 134) contain additional examples of the enumeration of the angular momentum values of product wave functions of definite permutation symmetry. Table 1C-4 refers to the configurations p^n, while Table 1C-5 gives the results for the spin-isospin wave functions.

1C-3 Unitary Symmetry

1C-3a Shift operators

A systematic study of the relationship between the states with different quantum number tableaux ρ_m, associated with a given permutation symmetry $[f]r$ of the particle coordinates, can be based on the algebra of the set of operators $E(m_b, m_a)$ that transfer a particle from the one-particle state m_a to the state m_b. These "shift operators" act symmetrically on all the particles, and are thus given by

$$E(m_b, m_a) = \sum_{k=1}^{n} E_{m_b, m_a}(x_k) \tag{1C-37}$$

where the single-particle operator $E_{m_b, m_a}(x)$ is defined by its matrix elements

$$\langle m_d | E_{m_b, m_a} | m_c \rangle = \delta(m_a, m_c)\, \delta(m_b, m_d) \tag{1C-38}$$

For $m_b = m_a$, we have

$$E(m_a, m_a) = n_a \tag{1C-39}$$

with n_a representing the number of particles occupying the quantum state m_a. Summing over a, we obtain

$$\sum_a E(m_a, m_a) = n \tag{1C-40}$$

and this particular combination of shift operators is therefore a constant for the states considered.

The g^2 shift operators may be considered as the elementary units, from which all operators acting symmetrically on the particles (and conserving the number of particles) can be constructed. Thus, an arbitrary single-particle operator can be written

$$F = \sum_{k=1}^{n} F(x_k) = \sum_{m_a, m_b} \langle m_b | F | m_a \rangle E(m_b, m_a) \tag{1C-41}$$

Two-particle operators can be expressed as bilinear forms in the shift operators, and so on.

If we are dealing with a system of fermions, for which the state is totally antisymmetric with respect to permutations acting simultaneously on the x and ξ variables (see Eq. (1C-34)), we can also express the shift operators in the form

$$E(m_b, m_a) = \sum_{\alpha} a^{\dagger}(m_b, \mu_\alpha) a(m_a, \mu_\alpha) \tag{1C-42}$$

where $a^{\dagger}(m, \mu)$ creates a one-particle state with quantum numbers m (referring to x space) and μ (referring to ξ space). In analogy to Eq. (1C-42), one can also define shift operators $E(\mu_\beta, \mu_\alpha)$ acting in ξ space.

Since the shift operators act symmetrically on all the particles, they do not affect the permutation symmetry and are therefore diagonal in the quantum numbers $[f]$ and r, with matrix elements

$$\langle [f']r'\rho'_m | E(m_b, m_a) | [f]r\rho_m \rangle = \delta([f], [f'])\, \delta(r, r') \langle [f]\rho'_m | E(m_b, m_a) | [f]\rho_m \rangle \tag{1C-43}$$

These matrix elements are nonvanishing only if the tableaux ρ_m and ρ'_m are associated with configurations $\mathscr{C}(m)$ and $\mathscr{C}'(m)$, for which $n'_a = n_a - 1$ and $n'_b = n_b + 1$, while $n'_c = n_c$ for $c \neq a, b$. (If we consider totally antisymmetric states specified by $[f]\rho_m \rho_\mu$, the matrix elements of $E(m_b, m_a)$ are diagonal in $[f]$ and ρ_μ, and are independent of ρ_μ.)

The shift operators $E(m_b, m_a)$ are the basic elements for the study of the relationship between the states $[f]\rho_m$ (with fixed r or ρ_μ), since, from any given state $[f]\rho_m$, it is possible to produce any other state $[f]\rho'_m$ by acting with a suitable linear combination of products of shift operators. This "completeness" corresponds to the fact that any operator acting symmetrically on the n-particle wave function can be constructed from the shift operators, and may also be verified by using the explicit construction of the symmetrized states in Eq. (1C-31).

1C-3b Algebra of shift operators. The group of unitary transformations

The shift operators obey the simple commutation relations

$$[E(m_b, m_a), E(m_d, m_c)] = \delta(a, d) E(m_b, m_c) - \delta(b, c) E(m_d, m_a) \tag{1C-44}$$

as follows from Eqs. (1C-37) and (1C-38) (or from Eq. (1C-42)). Since the commutator of two shift operators is a linear combination of such operators, the set of g^2 shift operators is said to be closed under commutations. One also refers to such a set as forming a Lie algebra with a structure defined by Eq. (1C-44).

The shift operators are the generators of infinitesimal unitary transformations

$\mathscr{U}$ acting simultaneously on the wave functions of the n individual particles. Under a unitary transformation, the single-particle states transform as

$$\varphi_{m_a}(x) \rightarrow \sum_{m_b} \mathscr{U}_{m_a, m_b} \varphi_{m_b}(x) \tag{1C-45}$$

where $\mathscr{U}_{m_a, m_b}$ is a unitary matrix in g dimensions. For infinitesimal transformations,

$$\mathscr{U}_{m_a, m_b} = \delta_{m_a, m_b} + i\varepsilon_{m_a, m_b} \tag{1C-46}$$

where ε is Hermitian (and infinitesimal). The operator $\mathscr{U}$ acting in the space of the n-particle states can therefore be expressed in the form

$$\mathscr{U} = 1 + i \sum_{m_a, m_b} \varepsilon_{m_a, m_b} E(m_b, m_a) \tag{1C-47}$$

where 1 is the identity operator.

By superposing infinitesimal transformations, one can form the full group of unitary transformations, which is denoted by U_g. It is a Lie group whose structure is determined by the algebra of the generators, expressed by the relations (1C-44).

The states $[f]\rho_m$ based on n-particle product wave functions can be characterized as carrying representations of the group U_g, and the "completeness" properties of the shift operators discussed in the previous section imply that these representations are irreducible. The partition quantum numbers $[f]$ therefore label the irreducible representations of U_g as well as those of S_n. (The representations of U_g comprise partitions for all values of n, but with the number of rows k limited to $k \leq g$ (see p. 117).) The Clebsch-Gordan series for U_g, that is the reduction of the Kronecker product, denoted by $[f^{(1)}] \otimes [f^{(2)}]$, into irreducible representations $[f]$ of U_g can be obtained from the rules for decomposing outer products (see p. 116).

The determinant of a unitary matrix is a number $e^{i\varphi}$ of absolute magnitude unity. (The determinant equals the product of the eigenvalues, each of which is of magnitude unity on account of the relation $\mathscr{U}^\dagger \mathscr{U} = 1$.) The special unitary transformations associated with matrices $\mathscr{U}_{m_a, m_b}$ with determinant unity ($\varphi = 0$; unimodular matrices) form a subgroup of U_g, referred to as the special unitary group in g dimensions (SU_g). The infinitesimal unimodular unitary transformations have a traceless matrix ε_{m_a, m_b}. and the generators are therefore the set of shift operators that are linearly independent of the total number operator n given by Eq. (1C-40). (For example, one may take the $E(m_b, m_a)$ with $m_b \neq m_a$ and $(g - 1)$ linearly independent combinations of the type $E(m_a, m_a) - E(m_b, m_b)$; it is seen that such a set is also closed under commutations and therefore forms a Lie algebra.)

The irreducible representations of SU_g are the same as those of U_g, but representations $[f]$ differing only by completed columns are identical with respect to SU_g; thus, the representations of SU_g can be specified by the set of $(g - 1)$ numbers $(f_1 - f_g, f_2 - f_g, \ldots, f_{g-1} - f_g)$. With respect to U_g, the representations differing by completed columns, though trivially related, are distinguished by the quantum number $n = \sum_i f_i$.

One can construct combinations of shift operators that commute with all the shift operators and are therefore invariants under U_g. These invariants are referred to as Casimir operators. The eigenvalues of the invariants are functions of the partition quantum numbers, labeling the representations of U_g. The linear invariant is the number operator Eq. (1C-40). The quadratic invariant is

$$G_2(U_g) = \sum_{m_b, m_a} E(m_a, m_b)E(m_b, m_a) \tag{1C-48}$$

whose matrix elements are

$$\langle [f']\rho'_m |G_2(U_g)| [f]\rho_m \rangle = \delta([f], [f'])\, \delta(\rho_m, \rho'_m) \sum_{i=1}^{g} f_i(f_i - 2i + 1 + g) \tag{1C-49}$$

as can be seen, for example, by acting with G_2 on the state of maximal weight (see p. 118). The corresponding Casimir operator for SU_g is

$$G_2(SU_g) = G_2(U_g) - \frac{1}{g}\left(\sum_{m_a} E(m_a, m_a)\right)^2$$

$$= G_2(U_g) - \frac{1}{g} n^2 \tag{1C-50}$$

Higher-order invariants can be similarly constructed by forming expressions completely symmetric in the quantum numbers m_a. Thus, the third-order invariant is

$$G_3(U_g) = \sum_{m_a, m_b, m_c} E(m_a, m_c)E(m_c, m_b)E(m_b, m_a) \tag{1C-51}$$

The eigenvalues of the invariants can be used to label the representations of U_g as alternatives to the partition quantum numbers.

For $g = 2$, the algebra of the shift operators obtains a familiar form if we introduce the linear combinations

$$\begin{aligned} n &= E(m_1, m_1) + E(m_2, m_2) \\ \lambda_0 &= \tfrac{1}{2}(E(m_1, m_1) - E(m_2, m_2)) \\ \lambda_+ &= E(m_1, m_2) \\ \lambda_- &= E(m_2, m_1) \end{aligned} \tag{1C-52}$$

The commutation relations (1C-44) imply that the quantities $\lambda_0, \lambda_+, \lambda_-$, which are the generators of SU_2, have the commutators

$$\begin{aligned} [\lambda_0, \lambda_\pm] &= \pm\lambda_\pm \\ [\lambda_+, \lambda_-] &= 2\lambda_0 \end{aligned} \tag{1C-53}$$

corresponding to the components of an angular momentum vector $\boldsymbol{\lambda} = (\lambda_1, \lambda_2, \lambda_3)$ with $\lambda_0 = \lambda_3$, $\lambda_\pm = \lambda_1 \pm i\lambda_2$.

The group SU_2 can therefore be viewed as a rotation group R_3 in a three-dimensional space, generated by the angular momentum operator $\boldsymbol{\lambda}$, and the representations can be labeled by the quantum number λ taking the values 0, 1/2, 1, ... The Casimir operator for SU_2 given by Eqs. (1C-48), (1C-49), and (1C-50) is $G(SU_2) = 2|\boldsymbol{\lambda}|^2 = 2\lambda(\lambda + 1)$. The equivalence between the sets of quantum numbers $n\lambda$ and

$[f_1 f_2]$ has already been exhibited (p. 120), using the example of particle states specified by the isospin component ($m_1 = 1/2, m_2 = -1/2$). In this case, the vector $\boldsymbol{\lambda}$ represents the total isospin $\mathbf{T}$.

The groups SU_2 and R_3 are homomorphic rather than isomorphic, since to each element in R_3 there correspond two elements in SU_2. (Isomorphism implies a one-to-one correspondence of the elements.) Thus, if we denote an element of R_3 by the Euler angles $\omega = (\phi\theta\psi)$ (see Fig. 1A-1), the associated elements of SU_2 are the two-dimensional unimodular unitary matrices $\pm\mathscr{D}^{1/2}_{m_1 m_2}(\omega)$, where $\mathscr{D}^{1/2}_{m_1 m_2}$ are the $\mathscr{D}$ functions for angular momentum 1/2 (see Sec. 1A-3). The existence of two elements in SU_2 for given ω is connected with the fact that a rotation of 360°, which does not affect ω, changes the sign of $\mathscr{D}^{1/2}$. Thus, the representations with half-integer angular momenta are double valued with respect to R_3 but single valued in SU_2.

For $g > 2$, one can introduce linear combinations of generators with angular momentum-like properties in several essentially different ways.

One possibility is illustrated by the states of the configuration $(j)^m$ having $g = 2j + 1$. (The configuration $(l)^m$ is included by letting j take integer as well as half-integer values.) The total angular momentum $\mathbf{J}$ is given by (see Eq. (1A-62))

$$J_\mu = (j(j+1))^{1/2} \sum_{m, m'} \langle jm1\mu | jm' \rangle E(m', m) \tag{1C-54}$$

in terms of its spherical components ($J_{\mu=\pm 1} = \mp 2^{-1/2} J_\pm$). It can also be verified that the operators (1C-54) satisfy the commutation relations of an angular momentum as a consequence of Eq. (1C-44).

Irrespective of the physical significance of the g single-particle states, we may formally associate these with the magnetic substates of an angular momentum $j = \frac{1}{2}(g - 1)$ and thus define an angular momentum-like operator (a "quasispin") by means of Eq. (1C-54). In this manner, the states belonging to a representation of U_g may always be labeled by a quantum number J (and the associated M_J).

In addition to the first-rank tensor J_μ in Eq. (1C-54), one can introduce spherical tensors of higher rank. In fact, the g^2 generators can be represented by a scalar ($=n$), and a set of tensors of rank $\lambda = 1, 2, \ldots, 2j = g - 1$. For example, the generators of U_3 comprise a second-rank tensor in addition to n and an angular momentum vector. (See the example in Appendix 7B.)

An alternative way of defining angular momentum-like operators is to select two m values (for example, m_1 and m_2) and introduce the vector operator $\boldsymbol{\lambda}$ as in Eq. (1C-52). For example, in the U_3 classification of the hadronic spectra, the isospin vector $\mathbf{T}$ is represented in this manner. The operator $n_3 = E(m_3, m_3)$ commutes with $\mathbf{T}$, and the states belonging to a given representation $[f]$ of U_3 can therefore be classified by the eigenvalue of n_3 ($= 0, 1, 2, \ldots$) in addition to T and M_T. In terms of the generators of SU_3, the additional quantum number is conventionally defined by

$$Y = \tfrac{1}{3}n - n_3 \tag{1C-55}$$

representing the hypercharge (see Eq. (1-62)). An alternative choice of the U_2 subspace gives the quasispin $\mathbf{U}$ and charge Z instead of $\mathbf{T}$ and Y (see p. 40).

The different ways of forming angular momentum-like operators from the generators of the unitary groups correspond to different ways of choosing R_3 (or SU_2) subgroups of U_g. The problem is part of the more general one of classifying the states belonging to a given representation $[f]$ of U_g in terms of the representations of subgroups of U_g. The different decompositions of U_g correspond to different choices of basis states, that is, to different coupling schemes for the n-particle system.[9]

A complete chain of subgroups can always be obtained in terms of the set of unitary groups U_{g-1}, U_{g-2} ..., U_2, U_1 formed by successively removing single-particle states from the basis m_a $(a = 1, 2, \ldots, g)$. The "m-coupling scheme," represented by the states with specified tableaux ρ_m (see Sec. 1C-2b), corresponds to such a reduction of U_g. For U_2, this reduction yields the magnetic quantum number. For U_3, we obtain a labeling in terms of Y, T, and M_T. Such a reduction of U_g into products of U_{g_1} and U_{g_2} with $g = g_1 + g_2$ can be obtained from the rules for decomposing outer products of partitions. Another reduction into products of U_{g_1} and U_{g_2} occurs if the single-particle states are products of functions having the dimensions g_1 and g_2, with $g = g_1 g_2$. (See the spin-isospin states in Table 1C–5.) This decomposition involves the Clebsch-Gordan series for the inner product of representations of S_n.[10]

If it is desirable to employ eigenstates of the total angular momentum operator (1C-54), one is faced with the problem of finding additional subgroups of U_g that contain this R_3 group as a subgroup. For odd g (and $g \geq 5$), one such additional subgroup is the group R_g of orthogonal (real and unitary) transformations in g dimensions; these transformations have the property of leaving invariant the two-particle state $(l)^2; L = 0$, with $(2l + 1) = g$. For even g, a corresponding subgroup is provided by the group Sp_g of symplectic transformations, which leave invariant the two-particle state $(j)^2; J = 0$ with $(2j + 1) = g$.

The representations of R_g and Sp_g are labeled by a set of quantum numbers that include the seniority number. (For a discussion of the representations of R_g and Sp_g, see Hamermesh, 1962, pp. 391 ff., and de-Shalit and Talmi, 1963, pp. 389 ff.) Only in special cases do there exist additional subgroups containing the R_3 group with the generators (1C-54), and it is therefore in general not possible in this manner to give a complete classification of the n-particle states, which requires $\frac{1}{2}g\,(g-1)$ quantum numbers, in addition to the set $(f_1, \ldots, f_g)$. For example, in the U_3 scheme, the third quantum number, $\tilde{\Lambda}$, employed on p. 133, has no group theoretical significance.

While the states with specified permutation symmetry, describing systems of equivalent particles each occupying one out of g substates, provide a simple construction of all the representations of U_g, it should be emphasized that it is also possible to consider the unitary symmetry directly in terms of the algebra of the generators without any reference to permutation symmetry.

---

[9] The group theoretical approach to the classification of many-particle states in terms of U_g and its subgroups has been especially exploited by Racah (1951). For a discussion of the reduction of U_g, see also Boerner (1963), Nagel and Moshinsky (1965), and references contained therein.

[10] Multiplication tables for outer and inner products of representation of S_n, yielding decompositions of U_g, are given by Itzykson and Nauenberg (1966).

Thus, for example, a system consisting of nucleons and pions may be characterized by SU_2 symmetry (isospin) and systems that in addition involve strange particles, by SU_3 symmetry, without any obvious role for the permutation symmetry. However, one may also attempt to view such systems as built out of basic entities that each carry the fundamental g-dimensional representation of SU_g (nucleons in the case of SU_2; quarks in the case of SU_3). The symmetric group then again appears as an equally valid starting point for the symmetry classification.

▼

ILLUSTRATIVE EXAMPLES TO APPENDIX 1C

Four-particle wave functions of definite symmetry (*Table 1C-1*)

Functions illustrating the different permutation symmetries for four-particle wave functions are listed in Table 1C-1.

The dimensions of the different representations may be obtained by counting the different ways in which the given function may be formed by coupling the fourth particle to a three-particle state of definite symmetry. A completely symmetric function, [4], can be formed only by adding the fourth particle to the symmetric three-particle state [3], and so [4] is one dimensional. The symmetry [31] can be formed by adding the fourth particle to a state of type [3] or to either of the two states of a representation of type [21]; hence, the representation [31] is three dimensional. The representation [22] can only be formed from three-particle states of type [21] and so is two dimensional. The representation [211] can be built from [21] or [111] and thus has the dimensions $2 + 1 = 3$. Finally, the totally antisymmetric representation [1111] can only be built from [111] and so is one dimensional.

As discussed on p. 111, one may systematize the counting of the dimensions in terms of the Young tableaux. This method of enumeration is shown in the third column of the table, which gives the complete set of tableaux for each symmetry type.

The functions illustrating the symmetries [4] and [31] correspond to a configuration of the type (s^3p). Assuming the s-state wave function to be a constant and the p state to be proportional to x, these functions are linear in the coordinates x_1, x_2, x_3, x_4. The representation [4] contains the unique linear function that is symmetric in all four coordinates, while [31] contains the three functions that are orthogonal to the symmetric functions. The Young tableaux have been assigned to the basis functions following the rules given on p. 112. Thus, $\begin{array}{|c|c|c|}\hline 1 & 2 & 3 \\ \hline 4 \\ \cline{1-1}\end{array}$ implies a function that is symmetric in the coordinates of 1, 2, and 3, while $\begin{array}{|c|c|c|}\hline 1 & 2 & 4 \\ \hline 3 \\ \cline{1-1}\end{array}$ has the symmetry $\begin{array}{|c|c|}\hline 1 & 2 \\ \hline 3 \\ \cline{1-1}\end{array}$ with respect to the coordinates of the first three particles.

It is impossible to generate the lower symmetries with the configuration s^3p since, for this configuration, the functions must be symmetric in the three s-state particles, and so configurations of the type (s^2p^2) have been used to illustrate [22] and [211]. For [22], both p orbits are taken to be in the x direction, while for [211], the antisymmetry among three particles makes it necessary to employ two different

▲

$[f]$	Young diagram	Young tableaux, r	Illustrative functions	ρ_m
[4]	□□□□	1 2 3 4	$x_1 + x_2 + x_3 + x_4$	p_x s s s
[31]	□□□ / □	1 2 3 / 4	$x_1 + x_2 + x_3 - 3x_4$	p_x s s / s
		1 2 4 / 3	$x_1 + x_2 - 2x_3$	
		1 3 4 / 2	$x_1 - x_2$	
[22]	□□ / □□	1 2 / 3 4	$2x_1x_2 - (x_1 + x_2)(x_3 + x_4) + 2x_3x_4$	p_x p_x / s s
		1 3 / 2 4	$(x_1 - x_2)(x_3 - x_4)$	
[211]	□□ / □ / □	1 2 / 3 / 4	$(x_1 + x_2 - 2x_3)y_4 - (y_1 + y_2 - 2y_3)x_4$	p_x s / p_y / s
		1 3 / 2 / 4	$(x_1 - x_2)y_4 - (y_1 - y_2)x_4$	
		1 4 / 2 / 3	$\begin{vmatrix} x_1 & y_1 & 1 \\ x_2 & y_2 & 1 \\ x_3 & y_3 & 1 \end{vmatrix}$	
[1111]	□ / □ / □ / □	1 / 2 / 3 / 4	$\begin{vmatrix} x_1 & y_1 & z_1 & 1 \\ x_2 & y_2 & z_2 & 1 \\ x_3 & y_3 & z_3 & 1 \\ x_4 & y_4 & z_4 & 1 \end{vmatrix}$	p_x / p_y / p_z / s

Table 1C-1 Permutation symmetry for four-particle states.

▼ *p* orbits (which are taken to be proportional to *x* and *y*, respectively). For [1111], the chosen configuration sp^3 with three different *p* orbits is the simplest possible.

The last column in Table 1C-1 gives the quantum number tableaux ρ_m, which may be used to label the different states of symmetry $[f]r$, belonging to a given configuration. Such classifications are discussed in Section 1C-2. For the configurations chosen, there is only a single state with specified $[f]r$ and therefore only a single tableau

▲ ρ_m for each configuration and $[f]$.

Multiplication table for inner products of representations of S_3 (*Table 1C-2*)

The representations contained in the inner product $[f^{(1)}] \times [f^{(2)}]$ for the different representations of S_3 are shown in Table 1C-2. The order of the factors has no effect on the inner product and so the table is symmetric about the main diagonal.

		$[f^{(1)}]$		
		[3]	[21]	[111]
	[3]	[3]	[21]	[111]
$[f^{(2)}]$	[21]		[3] + [21] + [111]	[21]
	[111]			[3]

Table 1C-2 Inner products of representations of S_3.

The table may be constructed by explicitly writing out the products of functions of definite symmetry, such as the examples in Eq. (1C-7), and then projecting out product functions of definite symmetry by means of the operators $\mathscr{A}$, $\mathscr{S}$, $\mathscr{P}_1$, and $\mathscr{P}_2$.

The entries in the table can also be obtained from simple features of the inner product. Thus, $[n] \times [f] = [f]$, since multiplication by the completely symmetric function $[n]$ cannot change the symmetry of the function $[f]$. Similarly, $[111 \ldots 1] \times [f] = [\tilde{f}]$, since multiplication by a completely antisymmetric function interchanges symmetric and antisymmetric pairs, and this is just the relation of $[f]$ to its conjugate $[\tilde{f}]$. The inverse of these two results also hold: $[f] \times [f]$ always contains $[n]$ just once and $[f] \times [\tilde{f}]$ contains $[1111 \ldots 1]$ once.

A count of dimensions yields further results. For example, since [21] is two dimensional, the product $[21] \times [21]$ must give representations whose dimensions add to four; thus, after we have recognized from the above rules that the one-dimensional representations [3] and [111] each appear once, we may conclude that [21] also appears once in the product. (For a systematic discussion of inner products, see, for example, Hamermesh, 1962, p. 254; tables of inner products, for $n \leq 8$, are given by Itzykson and Nauenberg, 1966).

The connection between the irreducible representations of the symmetric groups S_n and the unitary groups U_g implies that the decomposition of inner products of representations of S_n corresponds to the reduction of $U_{g_1 g_2}$ in terms of the product of the groups U_{g_1} and U_{g_2}. (See the discussion in connection with Table 1C-5.)

Quantum numbers and wave functions for states of configuration p^3 (*Table 1C-3*)

The states of definite permutation symmetry that can be constructed from product states of the type p^3 are enumerated in Table 1C-3. The configurations are specified by the m values ($=1$, 0, and -1) and are arranged according to the total M value ($= m_1 + m_2 + m_3$).

M	Configuration	[3]	[21]	[111]
3	1^3	1		
2	$1^2\ 0$	1	1	
1	$1^2\ \ -1$	1	1	
	$1\ \ 0^2$	1	1	
0	$1\ \ 0\ -1$	1	2	1
	0^3	1		

Table 1C-3 Classification of states belonging to p^3 configuration.

The number of times each symmetry occurs for a given configuration can be found by writing out the possible Young tableaux ρ_m in m space (see p. 117). We shall adopt the order $m = 1, 0, -1$ for writing the m values into the tableaux.

For $M = 3$, we have only the configuration $(m = 1)^3$, which must be a symmetric function

$$\Phi\left(\rho_m = \begin{array}{|c|c|c|}\hline 1 & 1 & 1 \\ \hline\end{array}\right) = (1\ 1\ 1)$$

with the notation

$$(m_1 m_2 m_3) \equiv \varphi_{m_1}(1)\varphi_{m_2}(2)\varphi_{m_3}(3)$$

for three-particle product states.

For $M = 2$, the configuration $((m = 1)^2,\ m = 0)$ yields a single symmetric state

$$\Phi\left(\rho_m = \begin{array}{|c|c|c|}\hline 1 & 1 & 0 \\ \hline\end{array}\right) = \frac{1}{\sqrt{3}}\,[(110) + (101) + (011)]$$

The same configuration also yields the symmetry type [21] once, corresponding to the tableau in m space $\begin{array}{|c|c|}\hline 1 & 1 \\ \hline 0 \\ \cline{1-1}\end{array}$; this representation is two dimensional under permutation of the coordinates and, hence, there are two states of this symmetry distinguished by the two different tableaux r in particle number space

$$\Phi\left(r = \begin{array}{|c|c|}\hline 1 & 2 \\ \hline 3 \\ \cline{1-1}\end{array}\quad \rho_m = \begin{array}{|c|c|}\hline 1 & 1 \\ \hline 0 \\ \cline{1-1}\end{array}\right) = \frac{1}{\sqrt{6}}\,[2(110) - (101) - (011)]$$

$$\Phi\left(r = \begin{array}{|c|c|}\hline 1 & 3 \\ \hline 2 \\ \cline{1-1}\end{array}\quad \rho_m = \begin{array}{|c|c|}\hline 1 & 1 \\ \hline 0 \\ \cline{1-1}\end{array}\right) = \frac{1}{\sqrt{2}}\,[-(101) + (011)]$$

The two different configurations for $M = 1$ are each like the $M = 2$ configuration (are of the type $m_1^2 m_2$) and thus yield [3] and [21] each once.

For $M = 0$, the configuration $(m = 0)^3$ must be symmetric ([3]), corresponding to the wave function (000). The wave functions for the configuration $(m = 1,\ m = 0,\ m = -1)$ are

$$\Phi\left(\rho_m = \begin{array}{|c|c|c|}\hline 1 & 0 & -1 \\ \hline\end{array}\right) = \frac{1}{\sqrt{6}}\,[(10-1) + (01-1) + (-101) + (1-10) + (0-11) + (-110)]$$

$$\Phi\left(r = \begin{array}{|c|c|}\hline 1 & 2 \\ \hline 3 \\ \cline{1-1}\end{array}\quad \rho_m = \begin{array}{|c|c|}\hline 1 & 0 \\ \hline -1 \\ \cline{1-1}\end{array}\right) = \frac{1}{\sqrt{12}}\,[2(10-1) + 2(01-1) - (-101) - (1-10) - (0-11) - (-110)]$$

$$\Phi\left(r = \begin{array}{|c|c|}\hline 1 & 3 \\ \hline 2 \\ \cline{1-1}\end{array}\quad \rho_m = \begin{array}{|c|c|}\hline 1 & 0 \\ \hline -1 \\ \cline{1-1}\end{array}\right) = \frac{1}{\sqrt{4}}\,[-(-101) + (1-10) + (0-11) - (-110)]$$

$$\Phi\left(r = \begin{array}{|c|c|}\hline 1 & 2 \\ \hline 3 \\ \cline{1-1}\end{array}\quad \rho_m = \begin{array}{|c|c|}\hline 1 & -1 \\ \hline 0 \\ \cline{1-1}\end{array}\right) = \frac{1}{\sqrt{4}}\,[-(-101) + (1-10) - (0-11) + (-110)]$$

$$\Phi\left(r = \begin{array}{|c|c|}\hline 1 & 3 \\ \hline 2 & \\ \cline{1-1}\end{array}\quad \rho_m = \begin{array}{|c|c|}\hline 1 & -1 \\ \hline 0 & \\ \cline{1-1}\end{array}\right) = \frac{1}{\sqrt{12}}[2(10-1) - 2(01-1) + (-101) + (1-10) - (0-11) - (-110)]$$

$$\Phi\left(\rho_m = \begin{array}{|c|}\hline 1 \\ \hline 0 \\ \hline -1 \\ \hline\end{array}\right) = \frac{1}{\sqrt{6}}[(10-1) - (01-1) - (-101) - (1-10) + (0-11) + (-110)]$$

In assigning the tableaux ρ_m to definite basis functions, we have followed the same principle as employed in the tableaux r; thus, if we neglect the last orbit (with the assumed standard order, this means neglecting the orbit $m = -1$ in the present example), the remaining function has definite symmetry under exchange of the two remaining orbits ($m = 1$ and 0), and this symmetry corresponds to the Young diagram obtained by removing the block $\boxed{-1}$ from the m-space tableau. (The general construction of states with specified r and ρ_m is given by Eq. (1C-31).)

From the different M values associated with each symmetry, we can conclude that, for the configuration p^3, we obtain symmetric states [3] with $L = 3$ and 1, states of mixed symmetry [21] with $L = 2$ and 1, and a single antisymmetric state [111] with $L = 0$. The [111] state may be recognized as the unique Slater determinant that can be formed out of the configuration p^3 (closed shell configuration). The wave functions of definite L may be obtained by starting with the $M = L$ component given by the expressions above and acting with the lowering operator $L_x - iL_y$, which can be written in terms of the shift operators $E(m' = m - 1, m)$. Thus, from Eq. (1C-54), we obtain the relation $L_x - iL_y = 2^{1/2}(E(0, 1) + E(-1, 0))$.

The generators (1C-37) of the unitary group, U_3, change the configuration (the m_i values) and the tableau ρ_m, but leave the permutation symmetry $[f]r$ unchanged. Thus, in the present example, the states of symmetry [3] form a ten-dimensional representation of the group U_3, while each such state is a one-dimensional representation of the permutation group S_3. Similarly, the states of type [21] form an eight-dimensional representation of U_3 and a two-dimensional representation of S_3, while the representation [111] is one dimensional in both U_3 and S_3.

Classification of states with configurations p^n (Table 1C-4)

The states belonging to the configuration p^n can be classified by the orbital symmetry $[f]$ and the total angular momentum L. (The full specification of the states in general requires an additional quantum number besides $[f]LM$, such as the quantity $\tilde{\Lambda}$ considered below.) Because there are three substates of the p orbital, the partition $[f]$ can contain at most three numbers $[f_1 f_2 f_3]$ (the wave function can be antisymmetric in at most three particles at a time).

The classification in terms of $[f]$ and L is shown in Table 1C-4, for $n \leq 6$. In constructing the table, it is simplest to start with the low values of n and successively add particles.

For $n = 2$, we immediately obtain the listed result from the symmetry properties of the vector addition coefficients.

For $n = 3$, we can obtain the L structure by counting the number of states with given $[f]$ in the m representation (see Table 1C-3). We can give an alternative derivation of the L structure for $n = 3$, which is also instructive. We start by noting that the state

n	$[f]$	L values
1	[1]	1
2	[2]	02
	[11]	1
3	[3]	13
	[21]	12
	[111]	0
4	[4]	024
	[31]	123
	[22]	02
	[211]	1
5	[5]	135
	[41]	1234
	[32]	123
	[311]	02
	[221]	1
6	[6]	0246
	[51]	12345
	[42]	02^234
	[33]	13
	[411]	13
	[321]	12
	[222]	0

Table 1C-4 p^n configurations.

▼ with symmetry [111] must be the Slater determinant formed of the three p substates; this unique state is the only totally antisymmetric state of p^3 that we can form, and may be thought of as a closed shell structure. The uniqueness of the state (a one-dimensional representation in U_3) immediately implies $L = 0$. The L content of [21] may now be obtained by noting that the outer product of [11] and [1] contains [21] once and [111] once (see the rules for multiplying symmetries, p. 116). When we combine this result with the rules for coupling angular momenta, we obtain

$$\begin{aligned}[21] &= [11] \otimes [1] - [111] \\ &\rightarrow (L = 1) \otimes (L = 1) - (L = 0) \\ &= (L = 0, 1, 2) - (L = 0)\end{aligned}$$

so [21] contains $L = 1$ and 2. Continuing in the same manner, we obtain

$$\begin{aligned}[3] &= [2] \otimes [1] - [21] \\ &\rightarrow (L = 0, 2) \otimes (L = 1) - (L = 1, 2) \\ &= (L = 1, 3)\end{aligned}$$

A check on these results is provided by the dimension formula (1C-27), which gives $h[21] = 8$ and $h[3] = 10$, for U_3. ▲

▼ For $n = 4$, again we may either use an explicit count of M values for each $[f]$ or we may start with the most antisymmetric type of state [211] and notice that this is like a single particle outside the closed shell [111] (it is the only state obtained by multiplying $[111] \otimes [1]$ since [1111] is impossible for p^4) and thus this symmetry has the single L value $L = 1$. The other symmetries may then be obtained by using simultaneously the rules for multiplying symmetries and for coupling angular momenta.

Having worked out these examples, we can now obtain the general rule for the L content of the configurations p^n. It is convenient to start with the completely symmetric states $[n]$. The enumeration of these states is the same as that of a single particle in a harmonic oscillator with principal quantum number $N = n$, for which we have the well-known result

$$L = n, n-2, \ldots, 0 \text{ or } 1 \qquad [n] \tag{1C-56}$$

From this result the L content of $[n1]$ follows by methods similar to those employed for $(p)^3$,

$$[n1] = [n] \otimes [1] - [n+1]$$

$$\rightarrow (L = n, n-2, \ldots, 1 \text{ or } 0) \otimes (L = 1) - (L = n+1, n-1, \ldots, 0 \text{ or } 1)$$

Thus, $[n1]$ contains

$$L = n, n-1, n-2, \ldots, 1 \qquad [n1] \tag{1C-57}$$

Continuing in this way we can obtain the general rule for the L content of $[f_1 f_2 f_3]$. Since the closed shell $[fff]$ has zero angular momentum, we may remove such completed columns from the Young diagram without affecting the angular momentum properties of the state. Hence, the L content only depends on the two numbers $f_1 - f_3$ and $f_2 - f_3$. To exploit the symmetry between particles and holes (particles removed from closed shells), it is useful to express these two numbers in terms of

$$\begin{aligned} \lambda &= f_1 - f_2 \\ \mu &= f_2 - f_3 \end{aligned} \tag{1C-58}$$

The interchange of λ and μ is equivalent to a particle-hole conjugation and thus gives rise to symmetries with the same L content. The final result for the L structure belonging to the symmetry $(\lambda\mu)$ can be expressed by introducing a quantity $\tilde{\Lambda}$ which takes the values

$$\tilde{\Lambda} = \min(\lambda, \mu), \min(\lambda, \mu) - 2, \ldots, 0 \text{ or } 1 \tag{1C-59}$$

Then, for each value of $\tilde{\Lambda}$, there is a series of L values

$$\begin{aligned} L &= \tilde{\Lambda}, \tilde{\Lambda} + 1, \ldots, \tilde{\Lambda} + \max(\lambda, \mu) \qquad && (\tilde{\Lambda} \neq 0) \\ L &= \max(\lambda, \mu), \max(\lambda, \mu) - 2, \ldots, 0 \text{ or } 1 \qquad && (\tilde{\Lambda} = 0) \end{aligned} \tag{1C-60}$$

In the nuclear p-shell configurations, we are restricted to partitions with $f_i \leq 4$ $(\lambda + \mu \leq 4)$, since we must combine these functions with spin-isospin wave functions to form totally antisymmetric wave functions. However, the general classification of states according to U_3 finds application in the characterization of states in a harmonic oscillator potential (see Appendix 7B).

Classification of spin-isospin functions (*Table 1C-5*)

The decomposition of states with definite permutation symmetry $[f]$ in spin-
▲ isospin space (and conjugate symmetry $[\tilde{f}]$ in orbital space) into components (T, S)

n	$[f]$	(T, S)
1	[1]	(1/2, 1/2)
2	[2]	(1, 1) (0, 0)
	[11]	(1, 0) (0, 1)
3	[3]	(3/2, 3/2) (1/2, 1/2)
	[21]	(3/2, 1/2) (1/2, 3/2) (1/2, 1/2)
	[111]	(1/2, 1/2)
4	[4]	(2, 2) (1, 1) (0, 0)
	[31]	(2, 1) (1, 2) (1, 1) (1, 0) (0, 1)
	[22]	(2, 0) (0, 2) (1, 1) (0, 0)
	[211]	(1, 1) (1, 0) (0, 1)
	[1111]	(0, 0)
5	[5]	(5/2, 5/2) (3/2, 3/2) (1/2, 1/2)
	[41]	(5/2, 3/2) (3/2, 5/2) (3/2, 3/2) (3/2, 1/2) (1/2, 3/2) (1/2, 1/2)
	[32]	(5/2, 1/2) (1/2, 5/2) (3/2, 3/2) (3/2, 1/2) (1/2, 3/2) (1/2, 1/2)
	[311]	(3/2, 3/2) (3/2, 1/2) (1/2, 3/2) (1/2, 1/2)
	[221]	(3/2, 1/2) (1/2, 3/2) (1/2, 1/2)
	[2111]	(1/2, 1/2)
6	[6]	(3, 3) (2, 2) (1, 1) (0, 0)
	[51]	(3, 2) (2, 3) (2, 2) (2, 1) (1, 2) (1, 1) (1, 0) (0, 1)
	[42]	(3, 1) (1, 3) (2, 2) (2, 1) (1, 2) $(1, 1)^2$ (2, 0) (0, 2) (0, 0)
	[411]	(2, 2) (2, 1) (1, 2) (1, 1) (1, 0) (0, 1)
	[33]	(3, 0) (0, 3) (2, 1) (1, 2) (1, 0) (0, 1)
	[321]	(2, 1) (1, 2) (2, 0) (0, 2) $(1, 1)^2$ (1, 0) (0, 1)
	[3111]	(1, 1) (0, 0)
	[222]	(1, 1) (0, 0)
	[2211]	(1, 0) (0, 1)

Table 1C-5 Isospin-spin components of supermultiplets (U_4 classification).

▼ with total isospin T and total spin S is shown in Table 1C-5, for $n \leq 6$. The construction of the table follows lines very similar to those employed in Table 1C-4.

For $n = 2$, we shall enumerate the tableaux ρ_m in m space corresponding to the different values of M_T and M_S; we write $+$ for $m = +1/2$ and $-$ for $m = -1/2$ and adopt the standard order $++$, $+-$, $-+$, $--$ for filling out the tableaux. The first quantum number is always m_t while the second is m_s. The following tableaux occur:

$M_T = 1 \quad M_S = 1$ [$++$ | $++$]

$M_T = 1 \quad M_S = 0$ [$++$ | $+-$]   [$++$ / $+-$]

$M_T = 0 \quad M_S = 1$ [$++$ | $-+$]   [$++$ / $-+$]

▲

$M_T = 0 \qquad M_S = 0$

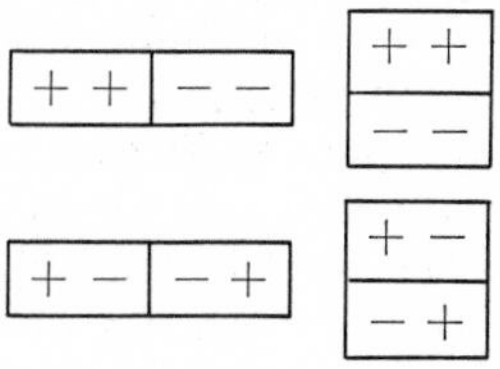

Thus, we obtain the well-known result that the symmetric spin-isospin functions [2] have $(T, S) = (1, 1)$ and $(0, 0)$, while the antisymmetric functions [11] have $(0, 1)$ and $(1, 0)$. Writing out the m space tableaux for $n = 3$, we obtain

$M_T = \frac{3}{2} \quad M_S = \frac{3}{2}$

$M_T = \frac{3}{2} \quad M_S = \frac{1}{2}$

$M_T = \frac{1}{2} \quad M_S = \frac{3}{2}$

$M_T = \frac{1}{2} \quad M_S = \frac{1}{2}$

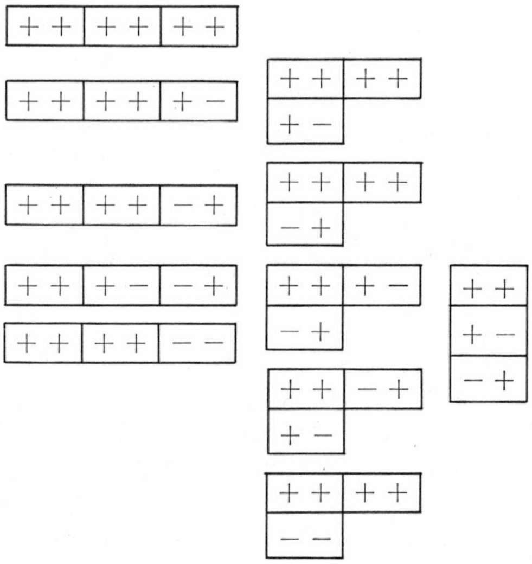

which leads to the (T, S) structure listed in the table.

We may also give an alternative derivation of the result for $n = 3$. Starting from [111] we note that this symmetry lacks just one particle from forming the unique configuration [1111] of the closed shell. Thus, [111] may be thought of as a single hole in the closed shell and has the same quantum numbers as a single particle, $(T, S) = (1/2, 1/2)$. Now we may construct the other symmetries by taking products of two-particle states and the states of the third particle

$$\begin{aligned}
[21] &= [11] \otimes [1] - [111] \\
&\rightarrow [(1, 0) + (0, 1)] \otimes (\tfrac{1}{2}, \tfrac{1}{2}) - (\tfrac{1}{2}, \tfrac{1}{2}) \\
&= (\tfrac{3}{2}, \tfrac{1}{2}) + (\tfrac{1}{2}, \tfrac{3}{2}) + (\tfrac{1}{2}, \tfrac{1}{2}) \\
[3] &= [2] \otimes [1] - [21] \\
&\rightarrow [(1, 1) + (0, 0)] \otimes (\tfrac{1}{2}, \tfrac{1}{2}) - ((\tfrac{3}{2}, \tfrac{1}{2}) + (\tfrac{1}{2}, \tfrac{3}{2}) + (\tfrac{1}{2}, \tfrac{3}{2})) \\
&= (\tfrac{3}{2}, \tfrac{3}{2}) + (\tfrac{1}{2}, \tfrac{1}{2})
\end{aligned}$$

The rest of Table 1C-5 can be constructed by means of the continued application of the methods indicated above.

Since there are four basis states of a nucleon in spin-isospin space, the classification involves the representations of U_4, referred to as supermultiplets. The assignment of T and S quantum numbers corresponds to the reduction of U_4 in terms of the product of two U_2 groups.

Table 1C-5 can also be read as a table of inner products of representations of S_n. For example, for $n = 3$, a U_2 representation with $T = 1/2$ or $S = 1/2$ refers to the partition [21], and the fact that $(T, S) = (1/2, 1/2)$ occurs for all the symmetries [3], [21], and [111] corresponds to the fact that the product $[21] \times [21]$ contains each of these symmetries (see Table 1C-2).

CHAPTER 2

Independent-Particle Motion

2-1 BULK PROPERTIES OF NUCLEI

2-1a Nuclear Size

At an early stage in the study of nuclear structure, evidence from α-decay lifetimes and scattering cross sections for α particles on light nuclei suggested that nuclei are characterized by an approximately constant density within a volume that increases roughly in proportion to the mass number, A (see Rutherford *et al.*, 1930, pp. 280, 331). This conjecture has been tested in greatest detail by means of high-energy electron scattering experiments (as illustrated in Fig. 2-1, p. 159), which yield

$$\rho(0) = 0.17 \text{ nucleon fm}^{-3} \tag{2-1}$$

for the value of the central density. The density decreases from the value (2-1) to zero over a distance of the order 2–3 fm, and thus, with the exception of the lightest nuclei, the surface thickness is appreciably smaller than the radial extent of the nucleus, and it is useful to describe the density in terms of a radius, R, which varies approximately as

$$R = r_0 A^{1/3} \tag{2-2}$$

The electron scattering data determine the value of $r_0 = 1.1$ fm for the radius parameter that describes the distance at which the nuclear density has decreased to half of the central value (2-1) (see Fig. 2-1). This value of the radius is also consistent with the evidence on the nuclear charge distribution obtained from μ-mesic atoms. (For summaries and reviews of nuclear radius determinations, see Stanford Conference, 1958; Elton, 1961; Hofstadter, 1963.) Since the nuclear surface is not sharp, but, as indicated in Fig. 2-1, has a finite "diffuseness," the definition of the nuclear radius depends somewhat on the property considered. (See p. 160 for a discussion of the various moments of the nuclear charge distribution, as determined from the electron scattering data.)

The available evidence on the nuclear matter distribution is mainly confined to the proton density. In heavy nuclei, because of the Coulomb forces and associated neutron excess, there may be some difference between the density distributions of neutrons and protons. Tentative evidence bearing on this interesting problem is discussed in connection with the isotope shift data in Fig. 2-2 (p. 163) and the isospin mixing produced by the Coulomb force illustrated in Fig. 2-6 (p. 174); see also the discussion by Elton (1961, pp. 93ff.) of the evidence from the scattering of fast π^+ and π^- mesons, and the recent evidence derived from the capture of K^- mesons (Davis *et al.*, 1967; Burhop, 1967).

The almost constant density of nuclear matter is associated with the finite range of the nuclear forces; the range of the forces is of the order of r_0 and thus small compared with the nuclear size. This "saturation" of nuclear matter is also reflected in the fact that the total binding energy of the nucleus is roughly proportional to A. In a minor way, these features are modified by surface effects and the long-range Coulomb forces acting between the protons (see below).

2-1b Mean Free Path of Nucleons

A fundamental characteristic of any many-body system is the mean free path for collisions between constituent particles. A wide variety of evidence testifies to the fact that, in the nucleus, this mean free path is large compared to the distance between the nucleons and even, under many circumstances, is larger than the dimensions of the nucleus.

A very direct way to explore the nuclear opacity is provided by scattering experiments involving incident neutrons and protons. Figure 2-3, p. 165 shows typical examples of the energy dependence of the total cross section for interaction of neutrons with nuclei. For a system with a mean free path small compared to the radius, the total cross section would vary monotonically with energy, decreasing slowly over the energy region considered, toward the limiting value $2\pi R^2$. (For a discussion of general scattering theory as applied to nuclei, and for the estimate of cross sections for totally absorbing systems, see, for example, Blatt and Weisskopf, 1952, Chapter 8.) The pronounced variations in the observed cross sections must be attributed to the interference between the incident and transmitted waves, and thus establish the fact that the mean free path is at least comparable with the nuclear radius. (We later return to the more quantitative analysis of such scattering experiments (Sec. 2-4c); see also the discussion in connection with Fig. 2-3.)

The relatively long mean free path of the nucleons implies that the interactions primarily contribute a smoothly varying average potential in which the particles move independently. As a first approximation of heavy nuclei, we may neglect surface effects, and the resulting Fermi gas model provides a useful starting point for the discussion of many of the bulk properties of nuclei.

2-1c Momentum Distribution (Fermi Gas Approximation)

If we consider a volume Ω of constant potential, the individual-particle states are described by plane waves,

$$\varphi_\nu = \Omega^{-1/2} \exp(i\mathbf{k} \cdot \mathbf{r})\chi_{m_s}\xi_{m_t} \tag{2-3}$$

where χ and ξ are the spin and isospin wave functions specified by the "magnetic" quantum numbers describing the nucleon spin, $m_s = \pm 1/2$, and isospin, $m_t = +1/2$ (neutron) and $m_t = -1/2$ (proton).

The allowed values of **k** are determined by periodic boundary conditions (since we are neglecting surface effects)

$$\varphi(x, y, z) = \varphi(x + L, y, z) = \varphi(x, y + L, z) = \varphi(x, y, z + L) \qquad (2\text{-}4)$$

where L is the length of the volume element in which the particles are quantized ($\Omega = L^3$). The boundary conditions (2-4) lead to the eigenvalues

$$k_x = \frac{2\pi}{L} n_x \qquad k_y = \frac{2\pi}{L} n_y \qquad k_z = \frac{2\pi}{L} n_z$$

$$\left.\begin{matrix} n_x \\ n_y \\ n_z \end{matrix}\right\} = 0, \pm 1, \pm 2, \cdots \qquad (2\text{-}5)$$

and the label ν in Eq. (2-3) thus represents the set of quantum numbers n_x, n_y, n_z, m_s, and m_t.

The average one-particle level density in k space is

$$dn = 4\left(\frac{1}{2\pi}\right)^3 \Omega \, d^3k \qquad (2\text{-}6)$$

where the factor 4 reflects the fact that there are four different spin-isospin states for each eigenvalue **k**.

The ground state of the Fermi gas is obtained by forming a product state in which the lowest-energy one-particle states (2-3) are filled (the effects of the antisymmetrization are considered in Sec. 2-1h). The dividing line between the filled and unfilled states is referred to as the Fermi surface, and the corresponding wave number is denoted by $k_F^{(n)}$ and $k_F^{(p)}$ for the neutrons and protons, respectively. The value of k_F is determined from the condition that the total number of occupied orbits must be equal to the number of particles (N for neutrons and Z for protons). Thus, we obtain from Eq. (2-6)

$$\begin{aligned} k_F^{(n)} &= \left(3\pi^2 \frac{N}{\Omega}\right)^{1/3} \\ k_F^{(p)} &= \left(3\pi^2 \frac{Z}{\Omega}\right)^{1/3} \end{aligned} \qquad (2\text{-}7)$$

Using the observed particle density (2-1), we obtain

$$k_F \approx 1.36 \text{ fm}^{-1} \qquad (2\text{-}8)$$

as an average value for neutrons and protons ($N = Z = A/2$).

A measurement of the momentum distribution of the nucleons in a nucleus would provide an especially direct test of the Fermi gas model. Various experiments utilizing high-energy incident particles have attempted to explore this distribution, but the results, so far, have been mainly confined to light nuclei, and a quantitative analysis is plagued with difficulties in the description of the reaction mechanism. (See, for example, the discussion of the high-energy $(p, 2p)$ experiment shown in Fig. 2-27; for a critical review of the available evidence on the momentum distribution in nuclei, see Gottfried, 1963.)

The Fermi energy, obtained from Eq. (2-7), represents the maximum kinetic energy of a particle in the Fermi gas, *at 0 temperature,*

$$\varepsilon_F = \frac{(\hbar k_F)^2}{2M} \approx 37 \text{ MeV} \qquad (2\text{-}9)$$

The total kinetic energy of the Fermi gas is obtained by summing over all the occupied orbits, $= \int_0^N \varepsilon \, dn$

$$\mathscr{E}_{\text{kin}} = \tfrac{3}{5}(N\varepsilon_F^{(n)} + Z\varepsilon_F^{(p)}) \approx \tfrac{3}{5}A\varepsilon_F \qquad (2\text{-}10) \qquad \checkmark$$

The magnitude of the Fermi energy implies that, under normal experimental conditions, the nucleus is a highly degenerate Fermi gas. Only for excitation energies of order $\varepsilon_F A \sim 10^3$ MeV will an appreciable fraction of all the nucleons be excited. $\checkmark$

2-1d   Nuclear Binding Energies

The total nuclear binding energy, $\mathscr{B}$, represents the difference between the observed mass, $\mathscr{M}$ (or, equivalently, the total nuclear energy $\mathscr{E}$), in the ground state and the masses of the separated nucleons,

$$\mathscr{M}(N, Z) = \frac{1}{c^2}\mathscr{E}(N, Z) = NM_n + ZM_p - \frac{1}{c^2}\mathscr{B}(N, Z) \qquad (2\text{-}11)$$

The main trends in $\mathscr{B}$ are illustrated in Fig. 2-4, p. 168, and can be understood in terms of a simple expression (the semi-empirical mass formula), the separate terms of which can be motivated on the basis of the gross features of nuclei as described above (Weizsäcker, 1935; Bethe and Bacher, 1936)

$$\mathscr{B} = b_{\text{vol}} A - b_{\text{surf}} A^{2/3} - \tfrac{1}{2}b_{\text{sym}} \frac{(N-Z)^2}{A} - \frac{3}{5}\frac{Z^2 e^2}{R_c} \qquad (2\text{-}12)$$

That the main term in the nuclear binding energy should be linear in A is strongly suggested by the approximate A independence of the nuclear density. Thus, the first term in Eq. (2-12) is the volume energy representing the binding in the limit of large A, for $N = Z$, and in the absence of Coulomb forces.

The second term in Eq. (2-12) represents the surface energy, which is a general feature of finite systems reflecting the fact that particles in the surface have fewer neighbors than at normal density. However, in contrast to classical liquids and crystals, the structure of the nuclear surface and the associated energy are also affected in an important manner by the kinetic energy. The surface energy term is responsible for the increase in binding energy per particle with increasing A, which can be seen for the lighter nuclei in Fig. 2-4.

The binding energy term proportional to $A^{2/3}$ represents, quite generally, the leading-order correction to the linear term describing the energy of a saturating system. Thus, the observed coefficient, b_{surf}, might contain contributions from many effects, such as an A dependence of the density or of the correlations, which need not be proportional to the surface area of the nucleus. An experimental test of the interpretation of this term as a surface energy is provided by the data on the height of the potential energy barrier for the fission process. The barrier height is a very sensitive function of the ratio between the nuclear surface energy and Coulomb energy. (See the discussion of the fission process in Chapter 6.) The surface energy parameter determined from the observed fission "thresholds" is $b_{surf} = 17$ MeV, in excellent agreement with the value (2-14) determined from the systematics of the nuclear masses (Burnett *et al.*, 1964; Myers and Swiatecki, 1966).

The tendency toward stability for $N = Z$ (the nuclear symmetry energy) is expressed by the third term in Eq. (2-12), which represents the leading effect for small values of $(N - Z)/A$. The symmetry energy may be divided into a kinetic and a potential part. For given A, the kinetic energy of the nuclear Fermi gas is a minimum for $N = Z$. The kinetic part of b_{sym} may be estimated by expanding the energy (2-10) in powers of $(N - Z)$, which yields

$$(b_{sym})_{kin} = \tfrac{2}{3}(\varepsilon_F)_{N=Z} \approx 25 \text{ MeV} \tag{2-13}$$

The potential energy part of b_{sym} is associated with a specific feature of the nuclear forces, which implies that the neutron-proton interaction is on the average stronger than that between like particles (see Sec. 2-5b). The empirical value of b_{sym}, which is about 50 MeV (see Eq. (2-14)), together with the estimate (2-13) implies that the potential energy part of b_{sym} is about 25 MeV.

The last term in the semi-empirical mass formula (2-12) is the Coulomb energy corresponding to a uniformly charged sphere of radius R_c. The Coulomb repulsion is responsible for the gradual decrease in the binding energy per particle that is observed for heavy nuclei (see Fig. 2-4).

The observed binding energies are fitted rather well by the semi-empirical mass formula if one chooses the parameters (see Fig. 2-4)

$$\begin{aligned} b_{vol} &\approx 16 \text{ MeV} \\ b_{surf} &\approx 17 \text{ MeV} \\ b_{sym} &\approx 50 \text{ MeV} \\ R_c &\approx 1.24\, A^{1/3} \text{fm} \end{aligned} \tag{2-14}$$

These values of the parameters also account for the observed neutron excess of the β-stable nuclei (see Fig. 2-18). More exacting tests of the semi-empirical mass formula are encountered when one tries to predict the masses of nuclei far from the line of β stability (as is of special interest in connection with the theories of nucleogenesis; see Sec. 2-3b) and of nuclei much heavier than those so far studied. It is likely that for these purposes additional terms in the mass formula may be required, describing, for example, a dependence of the surface energy and of the average nuclear density on the charge symmetry parameter, $N-Z$.

A more detailed examination of the nuclear binding energies reveals systematic deviations from a smoothly varying function of Z and N, which may amount to about 10 MeV in the total binding, as indicated in Fig. 2-4. A quantitative treatment of these quantal effects requires a rather complete description of the nuclear structure, including detailed configuration assignments, evaluation of correlation effects, and so on. The largest of the quantal effects are associated with the shell structure and the nuclear deformations, as discussed in Sec. 9-1. For attempts to generalize the binding energy formula to include quantal effects in terms of a number of average parameters, see Zeldes *et al.* (1967); Myers and Swiatecki (1966). We consider in the next section a part of the quantal effect, the pairing energy, which has an especially simple structure.

2-1e Pairing Energy

The nuclear binding energies are found to exhibit a systematic variation depending on the evenness or oddness of Z and N

$$\delta\mathscr{B} = \begin{cases} \Delta & Z \text{ even} \quad N \text{ even} \\ 0 & A \text{ odd} \\ -\Delta & Z \text{ odd} \quad N \text{ odd} \end{cases} \tag{2-15}$$

From the Fermi gas model, we expect an odd-even difference (pairing energy) resulting from the fact that each orbit, **k**, can be occupied by two protons and by two neutrons. Thus, we obtain an odd-even parameter Δ that is of the order of the spacing between the one-particle energies in the neighborhood of the Fermi energy

$$(\Delta)_{\text{kin}} \approx \frac{2}{3}\frac{\varepsilon_F}{A} \approx \frac{25}{A} \quad \text{MeV} \tag{2-16}$$

The observed pairing energies are shown in Fig. 2-5, p. 170, and are seen to be almost an order of magnitude larger than the estimate (2-16).

The large observed odd-even effect may be described in terms of a pairwise correlation of identical particles, which contributes an additional binding energy of 2Δ per pair (for nucleons near the top of the Fermi distribution).

This interpretation is supported by the paucity of levels in even-even nuclei for excitation energies less than that required to break a pair. (The experimental evidence for this energy gap is presented in Chapter 8.) The correlation of the particles in the pair is associated with a superposition of single-particle states within an energy interval of order Δ. Thus, the transition from occupied to unoccupied states, which in a noninteracting Fermi gas takes place sharply at the energy ε_F, is smeared out over an interval of order Δ.

The pairing effect plays a very important role in the low-energy nuclear phenomena. It can be treated in terms of a simple generalization of the independent-particle description, which will be considered in Chapter 8, following the analysis in Chapter 7 of correlations between two particles moving in orbits outside the Fermi distribution. The correlation effect is brought about by the predominantly attractive character of the nucleonic force; thus, in atoms with the repulsive Coulomb interactions of the electrons, no similar pairing effect is observed (see Fig. 2-13).

2-1f Isospin Quantum Number

Isospin dependence of nuclear binding

The expression (2-12) describes the binding energy for the ground state of a nucleus with given Z and N, that is, with given $A = Z + N$ and $M_T = \frac{1}{2}(N - Z)$. The ground state of the Fermi gas is obtained by filling the lowest neutron orbits up to the neutron Fermi energy, and similarly for the protons. The resulting state has a total isobaric spin $T = |M_T|$. In fact, a neutron and a proton in the same orbit form a system with zero isospin, since the wave function is symmetric in spin-orbital space. Thus, in the ground state, the isospin of the Fermi gas is contributed entirely by the extra neutrons, and we obtain a totally "aligned" isospin, $T = |M_T|$.

By exploiting the charge independence of the nucleonic interactions, we can also obtain, from Eq. (2-12), the binding energy for the lowest state with any given higher value of T. Such a state is the isobaric analog of the ground state of the nucleus with M_T equal to the T value considered.

In order to express the binding energy as a function of T and M_T, we note that the only M_T-dependent term is the Coulomb energy, which is a function of $Z = \frac{1}{2}A - M_T$. The remaining part of the binding energy can only depend on T (and A). The term proportional to $(N - Z)^2$ may thus be regarded as the leading term in an expansion in powers of the isospin,

$$\mathscr{E}(A, T, M_T) = \mathscr{E}_0(A) + 2b_{\text{sym}}\frac{T^2}{A} + \frac{3}{5}(\tfrac{1}{2}A - M_T)^2\frac{e^2}{R_c} \tag{2-17}$$

The symmetry energy may also contain a term linear in T; this term is associated with neutron-proton exchange interactions and involves more detailed features of the nuclear structure. Thus, the potential (2-29) gives a contribution proportional to $T(T+1)$, while the assumption of the full supermultiplet symmetry gives an interaction energy proportional to $T(T+4)$ (see Blatt and Weisskopf, 1952, p. 243). The experimental evidence on the masses of nuclei with small values of T provides support for the existence of a linear term (see, for example, Myers and Swiatecki, 1966); however, we have retained the somewhat simpler form, T^2, in Eq. (2-17), since this gives the main effect for heavy nuclei.

The difference in binding energy for states in the same nucleus having different values of T (but the same M_T and A) is given by the symmetry energy. Thus, the lowest states with $T = M_T + 1$ occur at an excitation energy of about

$$\mathscr{E}(A, T+1, M_T = T) - \mathscr{E}(A, T, M_T = T) \approx 4b_{\text{sym}} \frac{(T+\frac{1}{2})}{A} \tag{2-18}$$

This estimate represents an average neglecting the effects of shell structure and pairing.

The binding energy difference between isobaric analog states (which have the same A and T, but different M_T) is given by the Coulomb energy. The estimate of the Coulomb energy in Eq. (2-12) is based on a very simple description of an averaged nuclear charge distribution. However, the interaction of each charge with itself is included in the rest mass of the proton, and the nuclear Coulomb energy should therefore only include the interaction with the $Z-1$ other charges. Thus, one may obtain a slight improvement by replacing the factor Z^2 by $Z(Z-1)$.

In a quantal description of the Coulomb energy, one must take into account the correlation of the protons that is implied by the antisymmetrization of the wave function. The estimate of this effect is considered below (see Eq. (2-45)), and one finds, for a heavy nucleus,

$$\begin{aligned} \mathscr{E}_{\text{Coul}} &= \frac{3}{5}\frac{Z^2e^2}{R_c}\left[1 - 5\left(\frac{3}{16\pi Z}\right)^{2/3}\right] \\ &\approx 0.70 \frac{Z^2}{A^{1/3}} [1 - 0.76 Z^{-2/3}] \quad \text{MeV} \end{aligned} \tag{2-19}$$

$$(R_c = 1.25 A^{1/3}\ \text{fm};\ A \gtrsim 40)$$

Since the correlation produced by the antisymmetry of the wave function extends over distances of order $k_F^{-1} \sim r_0$ (see below), the second term in the quantal estimate (2-19) is larger by a factor of order $A^{1/3}$ than the classical correction obtained by replacing Z^2 by $Z(Z-1)$. The radius parameter in Eq. (2-19) has been determined from the observed energy differences between isobaric analog states (see, for example, Anderson *et al.*, 1965; Batty *et al.*, 1966). This value of R_c is significantly larger than the value (2-66) describing the total charge density, as determined from the electron scattering data. Such a difference may be expected from the fact that the isobaric displacement energy represents the Coulomb energy of an extra charge having a radial density distribution corresponding to that of the excess neutrons; these neutrons have somewhat larger average radii than the total proton distribution.

In lighter nuclei ($A \lesssim 20$), the Coulomb energy cannot be described by a simple expression such as Eq. (2-19), partly because the diffuseness in the charge distribution is comparable to the nuclear radius and thus R_c does not vary as $A^{1/3}$, and partly because the exchange term becomes increasingly important and depends on the more specific details of the nuclear configuration. (Discussions of the Coulomb energies in light nuclei have been given by Carlson and Talmi, 1954; Sood and Green, 1957; Harchol *et al.*, 1967.)

Violation of isospin conservation by Coulomb potential

The primary effect of the Coulomb forces is to add to the nuclear Hamiltonian a term depending only on M_T (and A). This energy splits the components of the T multiplets by large amounts but is diagonal in T (conserves isospin).

The Coulomb interaction, however, also contains T-violating effects. Thus, the Coulomb repulsion between the protons implies that the ratio of proton to neutron density increases slightly as one moves from the nuclear center toward the surface. An estimate of the resulting isospin mixing is given in Fig. 2-6, p. 174. It is seen that, even in heavy nuclei, the average Coulomb field implies admixed components with $T > M_T$ with a probability of only a fraction of a percent in the nuclear ground state.

In the higher-energy part of the spectrum, there occur approximate degeneracies between states of different isospin. In such situations, even a very small isospin-violating coupling can produce large admixtures of near-lying states with different isospin (see, for example, p. 50).

2-1g Nuclear Potential

Average potential for particles at Fermi surface

From the observed binding energies, we can approximately estimate the magnitude of the potential energy of a single nucleon in the nucleus. If we assume that the nucleonic interaction energy can be represented in terms of the potential energies of the individual particles, the energy required to remove a neutron from the nucleus (the neutron separation energy) is

$$S_n(N, Z) \equiv \mathscr{B}(N, Z) - \mathscr{B}(N-1, Z) \approx -(V_n + \varepsilon_F) \tag{2-20}$$

and a similar expression for protons. Since S is of order 10 MeV, and ε_F is ~ 40 MeV (see Eq. (2-9)), the potential V is about -50 MeV. We shall see later that this estimate is compatible with that obtained from nucleonic scattering experiments (Sec. 2-4c). It may be noted that the separation energy represents a relatively small difference between the larger kinetic and potential energies of the nucleon.

Velocity dependence of potential

The above estimate of the potential energy refers to particles at the top of the Fermi distribution. It is to be expected that the effective potential, V, depends somewhat on the momentum of the particle, as a result of the velocity dependence of the nucleonic interaction and of the correlations in the nucleonic motion.

Indeed, it follows from simple arguments that a saturating system like the nucleus, with an independent-particle structure, must be described in terms of a velocity-dependent potential (Weisskopf, 1957). Thus, the nuclear binding energy per particle is

$$\frac{\mathscr{B}}{A} = -(\tfrac{1}{2}\langle V\rangle + \langle \varepsilon_{\text{kin}}\rangle) \tag{2-21}$$

The factor $\frac{1}{2}$ arises from the fact that the interaction is assumed to result from a two-body force and thus should be counted once for each pair. (If there were significant n-body forces, the corresponding factor would be $1/n$.) The mean values of the potential and kinetic energies in Eq. (2-21) refer to averages for the occupied orbits. The velocity dependence of the potential V is obtained by combining Eqs. (2-20) and (2-21) with the relation $S = \mathscr{B}/A$, which applies to an infinite saturating system, where the separation energy S is independent of A. (Comparison of Fig. 2-4 with Figs. 2-15 and 2-16 shows that this relation is approximately true for heavy nuclei along the line of β stability.) Using the Fermi gas value (2-10) for the mean kinetic energy, we then find

$$\langle V\rangle \approx V(\varepsilon_F) - \tfrac{1}{5}\varepsilon_F - \frac{\mathscr{B}}{A} \tag{2-22}$$

where $V(\varepsilon_F)$ is the binding field for the most weakly bound nucleons (which is the potential appearing in Eq. (2-20)). Thus, the average binding potential must be deeper than $V(\varepsilon_F)$. (Remember that V is a negative quantity.)

Effective mass

The state dependence of the average potential is sometimes described approximately in terms of an effective mass. This approximation is obtained by expanding V in powers of ε_{kin} and keeping only the first two terms

$$V = V(\varepsilon_{\text{kin}} = 0) + a\varepsilon_{\text{kin}} \tag{2-23}$$

(which is probably a very crude approximation for $\varepsilon_{\text{kin}} \sim \varepsilon_F$). If the relation

(2-23) is combined with the usual kinetic energy term, we obtain a Hamiltonian describing motion in a constant static potential; the velocity dependence is expressed through a modified kinetic energy term, in which the nucleon mass M is replaced by the effective mass M^* given by

$$\frac{M}{M^*} = 1 + a \tag{2-24}$$

From Eqs. (2-23) and (2-22) we obtain

$$a \approx \frac{1}{2} + \frac{5}{2}\left(\frac{\mathscr{B}}{A}\right)\frac{1}{\varepsilon_F} \tag{2-25}$$

which implies an effective mass, $M^* \sim M/2$. Such an energy dependence of the potential is similar to that observed in the scattering experiments (see Figs. 2-3 and 2-29) and in the analysis of bound states (see Fig. 3-5).

It should be emphasized that the use of an effective mass is simply a device for expressing the state dependence of the binding field appearing in the effective one-particle Hamiltonian. The consequences of this state dependence for other properties cannot, in general, be obtained by replacing the nucleon mass, M, by M^* in the expressions appropriate to a static binding field. (See, for example, the comments on the magnetic moments on p. 394 and on the moment of inertia in Sec. 9-2.)

Symmetry potential

In heavy nuclei, the neutron excess implies that the neutrons and protons are subject to somewhat different average nuclear potentials. The effect is related to the symmetry energy, and we can write

$$V = V_0 + \tfrac{1}{2}t_z \frac{N-Z}{A} V_1 \qquad \left(t_z = \begin{matrix} \tfrac{1}{2} & \text{neutron} \\ -\tfrac{1}{2} & \text{proton} \end{matrix}\right) \tag{2-26}$$

for the nuclear potentials acting on the protons and neutrons. In the independent-particle approximation, the total potential energy is obtained as one-half the sum of the one-particle potential energies (for two-body forces) and thus

$$(\mathscr{E}_{\text{sym}})_{\text{pot}} \approx \frac{1}{8}\frac{(N-Z)^2}{A} V_1 \tag{2-27}$$

Combining Eq. (2-27) with Eqs. (2-13) and (2-14), we obtain the estimate

$$V_1 \approx 4(b_{\text{sym}})_{\text{pot}} = 4[b_{\text{sym}} - (b_{\text{sym}})_{\text{kin}}] \approx 100 \text{ MeV} \tag{2-28}$$

Thus, for a heavy nucleus ($A \sim 200; Z \sim 80$), the symmetry term in the potential (2-26) amounts to about 5 MeV. In the case of protons, the total potential is obtained by adding to Eq. (2-26) the Coulomb potential which, for a heavy nucleus ($A \sim 200$), is about 20 MeV at the nuclear center, decreasing to about 13 MeV at the nuclear surface.

Charge exchange potential

The isobaric invariance of the forces responsible for the symmetry term in the nuclear potential implies a corresponding neutron-proton exchange potential (Lane, 1962). The expression (2-26) involves the product of the z components of the isospins of the nucleon and the nucleus, and the generalized potential that is invariant to rotations in isospace has the form

$$V = V_0 + \frac{V_1}{A} \mathbf{t} \cdot \mathbf{T}_{A-1} \tag{2-29}$$

where $\mathbf{t}$ is the nucleon isospin and $\mathbf{T}_{A-1}$ that of the rest of the nucleus.

The exchange terms in Eq. (2-29) (the terms involving $t_{\pm} = t_x \pm it_y$) have no effect for the low configurations of a nucleus, which are fully aligned in isospace, but in higher configurations these terms are of significance in ensuring the constancy of the total nuclear isospin. (See, for example, Fig. 3-1 and Eq. (3-19).)

The exchange potential can be studied directly by means of the charge exchange scattering of nucleons ((*pn*) reactions on nuclei with neutron excess). The quantitative information on the symmetry potential obtained from the analysis of scattering experiments is discussed in Section 2-4c.

2-1h Antisymmetrized Fermi Gas Wave Functions

A proper quantal description of a Fermi gas introduces certain refinements of the semiclassical treatment. The antisymmetrized wave function for a system of independent nucleons is a Slater determinant, constructed from the wave functions of the individual particles (Slater, 1929). The calculation of matrix elements for such determinantal wave functions can be carried out especially simply by exploiting a formalism based on operators that create or destroy a nucleon moving in a single-particle orbit. The main features of this formalism are described in Appendix 2A.

The structure of the antisymmetrized state $|\nu_1 \nu_2 \cdots \nu_A\rangle_a$ constructed from the one-particle states (2-3) may be exhibited in terms of the different density functions. The one-particle spatial density operator is

$$\rho(\mathbf{r}) = \sum_{k=1}^{A} \delta(\mathbf{r} - \mathbf{r}_k) \tag{2-30}$$

The expectation value of this density operator in the ground state of the Fermi gas may be obtained by a direct evaluation in the Slater determinant constructed from the states (2-3). One finds, as a general result applying to any one-particle operator, that the expectation value is equal to the sum of the expectation values for the individual occupied particle orbits and is thus not affected by the antisymmetrization (see Eq. (2A-26)). We therefore have

$$\langle \nu_1 \, \nu_2 \cdots \nu_A | \rho(\mathbf{r}) | \, \nu_1 \, \nu_2 \cdots \nu_A \rangle_a$$
$$= \sum_{i=1}^{A} |\varphi_{\nu_i}(\mathbf{r})|^2 = \frac{A}{\Omega} = \rho_0 \tag{2-31}$$

where the average density can be expressed by means of Eq. (2-7),

$$\rho_0 = 4 \frac{k_F^3}{6\pi^2} \tag{2-32}$$

Since the plane wave states (2-3) ignore surface effects, we obtain a constant density equal to the value (2-32).

The effect of antisymmetrization appears when we consider the two-particle density functions, such as

$$\rho(\mathbf{r}, \mathbf{r}') = \sum_{j<k} [\delta(\mathbf{r} - \mathbf{r}_j)\delta(\mathbf{r}' - \mathbf{r}_k) + \delta(\mathbf{r} - \mathbf{r}_k)\delta(\mathbf{r}' - \mathbf{r}_j)] \tag{2-33}$$

whose expectation value gives the probability of finding one particle at $\mathbf{r}$ and another at $\mathbf{r}'$. Again, we may evaluate the operator (2-33) directly in the Slater determinant, or may employ the general relations obtained in Appendix 2A. According to Eq. (2A-32), the expectation value of $\rho(\mathbf{r}, \mathbf{r}')$ is given by

$$\langle \nu_1 \, \nu_2 \cdots \nu_A | \rho(\mathbf{r}, \mathbf{r}') | \, \nu_1 \, \nu_2 \cdots \nu_A \rangle_a$$
$$= \sum_{\nu_i < \nu_k \leq \nu_F} \langle \nu_i \, \nu_k | \rho(\mathbf{r}, \mathbf{r}') | \, \nu_i \, \nu_k \rangle_a \tag{2-34}$$

On inserting the one-particle wave functions (2-3), we obtain for the antisymmetrized two-particle matrix elements in Eq. (2-34)

$$\langle \nu_1 \nu_2 | \rho(\mathbf{r}, \mathbf{r}') | \, \nu_1 \nu_2 \rangle_a$$
$$= \langle \nu_1 \nu_2 | \rho(\mathbf{r}, \mathbf{r}') | \, \nu_1 \nu_2 \rangle - \langle \nu_2 \nu_1 | \rho(\mathbf{r}, \mathbf{r}') | \, \nu_1 \nu_2 \rangle$$
$$= \frac{1}{\Omega^2} \{1 - \delta(m_s(1), m_s(2))\delta(m_t(1), m_t(2)) \cos[(\mathbf{k}_1 - \mathbf{k}_2) \cdot (\mathbf{r} - \mathbf{r}')]\} \tag{2-35}$$

Replacing the sums in Eq. (2-34) by integrals, and using Eqs. (2-6) and (2-32), we obtain

$$\langle \rho(\mathbf{r}, \mathbf{r}') \rangle_{\text{gr.st.}} = \rho_0^2[1 - \tfrac{1}{4}C^2(k_F |\mathbf{r} - \mathbf{r}'|)] \tag{2-36}$$

where

$$C(x) = \frac{3}{x^2}\left(\frac{\sin x}{x} - \cos x\right) \tag{2-37}$$

The second term in Eq. (2-36) describes the correlation of the nucleons resulting from the antisymmetrization; the factor 1/4 results from the fact that the spatial correlation occurs only for nucleons with the same spin and isospin orientation (see Eq. (2-35)) and such pairs represent one fourth of the total (for simplicity, we assume $N=Z=A/2$). This correlation implies that, in the neighborhood of each nucleon, there is one less nucleon than would have been expected for a homogeneous uncorrelated system,

$$\frac{1}{\rho_0}\int d^3r'(\langle\rho(\mathbf{r},\mathbf{r}')\rangle_{\text{gr.st.}} - \rho_0^2)$$
$$= -\frac{1}{4}\rho_0\int C^2(k_F r)\,d^3r = -1 \tag{2-38}$$

This correlation effect is sometimes referred to as the "exchange hole." The function $1 - C^2(k_F r)$ is plotted in Fig. 2-7, p. 177.

We may also be interested in two-particle density functions characterizing pairs that are specified by additional quantum numbers beside the positions $\mathbf{r}$ and $\mathbf{r}'$. For example, the operator describing the density of pairs having spatially symmetric wave functions is

$$\rho(\mathbf{r},\mathbf{r}',\pi=+1)$$
$$= \sum_{j<k}[\delta(\mathbf{r}-\mathbf{r}_j)\,\delta(\mathbf{r}'-\mathbf{r}_k) + \delta(\mathbf{r}-\mathbf{r}_k)\delta(\mathbf{r}'-\mathbf{r}_j)]\tfrac{1}{2}[1+P^r_{jk}] \tag{2-39}$$

The matrix elements of this operator may be evaluated in exact analogy to the derivation of Eqs. (2-34) and (2-35),

$$\langle\nu_1\nu_2|\rho(\mathbf{r},\mathbf{r}',\pi=+1)|\nu_1\nu_2\rangle_a$$
$$= \frac{1}{\Omega^2}\frac{1}{2}[1-\delta(m_s(1),m_s(2))\delta(m_t(1),m_t(2))][1+\cos(\mathbf{k}_1-\mathbf{k}_2)\cdot(\mathbf{r}-\mathbf{r}')] \tag{2-40}$$

Summing over the occupied orbits in the ground state of the Fermi gas, we obtain

$$\langle\rho(\mathbf{r},\mathbf{r}',\pi=+1)\rangle_{\text{gr.st.}} = \tfrac{3}{8}\rho_0^2[1+C^2(k_F|\mathbf{r}-\mathbf{r}'|)] \tag{2-41}$$

In a similar manner, we may evaluate the two-body density function for nucleons with spatially antisymmetric wave functions,

$$\langle\rho(\mathbf{r},\mathbf{r}',\pi=-1)\rangle_{\text{gr.st.}} = \tfrac{5}{8}\rho_0^2[1-C^2(k_F|\mathbf{r}-\mathbf{r}'|)] \tag{2-42}$$

We could also have characterized the pairs by their total spin, S, and isospin, T. The $\pi=-1$ pairs contain ($S=0, T=0$) and ($S=1, T=1$) states with probabilities (proportional to $(2S+1)(2T+1)$) in the ratio 1 to 9, while the $\pi=+1$ pairs contain the states ($S=1, T=0$) and ($S=0, T=1$) with equal probability. Thus, the coefficients 3/8 and 5/8 in Eqs. (2-41) and (2-42) represent the relative statistical weights of the spatially symmetric and antisymmetric two-particle states.

The pair correlation function can, in principle, be determined from various scattering and reaction processes, but there is at present little direct evidence on this point. The correlations associated with the antisymmetrization play an important role in the evaluation of matrix elements for two-particle operators, such as the nucleonic interactions (the exchange contributions).

As an example, we consider the effect of the exchange hole on the estimate of the total Coulomb energy. For this purpose, we need the two-particle density function for the protons,

$$\rho_{pp}(\mathbf{r}_1, \mathbf{r}_2) = \rho_p(\mathbf{r}_1)\rho_p(\mathbf{r}_2)[1 - \tfrac{1}{2}C^2(k_F^{(p)} r_{12})] \tag{2-43}$$

The correlation occurs for protons with the same spin orientation, and since these represent one half of all proton pairs, the coefficient of the function C^2 is 1/2. The Coulomb energy is

$$\mathscr{E}_{\text{Coul}} = \tfrac{1}{2}e^2 \iint \frac{\rho_{pp}(\mathbf{r}_1, \mathbf{r}_2)}{|\mathbf{r}_1 - \mathbf{r}_2|}\, d^3r_1\, d^3r_2 \tag{2-44}$$

and thus the first term in the density (2-43) yields just the classical expression (2-3). The second term in Eq. (2-43) gives the exchange contribution which may be easily evaluated for a system with constant density (Bethe and Bacher, 1936)

$$\begin{aligned}(\mathscr{E}_{\text{Coul}})_{\text{exch}} &\approx -\frac{3}{16\pi}\frac{Z^2e^2}{R^3}\int \frac{1}{r}\, C^2(k_F^{(p)} r)\, d^3r \\ &= -\frac{27}{16}\frac{Z^2e^2}{(k_F^{(p)})^2 R^3}\end{aligned} \tag{2-45}$$

Using the value of k_F given by Eq (2-7), we obtain the Coulomb energy corrected for exchange, as given in Eq. (2-19).

2-1i Statistical Features of Excitation Spectrum

The bulk properties of nuclei, discussed above, serve to define certain important qualitative features, but the main source of evidence on nuclear structure is provided by the rich body of information relating to the nuclear spectra and the properties of individual levels. As we shall discuss in the following chapters, the low-energy spectra are dominated by correlation effects that give rise to pair correlations and collective modes of rotational and vibrational type, superimposed on the single-particle motion. However, the number of collective modes is small compared with the total number of degrees of freedom of the particles. Thus, at sufficiently high excitation energies, it is expected that the particle degrees of freedom will dominate and that the Fermi gas model may provide useful guidance in the discussion of average properties of the spectrum.

Level density of Fermi gas

The calculation of the density of states for the Fermi gas amounts to counting the number of different ways in which the excitation energy

$$E = \mathscr{E} - \mathscr{E}_{\text{ground state}} \tag{2-46}$$

can be distributed among the single-particle states (2-3). This is a well-defined combinatorial problem, which is the same as that encountered in the characterization of the equilibrium state of a large system by means of statistical mechanics. The mathematical tools employed in the solution of this problem are summarized in Appendix 2B. As compared with the usual macroscopic systems described by statistical mechanics, there are relatively few particles in a nucleus, and this implies that, in evaluating the thermodynamic functions, it is necessary to be somewhat more careful in treating certain terms that are often neglected in statistical mechanics.

The result of the calculation of the total level density for the Fermi gas is (see Eq. (2B-42))

$$\rho(N, Z, E) = \frac{6^{1/4}}{12} \frac{g_0}{(g_0 E)^{5/4}} \exp\left\{2\left(\frac{\pi^2}{6} g_0 E\right)^{1/2}\right\} \qquad N \approx Z \tag{2-47}$$

where E is the excitation energy and g_0 is the one-particle level density at the Fermi energy, representing the sum of the proton and neutron level densities,

$$g_0 \equiv g(\varepsilon_F) \approx \frac{3}{2} \frac{A}{\varepsilon_F} \tag{2-48}$$

In Eq. (2-47), we have assumed that $Z = N = A/2$; the corrections for neutron excess can be evaluated by the same methods, but are found to be negligibly small.

In obtaining the expression (2-47), it is necessary to assume

$$E \ll \varepsilon_F A^{1/3} \tag{2-49}$$

This limit results from the fact that the one-particle level spacing (2-48) is a function of the one-particle energy ($g(\varepsilon) \propto \varepsilon^{1/2}$). This variation can be accounted for by employing the methods described in Appendix 2B, but the level density then becomes a more complicated function of the excitation energy (non-degenerate Fermi gas). In addition, the derivation of Eq. (2-47) assumes $E \gg \varepsilon_F A^{-1}$, which is simply the condition that the excitation energy be great compared to the energy of the first excited state. (There must be many excited levels in order that the level density be defined.) However, the Fermi gas model is inappropriate for a much larger region of the low-energy spectra due to the neglect of various systematic correlation effects associated with collective modes of excitation.

The most striking feature of the level density expression (2-47) is the very rapid increase in the number of levels with increasing excitation energy. This is a reflection of the increasing number of degrees of freedom, which can be excited at higher energies. In discussing this increase, it is often useful to employ the concept of the nuclear temperature,[1] T, which is the inverse of the logarithmic derivative of ρ; for the Fermi gas, we have

$$T^{-1} = \frac{1}{\rho}\frac{\partial \rho}{\partial E} = -\frac{5}{4}E^{-1} + \left(\frac{\pi^2}{6}\frac{g_0}{E}\right)^{1/2} \tag{2-50}$$

The condition $g_0 E \gg 1$, mentioned above, implies that the second term in Eq. (2-50) will be larger than the first, but the first term may still be a significant correction in many cases of interest.

The significance of the temperature may be seen in a somewhat different light if we ask for the average occupation number $f(\nu)$ of a given one-particle state of the Fermi gas, as a function of the excitation energy E; we find (see Sec. 2B-3)

$$f(\nu) \approx \frac{1}{1 + \exp\left(\dfrac{\varepsilon(\nu) - \varepsilon_F}{T}\right)} \tag{2-51}$$

Thus, the temperature determines the region around the Fermi energy in which the average occupation number is significantly different from that in the ground state of the system. The average number of particles excited with respect to the ground state is

$$\begin{aligned} n_{ex} &= \sum_{\nu<\nu_F} \left(1 - f(\nu)\right) + \sum_{\nu>\nu_F} f(\nu) \\ &= g_0 T \ln 4 \approx \left(\frac{6}{\pi^2} g_0 E\right)^{1/2} \ln 4 \end{aligned} \tag{2-52}$$

One can also recognize, in the relation (2-51), the origin of the main features of the level density given in Eq. (2-47). Thus, the single particles that occupy excited orbits with respect to the ground state of the Fermi gas are mainly

[1] Thermodynamic concepts were introduced into the discussion of the nuclear excitation spectra by Frenkel (1936), Bohr and Kalckar (1937), Weisskopf (1937), Landau (1937), and Bethe (1937).

confined to an energy region of width $\sim T$ around ε_F, which implies an average energy per excited nucleon

$$\frac{E}{n_{\text{ex}}} \sim T \tag{2-53}$$

The number of orbits in the interval $\sim T$ determines the number of excited nucleons

$$n_{\text{ex}} \sim T g_0 \tag{2-54}$$

in agreement with Eq. (2-52). The estimates (2-53) and (2-54) give

$$E \sim g_0 T^2 \tag{2-55}$$

corresponding to the leading term in Eq. (2-50). The total number of levels is of the order of the number of ways in which the n_{ex} particles can be distributed over a number of levels of order $2n_{\text{ex}}$, and thus the main term in the level density is

$$\rho \sim \frac{(2n_{\text{ex}})!}{[(n_{\text{ex}})!]^2} \sim \exp\{n_{\text{ex}}\} \sim \exp\left(\frac{E}{T}\right) \sim \exp(aE)^{1/2} \tag{2-56}$$

where a is a parameter of order g_0.

One may also be interested in the density of states characterized by a definite value of the total angular momentum, I, and parity π; the calculation for the Fermi gas with $N = Z = A/2$ is carried out in Sec. 2B-6 and yields (see Eq. (2B-62))

$$\rho(A, E, I\pi) = \frac{2I+1}{24}\left(\frac{\pi^2}{6} g_0\right)^{1/2}\left(\frac{\hbar^2}{2\mathscr{I}_{\text{rig}}}\right)^{3/2}\left[E - \frac{\hbar^2}{2\mathscr{I}_{\text{rig}}} I(I+1)\right]^{-2}$$
$$\times \exp\left\{2\left[\frac{\pi^2}{6} g_0\left(E - \frac{\hbar^2}{2\mathscr{I}_{\text{rig}}} I(I+1)\right)\right]^{1/2}\right\} \tag{2-57}$$

where the coefficient of the I-dependent term depends on the moment of inertia for rigid rotation,

$$\mathscr{I}_{\text{rig}} = \tfrac{2}{3}\int \rho(\mathbf{r}) r^2 \, d^3r \tag{2-58}$$

The approximations made in obtaining the expression (2-57) imply a range of validity similar to that of Eq. (2-47).

The enumeration of the levels on the basis of the Fermi gas ascribes to each level a definite configuration specified by the orbits of the individual particles. In any experiment aimed at measuring the total nuclear level density, it is crucial to know whether the actual levels represent pure configurations or involve configuration mixing that will remove the selection rules associated with single configurations. We shall, therefore, in the following section, consider the evidence relating to configuration mixing in highly excited states.

Configuration mixing and the compound nucleus

The first evidence on nuclear level densities at high excitation energies came from the discovery of densely spaced, sharp resonances in the slow neutron capture reaction. (The development leading to this discovery has been reviewed by Bethe, 1937, pp. 113ff.) The density of these levels is of the order 10^6 times greater than that corresponding to single-particle motion (in a nucleus with $A \sim 100$); see, for example, the levels of ^{233}Th shown in Fig. 2-8, p. 178. This evidence implies that the neutron, on entering the nucleus, can share its energy with a large number of degrees of freedom of the target, and thus establish a highly complex state of motion, the compound nucleus (Bohr, 1936). In terms of the Fermi gas model, the compound nucleus corresponds to very extensive configuration mixing in the stationary states and resonances. Such configuration mixing implies that the component representing one-particle motion with respect to the target is distributed over the wave functions of a large number of different resonance states. All these resonances may therefore be excited in neutron scattering, and at the same time the neutron width of each resonance will be small, when measured in single-particle units. (The analysis of resonance scattering and the estimate of single-particle units for resonance widths are discussed in Appendix 3F.)

The occurrence of configuration mixing leading to the compound nucleus can be understood in terms of the increasing importance of small perturbations in the independent-particle motion, with increasing excitation energy of the system. Partly, the number of excited particles, and thus the number of possible interactions, increases; partly, there is an increase in the excitation energy per particle and therefore of the density of final states available in a collision between two particles. Thus, at sufficiently high excitation energy, each configuration will be strongly coupled to some similar configuration. In turn, this second configuration is strongly coupled to a third, and in this manner the properties of any given configuration become distributed over the quantum states lying within some characteristic energy region.

A more detailed picture of the compound nucleus may be obtained from a statistical analysis of level spacings and widths. As a limiting case, one may consider the spectrum resulting from the diagonalization of large matrices with random elements. This model represents the extreme case of complete mixing between all the available degrees of freedom within an appropriate energy interval. Some of the properties of such systems are considered in Appendix 2C.

Such a more detailed model makes possible a discussion of the probability distributions and correlations between the various properties of the nuclear levels. For example, the distribution $P(s)$, for spacings s between adjacent levels of the same $I\pi$, is given to a good approximation by the Wigner distribution

$$P(s) = \frac{\pi s}{2D^2} \exp\left(- \frac{\pi s^2}{4D^2} \right) \tag{2-59}$$

where D is the average level spacing.

The distribution (2-59) may be contrasted with the Poisson distribution

$$P(s) = \frac{1}{D} \exp\left(- \frac{s}{D} \right) \tag{2-60}$$

which follows from the assumption that the eigenvalues E_i are randomly distributed, as would be approximately true, for example, in the Fermi gas model with no configuration mixing. The greatly reduced fluctuations in the spacings implied by the distribution (2-59) as compared with the Poisson distribution (2-60) reflect the fact that the configuration mixing effects included in the random matrices imply a tendency for neighboring levels to repel each other.

As discussed in connection with Fig. 2-9, p. 180, the spacing distributions of the resonance levels observed in the slow neutron capture reaction are consistent with the expression (2-59) obtained from the model of random matrices and disagree with the distribution (2-60). A similar analysis of the distribution of neutron widths of these resonance levels lends further support to the assumption of extreme configuration mixing, as embodied in the model of random matrices (see Fig. 2-10, p. 182).

Thus, the present evidence is compatible with the picture of complete mixing between all configurations that are sufficiently close in energy; this mixing implies that, in the slow neutron resonance studies, it is possible to observe all the levels permitted by angular momentum and parity selection rules. (These selection rules are discussed in connection with Fig. 2-8). One therefore obtains a measure of the total density of levels $\rho(E, I\pi)$ at the excitation energy, E, corresponding to the neutron separation energy.

Evidence on the nuclear level density over a much wider range of energies can be obtained by exploiting the compound nucleus concept to interpret the yields of nuclear reaction processes (evaporation spectra). The example shown in Fig. 2-11, p. 183, exhibits the striking exponential increase in level density that has been found in all such measurements. The Fermi gas level densities (2-47) and (2-57) contain this important qualitative feature, and the coefficient in the exponent is of the same order of magnitude as the estimate (2-48); see Figs. 2-11 and 2-12. However, as illustrated in Fig. 2-12, this coefficient is found to exhibit marked variations as a function of the nucleon number A. This variation can be associated with the shell structure, which implies a departure from a uniform single-particle spectrum with a resulting modification in the form of the level density expression (see Sec. 2B-2). At the present time, the detailed variation of the nuclear level densities as a function of energy and angular momentum is not well understood; thus, it is sometimes found that the Fermi gas expression (2-57) gives a very good description of the available data (see, for example, Fig. 2-12), while in other nuclei the temperature varies more slowly ($T \approx$ const) or the effective moment of inertia is considerably smaller than $\mathscr{I}_{\text{rig}}$.

It should be emphasized that the available evidence on nuclear level densities is still of a rather qualitative nature and thus leaves open many important questions concerning correlation effects in the high-energy nuclear spectra. Because of the many possible ways in which such correlations might occur and manifest themselves in the properties of the nuclear levels, the subject is one of great potential scope.

▼

ILLUSTRATIVE EXAMPLES TO SECTION 2-1

Determination of nuclear charge distribution from electron scattering (Fig. 2-1)

The primary source of information on the nuclear charge distribution has been the study of electron scattering on nuclei. Low-energy electrons are mainly scattered by the Coulomb field outside the nucleus and the cross section is approximately described by the scattering from a point charge (Mott scattering). For higher energies, the electron wavelength

$$\lambda\!\!\!^{-}_e = \frac{\hbar c}{E_e} \approx \frac{200}{E_e(\text{MeV})} \quad \text{fm} \tag{2-61}$$

becomes comparable with or smaller than the nuclear dimensions, and the scattering is sensitive to the spatial distribution of charge within the nucleus.

Figure 2-1 shows the differential cross section observed for electrons of 153 MeV scattered from a gold target. It is seen that, for the angles studied, the intensity of the scattering is at least an order of magnitude weaker than for a point charge of $Z = 79$. The angular distribution exhibits mild oscillations characteristic of scattering by a system with a rather well-defined radius. A simple estimate of the radius can be obtained by observing that in such diffraction

▲ patterns the successive maxima or minima are separated by angles corresponding

▼ to $\Delta(qR) \approx \pi$, where $\hbar q$ is the momentum transfer associated with the given scattering angle ($q \approx 2\lambda\!\!\!^{-}{}^{-1} \sin(\theta/2)$). From the existence of minima at $\theta \approx 45°$
▲ and $\theta \approx 85°$, we obtain $R \approx 7$ fm.

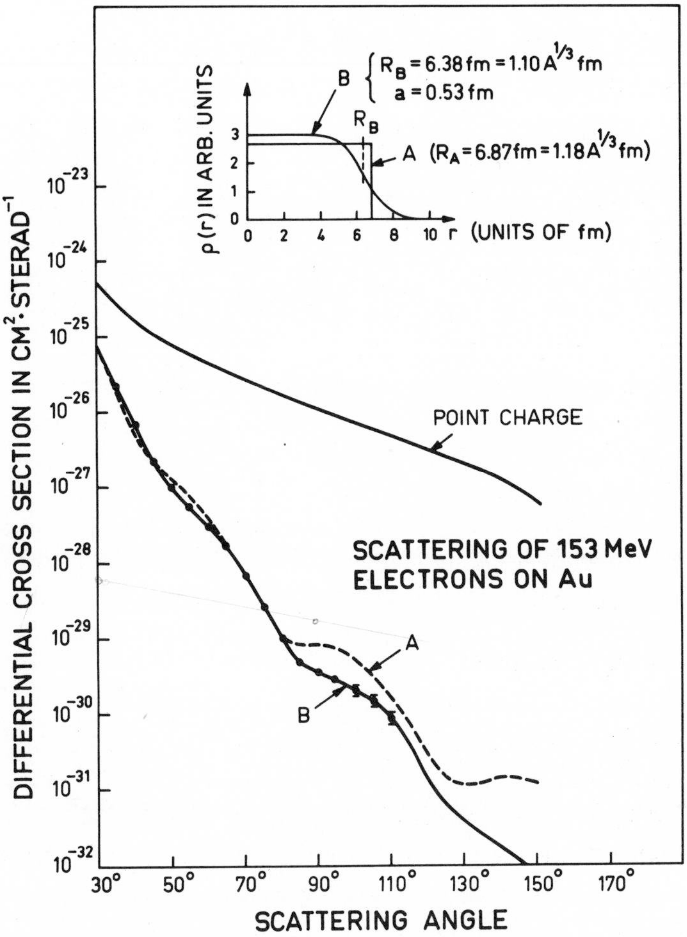

Figure 2-1 The experimental data and the theoretical analysis are taken from B. Hahn, D. G. Ravenhall, and R. Hofstadter, *Phys. Rev.* **101**, 1131 (1956); D. R. Yennie, D. G. Ravenhall, and R. N. Wilson, *Phys. Rev.* **95**, 500 (1954); R. Herman and R. Hofstadter, *High Energy Electron Scattering Tables*, Stanford Univ. Press, Stanford, California, 1960. We wish to thank G. Jacob for help in the preparation of the figure.

▼ A more detailed interpretation of the scattering may be obtained by assuming a charge distribution, calculating the resulting potential, and then solving the Dirac equation for scattering in such a potential. (A collection of articles describing the experiments and their analysis is contained in Hofstadter,
▲ 1963.) The solutions are usually obtained with the help of electronic computers,

▼ since more than 100 partial waves may be significantly involved. Figure 2-1 shows the best fits to the experimental points that can be obtained if one assumes (*A*) a uniform charge distribution or (*B*) a distribution of the form

$$\rho = \rho_0\left[1+\exp\left(\frac{r-R}{a}\right)\right]^{-1} \tag{2-62}$$

These two distributions and the parameters obtained are shown in the insert to the figure. It is seen that the experiments provide definite evidence for a finite surface thickness. A satisfactory fit can also be obtained from distributions differing somewhat from (B), as, for example, a distribution with a slight increase or decrease in density at the center of the nucleus. These scattering data, thus, primarily determine two parameters, the mean radius and the surface thickness. The thickness of the surface region is often expressed in terms of the interval, t, in which the density falls from 90% to 10% of the central value ρ_0. For the distribution (2-62), we have

$$t = (4\ \ln 3)a \approx 4.40a \tag{2-63}$$

It may become possible to determine finer details in the charge distribution by employing electrons of still higher energy.

The distribution (2-62) is used extensively in the discussion of nuclear charge distributions and, for convenience, we give some of the moments of this distribution, which are encountered in the analysis of various nuclear properties. The central density ρ_0 is determined by the normalization integral

$$\int \rho\, d\tau = \rho_0 \frac{4\pi}{3} R^3\left(1+\pi^2\left(\frac{a}{R}\right)^2\right) \tag{2-64}$$

In this expression, we have neglected terms of relative order $\exp\{-R/a\}$. The radial moments of ρ are conveniently expressed as an expansion in a/R,

$$\langle r^n \rangle = \frac{\int \rho(r) r^n\, d\tau}{\int \rho(r)\, d\tau} \approx \frac{3}{n+3} R^n\left[1+\frac{n(n+5)}{6}\pi^2\left(\frac{a}{R}\right)^2+\cdots\right] \tag{2-65}$$

where the neglected terms in the expansion are of order $(a/R)^4$. The Coulomb self-energy of the charge distribution ρ can be expressed in terms of the effective Coulomb radius, R_c,

$$\frac{1}{R_c} \equiv \frac{5}{6}\frac{\int \frac{\rho(\mathbf{r}_1)\rho(\mathbf{r}_2)}{|\mathbf{r}_1-\mathbf{r}_2|} d\tau_1\, d\tau_2}{\left(\int \rho(r)\, d\tau\right)^2} = \frac{1}{R}\left[1-\frac{7}{6}\pi^2\left(\frac{a}{R}\right)^2+\cdots\right] \tag{2-66}$$

The derivation of these expressions involves the evaluation of the same integrals as encountered in Eq. (2B-10) (see, for example, Elton, 1961). Since the expansions in powers of $(a/R)^2$ are rapidly convergent (except for the lightest nuclei), one ▲

▼ may, for many purposes, employ the expansion of the density (2-62) in the form

$$\rho(r) = \rho_0 \left[S(r - R) - \frac{\pi^2}{6} a^2 \delta'(r - R) + \cdots \right] \tag{2-67}$$

where S is the step function

$$\begin{aligned} S(x) &= 1 \qquad x < 0 \\ &= 0 \qquad x > 0 \end{aligned} \tag{2-68}$$

and δ' is the derivative of the δ function. The coefficient of the δ' function may be found, for example, from Eq. (2-64), and one may then immediately derive the moments (2-65) and (2-66).

As discussed on p. 138, the experimental scattering data and the measurements on μ-mesic atoms are consistent with the parameters

$$\begin{aligned} \rho_0 &= 0.17 \quad \text{nucleon fm}^{-3} \\ a &= 0.54 \quad \text{fm} \end{aligned} \tag{2-69}$$

for all nuclei with $A > 16$. From Eqs. (2-69) and (2-64) we obtain

$$R \approx (1.12A^{1/3} - 0.86A^{-1/3} + \cdots) \ \text{fm} \tag{2-70}$$

for the radius parameter appearing in the distribution (2-62). From Eqs. (2-69) and (2-65) we thus obtain

$$\begin{aligned} \langle r^2 \rangle &= \frac{3}{5}(1.12A^{1/3})^2(1 + 3.84A^{-2/3} + \cdots) \ (\text{fm})^2 \\ &\approx \frac{3}{5}(1.2A^{1/3})^2 \ (\text{fm})^2 \end{aligned} \tag{2-71}$$

and similarly, from Eq. (2-66),

$$R_c \approx 1.2A^{1/3} \ \text{fm} \tag{2-72}$$

for a medium heavy nucleus ($A \approx 100$).

Evidence on nuclear charge distribution obtained from isotope shift in atomic spectra (Fig. 2-2)

A very sensitive measure of the changes in the nuclear charge distribution resulting from the addition of neutrons to the nucleus is provided by the measurements of the isotope shifts in the atomic spectra. Since the electron wave function is approximately constant over the nuclear volume, the effect of the finite nuclear size is mainly determined by the mean square radius $\langle r^2 \rangle$ of the nuclear charge distribution, that is,

$$\Delta E = E - E_{\text{point nucleus}} \approx \frac{2\pi}{3} Ze^2 \langle r^2 \rangle \rho_e(0) \tag{2-73}$$

where $\rho_e(0)$ is the electron density in the region of the nucleus. The expression (2-73) is readily obtained by comparing the binding energy for a charge located at the nuclear center with that of a charge distributed on a spherical surface with ▲ radius r. The electron density $\rho_e(0)$ may be calculated from a knowledge of the

▼ Coulomb field in which the electron moves; in heavy atoms one must include the enhancement of $\rho_e(0)$ by relativistic effects (Breit, 1958; Kopfermann, 1958).

The evidence discussed in connection with Fig. 2-1 suggests that, on the average, the nuclear charge distribution varies with atomic number as

$$\langle r^2 \rangle \approx \frac{3}{5}(r_0 A^{1/3})^2 \tag{2-74}$$

with

$$r_0 \approx 1.2 \quad \text{fm} \tag{2-75}$$

The variation in the charge distribution described by Eqs. (2-74) and (2-75) is appropriate to the overall trend among the stable nuclear species, that is, to variations in A by which roughly equal numbers of neutrons and protons are added to the nucleus. The isotope shift involves the variation of the charge distribution when only neutrons are added to the system and is thus a quite new property. The observed shifts are conveniently expressed in terms of a standard unit obtained by assuming the variation (2-74)

$$(\delta\langle r^2 \rangle)_{\text{std}} \equiv \frac{2}{3}\frac{\delta A}{A}\langle r^2 \rangle \tag{2-76}$$

▲ In Fig. 2-2, the observed isotope shifts of the even-even nuclei are

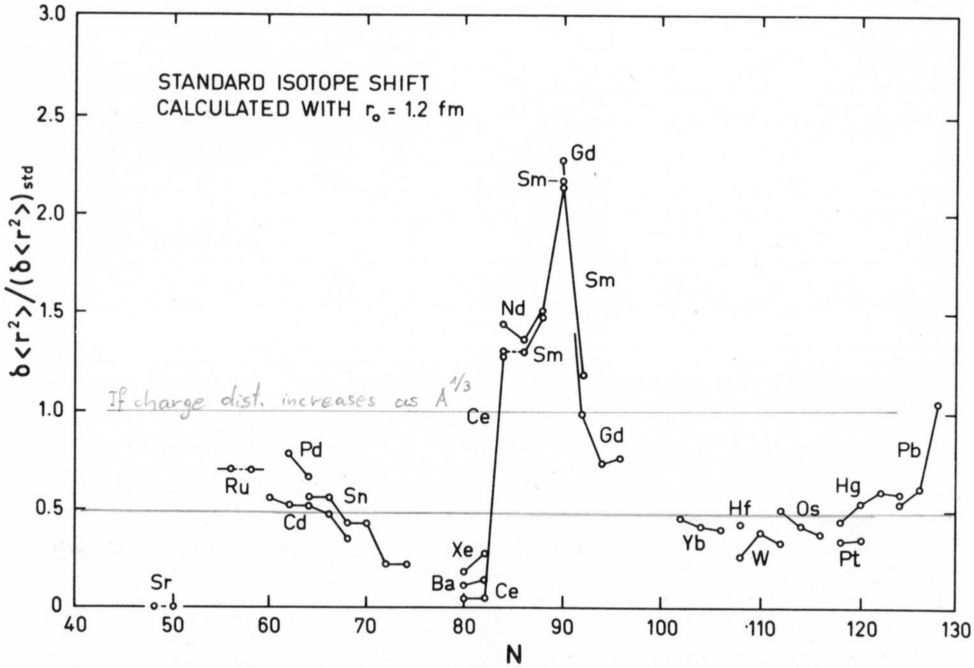

Figure 2-2 The figure is based on the review by P. Brix and H. Kopfermann, *Rev. Mod. Phys.* **30**, 517 (1958). The isotope shifts refer to even-even nuclei with neutron numbers $N-2$ and N. (See the comments on p. 165 concerning corrections for nuclear recoil.)

▼ given in terms of the standard unit. In most cases, the shifts are of the order of one-half the standard unit, but striking variations are also observed.

The fact that the radius of the charge distribution increases less rapidly than $A^{1/3}$, when neutrons are added, can be understood in terms of the dependence of the proton potential on the neutron excess (Perey and Schiffer, 1966; Swift and Elton, 1966; Uher and Sorensen, 1966). Thus, the addition of neutrons to the system implies that the proton potential is increased (see the symmetry potential given by Eq. (2-26)), and, with increasing binding, the protons are compressed in the nucleus. As a rough estimate, we have, for the change, δR_p, in the proton radius associated with an increase, δV_p, in the depth of the proton potential,

$$\delta R_p \approx \frac{\delta V_p}{(dV/dr)_R} \qquad (2\text{-}77) \quad \checkmark$$

where the radial derivative of the one-particle potential is taken at the nuclear surface. Taking

$$\frac{dV}{dr} \approx -\frac{V_0}{t} \qquad (2\text{-}78) \quad \checkmark$$

where t is the surface thickness (the estimates (2-63) and (2-69) yield $t \approx 2.5$ fm), and

$$\delta V_p \approx -\frac{1}{4}\frac{\delta N}{A}V_1 \qquad (2\text{-}79)$$

where V_1 is the isovector part of the one-particle potential (for an estimate, see Eq. (2-28)), we have

$V_1 \approx 100$ MeV
$V_0 \approx 50$ MeV

$$\delta R_p \approx \frac{1}{4}\frac{\delta N}{A}\frac{V_1}{V_0}t \approx -\frac{\delta N}{A} \quad \text{fm} \qquad (2\text{-}80)$$

This compression of the protons is about one half as great as the standard expansion (see Eq. (2-76))

$$R \approx r_0 A^{1/3} \quad \Longrightarrow$$

$$\delta R_{\text{std}} \approx \frac{1}{3}\frac{\delta A}{A}R \qquad (2\text{-}81) \quad \checkmark$$

(since $R \approx 6$ fm in a heavy nucleus). The symmetry effect as revealed in the isotope shift implies a tendency for the mean radius of the protons to be somewhat smaller than that of the neutrons in a nucleus with $N > Z$. The Coulomb force provides an effect in the opposite direction.

The striking maximum in the isotope shift at $N = 90$ can be understood in terms of the effect of deviations of the nuclear shape from spherical symmetry (Brix and Kopfermann, 1949). The effect of the nuclear deformations on the isotope shift may be simply evaluated if we assume (see Sec. 9-1)

(a) the surfaces of constant density enclose a constant volume as the system is

▲ deformed,

▼ (b) the surfaces of constant density all have the same eccentricity,
(c) the deformations are mainly of quadrupole type.

The charge density distribution of a deformed nucleus (in the intrinsic coordinate system) can then be written (to order β^2)

$$\rho(\mathbf{r}) = \rho\left(r\left[1 - \frac{1}{4\pi}\beta^2 + \beta Y_{20}\right]^{-1}\right) \tag{2-82}$$

and the mean square radius of the charge distribution is

$$\int \rho(\mathbf{r}) r^2 \, d\tau = \int \rho(r) r^4 \, dr \int \left[1 - \frac{1}{4\pi}\beta^2 + \beta Y_{20}\right]^5 d\Omega = \left(1 + \frac{5}{4\pi}\beta^2\right)\langle r^2 \rangle_0 \tag{2-83}$$

where $\langle r^2 \rangle_0$ represents the mean square radius of the charge distribution for a spherical nucleus ($\beta = 0$). The above derivation has assumed a deformation of axial symmetry; other components of quadrupole deformation are included by taking β to be the total deformation parameter. Since the change in $\langle r^2 \rangle$ is proportional to β^2, not only the static deformation (as revealed in the quadrupole moments or $E2$ transition probabilities between rotational states), but also the fluctuations in the nuclear shape (as revealed in $E2$ transition rates to vibrational states) contribute to the effective charge radius. For example, ${}^{150}_{62}\mathrm{Sm}_{88}$ appears to be a spherical nucleus with $\langle \beta^2 \rangle = 0.032$ as determined from the $E2$ transition to the first excited 2+ vibrational state (see Fig. 4-1 and Chapter 6), while ${}^{152}_{62}\mathrm{Sm}_{90}$ exhibits the rotational spectrum characteristic of a statically deformed nucleus with $Q_0 = 5.9 \times 10^{-24}$ cm^2, which implies $\beta^2 = 0.094$, since $Q_0 = 3(5\pi)^{-1/2} ZR^2\beta$ for a uniformly charged nucleus (see Chapter 4). The variation in β^2 between ^{150}Sm and ^{152}Sm thus implies a contribution to the isotope shift,

$$\frac{\delta\langle r^2 \rangle}{\delta\langle r^2 \rangle_{\mathrm{std}}} = \frac{15A}{16\pi}\delta\beta^2 \approx 2.8 \tag{2-84}$$

In Nd, Eu, and Gd, the change in β^2 between isotopes with $N = 88$ and $N = 90$ is found to be very similar to that in Sm, and thus accounts for the strikingly large isotope shifts observed in all these nuclei.

The observed isotope shifts exhibit large odd-even staggering (not shown in Fig. 2-2), which we may characterize by the parameter

$$\gamma \equiv \frac{\langle r^2 \rangle_{A+1} - \langle r^2 \rangle_A}{\frac{1}{2}(\langle r^2 \rangle_{A+2} - \langle r^2 \rangle_A)} \tag{2-85}$$

where $\langle r^2 \rangle_A$ represents the mean square radius of an even-even isotope, A. If the radius increased smoothly with increasing neutron number, as in the relation (2-76), the parameter γ would be unity. The observed values are usually somewhat less than unity, and in some cases negative values have been observed (see, for example, Kuhn and Turner, 1962). The origin of the odd-even staggering is not well understood, but it has been suggested that the effect may be related to the nuclear deformations and reveal a systematic tendency for odd-A nuclei ▲ to exhibit smaller values of $\langle \beta^2 \rangle$ than even-even isotopes (Sorensen, 1966).

▼ Recently, the isotope shift has been detected in x-ray transitions (Chesler and Boehm, 1968, and references given there) and in the spectra of muonic atoms (see the review by Wu, 1967). The new evidence has confirmed the main qualitative features discussed above. However, the comparison between ratios of isotope shifts in the same element has revealed unexpectedly large specific mass effects in the electronic spectra, which imply significant corrections to some of the values in Fig. 2-2 (Wu, 1968). Additional detailed information on the variation of the nuclear charge distribution has been obtained from the study of electron scattering on separated isotopes (see Van Oostrum *et al.* 1966).

Estimate of mean free path from neutron total cross sections (Fig. 2-3)

Information on the mean free path of nucleons in a nucleus can be obtained from a study of cross sections as a function of energy. The measured total cross section for the interaction of neutrons with Cu, Cd, and Pb are shown in Fig. 2-3.

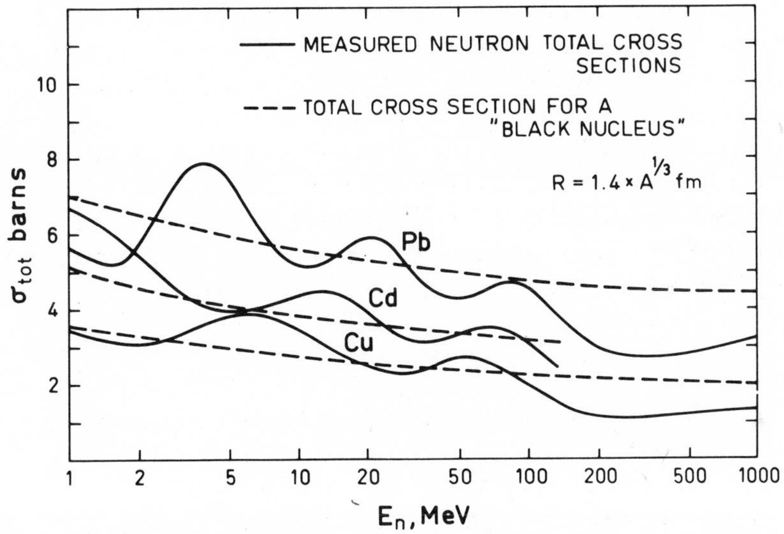

Figure 2-3 The experimental data for $E_n < 100$ MeV are taken from the review by J. M. Peterson, *Phys. Rev.* **125**, 955 (1962) and from the compilation *Neutron Cross Sections, BNL* **325**, Sigma Center, Brookhaven National Laboratory (1964). For energies above $E_n = 100$ MeV, the data are taken from V. A. Nedzel, *Phys. Rev.* **94**, 174 (1954) and T. Coor, D. A. Hill, W. F. Hornyak, L. W. Smith, and G. Snow, *Phys. Rev.* **98**, 1369 (1955). We wish to thank J. M. Peterson for help in the preparation of the figure.

The dotted lines give the cross sections that are calculated for a "black nucleus," that is, by assuming a boundary condition for $r = R$ expressing that neutrons may enter the nuclear volume, but that there is no outgoing flux approaching the nuclear surface from the inside (for the details of this calculation, see Blatt and Weisskopf, 1952, Chapter VIII). ▲

▼ The marked oscillations in the measured cross sections result from the fact that the scattering nuclei are not opaque and thus the transmitted wave is able to interfere with the incident wave. (A similar effect is observed in the scattering of electrons on atoms and is referred to as the Ramsauer-Townsend effect; see, for example, Massey and Burhop, 1952, pp. 8ff., 113ff.) The atom-atom interaction (molecular forces) can also be represented, for sufficiently low energies, by a real potential of finite range, and thus the cross sections exhibit marked oscillations of similar origin; see, for example, the review by Pauly and Toennies, 1965.)

A qualitative interpretation of the interference effect may be very simply obtained on the basis of a semiclassical approximation appropriate to high energies. The propagation of the neutron inside the nucleus is described in terms of the inside velocity, v_{in}, and a mean free path λ; these parameters can be expressed in terms of a complex wave number K, or in terms of motion in a complex potential $V + iW$,

$$K = \left(\frac{2M}{\hbar^2}(E - V - iW)\right)^{1/2} = \frac{Mv_{\text{in}}}{\hbar} + \frac{i}{2\lambda} \tag{2-86}$$

Since we shall consider incident energies large compared with the potential energy and wavelength small compared with the nuclear radius, we may calculate the amplitude of the transmitted wave assuming a straight line orbit through the nucleus. A ray that passes a distance b from the nuclear center thus emerges with an amplitude

$$\exp\{2i(K - k)(R^2 - b^2)^{1/2}\} \tag{2-87}$$

relative to the incident wave, which moves with the wave number k, where

$$k = \left(\frac{2ME}{\hbar^2}\right)^{1/2} = \frac{Mv_{\text{out}}}{\hbar} \tag{2-88}$$

Summing over the different impact parameters, b, we obtain for the scattering amplitude in the forward direction,

$$\begin{aligned} f(0) &= \frac{ik}{2\pi}\int_0^R [1 - \exp\{2i(K - k)(R^2 - b^2)^{1/2}\}]2\pi b\, db \\ &= \frac{ikR^2}{2}\left\{1 + \frac{2}{x^2}[1 - e^{ix}(1 - ix)]\right\} \qquad x \equiv 2(K - k)R \end{aligned} \tag{2-89}$$

The expression for $f(0)$ may be obtained from the partial wave expansion (3F-33) by replacing the variable l by kb.

The total cross section may be calculated from the scattering amplitude in the forward direction, since the attenuation of the incident beam (proportional to ▲ the total cross section) is the result of interference between the incident wave

▼ and the wave scattered in the forward direction. The relation, usually called the optical theorem, is

$$\sigma_{tot} = \frac{4\pi}{k} \operatorname{Im} f(0) \tag{2-90}$$

When the transmitted wave (2-87) is 180° out of phase with respect to the incident wave, there is a maximum in the cross section, while minima correspond to the situation in which the transmitted and incident waves are in phase. Since the parameter x that determines the relative phase is a decreasing function of energy and an increasing function of R, the corresponding maxima and minima shift to higher energy as R is increased. (This variation with E and R is the opposite of that characterizing the one-particle resonances in a potential well; see Sec. 3F-2. The relation of the interference phenomena discussed above to the one-particle resonances has been discussed by McVoy, 1967a.)

Examination of Eqs. (2-89) and (2-90) shows that the last maximum in the cross section is expected when the real part of x is about 4.1; the fact that this maximum occurs for an incident energy of about 90 MeV for Pb implies that the real potential V is about -22 MeV, using $R = 1.4 \times A^{1/3} = 8.3$ fm. This value of the radius seems the most appropriate for the present estimate, since the potential extends somewhat beyond the charge distribution. (The maxima and minima of the cross section given by Eqs. (2-89) and (2-90) have been tabulated by Franco, 1965, who has also discussed the validity of this simple approximation.) The increase in σ_{tot} for $E_n \gtrsim 400$ MeV is associated with meson production.

From the magnitude of the oscillations, we may also estimate the mean free path and thus the magnitude of the imaginary potential, W. If the potential were purely real ($\lambda = \infty$), the relations (2-89) and (2-90) would imply a difference of about a factor of 2 between the last maximum and minimum in the cross section. The observed difference in Pb is only about 15% and thus implies an attenuation of about a factor of 5 in the transmitted wave. From this we may conclude that $R/\lambda \approx 1.6$ or $W \approx -10$ MeV, as may also be confirmed by more detailed fitting of the experimental cross sections with the expressions (2-89) and (2-90).

Further comparisons of the theoretical expressions with the observed cross sections show that the real and imaginary potentials change with the bombarding energy. Thus, the minimum before the last maximum should occur when the real part of x is 7.7. The observation of this minimum at about 50 MeV in Pb implies that the potential has increased in strength to about 34 MeV. Indeed, the potential is found to increase steadily with decreasing energy, approaching a value of about 45 MeV for zero bombarding energy.

If the imaginary part of the potential were constant, the oscillations would become weaker as one went to lower energies, since the oscillatory term in the amplitude (2-89) varies inversely with x. In fact, the observed oscillations in the cross section get larger as the bombarding energy is decreased, implying a decrease in the imaginary potential. At low bombarding energies, the imaginary potential has decreased to about a fifth of its high-energy value. ▲

▼ In Sec. 2-4c, we shall consider the more quantitative description of the nucleon-nucleus cross sections and the potentials that are deduced from this analysis.

Binding energy per nucleon as function of A (Fig. 2-4)

▲ The experimentally determined binding energy per nucleon ($\mathscr{B}/A$) of the

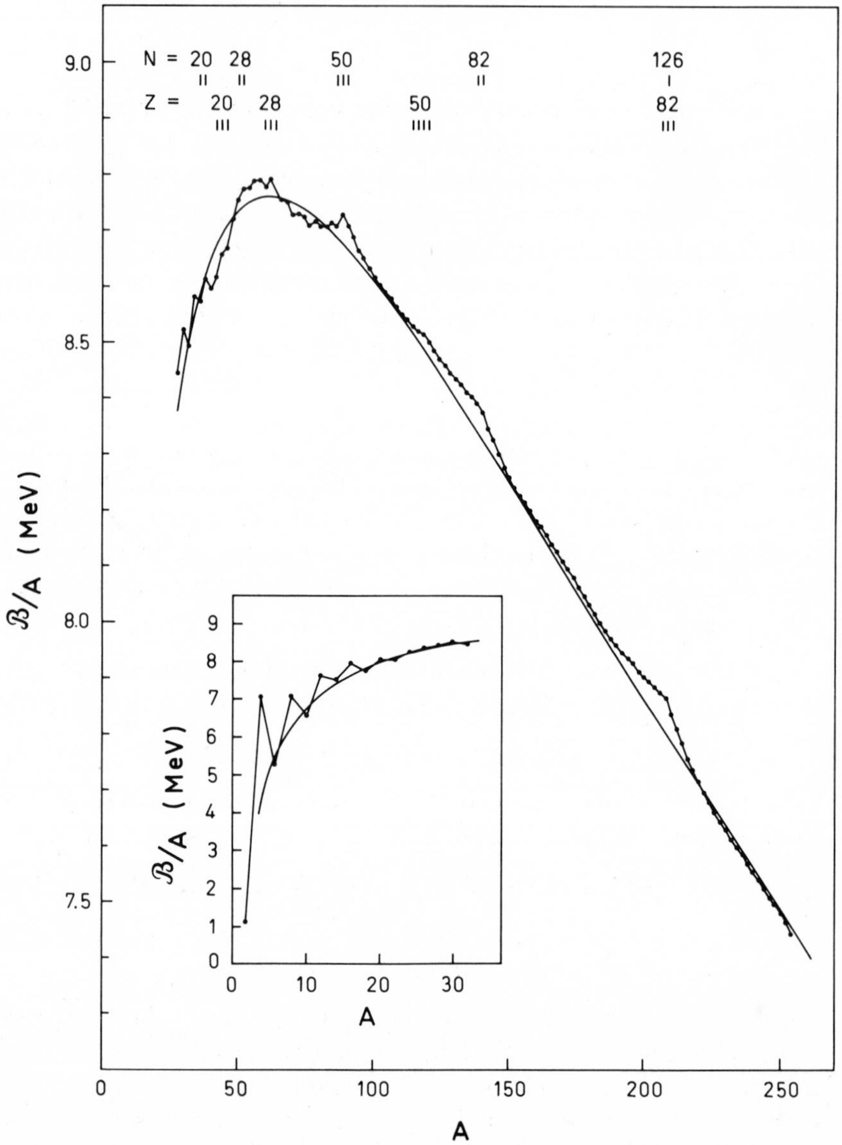

Figure 2-4 The experimental binding energies are taken from the compilation by J. H. E. Mattauch, W. Thiele, and A. H. Wapstra, *Nuclear Phys.* **67**, 1 (1965). The smooth curve represents the semi-empirical mass formula, Eq. (2-12), with the constants given by A. E. S. Green and N. A. Engler, *Phys. Rev.* **91**, 40 (1953).

▼ most stable isobar for each even value of the mass number A is plotted in Fig. 2-4. The restriction to even A avoids the systematic odd-even variation which is illustrated in Fig. 2-5.

The smooth curve in Fig. 2-4 is calculated from the mass formula (2-12) with the constants

$$\begin{aligned} b_{\text{vol}} &= 15.56 \text{ MeV} \\ b_{\text{surf}} &= 17.23 \text{ MeV} \\ b_{\text{sym}} &= 46.57 \text{ MeV} \\ R_c &= 1.24\, A^{1/3} \text{ fm} \end{aligned} \tag{2-91}$$

Besides the general trends described by the mass formula (2-12), one can see, in the measured binding energies, a number of significant local variations. Thus, in the light nuclei, the binding energy is systematically greater for mass numbers $A = 4n$ than for $A = 4n + 2$ (n an integer). These "short periods" are associated with the fact that the nuclear interactions favor states that are spatially symmetric (see, for example, Chapter 7). In heavier nuclei, the binding energies exhibit local maxima, which are associated with the completion of major shells.

Pairing energies (Fig. 2-5)

The odd-even mass parameter Δ defined by Eq. (2-15) can be determined from the empirical masses of a sequence of isotopes or isotones. Assuming that the masses are a smooth function of Z and N except for the pairing effect, we can define a local average of the masses of odd-A nuclei, and by comparing this value with the observed masses of the even-even nuclei, we obtain Δ. Thus, for even N, we may define

$$\begin{aligned} \Delta_n &= \tfrac{1}{4}\{\mathscr{B}(N-2,Z) - 3\mathscr{B}(N-1,Z) + 3\mathscr{B}(N,Z) - \mathscr{B}(N+1,Z)\} \\ &= -\tfrac{1}{4}\{S_n(N-1,Z) - 2S_n(N,Z) + S_n(N+1,Z)\} \\ S_n(N,Z) &\equiv \mathscr{B}(N,Z) - \mathscr{B}(N-1,Z) \end{aligned} \tag{2-92}$$

while, for odd N, the negative of the expression (2-92) is taken as the neutron pairing energy. Similarly, for even Z, we define the proton pairing energy

$$\begin{aligned} \Delta_p &= \tfrac{1}{4}\{\mathscr{B}(N,Z-2) - 3\mathscr{B}(N,Z-1) + 3\mathscr{B}(N,Z) - \mathscr{B}(N,Z+1)\} \\ &= -\tfrac{1}{4}\{S_p(N,Z-1) - 2S_p(N,Z) + S_p(N,Z+1)\} \\ S_p(N,Z) &\equiv \mathscr{B}(N,Z) - \mathscr{B}(N,Z-1) \end{aligned} \tag{2-93}$$

while, for odd Z, the negative of Eq. (2-93) is used. The pairing energies (2-92) and (2-93) obtained from the empirical masses are plotted in Fig. 2-5 as a function of the number of neutrons or protons in the nucleus. It is seen that the general trend in the observed pairing energies is fit by the simple expression

$$\Delta \approx \frac{12}{A^{1/2}} \text{ MeV} \tag{2-94}$$

▲ although significant local variations occur and appear to be correlated with the

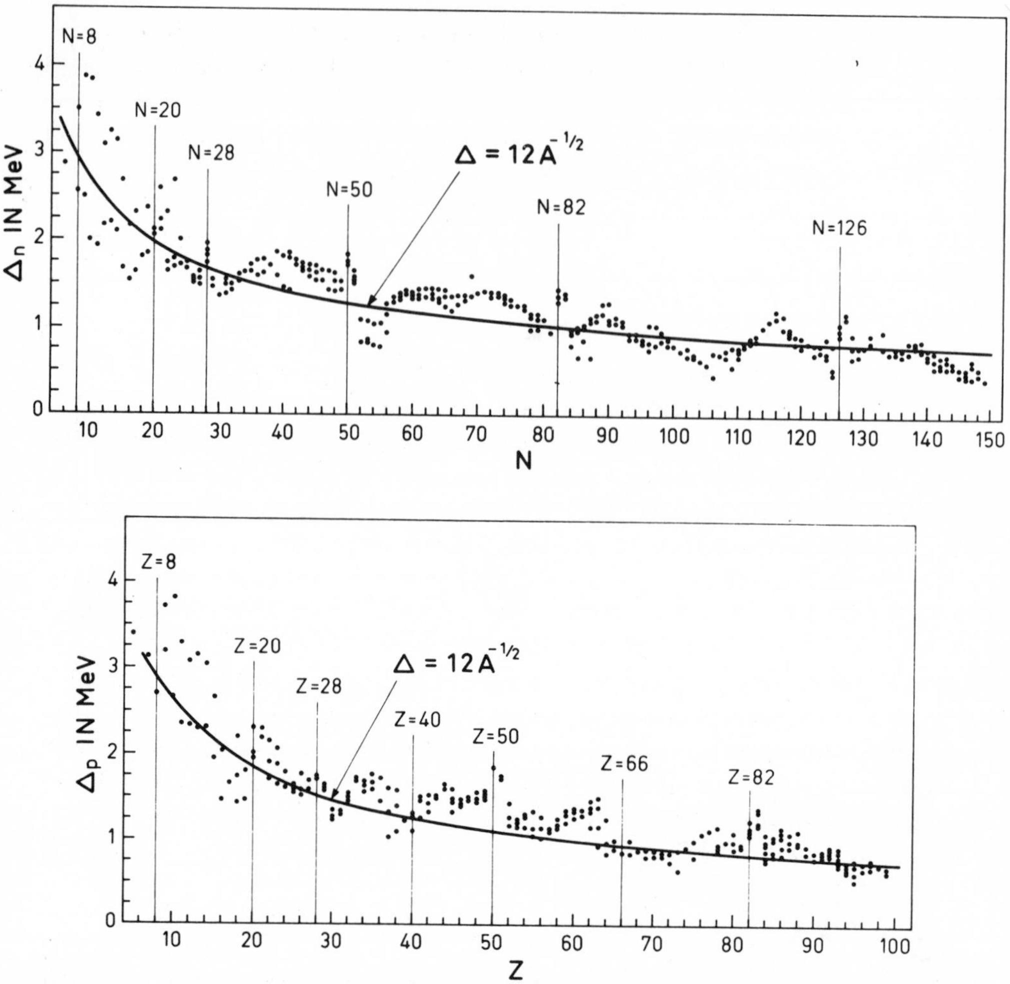

Figure 2-5 The odd-even mass differences for neutrons and protons are based on the analysis of N. Zeldes, A. Grill, and A. Simievic, *Mat. Fys. Skr. Dan. Vid. Selsk.* **3**, No. 5 (1967).

▼ shell structure. There is a slight tendency for Δ_p to exceed Δ_n. This fact leads to a predominance of odd-N nuclei among the β-stable species as compared with odd Z (53 odd-Z, compared to 68 odd-N β-stable nuclei with $A < 238$). In Chapter 8, we shall consider the origin and more detailed interpretation of the pairing energy.

The simple description of the pairing energy used in Eq. (2-15) implies that the extra energy of an odd-odd nucleus, as compared with an even-even configuration, is

$$\mathscr{E}_{\text{odd-odd}} - \mathscr{E}_{\text{even-even}} \approx \Delta_n + \Delta_p \approx 2\Delta \tag{2-95}$$

Comparison with the observed masses of odd-odd nuclei reveals that this relation is approximately fulfilled, but that there is a systematic tendency for the ▲

odd-odd masses to be slightly lower than this estimate. This extra binding of the odd-odd nuclei amounts on the average to about $20A^{-1}$ MeV (see, for example, Zeldes *et al.*, 1967), and may be thought of as resulting from the attractive residual interaction between the unpaired neutron and the unpaired proton.

The expression (2-92) represents an average pairing energy for the neutron number N and $N-1$. In order to avoid this averaging, one may attempt to derive Δ from a second difference of energies rather than the third difference employed in Eq. (2-92). Thus, for even N, we may define

$$\begin{aligned}\bar{\Delta}_n &= -\tfrac{1}{2}\{\mathscr{B}(N-1,Z) - 2\mathscr{B}(N,Z) + \mathscr{B}(N+1,Z)\} \\ &= +\tfrac{1}{2}\{S_n(N,Z) - S_n(N+1,Z)\}\end{aligned} \tag{2-96}$$

However, because the average energy (2-12) contains significant terms that are not linear in N, the linear interpolation (2-96) yields an estimate of Δ that is systematically too small. The correction may be approximately estimated by taking the second derivative of Eq. (2-12) with respect to N (for fixed Z), and in this way one obtains contributions to Δ_n of about 1 MeV for $A = 40$ and 0.1 MeV for $A = 200$. The estimate (2-96), corrected in this manner, is very similar to that obtained from Eq. (2-92) (see Nemirovsky and Adamchuk, 1962).

It is essential in the above estimate of Δ that the nuclear masses vary in a smooth manner except for the odd-even pairing effect. This condition is badly violated as one goes from one major shell to the next (see Fig. 2-14), and in such cases the quantity Δ obtained from Eqs. (2-92), (2-93), and (2-96) does not have any simple significance.

Isospin mixing caused by the Coulomb potential (Fig. 2-6)

The isospin mixing in the nuclear ground state resulting from the Coulomb interaction can be estimated in terms of the nuclear polarization associated with the tendency of the Coulomb potential to push the protons towards the nuclear surface.

We first consider a nucleus with $N = Z$ and describe the polarization by the local isovector density

$$\rho_1(\mathbf{r}) \equiv \rho_n(\mathbf{r}) - \rho_p(\mathbf{r}) \tag{2-97}$$

Variations in the isoscalar density, $\rho_n(\mathbf{r}) + \rho_p(\mathbf{r})$, will be neglected, since they do not affect the isospin. The Coulomb energy is given by

$$\mathscr{E}_{\text{Coul}} = \frac{1}{2}\int \rho_p(\mathbf{r}) V_{\text{Coul}}(\mathbf{r})\, d\tau \tag{2-98}$$

The tendency of the Coulomb potential to polarize the nucleus is counteracted by the same effects as those responsible for the symmetry term in the nuclear energy (see Eq. (2-12)). We therefore express the symmetry energy in terms of a local energy density,

$$\mathscr{E}_{\text{sym}} = \frac{1}{2}\frac{b_{\text{sym}}}{\rho_0}\int(\rho_1(\mathbf{r}))^2\,d\tau \tag{2-99}$$

$$\rho_0 = \frac{3A}{4\pi R^3}$$

where ρ_0 is the average particle density. Minimizing the sum of the energies (2-98) and (2-99) with respect to variations $\delta\rho_1(\mathbf{r}) = -2\delta\rho_p(\mathbf{r})$, we obtain the polarization produced by the Coulomb potential

$$\rho_1(\mathbf{r}) = \frac{1}{2}\frac{\rho_0}{b_{\text{sym}}}(V_{\text{Coul}}(\mathbf{r}) - \langle V_{\text{Coul}}\rangle) \tag{2-100}$$

We have subtracted the mean value $\langle V_{\text{Coul}}\rangle$ of the Coulomb potential in order to ensure that the integral of $\rho_1(\mathbf{r})$ over the nuclear volume vanishes.

To determine the isospin mixing connected with the density difference (2-100), we must express the polarization effect in terms of quantized excitations. For this purpose, we shall employ a collective description in which the excitations associated with nuclear polarization are viewed as normal modes of oscillation similar to those in a liquid drop consisting of two fluids. The properties of such normal modes are discussed in Appendix 6A.

The main nuclear polarization is of monopole type (we neglect the relatively small quadrupole effects in deformed nuclei), and the expansion of $\rho_1(\mathbf{r})$ into normal modes takes the form (see Eq. (6A-62))

$$\rho_1(\mathbf{r}) = \rho_0(4\pi)^{-1/2}\sum_n \alpha_n j_0(k_n r) \tag{2-101}$$

where the values of k_n are given by the boundary condition (6A-63) at the nuclear surface, which yields (for $\lambda = 0$)

$$\tan k_n R = k_n R$$

$$k_n R = \begin{cases} 4.49 & n = 1 \\ 7.72 & n = 2 \\ 10.8 & n = 3 \end{cases} \tag{2-102}$$

From Eqs. (2-100) and (2-101), we obtain

$$\alpha_n = -\frac{\int_0^R \rho_1(\mathbf{r}) j_0(k_n r)(4\pi)^{1/2} r^2\,dr}{\rho_0\int_0^R [j_0(k_n r)]^2 r^2\,dr}$$

$$= -\frac{\sqrt{\pi}}{2}\frac{Ze^2}{Rb_{\text{sym}}}\frac{\int_0^R j_0(k_n r) r^4\,dr}{R^2\int_0^R j_0^2(k_n r) r^2\,dr} \tag{2-103}$$

In the last expression, we have inserted the Coulomb potential produced by a

▼ uniformly charged sphere,

$$V_{\text{Coul}}(r) = \frac{Ze^2}{R}\left(\frac{3}{2} - \frac{1}{2}\frac{r^2}{R^2}\right) \qquad (r<R) \qquad \text{(2-104)}$$

The amplitude α_n given by Eq. (2-103) represents the mean value in the polarized state of the nth mode. Since α_n is small compared to the zero point amplitude $(\alpha_n)_0$, the polarized state is represented by the ground state of the oscillator on which is superimposed the state with one quantum of excitation, with amplitude $c_n = \frac{1}{2}\alpha_n(\alpha_n)_0^{-1}$. The zero point amplitude $(\alpha_n)_0$ can be expressed in terms of the eigenfrequency ω_n and the restoring force parameter C_n for the nth vibrational mode (see Eqs. (6A-67) and (6A-68)), and for the probability, $P_n = c_n^2$, for excitation of the nth mode, we therefore obtain

$$\begin{aligned} P_n &= \frac{C_n}{2\hbar\,\omega_n}\alpha_n^2 \\ &= \frac{\pi}{8\hbar}\rho_0 R^2 Z^2 e^4 M^{1/2}(b_{\text{sym}})^{-3/2}\varepsilon_n \qquad \text{(2-105)} \\ &= 7.2\times 10^{-5} Z^2 A^{2/3}\varepsilon_n \end{aligned}$$

with

$$\begin{aligned} \varepsilon_n &= \frac{1}{k_n R}\,\frac{\left(\int_0^R j_0(k_n r) r^4\,dr\right)^2}{R^7\int_0^R [j_0(k_n r)]^2 r^2\,dr} \\ &= \begin{cases} 4.36\times 10^{-3} & n=1 \\ 2.98\times 10^{-4} & n=2 \end{cases} \qquad \text{(2-106)} \end{aligned}$$

In Eq. (2-105), we have used the relations (6A-60) and (6A-64) for the eigenfrequencies.

Each excitation carries a unit of isospin ($\tau = 1$), and the polarized nuclear state thus contains $T = 1$ components with a total probability

$$P(T=1) = P(\tau=1) = \sum_n P_n = 3.50\times 10^{-7} Z^2 A^{2/3} \qquad \text{(2-107)}$$

as illustrated in Fig. 2-6.

For nuclei with a neutron excess, the ground state has $T = T_0 = M_T = \frac{1}{2}(N-Z)$ in the absence of the Coulomb interaction, and the polarization effect introduces small components with $T = T_0 + 1$. The intensity $P(T_0+1)$ of these components can be simply obtained from the above results, provided the properties of the collective polarization modes are only little affected by the neutron excess. The estimate (2-107) then continues to give the total probability $P(\tau = 1)$ for excitation of polarization modes. The isospin ($\tau = 1$) of the excitation can ▲ couple with the isospin T_0 of the excess neutrons to form states with $T = T_0$

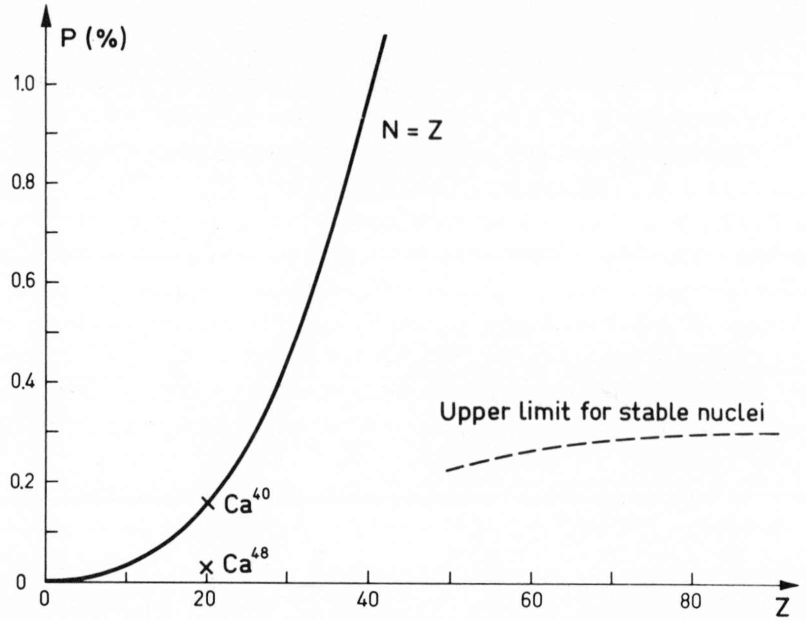

Figure 2-6 The figure shows the isospin impurities in nuclear ground states estimated on the basis of the hydrodynamical model (A. Bohr, J. Damgaard, and B. R. Mottelson, in *Nuclear Structure*, p. 1, eds. A. Hossain, Harun-ar-Rashid, and M. Islam, North-Holland, Amsterdam, 1967.)

▼ and $T_0 + 1$, and we obtain

$$P(T_0+1) = \langle T_0 T_0 1 0 | T_0+1, T_0\rangle^2 P(\tau=1)$$
$$= (T_0+1)^{-1} P(\tau=1) \tag{2-108}$$

This result, shown as a dotted line in Fig. 2-6, is, however, an overestimate because of the neglected interaction between the neutron excess and the polarization modes. Partly, this interaction produces a splitting between the excitations with $T = T_0$ and $T_0 + 1$, which pushes the $T = T_0 + 1$ state toward higher energies and thus reduces the probability for exciting this state. (An estimate of the coupling energy can be obtained from the isovector nuclear potential (see Eq. (2-29).) Partly, the presence of the excess neutrons, by more specific quantum effects, decreases the strength of the $(T_0 + 1)$ mode; this can be seen by analyzing the polarization modes in terms of the excitation of individual protons. The excitations lifting the protons to orbits that are occupied by neutrons cannot change the total isospin, since the system remains fully aligned in isospace. Thus, only the excitations to higher orbits can lead to an increase in the isospin. The main proton excitations contributing to the monopole mode are associated with an increase of the radial quantum number by one unit and, on account of the Pauli principle, only the protons in the two last major shells are therefore effective. ▲ In a heavy nucleus, the neutrons fill one more major shell than the protons,

▼ and thus the number of effective isospin-raising transitions is reduced by about a factor of 2. (An analysis of the modes with $T = T_0 + 1$, in terms of the effect of the nucleonic interactions in correlating the single-particle excitations, can be formulated by means of the methods discussed in Sec. 9-3.)

Estimates of the isospin admixing have also been made on the basis of an independent-particle description (MacDonald, 1956; Sliv and Kharitonov, 1965). The estimates obtained on this basis exceed those given in Fig. 2-6 by an order of magnitude. The reduction obtained by the present estimate may be attributed to the forces between the nucleons, which act against a separation of neutrons and protons. Thus, the eigenfrequency of the lowest collective monopole polarization mode given by the "hydrodynamic model" is $170A^{-1/3}\,\hbar^{-1}$ MeV (see Eq. (6A-65)), while the single-particle excitations with change of radial quantum number by one unit have a frequency of the order of $2\omega_0 \approx 80A^{-1/3}\hbar^{-1}$ MeV (see Eq. (2-131)).

It may be added that the dipole polarization mode has been studied in connection with the nuclear photoeffect (see Chapter 6). For this mode, the collective "hydrodynamical" eigenfrequency is also about twice the average single-particle frequency, and is found to account rather well for the observed frequency of the dipole resonance.

An especially sensitive test of the presence of isospin impurities is provided by the ft values for β transitions between isobaric analog states with $I = 0$. The transition operator for these β decays is proportional to a component $T_\pm = T_x \pm iT_y$ of the total isospin, and the matrix element is therefore independent of internal nuclear properties. Accurate ft measurements are available for a number of $0+ \rightarrow 0+$ transitions between members of isobaric triplets having two nucleons in addition to a "core" with $N = Z$ and $T = 0$ (see Fig. 1-10).

The above estimates yield admixtures of components with $T = 0$ and 2 into the predominantly $T = 1$ states with intensities

$$P(T) = \langle 1 M_T 1 0 | T M_T \rangle^2 \, P(\tau = 1)$$

where $P(\tau = 1)$ is given by Eq. (2-107) and is plotted in Fig. 2-6. Even these small admixtures, however, are only partially effective in modifying the transition matrix elements. In fact, in the approximation considered, in which the interaction between the excess nucleons and the excitations of the core is neglected, we can describe the nuclear states in terms of two independent components, the core and the extra particles with $T = 1$, M_T. The core state is predominantly isoscalar with small isovector components admixed by the Coulomb field, but these admixtures are independent of the M_T value of the extra nucleons. The operators $T_\pm$ can therefore only affect transitions between members of the triplet by acting on the extra nucleons carrying unit isospin, and the matrix element retains its unperturbed value.

An estimate of the modification in the ft value can be obtained by taking ▲ into account the splitting between the $T = 0, 1, 2$ states formed by coupling the

▼ isospin $\tau = 1$ of the core excitation to the isospin $T_0 = 1$ of the excess neutrons. If we assume the probability for virtual excitation of the various T components to be inversely proportional to the square of the excitation energy (corresponding to a matrix element unaffected by the interaction), and if we employ the estimate (2-29) for the coupling between τ and T_0, we obtain for the ft value

$$\frac{(ft)_0}{ft} \approx \left[1 - P(\tau=1) + \sqrt{3}\, P(\tau=1)\, \langle 1010|20\rangle\langle 1110|21\rangle \left(\frac{\hbar\omega_{n=1}}{\hbar\omega_{n=1} + V_1 A^{-1}}\right)^2\right]^2$$

$$\approx \left[1 - \frac{2V_1}{A\hbar\omega_{n=1}} P(\tau=1)\right]^2 \qquad V_1 \approx 100 \text{ MeV} \tag{2-109}$$

where $(ft)_0$ is the unperturbed ft value. The excitations with $T = 0$ and 1 do not contribute to the β decay, since the $T = 1$ component is missing in the nucleus with $M_T = 0$. The $T = 2$ component has a transition probability three times larger than for $T = 1$ (see Eq. (1-70)). For a nucleus with $A \approx 50$, the factor $2V_1(A\hbar\omega_{n=1})^{-1}$ is of the order of 10%. It should be emphasized that additional interaction effects between the core and the two extra nucleons may affect the Fermi matrix element by amounts comparable to the correction term estimated in Eq. (2-109).

Two-particle correlation function for Fermi gas (*Fig. 2-7*)

The antisymmetry of the wave functions of a Fermi gas implies correlations in the motion of the particles. The two-body correlation for nucleons in antisymmetric orbital states is proportional to the quantity $1 - C^2(k_F r_{12})$, which is plotted in Fig. 2-7 (see Eqs. (2-37) and (2-42)). The other two-body correlation functions in the Fermi gas can also be simply expressed in terms of this quantity (see Eqs. (2-36) and (2-41)).

The oscillations and long-range character of the correlation function ($C^2(x) \sim x^{-4} \cos^2 x$ for large x) are a consequence of the assumption of a sharp Fermi surface for the occupied momentum states. Whether or not such a sharp Fermi surface can ever be maintained in the presence of two-body interactions is an intriguing general question (see, for example, Kohn and Luttinger, 1965).

Average spacing and widths for resonances in low-energy neutron interaction (*Fig. 2-8*)

The principal source of evidence on the nature of the nuclear states at high excitation energy has been the study of the resonances observed in the interaction of low-energy neutrons with nuclei ($E_n <$ a few keV). As an example, Fig. 2-8 shows the total cross section for the reaction $n + {}^{232}\text{Th}$ in the region of $E_n \sim 100$ eV.

▲ The centrifugal barrier implies that, in the low-energy region, the $l = 0$

▼ resonances are much stronger than those with $l > 0$. Thus, from Eq. (3F-51) and Table 3F-1, we expect that on the average an $l = 1$ resonance in Th at 100 eV will have a neutron width about 10^{-4} times that of an $l = 0$ resonance (assuming similar one-particle parentage coefficients for the two resonances). ▲

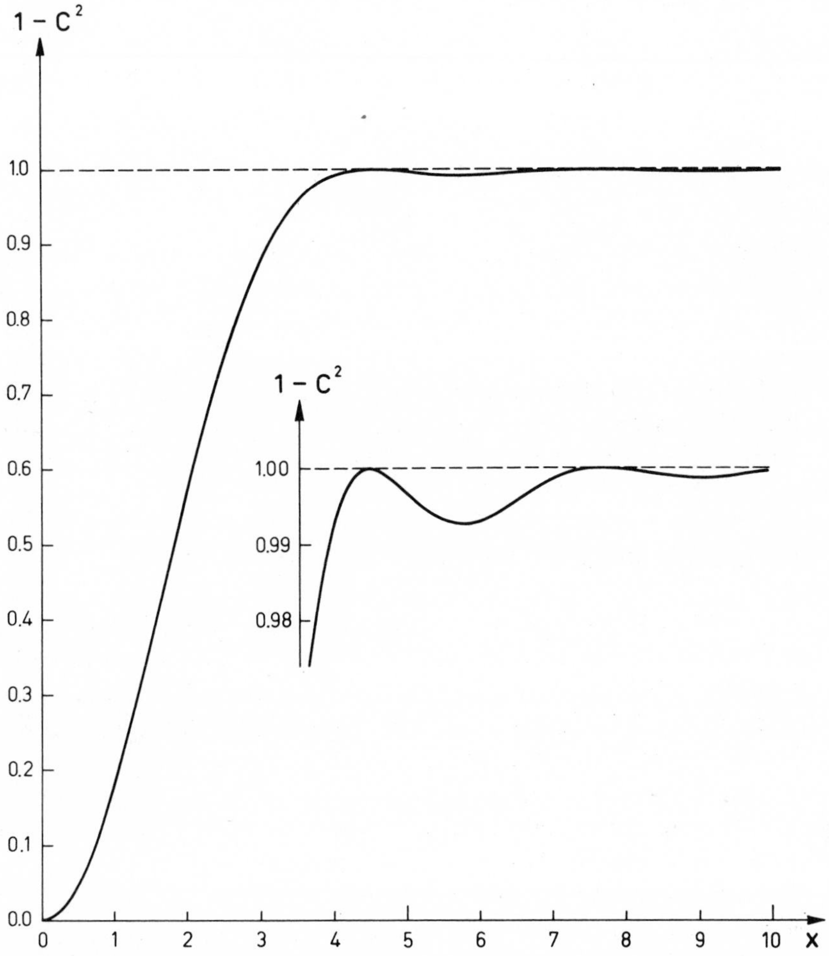

Figure 2-7 The two-particle density correlations in a Fermi gas involve the function $C(x)$ illustrated in the figure.

▼ The existence of very clear interference between the resonance and potential scattering in Fig. 2-8 provides further support for the $l = 0$ assignment to all of the strong resonances. Further improvements in the experimental resolution have revealed additional very weak resonances (not visible in Fig. 2-8), which are believed to arise from $l = 1$ interactions (see, for example, Bollinger and Thomas, 1964).

▲ The restriction to $l = 0$ implies that the angular momentum and parity

▼ $I_r\ \pi_r$ of the resonance states are limited by the selection rule

$$I_r = I_0 \pm \tfrac{1}{2} \qquad \text{(2-110)}$$
$$\pi_r = \pi_0$$

▲ where $I_0\ \pi_0$ are the angular momentum and parity of the ground state of the

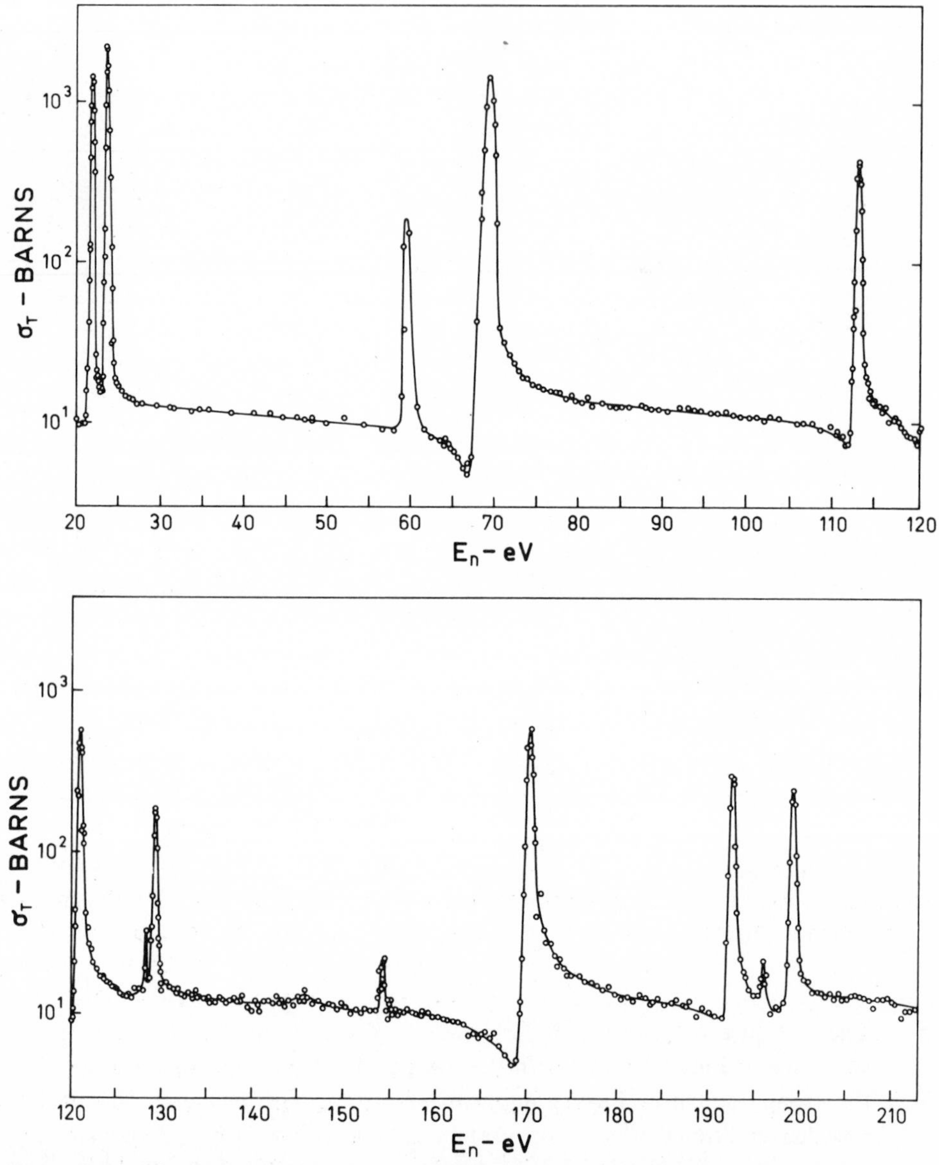

Figure 2-8 The figure gives the total cross section for the reaction $n + {}^{232}\text{Th}$ as a function of the neutron energy, E_n, in electron volts; the data are taken from the compilation *Neutron Cross Sections* (1964).

▼ target nucleus. For an even-even target, such as ^{232}Th, we have $I_0\pi_0 = 0+$, and thus the resonances are characterized by $I_r\pi_r = 1/2+$.

It is seen that the average spacing of the resonances is about 16 eV. This is about 10^6 times smaller than the single-particle spacing ($D_{sp} \approx 2\pi V_0(K_0R)^{-1} \approx 10^2 A^{-1/3}$ MeV for orbits of the same spin and parity in a square well potential). This high density of resonances is clear evidence that the states in this region of the spectrum involve the excitation of many degrees of freedom of the nucleus.

In the interpretation of the observed spacings of the levels, it is useful, as a first orientation, to compare with the expression (2-57) describing the level spectrum of a Fermi gas. The Fermi gas level density is very sensitive to the one-particle level density g_0, and therefore we may determine the value of g_0 that is necessary in order to give the observed level density. For ^{233}Th at an excitation energy of $E = S_n = 5.1$ MeV, we have $[\rho(I\pi = 1/2+)]^{-1} = 16$ eV, which implies $g_0 = 16\ \mathrm{MeV}^{-1}$. This value is of the same magnitude as the estimate $g_0 = 3A/2\varepsilon_F \approx 10\ \mathrm{MeV}^{-1}$ obtained from the Fermi gas model. The values of g_0 obtained from this and other estimates are discussed in connection with Fig. 2-12.

The observed neutron widths of the resonances fluctuate considerably from level to level (see Fig. 2-10), but the average is about

$$\bar{\Gamma}_n \approx 1.2 \times 10^{-3}(E_n(\mathrm{eV}))^{1/2} \quad \mathrm{eV} \tag{2-111}$$

where both the width and the resonance energy are in electron volts. This value is about 10^{-6} times the single-particle estimate (3F-51). The small widths of the resonances are directly connected with the high level density of the resonance states and provide additional evidence for the many-particle aspect of these states. The average of the neutron width divided by the level spacing provides a measure of the one-particle strength function and is further discussed in connection with Fig. 2-26.

Beside neutron emission, the resonance states may decay by γ-ray emission to any of the lower-lying levels of ^{233}Th. The total width for γ emission is found to be $\Gamma_\gamma \approx 2.5 \times 10^{-2}$ eV and to be approximately the same for all the resonances that have been measured in ^{233}Th. It is generally believed that the most important transitions contributing to the radiative decay are $E1$, although the available experimental evidence is not very conclusive (see, for example, Bartholomew, 1960). A detailed interpretation of Γ_γ would involve partly a discussion of the spectrum of the emitted γ radiation and partly an estimate of the $E1$ strength function for transitions of a few MeV.

Distribution of level spacings observed in neutron resonances (Fig. 2-9)

The statistical distributions of the resonance energies and widths provide information on the structure of the states involved. As an example, Fig. 2-9
▲ shows the distribution of the observed spacings between adjacent resonances in

▼ $n + {}^{232}\mathrm{Th}$. There is some uncertainty in the construction of the figure because of the observation of the very weak resonances mentioned in the discussion of Fig. 2-8 and believed to be $l = 1$ resonances. Since we are interested in the spacing ▲ distribution for levels of the same spin and parity, these weak levels have been

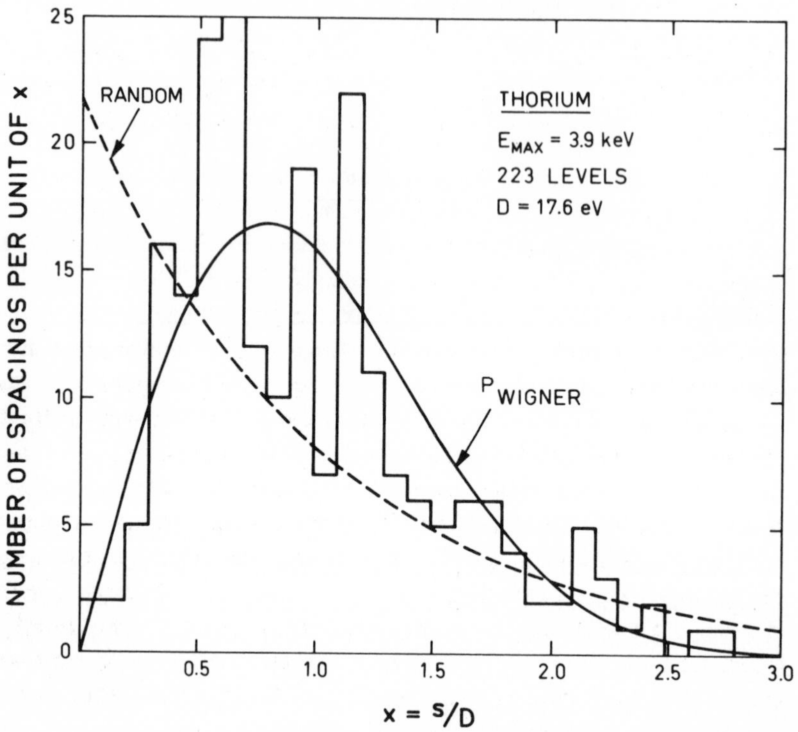

Figure 2-9 The figure plots the probability distribution of the observed spacings, s, between adjacent resonance levels in the reaction $n + {}^{232}\mathrm{Th}$ up to an energy $E_n = 3.9$ keV (223 resonances). The average level spacing is denoted by D. The data are taken from J. B. Garg, J. Rainwater, J. S. Petersen, and W. W. Havens, Jr., *Phys. Rev.* **134**, B985 (1964).

▼ omitted, but the conclusions drawn from the present analysis must be regarded as somewhat tentative, until the spin and parities of the weak levels have been directly determined. The Wigner distribution (2-59) and the Poisson distribution (2-60) are also drawn in the figure. It is seen that the data clearly exhibit the absence of small spacings, as expected in a situation where there is extensive configuration mixing, and are inconsistent with the Poisson distribution, which would apply if there were a large number of conserved quantities besides $I\pi$ characterizing the resonance states.

The description of the configuration mixing in terms of random matrices also implies the occurrence of a long-range order in the sequence of resonance ▲ energies (Dyson, 1962). Thus, if we let $N(E)$ be the function that gives the

▼ total number of levels up to the energy E, we may construct the quantity Δ that measures the mean square deviation of N from the best fitting linear function of E,

$$\Delta = \min_{A,B}\left[\frac{1}{2L}\int_{-L}^{L}[N(E) - AE - B]^2\,dE\right] \tag{2-112}$$

where the experimental data on the resonance energies are assumed to span the interval $(-L, L)$. The model of random matrices implies that, in the limit in which the number of resonances n included in the sample is very large,

$$\Delta = \frac{1}{\pi^2}\left[\ln(2\pi n) + \gamma - \frac{\pi^2}{8} - \frac{5}{4}\right]$$

$$= \frac{1}{\pi^2}[\ln n - 0.0687] \tag{2-113}$$

(Dyson and Mehta, 1963). The long-range order in the level spacings is revealed in the logarithmic variation of Δ with n (compare with a random distribution of levels, which yields $\Delta = n/15$). The value of Δ has been computed for the first 154 resonances in ^{233}Th (Dyson and Mehta, *loc. cit.*) and yields $\Delta = 3.12$ compared with the value $\Delta = 0.50$ obtained from Eq. (2-113). The rather large disagreement between these values may represent a serious deviation from the model of complete configuration mixing (random matrices), but some caution is necessary before drawing this conclusion, since the value of Δ is sensitive to the inclusion of resonances that may have been incorrectly assigned (impurities or $l = 1$ resonances) and the omission of weak $l = 0$ resonances. To be in agreement with the model of random matrices, about 25% of the observed resonances in ^{233}Th would have to represent incorrect assignments.

The analysis of the ^{233}Th resonances is especially simple because the target nucleus has $I_0 = 0$, in which case, for $l = 0$, all the resonances have $I_r = 1/2$. For odd-A target nuclei ($I_0 \neq 0$), the resonance states can have either of the values $I_r = I_0 \pm 1/2$. Unless the spins of each resonance have been experimentally determined, it becomes necessary to analyze the statistics of resonance properties in terms of the superposition of two resonance sequences that are uncorrelated with respect to each other. The available data on the spacings of resonances observed in the reaction $n+$ (odd-A nucleus) seem to be consistent with such an interpretation if the Wigner distribution is assumed for the spacings in the separate sequences (see, for example, Desjardins *et al.*, 1960).

Distribution of neutron widths (Fig. 2-10)

Additional evidence on the structure of the neutron resonance levels can be obtained from an analysis of the distribution of the neutron widths. As an example, the probability distribution of the reduced widths, $\Gamma_n^{(0)}$, observed for ▲ the resonances in $n + {}^{232}$Th, is plotted in Fig. 2-10. From the discussion in

▼ Appendix 3F, we can obtain the one-particle parentage $P(r)$ of a resonant state, r, from the neutron width,

$$P(r) = \frac{\Gamma_n(r)}{\Gamma_{sp}} = \text{const } E_n^{-1/2}(r)\Gamma_n(r) \tag{2-114}$$

where $E_n(r)$ is the neutron energy at resonance. Thus, the intrinsic property of ▲ the resonance is proportional to the reduced width $\Gamma_n^{(0)} = E_n^{-1/2}(r)\,\Gamma_n(r)$.

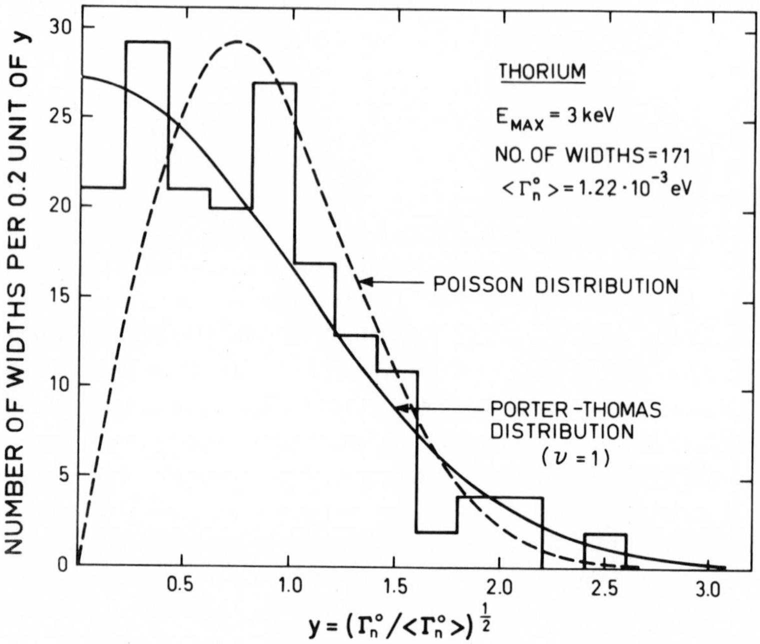

Figure 2-10 The figure plots the probability distribution of the reduced neutron widths observed in the reaction $n + {}^{232}$Th $(\Gamma_n^{(0)}(E_r) = \Gamma_n(E_r)E_r^{-1/2}(\text{eV}))$. The data are taken from J. B. Garg, J. Rainwater, J. S. Petersen, and W. W. Havens, Jr., *Phys. Rev.* **134**, B985 (1964).

▼ The theoretical distribution obtained in the limit of extreme configuration mixing (Porter and Thomas, 1956) is a χ^2 distribution with $\nu = 1$. Since such a distribution varies as $(\Gamma_n^{(0)})^{-1/2}$ for small values of $\Gamma_n^{(0)}$ (see Eq. (2C-28)),

$$P(\Gamma_n^{(0)}) = (2\pi\Gamma_n^{(0)}\langle\Gamma_n^{(0)}\rangle)^{-1/2} \exp\left\{-\frac{\Gamma_n^{(0)}}{2\langle\Gamma_n^{(0)}\rangle}\right\} \tag{2-115}$$

it is convenient to plot the distribution of $(\Gamma_n^{(0)})^{1/2}$. The observed widths in Fig. 2-10 follow the distribution (2-115) rather well, but are in disagreement with the Poisson distribution (a χ^2 distribution with $\nu = 2$; see Eq. (2C-29)).

The good agreement with the expression (2-115) provides some support for the exclusion from the analysis in Figs. 2-9 and 2-10 of the very narrow levels ▲ mentioned in connection with Fig. 2-8. These levels all have values of $\Gamma_n^{(0)}$ of the order $10^{-3}\langle\Gamma_n^{(0)}\rangle$ or smaller, and thus one may conclude that they are $l = 1$ or are characterized by some other quantum number that effectively excludes coupling to the channel corresponding to neutron emission.

Nuclear level density function from neutron evaporation spectra (*Fig. 2-11*)

The detailed study of neutron resonances provides information on the nuclear spectra that is confined to a very narrow energy interval above the neutron separation energy. Evidence on the nuclear level density over a much

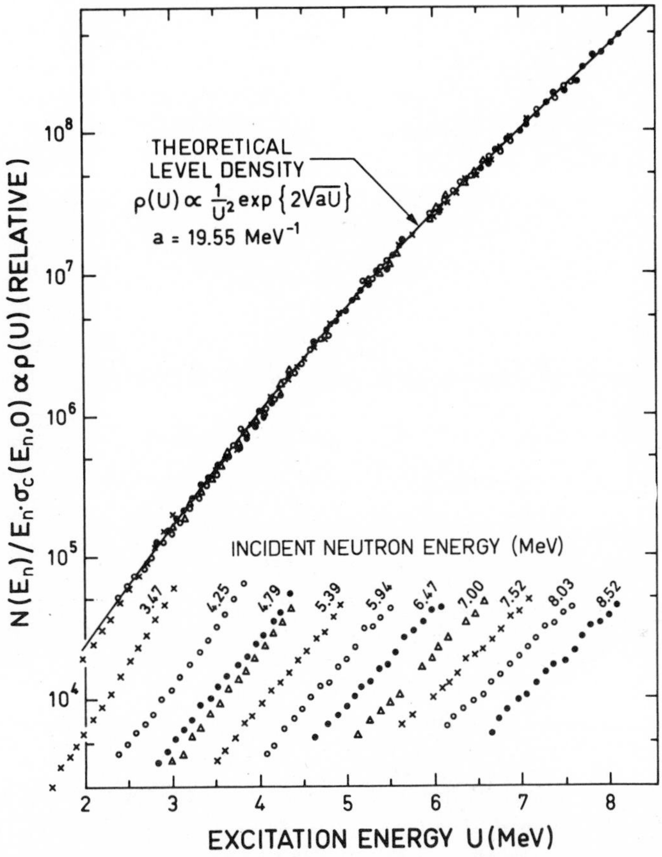

Figure 2-11 The figure gives the level density $\rho(U)$, in relative units, deduced from the energy distribution of neutrons inelastically scattered from Ag. The data are taken from K. Tsukada, S. Tanaka, M. Maruyama, and Y. Tomita, *Nuclear Phys.* **78**, 369 (1966).

wider interval can be obtained from the analysis of the energy distribution of nuclear reaction products. As an example, Fig. 2-11 shows the level density function obtained from neutron inelastic scattering on Ag.

The level density $\rho(U)$, at the excitation energy U, is deduced from the

▼ yield of neutrons, $N(E_n)$, of energy E_n, by employing the statistical relation

$$N(E_n) = \text{const } \rho(U) E_n \sigma_c(E_n, U) \tag{2-116}$$

where $\sigma_c(E_n, U)$ is the cross section for formation of the compound nucleus when the final nucleus at excitation energy U is bombarded by neutrons of energy E_n. (The physical basis of Eq. (2-116) will be further discussed below.)

The cross section $\sigma_c(E_n, U)$ is not directly observable but is expected to be approximately equal to $\sigma_c(E_n, 0)$; in the analysis, the latter cross section has been calculated from the optical model. Owing to the exponential variation of ρ, the main features of the results of the analysis are not very sensitive to the values of σ_c.

Since the yield predicted by Eq. (2-116) decreases approximately as $\exp(-E_n/T)$, where T is the nuclear temperature, reactions that do not proceed through the compound nucleus (direct interactions) are often found to contribute significantly for $E_n \gg T$. Thus, in the present study, the level density has been deduced from a series of experiments, in each of which only the low-energy part of the neutron spectrum ($E_n \leq 1.9$ MeV) has been employed to determine the variation of ρ. By employing different bombarding energies, E_{inc}, the whole range of excitation energies 2 MeV $< U <$ 8 MeV has been covered. The separate results for each bombarding energy are shown at the bottom of the figure, while the upper part represents a composite result obtained by normalizing successive experiments in the region of mutual overlap.

The level density that is determined by this experiment is a weighted average of $\rho(U, I)$, corresponding to the angular momenta I of the final states that are populated. As discussed below, we expect a simple expression of the type (2-116) only if $\rho(U, I)$ is approximately proportional to $\rho(U, I=0)$ (see Eq. (2-122)) for the relevant I values. Therefore, the smooth curve in the figure has been drawn to represent the Fermi gas expression for the density of levels with angular momentum $I = 0$ (see Eq. (2-57)),

$$\rho(U, I=0)_{\text{F.g.}} = \text{const} \frac{1}{U^2} \exp\{2(aU)^{1/2}\} \tag{2-117}$$

in which the coefficient a has been adjusted to fit the data as well as possible.

The level density function obtained from the present data is described rather well by Eq. (2-117), but it is found that in other cases there are significant deviations (Tsukada *et al.*, *loc. cit.*, Fig. 2-11). In a detailed analysis one might attempt to relate these effects to the shell structure (see Sec. 2B-2) and to the pair correlations (see Chapter 8). It is likely that more detailed studies of nuclear level densities may reveal the effects of still other correlation phenomena in the high-energy nuclear spectra.

The essential assumption underlying the above relation (2-116) is that the reaction can be described as a two-stage process of which the first is the formation ▲ of a definite state, the compound nucleus, which subsequently decays in a manner

▼ that is independent of the mode of formation (Bohr, 1936; Weisskopf, 1937). The cross section for going from channel α to channel β can thus be written

$$\sigma(\alpha \to \beta) = \sigma_c(\alpha)\frac{\Gamma_\beta}{\Gamma} \tag{2-118}$$

where $\sigma_c(\alpha)$ is the total cross section for forming the compound nucleus in a channel α. The decay probability per unit time to the channel β is denoted Γ_β, while the total decay rate of the compound nucleus is Γ. The inverse reaction can be written in a similar manner,

$$\sigma(\beta \to \alpha) = \sigma_c(\beta)\frac{\Gamma_\alpha}{\Gamma} \tag{2-119}$$

and thus, from the reciprocity relation (see Eq. (1-43)),

$$\sigma(\alpha \to \beta) = \frac{k_\beta^2}{k_\alpha^2}\sigma(\beta \to \alpha) \tag{2-120}$$

we obtain for the energy spectrum of emitted particles in the channel β

$$\begin{aligned} dN(\beta) &= \sigma(\alpha \to \beta)\rho(\beta)\, dE_\beta \\ &= f(\alpha)k_\beta^2\sigma_c(\beta)\rho(\beta)\, dE_\beta \end{aligned} \tag{2-121}$$

where $f(\alpha)$ depends only on the channel α, and where $\rho(\beta)$ is the density of states of the residual nucleus in channel β. The practical application of Eq. (2-121) requires the additional assumption, noted above, that the cross section $\sigma_c(\beta)$ is approximately the same for each of the channels β of given energy; some direct support for this assumption is provided by the observation that the total reaction cross sections depend in a smooth way on Z and N of the target, and are independent of the detailed configuration of the target state.

The assumption of a unique compound state, depending only on the energy and nucleon numbers, is violated by the conservation of angular momentum and parity. One must therefore consider the above relations for each channel specified by the appropriate angular momentum and parity quantum numbers (for example, lj of the particle, $I\pi$ of the nuclear state, and the total angular momentum of the compound system). One thus obtains the total number of emitted particles per unit energy in terms of a sum of terms of the type (2-121) describing the contribution of each of the angular momentum channels. In order to evaluate this sum and obtain an expression proportional to the total compound nucleus cross section as in Eq. (2-116), it is necessary to make the additional assumptions (see, for example, Goldstein, 1963) that the compound nucleus cross section for specified ljm of the projectile and IM of the target does not depend on the angle between the angular momenta j and I, and further that the angular momentum dependence of the level density of the final nucleus can be approximated by the simple leading-order expression (see Eq. (2-57))

$$\rho(E_\beta, I_\beta) = (2I_\beta + 1)\rho(E_\beta, I_\beta = 0) \tag{2-122}$$

These additional assumptions imply that the emitted particles in the channel β
▲ have an isotropic angular distribution.

▼ The fundamental assumption in the statistical analysis is that the cross section can be factored as in Eq. (2-118). Such a factorization would result automatically if the reaction proceeded through isolated (nonoverlapping) resonance states; the close connection of such resonance states to the bound stationary states of the many-particle system implies the independence of formation and decay in this case (see Sec. 3F-1). However, this picture is rarely applicable in situations where the expression (2-116) may be employed; the existence of many decay channels involving particle emission usually implies that the widths of the resonances are large compared with the spacings of the levels with the same angular momentum and parity. In such cases, when the compound system is formed, there are definite phase relations between the many overlapping resonances that are excited, and in general these phase relations may influence the mode of decay of the system. The relation (2-116) results only if we make the assumption that a truly chaotic (statistical) state of motion is established when the incident particle interacts with the target. We may then expect the memory of the initial formation to rapidly fade away in the subsequent evolution of the compound system (Bohr *et al.*, 1939). The precise significance of the concept of a nuclear level in this region of the spectrum raises interesting questions for further investigation.

Experimental evidence, testing the validity of the statistical assumptions discussed above, is obtained from comparison of the level densities deduced from Eq. (2-116) with a direct count of the number of nuclear levels (see below) from comparison of the yields of reaction products from the same compound system produced through different channels (see, for example, Goshal, 1950; Tanaka, 1960), and from comparison of the reaction yields leaving the final nucleus in definite resolved quantum states (see, for example, Barnard *et al.*, 1966). While this evidence seems to indicate that in most cases the dominant mode of nuclear reaction processes involves the formation of compound systems with statistical properties, a fraction of the total reaction products (typically of order 10%) exhibits energy and angular distributions that imply a completely different mechanism. (See, for example, Appendices 3E and 5A for a discussion of some of the features of these direct interaction processes.) In the analysis of statistical reactions it is thus important to verify that the observed yield is not significantly contaminated by direct reaction products. In the experiments discussed above, the possibility of such contamination was reduced by restricting the measurements to the dominant reaction products. In other studies, the data have been found to seriously violate the statistical assumption (see Wood *et al.*, 1965, and references quoted there.)

Systematics of nuclear level densities (Fig. 2-12)

The main sources of evidence on the nuclear level density function are the following:

▲ (a) the resonance spectra of slow neutrons (see, for example, Figs. 2-8 and 2-9);

▲ (b) the direct count of levels populated in charged particle reactions such as (pp'), (αp), and so on; in such studies it has been possible to establish the first one or two hundred levels in a number of nuclei with mass numbers up to about $A \approx 60$ (examples of this approach have been discussed by Ericson, 1959);

(c) the analysis of evaporation spectra (see, for example, Fig. 2-11).

The evidence on nuclear level densities from sources (a) and (c) is summa-▲ rized in Fig. 2-12. It has been assumed that the level densities follow the Fermi

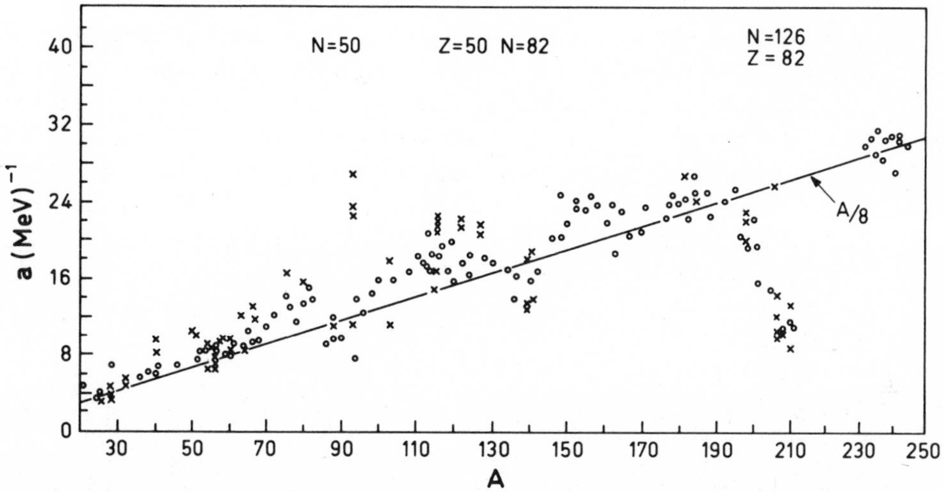

Figure 2-12 The parameter a appearing in the Fermi gas level density formula has been determined by comparison with the average spacings observed in slow neutron resonances (values indicated by o), and from evaporation spectra (values indicated by x). The figure is based on the analysis of E. Erba, U. Facchini, and E. Saetta-Menichella, *Nuovo cimento* **22**, 1237 (1961). This analysis also confirms the consistency with direct level counts.

▼ gas expression, Eq. (2-57), and the measurements determine the parameter

$$a = \frac{\pi^2}{6} g_0 \tag{2-123}$$

which appears in the exponent of the Fermi gas expression.

In the analysis in Fig. 2-12, a very rough correction for pairing effects has been included. Thus, in the level density formula (2-117), the excitation energy U has been replaced by an effective energy U^*, which is taken as

$$\begin{aligned} U^* &= U - 2\Delta && \text{for even-even nuclei} \\ &= U - \Delta && \text{for odd-}A\text{ nuclei} \\ &= U && \text{for odd-odd nuclei} \end{aligned} \tag{2-124}$$

where Δ is the odd-even mass parameter given in Fig. 2-5. This correction implies 20-40% increases in a for the even-even nuclei, and the resulting values do not show any systematic odd-even variation. The more systematic treatment of the ▲ effect of pair correlations on level densities is discussed in Chapter 8.

▼ It is seen that the different methods of estimating a give reasonably consistent results. However, it must be emphasized that, as discussed above, the form of the Fermi gas level density expression is not expected to be quantitatively correct, and in some cases the experimental data seem to establish the existence of deviations. Figure 2-12 should thus be regarded as a very rough summary of the present, very preliminary knowledge of nuclear level densities.

A most striking feature in Fig. 2-12 is the marked decrease in a for configurations near to closed shells. This effect can be understood qualitatively in terms of the appreciable energies required to excite particles from one shell into the next. However, we are not aware of any detailed estimates of the effect using the observed level spacings. The significant dependence of the effective a on the shell structure may also be expected to imply deviations from the simple expression (2-117) for the energy dependence of the level density.

For a uniform Fermi gas, the value of a is given by

$$a = \frac{\pi^2}{6} g(\varepsilon_F) = \frac{\pi^2}{4} \frac{A}{\varepsilon_F} \approx \frac{A}{15} \quad (\text{MeV})^{-1} \tag{2-125}$$

It is seen that the observed values of a are systematically larger than the estimate (2-125). However, $g(\varepsilon_F)$, as given in Eq. (2-125), represents a considerable underestimate of the one-particle level density, since it is based on the particle density at the center of the nucleus and fails to take into account the effect of the sloping sides of the actual nuclear potential (larger effective volume for the motion of particles near the top of the Fermi distribution). An estimate based on the harmonic oscillator potential gives

$$a = \frac{\pi^2}{6} \frac{2(N_{\text{max}} + 3/2)^2}{\hbar\omega_0} \approx \frac{A}{10} \quad (\text{MeV})^{-1} \tag{2-125a}$$

where N_{max} is the total oscillator quantum number of the last filled shell and ω_0 the oscillator frequency. (See Eqs. (2-131), (2-151), and (2-158) for estimates of $\hbar\omega_0$ and of the degeneracy of the oscillator shells.) Despite the rather good agreement between this estimate and the observed level densities, it is not clear that the main physical effects have been properly included in this very simple description of the level density. Further attention should be directed at

(a) the effects of shell structure;
(b) the effects of velocity dependence in the one-particle potential;
(c) a more proper treatment of pair correlations (see Sec. 8-6);
(d) the contribution of collective excitations.

Since both (b) and (c) are expected to systematically reduce the level density as compared with the above estimates, it may be suspected that the independent-quasiparticle description, when properly treated, will lead to an underestimate of the observed level densities. ▲

2-2 EVIDENCE FOR NUCLEAR SHELL STRUCTURE

While a mean free path larger than the average distance between the nucleons is sufficient to ensure the approximate validity of the Fermi gas model, a mean free path larger than the dimensions of the whole system, as indicated by the scattering experiments referred to above (see Fig. 2-3), leads to regularities associated with the quantized orbits of the individual nucleons. Especially striking effects occur if the system has a spherically symmetric shape. One can then characterize each orbital by the total nucleonic angular momentum j, and such orbits have a $(2j+1)$-fold degeneracy associated with the different spatial orientations of the angular momentum vector j. Just as in the electronic structure of atoms, the degeneracy of the single-particle orbits leads to marked discontinuities in many nuclear properties (shell structure effects).

We shall consider in this section a few very direct manifestations of the nuclear shell structure. (A more systematic presentation may be found in Mayer and Jensen, 1955.) The analysis of the nuclear spectra considered in the following chapters provides, almost at each step, further evidence for the shell structure.

It should be emphasized that the deviations from a uniform spacing of the single-particle levels have a significant effect on the binding of only the last few nucleons and are therefore of rather minor importance for the bulk properties of nuclei. In terms of the expansion of the total binding energy (2-12), the shell structure appears as a small correction compared to the surface energy, and the observed fluctuations in the binding energy function amount to only about 1% (see Fig. 2-4). Despite the smallness of these effects on the scale of the total nuclear energy, they are of decisive importance for the structure of the low-energy nuclear spectra, which are especially sensitive to the configurations of the few most weakly bound nucleons. This circumstance made it relatively difficult to discern the nuclear shell structure as long as the main information on nuclei was confined to binding energies. With the systematic measurement of nuclear moments and excitation spectra, the evidence for shell structure became overwhelming (Haxel, Jensen, and Suess, 1949; Mayer, 1949).

2-2a Binding Energies

Nuclear separation energies show discontinuities of the same type as those observed in the atomic ionization potentials, as is illustrated in Figs. 2-13 to 2-16, pp. 191ff. The major discontinuities in the nuclear binding energies occur for nucleon numbers 2, 8, 20, 28, 50, 82, and 126. These numbers are the counterpart in nuclear structure to the atomic numbers ($Z=2$, 10, 18, 36, 54, and 86) characterizing the noble gasses. As in the atomic case, these numbers correspond to the closing of shells that have an especially large energy separation from the next higher orbital (major shell closings). When other shells are completed, smaller effects are sometimes observed (subshell effects), as for the atomic numbers 4, 12, 30, 48, and 80 and nucleon numbers 6, 16, 40, and 58. The fact that the shell closures for protons and for neutrons occur at the same nucleon numbers implies that the shape of the binding field of the protons is similar to that for the neutrons.

From Figs. 2-13, 2-15, and 2-16, it is seen that the relative discontinuities in the nuclear binding energies are somewhat smaller (by a factor of about 2 or 3) than those observed in the atomic ionization potentials. This may be attributed to the different radial shape of the binding potential in the two systems.

2-2b Excitation Energies of Even-Even Nuclei

A very sensitive measure of the stability of the nucleus is the energy required to excite the nuclear ground state. On account of the pairing effect, the even-even nuclei (even Z and even N) show the simplest systematics. All such nuclei have vanishing total angular momentum and even parity in the ground state ($I\pi = 0+$), and with very few exceptions the first excited state has $I\pi = 2+$. We shall later see that these rules are simple consequences of the nucleonic interactions. The known excitation energies of the first (2+) excited states of even-even nuclei are given in Fig. 2-17, p. 197. It is seen that the excitation energies exhibit dramatic maxima at the shell closings superimposed on the gradual decrease with increasing A, which is a consequence of the increase in nuclear size.

VIP

The systematically occurring 2+ states represent the most easily excited nuclear degrees of freedom. For the nuclei with closed shells in both neutrons and protons, the excitations are associated with transitions of nucleons from the filled shells into higher orbits, while, for nuclei with particles in unfilled shells, the 2+ states involve rearrangements of the particles within the degenerate orbits.

2-2c Level Densities

Most of the evidence for the nuclear shell structure refers to the detailed features of the low-energy spectra. However, it is also found that, at excitation energies of 5–10 MeV, the total density of states is affected in a major way by the shell structure (see Fig. 2-12). In particular, nuclei with approximately closed shell configurations have level densities that are several orders of magnitude smaller than in other nuclei at similar excitation energies. Such an effect can be understood in terms of the large energy required to excite a particle from one shell to another, which in closed shell nuclei implies an effective reduction of the degrees of freedom available for a given total excitation energy.

ILLUSTRATIVE EXAMPLES TO SECTION 2-2

Ionization potential of neutral atoms (*Fig. 2-13*)

The separation energy (ionization potential) of the last electron of the neutral atoms is plotted in Fig. 2-13 as a function of the atomic number Z. The

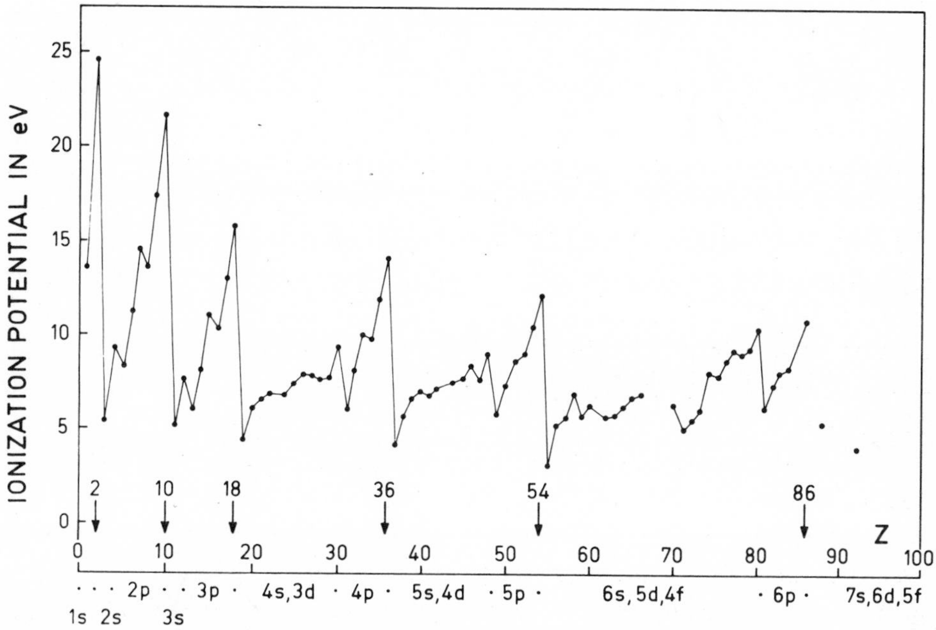

Figure 2-13 The values of the atomic ionization potentials are taken from the compilation by Moore (1949). The dots under the abscissa indicate closed shells.

shell structure is strikingly exhibited in the decrease of the separation energy after the completion of each major shell. Subshell structure is also discernible. (See, for example, the maxima at $Z = 4$ and 12 associated with the filling of the $2s$ and $3s$ orbits, and at $Z = 30$ and 48 associated with completion of the $(4s + 3d)$ and $(5s + 4d)$ shells.) The small maxima at $Z = 7$, 15, and 33 occur at the middle of the filling of the p shells, and reflect the fact that in these configurations it is possible to achieve a maximum number of antisymmetric bonds between the p

▼ electrons, and therefore a minimum in the Coulomb repulsion (see the more detailed discussion of these configurations in Chapter 7). This effect is analogous to the increased binding of the light nuclei with $A = 4n$ (see Fig. 2-4).

A rough measure of the adequacy of a shell model description of the atomic states may be obtained by comparing the energy differences between shells (as indicated by the magnitude of the discontinuities in Fig. 2-13) with the interaction energy of two electrons in a given configuration. The latter interaction effects are typically a few electron volts (see Chapter 7) and thus less by a factor of 3 to 10 than the major shell separations.

Separation energies of neutrons and protons (*Figs. 2-14, 2-15, and 2-16*)

The variations in the neutron and proton separation energies reveal the nuclear shell structure just as the variations in the ionization potentials reflect the corresponding shell structure of atoms. The nuclear counterpart to the plot of ▲ ionization potentials (Fig. 2-13) is illustrated in Fig. 2-14; the lines connect

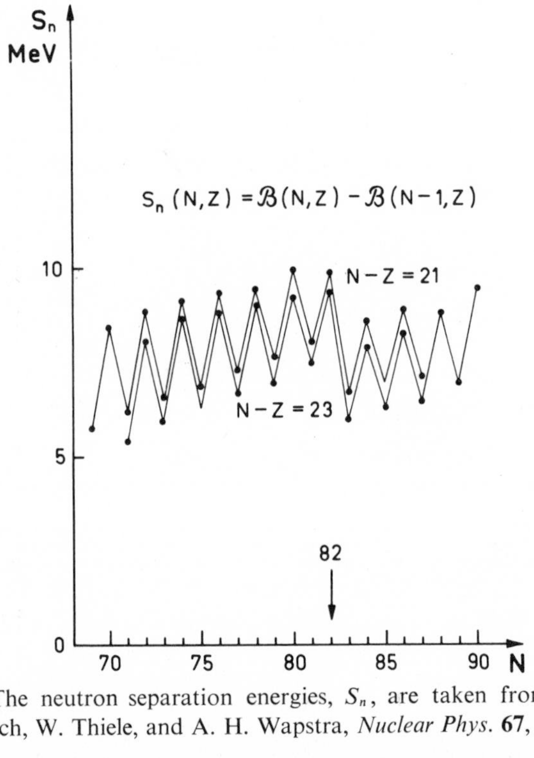

Figure 2-14 The neutron separation energies, S_n, are taken from the compilation by J. H. E. Mattauch, W. Thiele, and A. H. Wapstra, *Nuclear Phys.* **67**, 1 (1965).

▼ nuclides of constant neutron excess. Figure 2-14 differs most strikingly from Fig. 2-13 because of the rapid variations associated with the pairing energy effect in nuclei. These variations are of similar magnitude to the energy discontinuities associated with closed shells, and thus the shell structure effect is rather difficult to discern in Fig. 2-14.

▲ In order to avoid the rapid oscillations exhibited in Fig. 2-14, the neutron

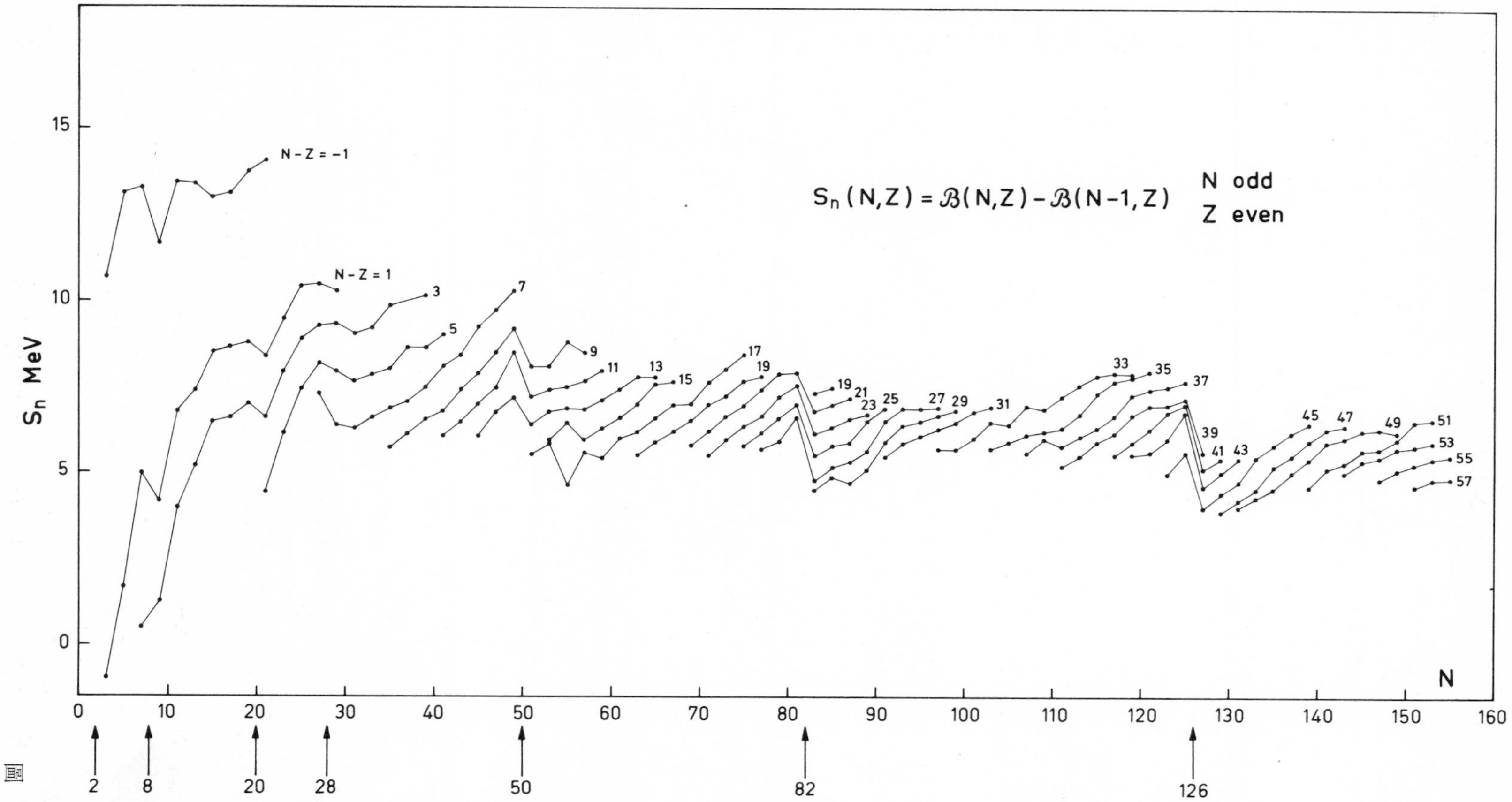

Figure 2-15 The neutron separation energies, S_n, are taken from the compilation by J. H. E. Mattauch, W. Thiele, and A. H. Wapstra, *Nuclear Phys.* **67**, 1 (1965).

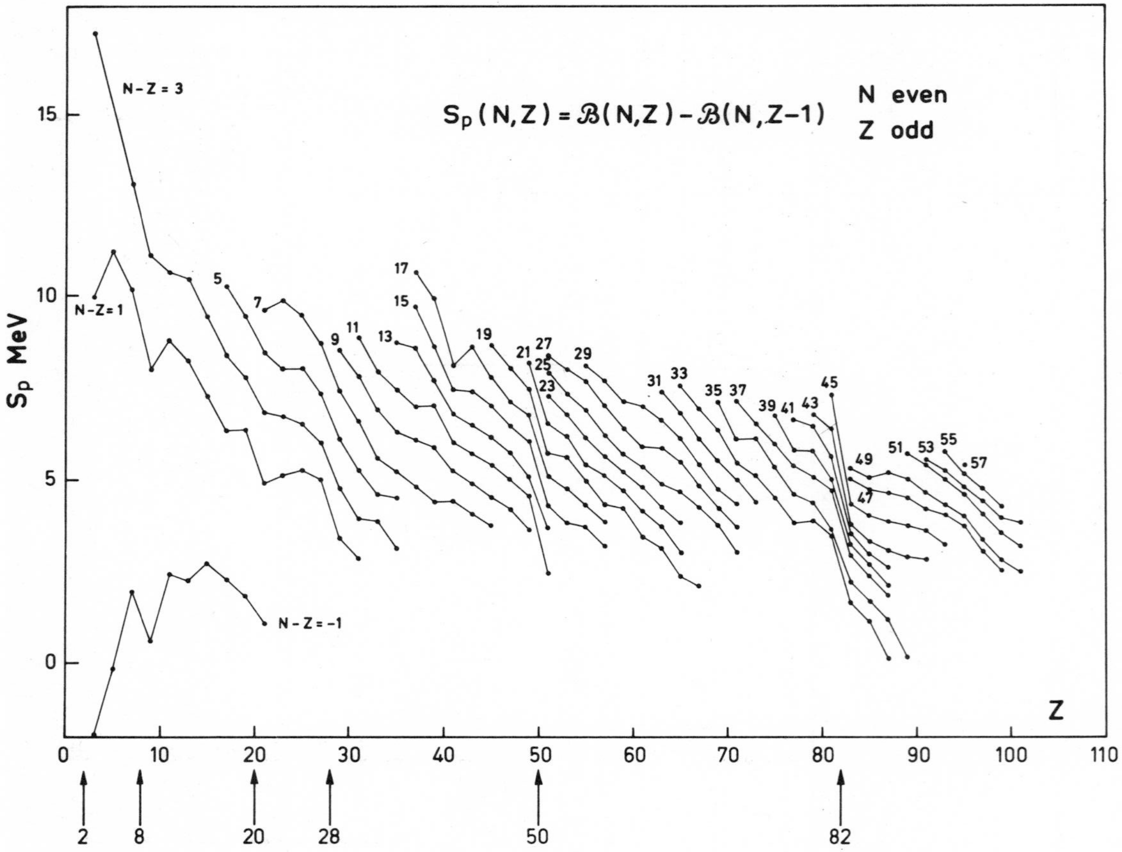

Figure 2-16 The proton separation energies, S_p, are taken from the compilation by J. H. E. Mattauch, W. Thiele, and A. H. Wapstra, *Nuclear Phys.* **67**, 1 (1965).

▼ separation energies of nuclei with odd N and even Z are plotted in Fig. 2-15 (the nuclei with odd Z are omitted only in order to slightly simplify the figure). Again, the lines connect nuclides with constant neutron excess. The neutron shell structure is exhibited, as in the corresponding plot for atoms (Fig. 2-13), by the maxima in the separation energies corresponding to closed shell configurations.

In estimating the magnitude of the energy differences between the major closed shells, it is necessary to take into account the fact that the pair correlation is much less effective in lowering the energy of a closed shell configuration than of other configurations with even nucleon numbers (see Chapter 8). Thus, the energy difference $\delta\varepsilon$ between shells, as obtained directly from the present figure, is an underestimate. For $\delta\varepsilon \gg \Delta$, a better estimate is obtained by adding 2Δ to the observed discontinuity in the masses. In this way, we estimate values of $\delta\varepsilon$ that are about 3 or 4 MeV between the major closed shells at $N = 50$, 82, and 126.

The proton separation energies for odd Z and even N are plotted as a function of the proton number Z in Fig. 2-16, and, as in Fig. 2-15, the lines connect nuclides with constant neutron excess. The proton shell structure is revealed by the sharp drops in the separation energy at the beginning of each new shell. It is seen that the proton closed shells occur for the same nucleon numbers as for neutrons and that the energy separations in the one-particle spectra are of similar magnitude.

The addition of equal numbers of neutrons and protons leads eventually to the limit $S_p = 0$ as a result of the Coulomb energy and therefore, in Fig. 2-16, the systematic trend of the lines is downward. Thus, the closed shells appear as sharp inflections in the curves of proton binding energies, rather than as maxima, in contrast to the corresponding figure for neutrons.

Systematics of excitation energies of 2+ states (Fig. 2-17)

In Fig. 2-17, the energy of the lowest state with $I\pi = 2+$ in each even-even nucleus is given as a function of the number of neutrons and protons, N and Z. The systematics of these levels not only reveals the shell structure in a dramatic manner, but is an important key to many features of the nuclear structure and will be a recurring theme in almost every chapter of the present work. Especially significant in this connection is the fact that the quadrupole transition probabilities connecting the 2+ states with the ground state are found to be strongly enhanced in comparison with the single-particle unit (see Fig. 4-1). This striking evidence for collective behavior provides the starting point for the analysis in terms of rotational and vibrational motion.

The 2+ states represent the first excited state in almost all even-even nuclei. The known exceptions are ^{4}He(0+), ^{14}C(1−), ^{16}O(0+), ^{40}Ca(0+), ^{72}Ge(0+), ^{90}Zr(0+), and ^{208}Pb(3−). ▲

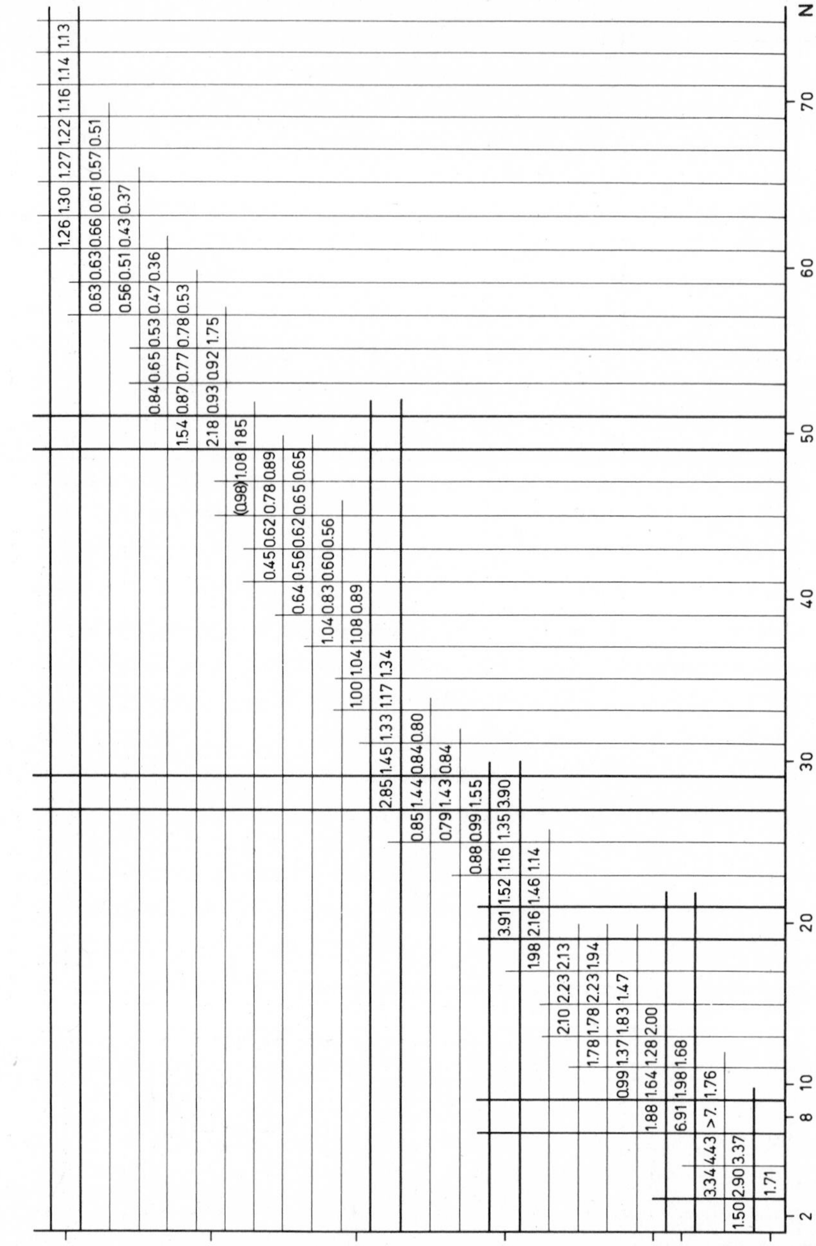

Figure 2-17a See caption to Figure. 2-17b.

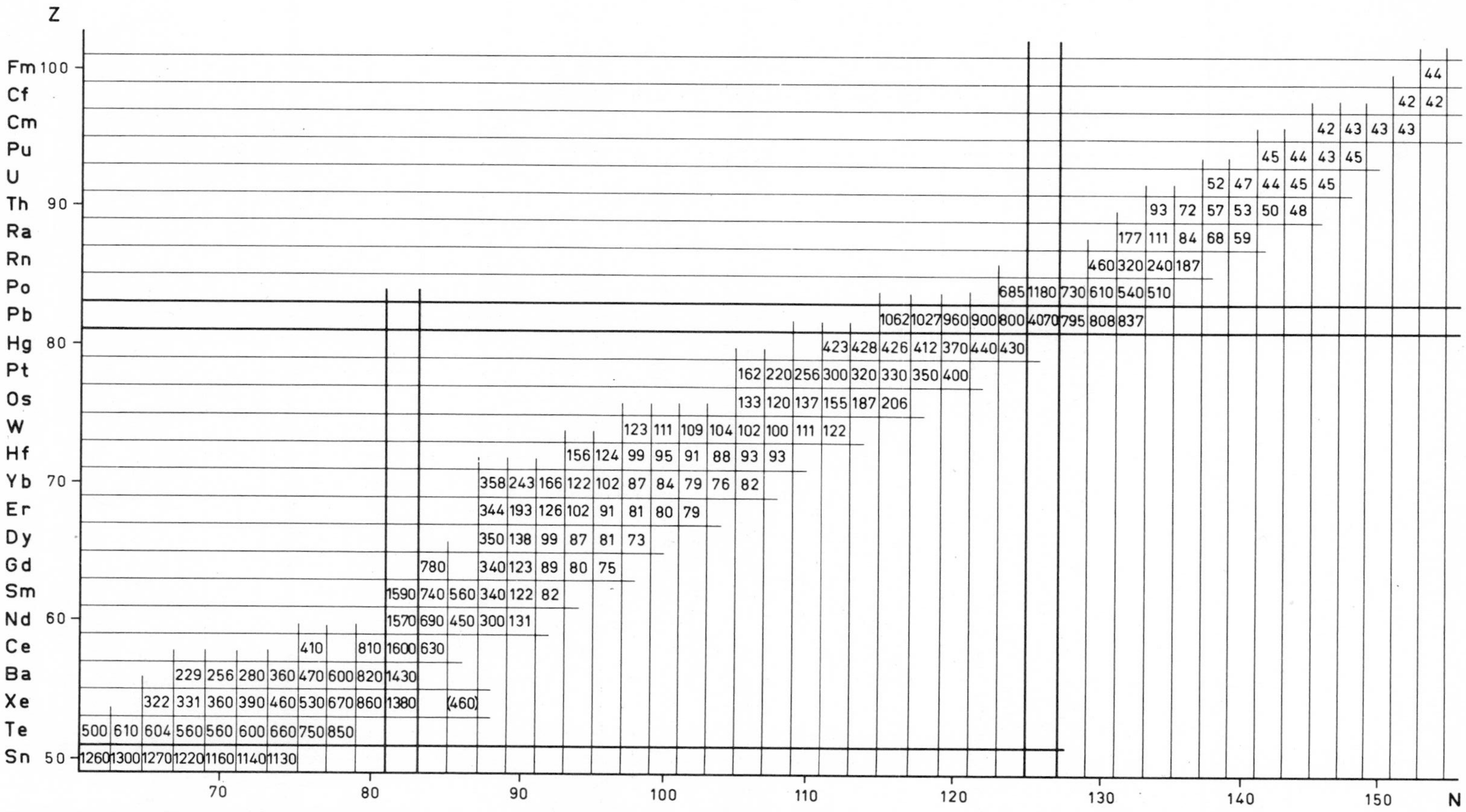

Figure 2-17b The energies of the first excited 2+ states of even-even nuclei are given as a function of N and Z. In Fig. 2-17a ($Z \leq 50$), the energies are in MeV, while in Fig. 2-17b ($Z \geq 50$), the energies are in keV. The data are taken from *Nuclear Data Sheets* and the *Table of Isotopes* by Lederer *et al.* (1967). The striking systematics in the energies of the first excited states of even-even nuclei was emphasized at an early stage in the development of nuclear spectroscopy (Stähelin and Preiswerk, 1951; Rosenblum and Valadares, 1952; Asaro and Perlman, 1952; Scharff-Goldhaber, 1952, 1953).

2-3 NUCLEAR SPECIES AND ABUNDANCES

On the basis of the energy systematics derived from the Fermi gas model with the added refinements of shell structure and pairing effects, it is possible to obtain a rather detailed interpretation of the stability of nuclei and the relative abundances of the naturally occurring nuclear species.

2-3a Nuclear Stability

Figure 2-18, p. 203, shows the known β-stable species. The broad variation of the β-stable region is determined by the competition between the symmetry and Coulomb energies. Superimposed on this smooth trend, the shell structure implies a tendency for the region of greatest stability to follow along the lines associated with closed shells of protons or neutrons. Another aspect of the same effect is the especially large number of stable isotopes or isotones that occur when the stability line crosses a closed shell line away from a region of doubly closed shells. (See especially $Z = 50$ and $N = 82$.)

The pairing energy, although small compared to binding energies, plays an interesting role in determining the naturally occurring nuclear species. For odd-A nuclei, there is only a single β-stable isobar, although in a few cases the β-decay energy is so low or the spin difference so high that the lifetime for β transformation becomes comparable with the age of the elements (^{87}Rb, ^{113}Cd, ^{115}In, ^{187}Re). For even-A nuclei, the pairing energy implies that the energies of even-even nuclei are systematically lower than those of odd-odd nuclei by the amount 2Δ, which, except for the lightest nuclei, is somewhat larger than the energy difference $2(b_{sym}/A + 3e^2/5R_c)$ associated with going one unit in Z away from the energy minimum in $N - Z$ (combine Eq. (2-12) and Fig. 2-5). As a consequence, there are no β-stable odd-odd nuclei after ^{14}N; the natural occurrence of ^{40}K, ^{50}V, ^{138}La, ^{176}Lu, and ^{180}Ta is associated with the very high spins of these nuclei, implying β-decay lifetimes comparable with the age of the elements. On account of the very long lifetime associated with double β decay (see Appendix 3D), all the even-even isobars whose masses are lower than the odd-odd neighbors are effectively β stable. Thus, one commonly finds two or three naturally occurring even-even isobars in the regions of heavy elements.

Estimates are also given in Fig. 2-18 of the domain of expected stability against proton or neutron emission, beyond which the experimental conditions for studying nuclear properties are radically altered. Although, in principle, this whole domain of semistable nuclei is available for nuclear spectroscopic studies, at the present time such evidence is practically confined to the β-stable isotopes and those immediately adjacent (see, for example, Fig. 2-17). In defining the upper limits of Z and N for the domain of nuclei that is in principle available to spectroscopic studies, the occurrence of spontaneous fission becomes of importance for nuclei with large Z. With increasing Coulomb energy, the spontaneous fission half-lives rapidly decrease. For sufficiently large A, spontaneous fission is expected to occur almost instantaneously even for nuclei near the neutron emission line, and thus to terminate the domain of semistable nuclei. Attempts to estimate the extent of the semistable region have been made on the basis of extrapolations of available systematics (Wheeler. 1955, and other references quoted in connection with Fig. 2-18). It has been suggested that the increased stability of expected new closed shell configurations may make possible the study of nuclei in the region around $A \sim 300$ (Myers and Swiatecki, 1966).

2-3b Relative Abundances and Nucleogenesis

The relative abundances with which the different nuclear species occur in our part of the universe are found to have many striking features that can be correlated with properties of the individual nuclei and which thereby have provided important clues regarding the processes by which the elements have been formed. The detailed examination of the different evidence seems to indicate that a multitude of nuclear processes occurring in stars at different stages of evolution have contributed to element formation. Without attempting to enter on a systematic description of these mechanisms, we shall briefly mention a few conclusions that appear to follow rather directly from the nuclear physics evidence. For a detailed discussion of this exciting chapter of nuclear astrophysics, see Burbidge *et al.* (1957), and, for more recent developments, the reviews by Burbidge (1962) and Strömgren (1968).

The empirical abundance curve for $A > 50$ exhibits two striking features (see Fig. 2-19, p. 206). First, the pronounced peak in the region of Fe and, second, a gradual decrease toward the heavier elements on which are superimposed a number of smaller peaks.

The peak near Fe has been explained as essentially reflecting the position of ^{56}Fe and the neighboring nuclei, as the most stable of all nuclear species; these nuclei would therefore acquire a maximum abundance under conditions of nuclear processes in thermal equilibrium. It is envisaged that the steps leading toward equilibrium involve first the collection of primordial matter resulting from the early development of the universe into stars and the nuclear "burning" of hydrogen to ^{4}He at temperatures of around 10^7 °K ($kT \sim 1$ keV). With the exhaustion of hydrogen in the core, the star contracts, and the associated rise in temperature makes it possible for α particles to react and to form ^{12}C and ^{16}O (at about $kT \sim 10$ keV). With a still further rise in temperature, these nuclei in turn react and ultimately produce the most stable nuclei in the region of $A \sim 60$. The detailed structure of the abundance peak at Fe is sensitive to temperature, density, and the duration of the extreme conditions in which the equilibrium has been established. The duration is important, since initially the material retains the equality $N = Z$ characteristic of the lighter elements from which it has been formed. With the passage of time, β^+ processes, and especially electron capture, create a neutron excess, which is characteristic of the most stable nuclei around $A \sim 60$. Indeed, the maximum binding energy occurs at ^{60}Ni (see Fig. 2-4), but of the $N = Z$ nuclei, the most stable is probably ^{56}Ni (as a result of the doubly closed shells, $N = Z = 28$). Detailed analysis of the observed abundances suggests that the elements around Fe were produced under the conditions $kT \approx 300$ keV, $\rho \approx 3 \times 10^6$ g/cm^3, and that these conditions prevailed for a time of order $t \sim 3 \times 10^4$ sec (Fowler and Hoyle, 1964). The appearance of this material in the earth and sun requires that some violent disruptive event terminated the approach to equilibrium and distributed some of the highly evolved stellar material into interstellar space, from where it has been reassembled to form the solar system.

The formation of nuclei heavier than Fe appears to involve principally the successive capture of neutrons followed by β-decay processes. This conclusion is partly suggested by the conspicuous peaks in the abundance curve associated with the closed shell neutron numbers 50, 82, and 126 (see Fig. 2-19). Additional support comes from the asymmetry in the observed abundances with respect to the line of greatest stability. Thus, there are a number of stable nuclei on the neutron-deficient side that cannot be formed by the neutron capture processes, and, as illustrated in Fig. 2-20, p. 207, these nuclei have abundances that are invariably smaller by more than an order of magnitude than the neighboring stable isotopes. On the contrary, the isotopes on the neutron excess side, which could not be formed by proton capture processes, are found to have abundances comparable with those on the stability line.

The isotopes produced in the neutron capture chain depend on the rate of the capture processes as compared with the β-decay rates, which are typically of order hours to days near the stability line and which decrease to a fraction of a second near the limits of stability for neutron emission shown in Fig. 2-18. Under conditions of low neutron flux, where β stability is established at every step before the next neutron capture can occur, the process follows the path shown in Fig. 2-20. The abundances along this path will depend inversely on the neutron capture cross sections, which determine the waiting time at each point. Since these capture cross sections are abnormally small for nuclei with closed neutron shells, a characteristic feature of the neutron capture process on a slow time scale (the *s* process) is the appearance of peaks in the abundance curves at the neutron numbers $N = 50, 82, 126$.

The smallness of the capture cross sections for closed shell nuclei may be understood from the fact that, in the relevant energy region $E_n \sim kT \sim 10 - 100$ keV, the capture is due to many well-separated resonances with $\Gamma_n > \Gamma_\gamma$. In such circumstances, the contribution of each resonance is simply proportional to Γ_γ, and the average cross section for any nucleus is proportional to Γ_γ/D, where D is the average spacing of the resonances. The total radiation width, Γ_γ, does not vary very much from nucleus to nucleus, corresponding to the fact that it represents a sum of many contributions from the different possible transitions to lower-lying states. Thus, the most important factor in the capture cross sections is the level spacing, D, at excitation energies approximately equal to the neutron separation energy. In closed shell nuclei, D is exceptionally large, partly because of the reduced binding energy of the added neutron, and partly because of the large energy required to excite a particle from the filled shells into the next empty shells (see Sec. 2-2c and the data in Fig. 2-12, p. 187).

The systematic measurement of capture cross sections has made possible a rather detailed correlation with abundance data for the nuclides produced in the *s* processes. (The cross sections are reviewed by Macklin and Gibbons, 1965 and 1967, while a "Handbuch der *s*-Prozesse" has been written by Seeger *et al.*, 1965.) This correlation has in turn provided information on the astrophysical conditions (temperature, neutron density, duration of exposure, and so on) in which these elements were synthesized.

If the neutron capture proceeds more rapidly than the corresponding β decays, the process leads initially to isotopes on the neutron excess side of the stability line, which subsequently decay, producing the most neutron-rich isobars. In this manner, many nuclides can be produced that are not reached by the slow process. The appreciable abundance observed for these neutron-rich isotopes indicates that such more rapid capture processes (*r* processes) have also played an important role in the evolution of the material found in the solar system.

For sufficiently great neutron fluxes, neutron capture continues at a given Z until the line of instability for neutron emission is approached. The relative abundances in such a process depend on the β-decay lifetimes of these extremely neutron-rich nuclides, since these lifetimes determine the waiting times for neutron addition. In Fig. 2-20, a tentative capture path is indicated for such a fast process. The shell structure, implying an exceptionally weak binding of the 83rd neutron, here manifests itself by the vertical break in the capture path. As a consequence, the path approaches rather close to the stability line near $A \sim 130$. The relatively low β-decay energies at this point thus imply a relatively long waiting and large abundance of nuclei with mass numbers in this region. In this way, the observed abundance peaks at $A \sim 80$, 130, and 194 have been correlated with the neutron shell closings at $N = 50$, 82, and 126.

The observed abundances for the elements above Fe thus suggest the operation of two essentially different synthesizing processes, the slow and fast neutron capture reactions. A number of finer details in the abundances and more quantitative theoretical estimates support this interpretation. Another mechanism is required for the production of the small amounts of very neutron-deficient nuclides, and it has been suggested that (p, γ) and (γ, n) processes are involved.

Considerable progress has been made in correlating the postulated element-synthesizing nuclear processes with astronomical evidence regarding the physical conditions and evolution of the stars. Thus, the slow neutron capture is supposed to take place in the Red Giant stage. In these rather highly evolved stars in which hydrogen has been exhausted in the core, the main source of energy is the burning of α particles. The neutrons for the s process may be produced by exothermic (α, n) reactions, such as $^{13}C(\alpha, n)^{16}O$ and $^{21}Ne(\alpha, n)^{24}Mg$, and in the slightly endothermic $^{22}Ne(\alpha, n)^{25}Mg$, as well as in the heavy ion reactions $^{12}C(^{12}C, n)^{23}Mg$ and $^{16}O(^{16}O, n)^{31}S$. The short duration and violent conditions of the equilibrium process responsible for the Fe group have suggested an association with supernovae (see the extensive discussion by Fowler and Hoyle, 1964). There exists much greater uncertainty concerning the site of the r process, but it may be that the necessary conditions are found in the extended and quasistellar radio objects (Hoyle and Fowler, 1963; Seeger *et al.*, 1965).

It should be emphasized that many of the deductions mentioned above are somewhat speculative, involving considerable extrapolation of the observational data. The great richness in the nuclear phenomena, however, opens wide perspectives for elucidating the events of cosmological evolution.

In connection with such cosmological considerations, it is of interest to bear in mind that the study of nuclear collisions at very high energies ($>10^9$ eV) has led to the discovery of antinucleons, the existence of which had been anticipated on the basis of Dirac's relativistic theory of spin 1/2 particles. The symmetry between particles and antiparticles, which appears to be a basic law of nature, implies that antinucleons will interact with each other with the same forces as observed for nucleons. One thus expects that there can exist antimatter built from antiparticles, with properties corresponding to those of ordinary matter. The two types of matter, however, annihilate each other and thus cannot coexist in the same domain of space. The asymmetry between the abundance of matter and antimatter in the immediate neighborhood of the earth may perhaps be related to the special history of this region of the universe (see Alfvén, 1965, and references given there).

ILLUSTRATIVE EXAMPLES TO SECTION 2-3

β-stable nuclides (*Fig. 2-18*)

Some of the qualitative trends in the nuclear stability are illustrated in Fig. 2-18. The boxes (both solid and open) represent the known β-stable species plotted as a function of the number of neutrons, N, and number of protons, Z. The general trend of this "valley of β stability" may be obtained by minimizing the total mass $\mathcal{M}$ for fixed total number of nucleons A,

$$\left.\frac{\partial \mathcal{M}}{\partial N}\right|_{A=\text{const}} = 0 \tag{2-126}$$

Using Eq. (2-12) for the binding energy $\mathcal{B}(N, Z)$ we obtain

$$(N - Z)_{\beta\text{-stable}} = \frac{\dfrac{3}{5}\dfrac{e^2}{R_c}A - (M_n - M_p)}{2\dfrac{b_{\text{sym}}}{A} + \dfrac{3}{5}\dfrac{e^2}{R_c}} \approx 6 \times 10^{-3} A^{5/3} \tag{2-127}$$

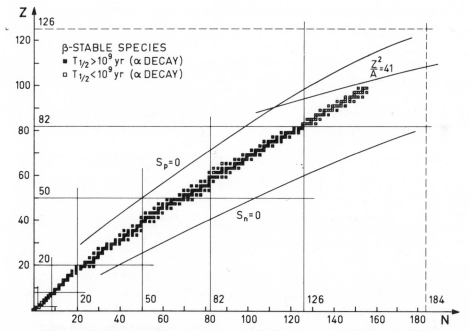

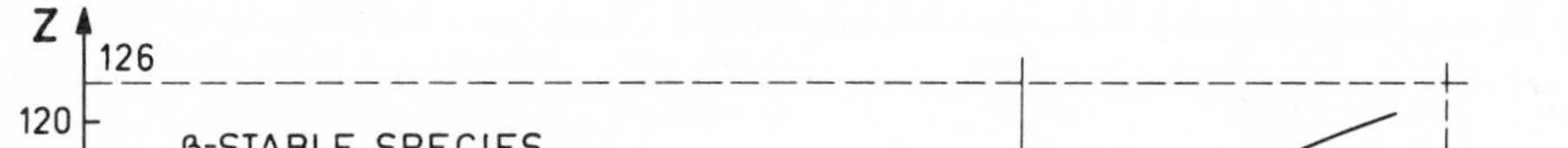

Figure 2-18 The β-stable nuclear species are plotted as a function of N and Z. The data are taken from the Table of Isotopes by D. Strominger, J. M. Hollander, and G. T. Seaborg, *Rev. Mod. Phys.* **30**, 585 (1958).

▼ Superimposed on the smooth trend described by Eq. (2-127), the valley of β stability exhibits a number of significant twistings and turnings. These local variations are mainly the result of the special stability associated with closed shell configurations (see, for example, the discontinuity at $Z = 20$ and 50 and at $N = 82$).

Another stability limit of significance for nuclear physics as well as for astrophysics is the value of the neutron excess for which the neutron separation energy is equal to zero ($S_n = 0$). This limit may be estimated from the average mass formula (2-12) by solving the equation

$$\left.\frac{\partial \mathscr{B}}{\partial N}\right|_{Z=\mathrm{const}} = 0 \tag{2-128}$$

and the resulting curve is drawn in Fig. 2-18. The limit for $S_p = 0$ has been estimated in a similar manner. These average estimates ignore the local deviations caused by shell structure as well as the interesting structure of the transition region (where S_n or $S_p \approx 0$), which is influenced by odd-even effects. For more detailed estimates of these limits, see Wheeler (1955), Baz *et al.* (1960), Karnaukhov and Ter-Akopyan (1964), and Myers and Swiatecki (1966). It should be emphasized that these estimates of stability with respect to particle emission represent rather extreme extrapolations of the available mass systematics, and therefore direct experimental measurements in the regions of particle instability would be very valuable.

In connection with the particle stability regions, it is important to recognize that expressions such as (2-12) represent expansions that are only valid in the neighborhood of the β-stable valley. Such expansions cannot answer questions concerning the possibility of particle-stable nuclear systems with very different composition and structure, as, for example, the possibility of a system consisting entirely of neutrons. Available estimates indicate that a pure neutron system would be unbound (Levinger and Simmons, 1961), but the question is a difficult one, since such a system might have a rather different structure from that of conventional nuclei.

In this connection, it should also be remembered that, for an electrically neutral system, the very weak, but long-range, gravitational forces will eventually come to dominate, with increasing nucleon number. The critical nucleon number for which the gravitational potential energy per nucleon ($\sim GAM^2R^{-1} \sim GA^{2/3}M^2r_0^{-1}$) is of the same magnitude as the nuclear energy ($\sim \hbar^2(Mr_0^2)^{-1}$) is

$$A_{\mathrm{crit}} \sim \left(\frac{\hbar^2}{GM^3r_0}\right)^{3/2} \sim 10^{56} \tag{2-129}$$

where G is the gravitational constant ($=7 \times 10^{-8}\ \mathrm{g}^{-1}\ \mathrm{cm}^3\ \mathrm{sec}^{-2}$). The nucleon number (2-129) corresponds to a total mass $A_{\mathrm{crit}}M \sim 2 \times 10^{32}$ g $\sim 10^{-1}\ M_\odot$, where $M_\odot$ is the mass of the sun. Such neutron stars may represent a stage in the evolution of stellar systems, and the problem of locating and identifying these ▲ objects presents a challenging question for theoretical and observational astron-

▼ omy. Because of the nonsaturating character of the gravitational interaction, the stability of systems with mass numbers appreciably greater than A_{crit} poses questions that cannot be answered within the framework of our present understanding of gravitation and nuclear systems. (See Wheeler, 1964, and the more detailed review by Harrison *et al.*, 1965.)

Spontaneous fission and instability with respect to α emission provide additional limitations to the available nuclear species. All nuclei heavier than about $A \approx 100$ are unstable with respect to fission, but the lifetime of this process is so long that it is unimportant, except in the heaviest nuclei. As discussed in Chapter 6, the liquid drop description of the fission process suggests that fissionability depends on the ratio of the Coulomb energy ($\propto Z^2 A^{-1/3}$) to surface energy ($\propto A^{+2/3}$). Thus, the lifetime for spontaneous fission depends on the parameter Z^2/A, and the *locus* $Z^2/A = 41$ drawn in Fig. 2-18 is expected to correspond to lifetimes in the region of seconds (compare $T_{1/2}^{\text{fiss}}(^{260}104) \approx 0.3$ sec (Flerov *et al.*, 1964)). It should be emphasized, however, that there are many features of the spontaneous fission lifetimes that are not understood. In particular, it appears that the fission barriers are strongly affected by the nuclear shell structure, and predictions concerning the stability of the heaviest nuclei, therefore, require a more detailed analysis of the potential energy of deformation (Gustafson *et al.*, 1967; Strutinski, 1967). It may also be noted that the fissionability of the heavy elements is rather sensitive to a possible symmetry-dependent term in the surface energy, which may imply a more severe limit resulting from fission instability in the heaviest elements.

Many nuclei throughout the periodic system are unstable with respect to α emission. However, below ^{208}Pb, only ^{5}He, ^{8}Be, ^{146}Sm, ^{148,150}Gd, and ^{154}Dy have lifetimes so short that this decay mode affects their abundance in nature or use in nuclear physics experiments. β-stable nuclides with α-decay half-lives less than 10^9 years are drawn in Fig. 2-18 as open boxes. The lowered stability of the nuclear configurations with only a few particles outside of closed shells is exhibited by the sudden drop in α-decay half-lives after the closed shells of $N = 82$ and especially after $N = 126$, $Z = 82$.

Abundances of even-even nuclear species with $A > 50$ (Fig. 2-19)

The relative abundances of the different nuclear species are derived from a many-sided analysis of available evidence concerning terrestrial abundances, solar wind, meteoric composition, and solar spectroscopy. The relative isotopic abundances, obtained from terrestrial and meteoric samples, play a special role in the analysis. A smooth curve has been drawn in Fig. 2-19 to approximately follow the experimental points. Considerable uncertainty still attaches to many of the determinations.

For elements lighter than those plotted in Fig. 2-19, the most conspicuous feature is the great preponderance of ^{1}H and ^{4}He. In the units employed, $H(^1\text{H}) \approx 4 \times 10^{10}$, and $H(^4\text{He}) \approx 3 \times 10^9$. ▲

▼ The odd-A species for the region of elements considered have abundances that are systematically somewhat less than those of neighboring even-A nuclei, which can be understood in terms of the tendency for neutron capture cross ▲ sections to be greater for odd than for even nuclei. (See the discussion of the

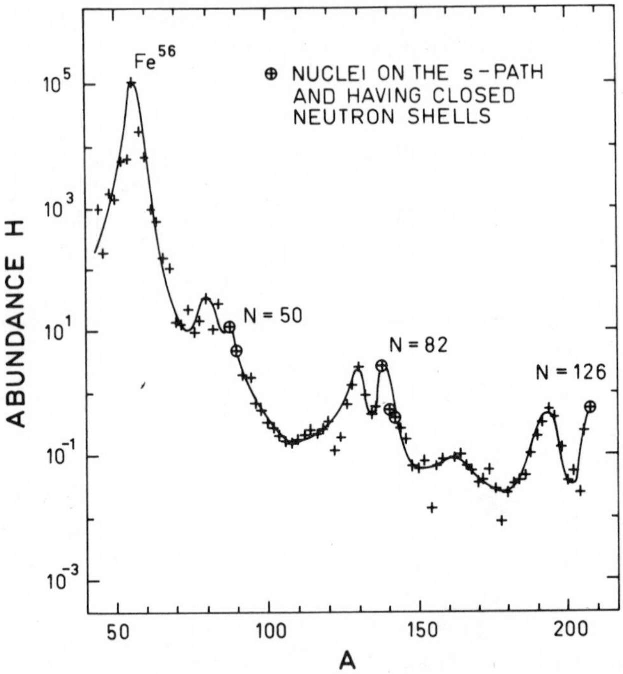

Figure 2-19 The relative abundance, H, in terms of numbers of atoms, for the different even-even nuclear species is plotted as a function of the atomic number A (for $A > 50$). The conventional unit is adopted, in which the abundances are measured relative to Si ($H(\text{Si}) = 10^6$). The data are based on the critical compilation of H. E. Suess and H. C. Urey, *Rev. Mod. Phys.* **28**, 53 (1956). More recent analyses have been reviewed by Aller (1961), Urey (1964), and Cameron (1968).

▼ synthesizing reactions on p. 200). In order not to complicate the figure, only abundances of even-A nuclei are shown.

The abundances in Fig. 2-19 refer to the solar system. The evidence on other stars or galaxies usually indicates qualitatively similar abundances of the elements, but in some cases striking differences are observed. Attempts have been made to relate these differences to the special stage of evolution of these systems or to their previous history. (See, for example, Burbidge, 1962.)

Details of abundances and capture paths for $105 < A < 145$ (Fig. 2-20)

The interpretation of the heavy element abundances in terms of neutron ▲ capture processes is illustrated in Fig. 2-20. The solid staircase line indicates the

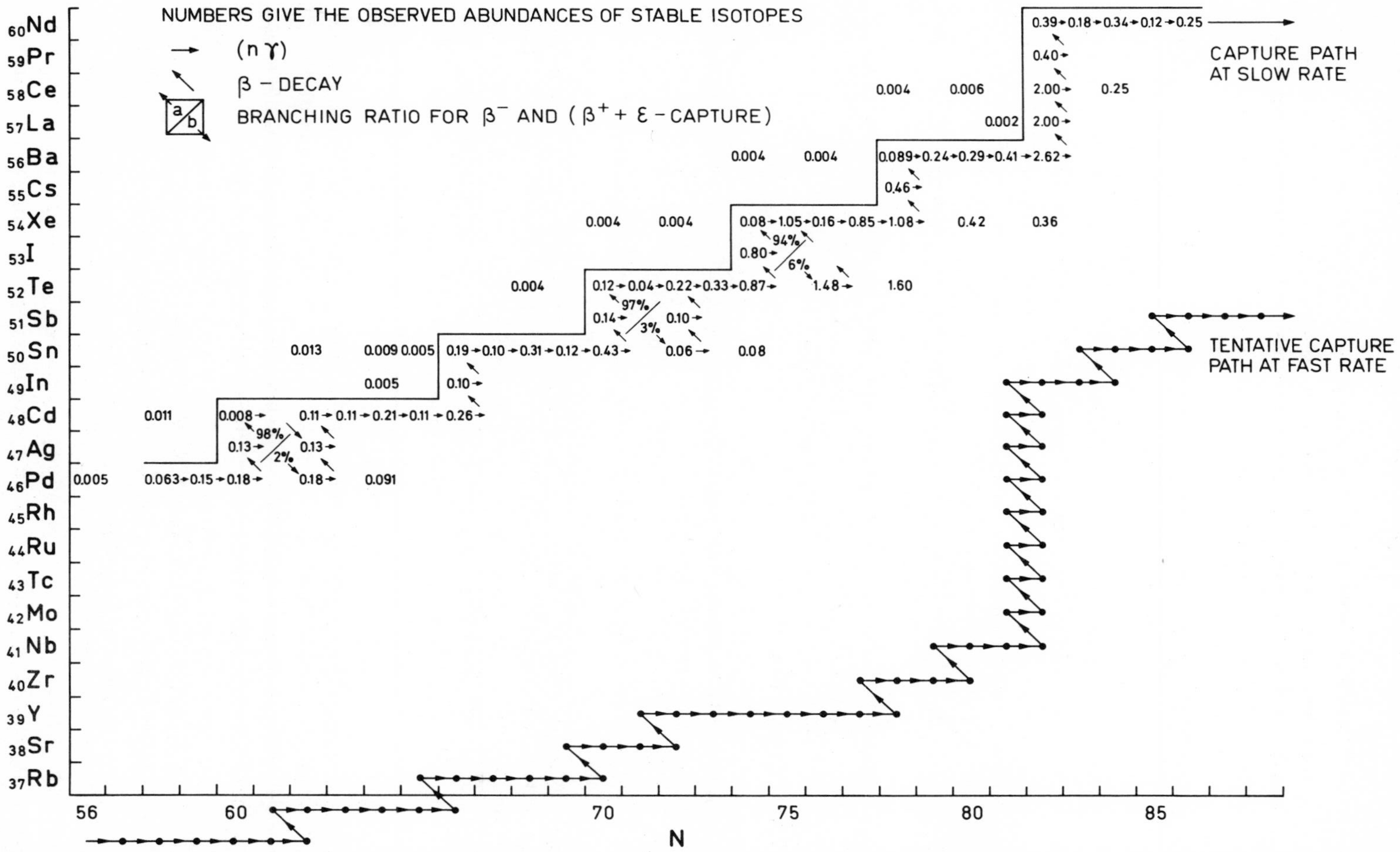

Figure 2-20 The figure is adapted from E. M. Burbidge, G. R. Burbidge, W. A. Fowler, and F. Hoyle, *Rev. Mod. Phys.* **29**, 547 (1957). The β^+/β^- branching ratios are taken from Strominger *et al.* (1958). The abundances are in the same units as in Fig. 2-19. In the figure, the abundance (0.07) of ^{116}Cd is missing.

▼ limits, toward neutron deficiency, of isotopes that can be produced by neutron capture. This limit can be obtained by following the indicated path appropriate to neutron capture processes on a time scale sufficiently slow that β-decay equilibrium is established at each point.

The line far to the neutron-rich side of the stability line represents a suggested path for element synthesis by neutron capture on a fast time scale (for details, see Burbidge *et al.*, 1957). It has been constructed by assuming that the neutron capture proceeds until the neutron binding energy has fallen to 2 MeV, representing the estimated equilibrium point for the combined action of (n, γ) and (γ, n) processes. The estimated neutron binding energies are obtained from the extrapolation of the empirical data on nuclear masses, including estimates of closed shell effects. Available evidence still leaves considerable uncertainty as to the details of this path.

In the interpretation of the relative abundances, it is of considerable importance that one can distinguish some isotopes that are only produced in the slow process ("shielded" from the fast capture products by a β-stable isobar of lower charge; see, for example, ^{108,110}Cd, ^{116}Sn, ^{122,123,124}Te, ^{128,130}Xe, ^{134,136}Ba, ^{142}Nd, etc.) and other isotopes which can only be produced in the fast process (see, for example, ^{110}Pd, ^{116}Cd, ^{124}Sn, ^{130}Te, ^{136}Xe, ^{142}Ce, etc.). The abundances of neighboring isotopes on the slow capture path are similar; typical variations are of the order of a factor of 2, reflecting the fact that the neutron capture cross sections for $E_n \approx 10$–100 keV do not vary strongly from isotope to isotope (see also the discussion on p. 201 in the text). The very low abundance of ^{108}Cd is an exception to this rule and has been interpreted in terms of the long β-decay half-life of ^{107}Pd ($T_{1/2}(^{107}\text{Pd}) \approx 7 \times 10^6$ years). If the mean time for capture of a neutron is short compared with this period, the capture path will be ^{106}Pd (n) ^{107}Pd (n) ^{108}Pd (n) ^{109}Pd (β^-) ^{109}Ag (n) ^{110}Ag (β^-) ^{110}Cd, and thus ^{108}Cd will be bypassed. Other evidence on the slow capture process is also consistent with the assumption that the mean time for neutron capture in the region of $A = 108$ is considerably shorter than 10^6 years. Indeed, analysis of a similar branch at ^{151}Sm (not shown in Fig. 2-20) suggests that the mean capture time in this region is of order 10^2 years. Thus, the β-decay lifetime of ^{151}Sm is $T_{1/2} = 80$ years; if ^{151}Sm decays before capturing a neutron, ^{152}Gd will be produced in the *s* process, while ^{152}Gd will be bypassed if the capture time is shorter than the β decay. The observed abundance of ^{152}Gd suggests that the neutron ▲ capture and β-decay lifetimes are comparable (Burbidge *et al.*, 1957, p. 558).

2-4 AVERAGE NUCLEAR POTENTIAL

2-4a Sequence of Single-Particle Levels. Spin-Orbit Coupling

As a first step in the study of the consequences of the nuclear shell structure, we must obtain the wave functions and eigenvalues corresponding to one-particle motion in the nuclear potential. The short range of the nucleonic forces suggests that the potential should approximately resemble the density distribution and, thus, as a rough first approximation, we might consider a square well potential. Still simpler and qualitatively similar is the harmonic oscillator potential, which is therefore widely used and plays a role in nuclear physics somewhat like that of the Coulomb potential in atomic physics. Some of the significant features of the binding states in the harmonic oscillator potential are summarized in Fig. 2-21, p. 221. It is usual to adjust the oscillator frequency ω_0 in order to reproduce the observed nuclear mean square radius. This requires

$$\sum_{k=1}^{A} \langle r_k^2 \rangle = \frac{\hbar}{M\omega_0} \sum_{k=1}^{A} (N_k + \tfrac{3}{2}) = \tfrac{3}{5} A R^2 \tag{2-130}$$

which yields (see the more detailed derivation based on Eqs. (2-157) and (2-158))

$$\hbar\omega_0 \approx \frac{5}{4}\left(\frac{3}{2}\right)^{1/3} \frac{\hbar^2}{M r_0^2} A^{-1/3} \approx 40 A^{-1/3} \quad \text{MeV} \tag{2-131}$$

We have neglected higher-order terms of relative magnitude $A^{-1/3}$ as well as the neutron excess, and have employed the value $r_0 = 1.2$ fm, which represents the effective radius for the estimate of $\langle r^2 \rangle$ (see Eq. (2-71)).

It is seen from Fig. 2-21 that, if the nuclear potential were very close to that of a harmonic oscillator, the major shell closings would occur at nucleon numbers 2, 8, 20, 40, 70, 112, and 168. The first three members of the series, but not the higher ones, correspond to observed major shell closings.

The choice of a more realistic radial dependence somewhat modifies the detailed sequence of orbits (see Fig. 2-22, p. 223). The main effect is to remove the harmonic oscillator degeneracy in such a sense that the orbits of highest l are depressed with respect to the low l orbits. This effect is schematically illustrated in Fig. 2-23, p. 224, from which is it seen that the observed major shell closings are still not accounted for.

A decisive step in the development of the nuclear shell model was the recognition that the assumption of a relatively strong spin-orbit interaction in the nucleonic motion leads to a natural explanation of the major shell closings (Haxel, Jensen, and Suess, 1949; Mayer, 1949). This coupling splits the levels with $j = l \pm 1/2$, which are degenerate in a spin-independent potential, and if the sign is such as to lower the levels with $j = l + 1/2$, the observed shell closings are obtained (see Fig. 2-23).

The sequence of single-particle levels that results when the spin-orbit force is added to the central potential is confirmed by a large body of evidence. The interpretation of the nuclear levels is particularly simple for low-lying configurations consisting of closed shells of neutrons and protons with only a single additional particle or with a single particle missing from such a closed configuration (a single hole). The spectra of these nuclei are considered in detail in Chapter 3 (see especially the comparison of the calculated and observed single-particle spectra shown in Figs. 3-3 and 3-5).

The observed spacings between the spin-orbit partners ($j = l \pm 1/2$) can be approximately represented by an energy term of the form

$$\Delta\varepsilon_{ls} \approx -20(\mathbf{l} \cdot \mathbf{s})A^{-2/3} \quad \text{MeV} \tag{2-132}$$

although, especially in the light nuclei, there are individual variations that are not fitted by such an average term. For orbits in the last shell, the maximum value of l is of order $A^{1/3}$. Thus, the spin-orbit splittings are an appreciable fraction of the harmonic oscillator separation, $\hbar\omega_0$, and of a sufficient magnitude to cause the level sequence implied by the major shell discontinuities (see Fig. 2-23).

Another direct consequence of the spin-orbit interaction is the occurrence of polarization phenomena in the nucleon-nucleus scattering process. Thus, the potential acting on a nucleon depends on the orientation of its spin with respect to the scattering plane. As a result of this interaction, unpolarized beams become partially polarized in the scattering process; if polarized beams are employed, the scattered intensity may exhibit azimuthal asymmetries. These polarization effects have been systematically observed and have been found to imply a spin-orbit coupling of the same sign as the estimate (2-132) and of similar magnitude (see, for example, Fig. 2-28b).

For nuclei with several particles outside closed shells, one might expect a rather complicated pattern of levels associated with the different ways of coupling the angular momenta of these particles. However, because of the pairing effect, one can obtain a qualitative description of the lowest states of an odd-A nucleus in terms of the orbits available to the unpaired odd particle. In this approximation, the degrees of freedom of the rest of the nucleons are neglected and these nucleons are assumed to remain as in the ground state of an even-even nucleus, that is, in the paired state with $I\pi = 0+$. As indicated in Fig. 2-24, p. 225, many of the properties of the low-lying levels receive an immediate interpretation in terms of such a one-particle model. The occurrence of other levels in the low-energy spectra (circled in Fig. 2-24) indicates the limitations of this simple description.

It should be emphasized that the single-particle spectra discussed in this section depend essentially on the assumption of a spherical nuclear potential. While this assumption is appropriate to many nuclei and especially to configurations near closed shells, there is also an extensive group of nuclei that possess a nonspherical equilibrium shape. Even though the anisotropic component of the potential is relatively small compared to the spherical part (eccentricity $\lesssim$ 0.3), it produces level shifts that are comparable with the distance between shells. The low-lying states in odd-A deformed nuclei bear no simple relation to the one-particle spectra in a spherical potential and no assignments have been attempted in Fig. 2-24. The classification of single-particle orbits in such deformed potentials is considered in Chapter 5.

2-4b Single-Particle Strength Function

With increasing excitation energy, the nuclear level density rapidly increases owing to the increasing number of nucleons that may participate in the excitation. Thus, in a heavy nucleus at an excitation energy of a few MeV, there are several hundreds of levels per MeV. Under such conditions, even a very small coupling between the motion of an individual nucleon and the modes of excitation of the rest of the nucleus is sufficient to produce strong mixings of near-lying configurations. As discussed in connection with the concept of the compound nucleus (pp. 156ff.), the stationary states of the entire nucleus then acquire a more complicated structure and any single state contains only a small amplitude of the wave function describing the single-particle motion with the rest of the nucleus in a definite configuration, such as the ground state.

We can consider such a situation by using a time-dependent description; the state of simple single-particle motion is now a wave packet built out of all the stationary states that contain an appreciable amplitude of the single-particle component. Since these stationary states spread out over an energy interval, the wave packet will decay in time as its different components come out of phase with each other. Denoting by Γ the energy spread in the wave packet,[2] the decay time for the single-particle motion will be of the order $\hbar/\Gamma$. When the single-particle motion continues undisturbed for a time long compared with that required for traversal of the nucleus, we have $\Gamma \ll D_{sp} \approx \pi\hbar v/R$, where D_{sp} is the spacing between successive single-particle states with the same values of (lj). Thus, the persistence of the single-particle motion manifests itself in a "gross structure" in the spectrum; the amplitude for single-particle motion is mainly concentrated in the stationary states lying within the energy interval Γ around the position that would have corresponded with the undisturbed single-particle state. The probability amplitude that a nuclear state f can be decomposed into single-particle motion with quantum numbers $(nl)jm$ relative to a parent state 0, is represented by the parentage factor $\langle f | a^\dagger(jm) | 0 \rangle$, where $a^\dagger(jm)$

[2] The notation Γ for the width should not be taken to presuppose a Breit-Wigner shape for the strength function. Indeed, the line shape is in general more complicated, and the precise definition of Γ must be specified in each case.

is the nucleon creation operator (see Appendix 2A). If the parent state has angular momentum $I_0 = 0$, the single-particle strength of the level f, with angular momentum $I_f = j$, is characterized by the probability

$$P_j(f) = \langle I_f = j,\ M_f = m \,|\, a^\dagger(jm) \,|\, I_0 = 0 \rangle^2 \qquad \text{(2-133)}$$

(For arbitrary spin of parent and final states, the single-particle strength can be defined in terms of the reduced matrix element, $P_j(f) = (2j+1)^{-1} \langle I_f \| a^\dagger(j) \| I_i \rangle^2$; see Appendix 3E.) If the single-particle orbit j is empty in the parent state, the sum of the single-particle strengths is unity,

$$\sum_f P_j(f) = 1 \qquad \text{(2-134)}$$

In regions of high level density, the gross structure can be described by the strength per unit energy interval, $D_j^{-1} \langle P_j(f) \rangle$, where D_j is the average spacing of levels with $I_f = j$, and where the average of $P_j(f)$ is taken over levels within a small energy interval. The theoretical problem of characterizing the line shape and width of such strength functions involves an analysis of the coupling between the one-particle motion and the degrees of freedom of the parent nucleus. A schematic model illustrating some features of this problem is discussed in Appendix 2D.

Examples of strength functions determined by neutron transfer in the deuteron stripping reaction are illustrated in Fig. 2-25, p. 228. The value of the $l = 0$ neutron strength function at an excitation energy equal to the neutron separation energy, has been systematically measured by means of the neutron resonance studies, and the available data are summarized in Fig. 2-26, p. 230.

Strength functions can also be defined for hole states produced by taking a particle from a specified one-particle orbit in the nucleus. In this case, the creation operator $a^\dagger(jm)$ in Eq. (2-133) is replaced by the annihilation operator $a(jm)$. Figure 2-27, p. 232, provides illustrations of strength functions for hole states measured by means of the $(p, 2p)$ reaction. Additional evidence on strength functions is discussed in Chapter 3 in connection with the problem of locating the one-particle excitations in the closed shell nuclei (see Fig. 3-2 and Tables 3-7 and 3-8).

With increasing energy, the rapid increase in the number of degrees of freedom that can be coupled to the particle motion implies a decrease in the lifetime for the one-particle state; correspondingly, the width Γ of the strength function increases. (See, for example, the very large width of the highly excited $1s$ hole configuration studied in the $(p, 2p)$ reaction (Fig. 2-27).)

When the single-particle levels are unbound, they acquire an additional width owing to the possibility of the particle escaping from the nucleus (emission process). This broadening is to be added to that associated with the gross structure effect. For excitation energies comparable with the magnitude of the potential, the lifetime for escape becomes comparable with the traversal time, and it is no longer convenient to talk in terms of nucleon levels. The characteristic manifestation of the single-particle motion is now in terms of the interference phenomena like those discussed in Fig. 2-3.

2-4c Optical Potential

Extensive experimental studies have been made of the scattering of neutrons and protons on nuclei through the whole region of elements. The measurements include total cross sections, differential elastic scattering cross sections, and polarization studies for energies ranging from electron volts up to the highest available energies ($\sim 10^{10}$ eV). The analysis of these data provides a rather detailed determination of the main features of the nuclear potential.

To a first approximation, the phenomena can be described in terms of nucleon motion in a spherical potential to which an appropriate spin-orbit coupling is added. (The effects of nuclear distortion, important for a certain class of nuclei, are considered separately in Chapter 5.) For the detailed analysis, the coupling of the nucleon motion to the internal degrees of freedom of the target nucleus plays an important role. It is often a good approximation to represent this coupling by an imaginary potential added to the one-particle Hamiltonian. This corresponds to the physical assumption that the energy exchange between the nucleon and the target, which may initially involve simple modes of excitation, usually leads by further interaction effects to configurations so complicated that no detailed features of their spectrum need be considered. Under such conditions, the coupling acquires an irreversible character and can be described as an effective damping of the one-particle motion (see Appendix 2D).

The damping effect of an imaginary potential can be seen directly from the time-dependent Schrödinger equation

$$i\hbar \frac{\partial \psi(\mathbf{r}, t)}{\partial t} = \left\{ \frac{p^2}{2M} + V(\mathbf{r}) + iW(\mathbf{r}) \right\} \psi(\mathbf{r}, t) \tag{2-135}$$

Multiplying on the left by ψ^* and taking the imaginary part, one obtains

$$\operatorname{div} \mathbf{j}(\mathbf{r}, t) + \frac{\partial}{\partial t} \rho(\mathbf{r}, t) = \frac{2}{\hbar} W(\mathbf{r}) \rho(\mathbf{r}, t) \tag{2-136}$$

where the particle density $\rho(\mathbf{r}, t)$ and current $\mathbf{j}(\mathbf{r}, t)$ are defined in the usual way,

$$\begin{aligned} \rho(\mathbf{r}, t) &= \psi^* \psi \\ \mathbf{j}(\mathbf{r}, t) &= \frac{\hbar}{2iM} (\psi^* \nabla \psi - \psi \nabla \psi^*) \end{aligned} \tag{2-137}$$

From Eq. (2-136) it is seen that the particles are being absorbed at a rate

$$-\frac{2}{\hbar}W(\mathbf{r})$$

which corresponds to a mean free path λ given by

$$\frac{1}{\lambda} = -\frac{2}{\hbar v}W(\mathbf{r}) \tag{2-138}$$

In a nuclear scattering experiment, the nucleons are, of course, not absorbed in the sense that would violate baryon conservation, or the overall conservation of probability for the total reaction process. However, since the wave function $\psi(\mathbf{r}, t)$ describes the motion of a single nucleon in the average potential of the target, interactions that lead to more complicated states of motion imply a reduction in the probability of the state ψ, and it is this decay of the one-particle state that is approximately represented by the imaginary potential.

The description of nucleon propagation in nuclei in terms of a complex potential is called an optical model in view of the analogous use of a complex index of refraction in the analysis of the transmission of electromagnetic waves through matter.

The coupling described by the imaginary potential is the same as that responsible for the gross-structure phenomena considered above (Sec. 2-4b). The description of this coupling in terms of a simple absorption process implies that the one-particle motion decays exponentially with time. One then obtains a Breit–Wigner line shape for the strength function representing the probability for finding a given single-particle state j in the wave function of the stationary states lying in an energy interval around the value E,

$$\frac{\langle P_j(f)\rangle}{D_j} \approx (2\pi)^{-1}\frac{\Gamma}{(E - E_{sp}(j))^2 + (\Gamma/2)^2} \tag{2-139}$$

where Γ is the average of $-2W(\mathbf{r})$ for the one-particle resonant state.

In some situations, it is necessary to consider the more detailed structure of the coupling between the particle motion and the internal nuclear degrees of freedom. In such cases, the simple imaginary potential is inadequate and the line shape has more structure than Eq. (2-139). (See, for instance, the coupling to rotational motion discussed in Chapter 5.)

Parameters of the optical potential

The description of the nuclear one-particle motion involves a potential having a number of components; one must specify the strength and radial dependence of the real and imaginary parts of the central nuclear potential as well as of the spin-orbit force. Finally, in the case of protons, one must add the Coulomb potential for an appropriate charge distribution. In the analysis of the empirical data on the basis of the optical model, one usually solves the Schrödinger equation by a partial wave expansion. The parameters of the potential are varied to obtain a best fit to the experimental cross section. Since extensive numerical work is involved in obtaining such solutions, the analysis is usually performed with the aid of high-speed electronic computers.

Some examples of optical model fits are illustrated in Fig. 2-26, p. 230, Fig. 2-28, p. 234, and Table 2-1, p. 235. The best fits are remarkably good in representing many detailed features in the experimental cross sections and serve to define rather accurately the main parameters of the optical model. The parameters are found to vary smoothly with A and E, as expected. Indeed, if this were not the case, there would hardly be any direct physical significance to the potentials obtained. In the following paragraphs, we discuss the parameters of the nuclear potential as determined from these analyses.

The real potential $V(r)$ is expected to follow roughly the density distribution. A convenient radial dependence, which is found to account satisfactorily for both the nuclear potential and density distribution, is the Woods–Saxon potential, shown in Fig. 2-22, p. 223. This potential involves three parameters, V_0, R, and a, describing, respectively, the central strength of the potential, the range, and the surface thickness.

The surface thickness a is found to be approximately the same as that characterizing the charge distribution ($a = 0.6$ fm), but the radius R of the potential is found to be approximately 1 fm larger than the corresponding extension of the charge density as determined from the electron scattering analysis (see Fig. 2-1). This difference has been interpreted in terms of the finite range of the nucleon-nucleon interaction (see, for example, Kerman *et al.*, 1959).

It is more difficult to anticipate the radial dependence of the imaginary potential, and many different forms have been employed. The simplest assumption, which is often made, is to take $W(r)$ as a multiple of $V(r)$. Absorptive potentials that are stronger in the region of the nuclear surface have also been extensively investigated. The calculated cross sections are relatively insensitive to the location of the absorptive potential (provided that other parameters are appropriately adjusted) and, thus, it has been difficult to establish the radial dependence of $W(r)$ (Hodgson, 1964); the most recent analyses seem to lend tentative support to a predominant surface absorption for incident nucleons with energies less than 40–50 MeV (see, for example, Figs. 2-26 and 2-28).

Various arguments have been advanced, attempting to justify a stronger absorption in the surface region than in the interior of the nucleus. In this connection, there are two aspects of the surface that must be considered. First, there are various collective excitations of the nucleus that are associated with density changes in the surface regions (see the surface vibrations and collective rotations that are discussed in Chapters 6 and 4, respectively). The coupling between these modes and an incident nucleon is expected to be approximately localized in the surface. Although these couplings are often of considerable importance for the damping of the one-particle motion, for many purposes it may be a rather poor approximation to replace them by an absorptive potential. (The coupling to the rotational and vibrational motion is discussed in Chapter 5 and Chapter 6, respectively.)

A second aspect of the surface that has often been emphasized is the fact that, in this region, the nuclear density is considerably reduced as compared with the central regions. Since the exclusion principle plays an important role in inhibiting collisions between a low-energy projectile and the nucleons of the target (see Sec. 2-5b), a decrease in the Fermi momentum, as in a Fermi gas with lower density, would lead to a relaxation of this inhibition and might imply stronger absorption. In addition, the lower Fermi momentum implies smaller velocities relative to the incident nucleon, and hence larger collision cross sections. However, since in the surface region the nuclear density changes appreciably in a distance of the order of the Fermi wavelength, it may not be appropriate to consider this region in terms of a local Fermi gas of reduced density. Thus, a more detailed description of the structure of the nuclear surface is required in order to properly assess the contribution of this region to the absorptive potential. In this connection, it may also be noted that the treatment of the real potential in the surface region in terms of a diffuseness parameter may be an oversimplification in view of the nonlocal effects expected to result from the finite range and velocity dependence of the interaction (see Sec. 2-5b).

The experimentally determined strengths of the different components of the nuclear potential are summarized in Fig. 2-29, p. 237. It is seen that the magnitude of the central real potential $V(r)$ decreases with increasing energy of the incident nucleon. Indirect evidence for such a velocity dependence has already been discussed in connection with the analysis of the nuclear binding energies (p. 147). As will be discussed in more detail below (Sec. 2-5b), this effect is in part associated with the short-range repulsive element in the nucleonic interaction, which manifests itself in two-nucleon scattering at high energies ($E > 100$ MeV).

The absorptive potential W also has a marked energy dependence. For small energies of the incident particles, only a few degrees of freedom of the target can be excited and, thus, the configuration mixing (damping of the one-particle motion) is relatively inhibited as compared with higher energies, where a much richer spectrum of the target may be involved. This effect is often described using the Fermi gas model, in which case one may visualize the absorption in terms of the collisions between the incident nucleon and the nucleons of the filled Fermi sea. The exclusion principle requires that the collisions lead to final states in which the scattered projectile and the recoiling nucleon of the target are both outside the occupied Fermi distribution. For nucleons with total kinetic energy E only a little greater than ε_F, the phase space for such collisions is reduced by a factor of order $(E - \varepsilon_F)^2 \varepsilon_F^{-2}$ as compared with free collisions (see Eq. (2-221)), and this damping effect goes to zero as $E \to \varepsilon_F$. However, it cannot be concluded from this argument that the strength function collapses to a single line for the single-particle states in the neighborhood of the Fermi surface. In fact, for energies smaller than the separations between single-particle levels, it is necessary to take into account the finite size of the system. Thus, in the nucleus, the structure of the strength functions depends essentially on the coupling to the few low-lying collective modes associated with deformations of the nuclear shape (see Chapters 5 and 6). The observed strength functions for single-particle states within a few MeV of the Fermi surface are often found to have widths greater than 1 MeV (see Fig. 2-25).

The energy variation of the nuclear potentials can also be described in terms of energy-independent but nonlocal interactions, replacing the potential energy term in the wave equation,

$$V(\mathbf{r})\psi(\mathbf{r}) \to \int V(\mathbf{r}, \mathbf{r}')\psi(\mathbf{r}')\, d^3r' \tag{2-140}$$

It is readily seen that the nonlocality of $V(\mathbf{r}, \mathbf{r}')$ (the dependence on $\mathbf{r} - \mathbf{r}'$) is equivalent to a momentum dependence. Thus, if we expand the wave function in momentum eigenstates, we obtain

$$\int V(\mathbf{r}, \mathbf{r}')\psi(\mathbf{r}')\, d^3r' = \int U(\mathbf{r}, \mathbf{p})\varphi(\mathbf{p}) \exp\left\{\frac{i}{\hbar}\mathbf{p}\cdot\mathbf{r}\right\} d^3p \tag{2-141}$$

with

$$\begin{aligned} \psi(\mathbf{r}) &= (2\pi)^{-3/2} \int \exp\left\{\frac{i}{\hbar}\mathbf{p}\cdot\mathbf{r}\right\}\varphi(\mathbf{p})\, d^3p \\ U(\mathbf{r}, \mathbf{p}) &= (2\pi)^{-3/2} \int \exp\left\{\frac{i}{\hbar}\mathbf{p}\cdot\mathbf{x}\right\} V(\mathbf{r}, \mathbf{r}+\mathbf{x})\, d^3x \end{aligned} \tag{2-142}$$

The form (2-141) exhibits the momentum dependence of the interaction. For instance, if V is confined to a domain of $\mathbf{x}$ small compared to the wavelengths contained in $\psi(\mathbf{r})$, one can expand $U(\mathbf{r}, \mathbf{p})$ as a power series in $\mathbf{p}$, and Eq. (2-141) becomes equivalent to a local potential depending on powers of the momentum.

The observed energy dependence of the potential is fairly moderate, in the sense that it corresponds to a nonlocality with an extension somewhat less than k_F^{-1}. Hence, to a first approximation, the effect may be taken into account by simply letting the potential depend on the energy of the incident particle. (For analyses using nonlocal potentials and comparison with energy-dependent local potentials, see Wyatt *et al.*, 1960; Perey and Buck, 1962; Wilmore and Hodgson, 1964.)

The spin-orbit coupling is of necessity a surface term since, in a region of constant density, the only direction with local significance is that of the particle motion and, thus, it is impossible to define a pseudovector that can be coupled to the nuclear spin. In the surface region, however, the density gradient defines the radial direction and makes it possible to introduce a local potential of the form

$$V_{ls}(r) \propto \nabla\rho(r) \times \mathbf{p}\cdot\mathbf{s} = \hbar^{-1}(\mathbf{l}\cdot\mathbf{s})\frac{1}{r}\frac{\partial\rho(r)}{\partial r} \tag{2-143}$$

While the proportionality of V_{ls} with $\nabla\rho(r)$ follows from the above arguments, if the range of the force is small compared with the distance over which the nuclear density changes appreciably, the rapid density variation in the region of the nuclear surface implies that $V_{ls}(r)$ may have a somewhat different radial dependence. However, since the main effect is still concentrated near the surface, it has been found sufficient to employ spin-orbit potentials of the simple form

$$V_{ls}(r) = V_{ls}\,r_0^2(\mathbf{l}\cdot\mathbf{s})\frac{1}{r}\frac{\partial}{\partial r}f(r) \tag{2-144}$$

where $f(r)$ is a radial function of the type describing the central real potential (Woods–Saxon form with $R = r_0 A^{1/3}$), and where the strength of the spin-orbit potential is characterized by the constant V_{ls}.

One can make contact with the estimate (2-132) for the spin-orbit splitting of bound orbits by approximating $V_{ls}(r)$ by a δ function at the nuclear surface (that is, taking $f(r)$ to be a step function). The estimate (2-144) then gives

$$\langle V_{ls}(r)\rangle \approx V_{ls}(\mathbf{l}\cdot\mathbf{s})\,r_0^2 R\mathscr{R}^2(R) \tag{2-145}$$

where $\mathscr{R}(r)$ is the radial wave function of the nucleon. For nucleons bound by 5–10 MeV, the quantity $R^3\mathscr{R}^2(R)$ is fairly independent of the particular orbit involved and is on the average about 1.4 with fluctuations of 10–20%. (See the wave functions in Fig. 3-4.) In this simple approximation, the spin-orbit coupling implies energy shifts in the bound states

$$\Delta\varepsilon_{ls} \approx 1.4V_{ls}(\mathbf{l}\cdot\mathbf{s})A^{-2/3} \tag{2-146}$$

which agrees rather well with (2-132), when the strength of the spin-orbit potential, V_{ls}, is that obtained from the analysis of the scattering experiments (see Eq. (2-179)). The spin-orbit coupling may also involve an imaginary term, but the present experimental evidence is barely sufficiently detailed to exhibit such an effect.

The parameters of the nuclear potential are expected to depend on the nuclear species primarily through the variation of R. The simple proportionality to $A^{1/3}$ has been found to be adequate in most analyses. In addition, the neutron excess implies somewhat different potentials for neutrons and protons; most important is the effect of the nuclear symmetry energy in producing a stronger central real potential $V(r)$ for protons than for neutrons (see the discussion on p. 148). The symmetry term in the nuclear potential obtained from the scattering data is of similar magnitude to that deduced from the binding energies (see Eqs. (2-26) and (2-28)). The available data, however, are inconclusive concerning the possible symmetry dependence of the spin-orbit and absorptive terms in the nuclear potential.

Optical potential for other particles

We have considered so far only the potentials describing the interactions of nucleons (and electrons) with nuclei. Scattering and reaction measurements have been performed for a large variety of other particles, such as d, t, ^{3}He, α, heavier ions, μ, $\pi^{\pm}$, and $K^{\pm}$. These results have also been interpreted in terms of optical potentials with parameters depending on the particle in question. The absorptive potentials used to describe the scattering of composite particles are very large, corresponding to the fact that such particles are not able to travel as a single entity over appreciable distances in the nucleus. (For example, for deuterons with an incident energy of 10 MeV, the imaginary potential needed to fit the elastic scattering is of the order of 10 MeV, which corresponds to a mean free path of about 3 fm, that is, less than the average distances between the particles in the deuteron.) The potentials employed in such analyses therefore have a less well-defined significance than for the scattering of "elementary" particles.

We here briefly mention a special effect, which has been observed in π-nucleus scattering, and which exhibits an important limitation in the form of the optical model employed above. The description of the elastic scattering from a composite system, such as the nucleus, in terms of a potential approximately proportional to the density distribution, is valid if the scattering results from elementary processes (the collisions with the individual particles) each giving a small angle scattering, as in the description in terms of the index of refraction of the medium. If large angle individual scatterings are involved, which may especially be the case for backward scattering at large energies, the optical model assumes that the individual scattering process is approximately isotropic. (See the discussion of the relation between optical potential and scattering amplitude in Sec. 2-5b.) The π-nucleon scattering involves a very strong p-wave component, and it has been found that the π-nucleus scattering at large angles cannot be fitted by an optical potential with the usual shape. The p-wave component in the π-nucleon scattering can be taken into account by adding to the optical potential a term proportional to the gradient of the density and to the direction of the π momentum (Kisslinger, 1955); such a generalized potential is found to account rather well for the empirical π-nucleus scattering and the level shifts observed in pionic atoms (see Ericson and Ericson, 1966).

In the nucleon-nucleus scattering, the spin-orbit coupling is an effect of similar type, but there is as yet no definite evidence for the contribution of velocity-dependent surface interactions in the spin-independent interaction of nucleons with nuclei. This may be associated with the relative weakness of the p-wave nucleon-nucleon scattering (see Sec. 2-5).

Relation of scattering potential to energies of bound states

The detailed information on the radial dependence of the nuclear potential, as obtained from the scattering data, provides the starting point for a more quantitative calculation of the nucleon bound state orbits. Results of such a calculation are illustrated in Fig. 2-30, p. 239. It is found that one can obtain a rather good fit to the experimental binding energies using potential parameters consistent with those indicated by the scattering experiments. (See especially the analysis of binding energies for single-particle and single-hole configurations in Figs. 3-3 and 3-5.) The detailed radial wave functions obtained in these calculations should provide a significant improvement over the simplified harmonic oscillator or square well wave functions often employed.

▲

ILLUSTRATIVE EXAMPLES TO SECTION 2-4

Some properties of the harmonic oscillator potential (Fig. 2-21)

The spectrum of the three-dimensional oscillator potential is drawn in Fig. 2-21. The nucleonic motion in this potential has the properties

Hamiltonian

$$H = \frac{1}{2M}\mathbf{p}^2 + \frac{1}{2}M\omega_0^2\mathbf{r}^2 \qquad (2\text{-}147)$$

Quantum numbers: rectilinear coordinates

$$n_x, n_y, n_z, m_s \qquad N = n_x + n_y + n_z \qquad (2\text{-}148)$$

polar coordinates

$$n_r, l, m, m_s \qquad N = 2(n_r - 1) + l \qquad (2\text{-}149)$$

Spectrum

$$E = (N + \tfrac{3}{2})\hbar\omega_0 \qquad l = N, N-2, \ldots, 0 \text{ or } 1 \quad j = l \pm \tfrac{1}{2} \qquad (2\text{-}150)$$

Degeneracy

$$\sum_l 2(2l+1) = (N+1)(N+2) \underset{N \gg 1}{\approx} (N+\tfrac{3}{2})^2 \qquad (2\text{-}151)$$

▲

▼ Total number of states

$$\sum_{N'=0}^{N}(N'+1)(N'+2)=\tfrac{1}{3}(N+1)(N+2)(N+3)\underset{N\gg1}{\approx}(N+2)^3 \qquad (2\text{-}152)$$

Dimension of orbits

$$\langle r^2\rangle_{Nl}=\frac{\hbar}{M\omega_0}(N+\tfrac{3}{2}) \qquad (2\text{-}153)$$

Matrix elements

$$\langle n_x+1|x|n_x\rangle=(iM\omega_0)^{-1}\langle n_x+1|p_x|x\rangle=\left((n_x+1)\frac{\hbar}{2M\omega_0}\right)^{1/2}$$

$$\langle N+1, l\pm1|r|N, l\rangle=(iM\omega_0)^{-1}\langle N+1, l\pm1|p_r|N, l\rangle \qquad (2\text{-}154)$$

$$=\left(\left(N+\frac{5}{2}\pm\left(l+\frac{1}{2}\right)\right)\frac{\hbar}{2M\omega_0}\right)^{1/2}$$

The number of radial nodes equals $n_r - 1$, and we employ a phase convention such that the radial wave functions are all positive for r greater than the outermost nodal point. In the rectilinear coordinates, the one-dimensional oscillator ▲ functions are taken to be positive for large positive x.

N	l	DEGEN.	TOTAL
5	1,3,5	42	112
4	0,2,4	30	70
3	1,3	20	40
2	0,2	12	20
1	1	6	8
0	0	2	2

Figure 2-21 Harmonic oscillator spectrum.

▼ In attempting to visualize the shape of the radial wave function, it is useful to bear in mind the classical turning points, which correspond to the major and minor axes of the classical elliptical orbits

$$(r_{\max})^2\approx\frac{\hbar}{M\omega_0}\{N+(N^2-l^2)^{1/2}\} \qquad (2\text{-}155)$$

$$(r_{\min})^2\approx\frac{\hbar}{M\omega_0}\{N-(N^2-l^2)^{1/2}\} \qquad (2\text{-}156)$$

▲ The estimate of the oscillator frequency ω_0 given in Eq. (2-131) is obtained

▼ by summing the relation (2-153) over the occupied orbits

$$A\langle r^2\rangle = \frac{\hbar}{M\omega_0} 2 \sum_{N=0}^{N_{\max}} (N+\tfrac{3}{2})(N+1)(N+2) \approx \frac{\hbar}{2M\omega_0}(N_{\max}+2)^4$$

$$= \tfrac{3}{5}A^{5/3}r_0^2 \tag{2-157}$$

where the factor 2 reflects the fact that there are both neutrons and protons included in the total particle number, A. In a similar manner, we may employ Eq. (2-152) to relate A to the maximum principal quantum number N,

$$A = \tfrac{2}{3}(N_{\max}+2)^3 \tag{2-158}$$

Combining Eqs. (2-158) and (2-157), we obtain the relation (2-131).

Radial shape of nuclear potential (*Fig. 2-22*)

In Fig. 2-22, the harmonic oscillator potential is compared with a potential of more realistic shape, often referred to as the Woods-Saxon potential. The parameters correspond to a nucleus with $A = 100$. It is seen that the corrections to the oscillator potential involve a repulsive effect for short and large distances and an attractive effect for intermediate distances. These corrections, therefore, favor orbits of large l (circular orbits) as compared with those of small l (penetrating orbits); the radial density distributions are shown in the lower part of the figure for two representative orbits.

Schematic diagram of nuclear one-particle level sequence (*Fig. 2-23*)

The level sequence corresponding to one-particle motion in a spherical potential with a strong spin-orbit coupling is represented schematically in Fig. 2-23. On the extreme left, the levels of the harmonic oscillator potential are indicated by the total oscillator quantum number N and the parity $\pi = (-1)^N$. The next column in Fig. 2-23 shows the splittings of the harmonic oscillator degeneracies obtained by using a somewhat more realistic spherical potential (see Fig. 2-22); the quantum numbers labeling the orbits are $(n_r\, l)$. Finally, the spin-orbit coupling is turned on to obtain the level sequence indicated in the center, where the orbits are labeled by $(n_r\, lj)$. The degeneracy $(2j+1)$ of each orbit is given in parenthesis on the right, while the total nucleon number obtained by summing the degeneracies of all lower-lying orbits is given in brackets. The numbers on the far right are the observed nucleon numbers corresponding to the completion of major shells.

The schematic nature of the figure must be emphasized. The ordering of neutron orbits and proton orbits is known to be slightly different and, in addition, the sequence of orbits changes somewhat as a function of the nuclear size. (See the theoretical spectra in Fig. 2-30; experimental evidence on the one-particle level sequence is summarized in Figs. 3-3 and 3-5.) ▲

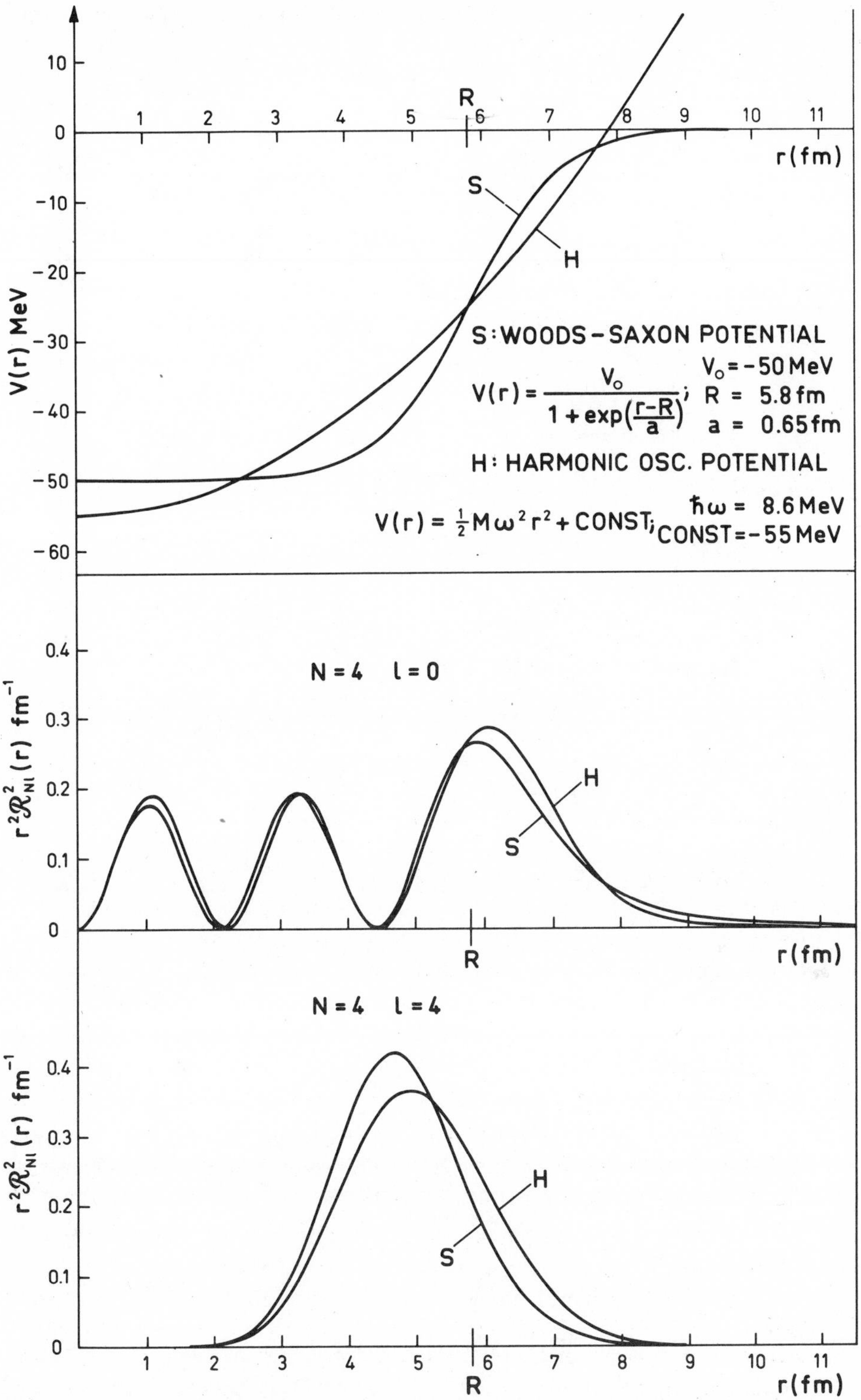

Figure 2-22 The square of the wave function times r^2 for the harmonic oscillator and the Woods-Saxon potential are plotted in units of fm^{-1}.

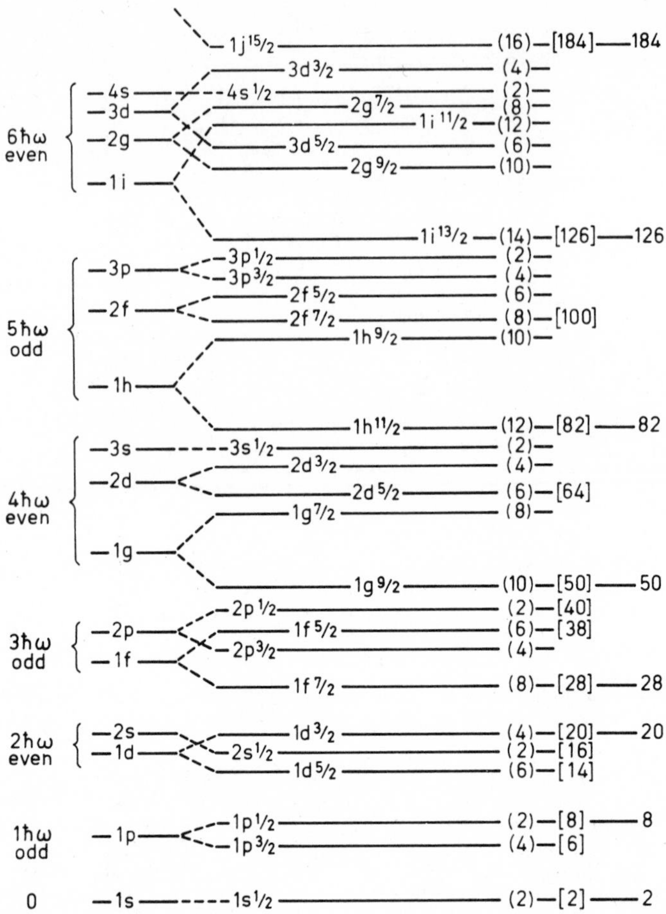

Figure 2-23 Sequence of one-particle orbits. The figure is taken from M. G. Mayer and J. H. D. Jensen, *Elementary Theory of Nuclear Shell Structure*, p. 58, Wiley, New York, 1955.

▼ *Spectra of odd-A nuclei compared with predictions of one-particle model (Fig. 2-24)*

The evidence on the spins and parities of the low-lying states of odd-A nuclei is summarized in Fig. 2-24 and is compared with the predictions of the simple one-particle model described in the text.

Since the one-particle model assumes that the core remains in the $I\pi = 0+$ configuration of the even-even ground state, we must expect to find states foreign to this model at excitation energies of the order of the energy, $E(2+)$, of the first excited $I\pi = 2+$ states of even-even nuclei (for the observed values of $E(2+)$, see Fig. 2-17). Thus, we have included in Fig. 2-24 only the states with excitation energies less than $\frac{1}{2}E(2+)$ in the case of states with the same parity as the ground ▲ state; for states of the opposite parity, the highest excitation energy included

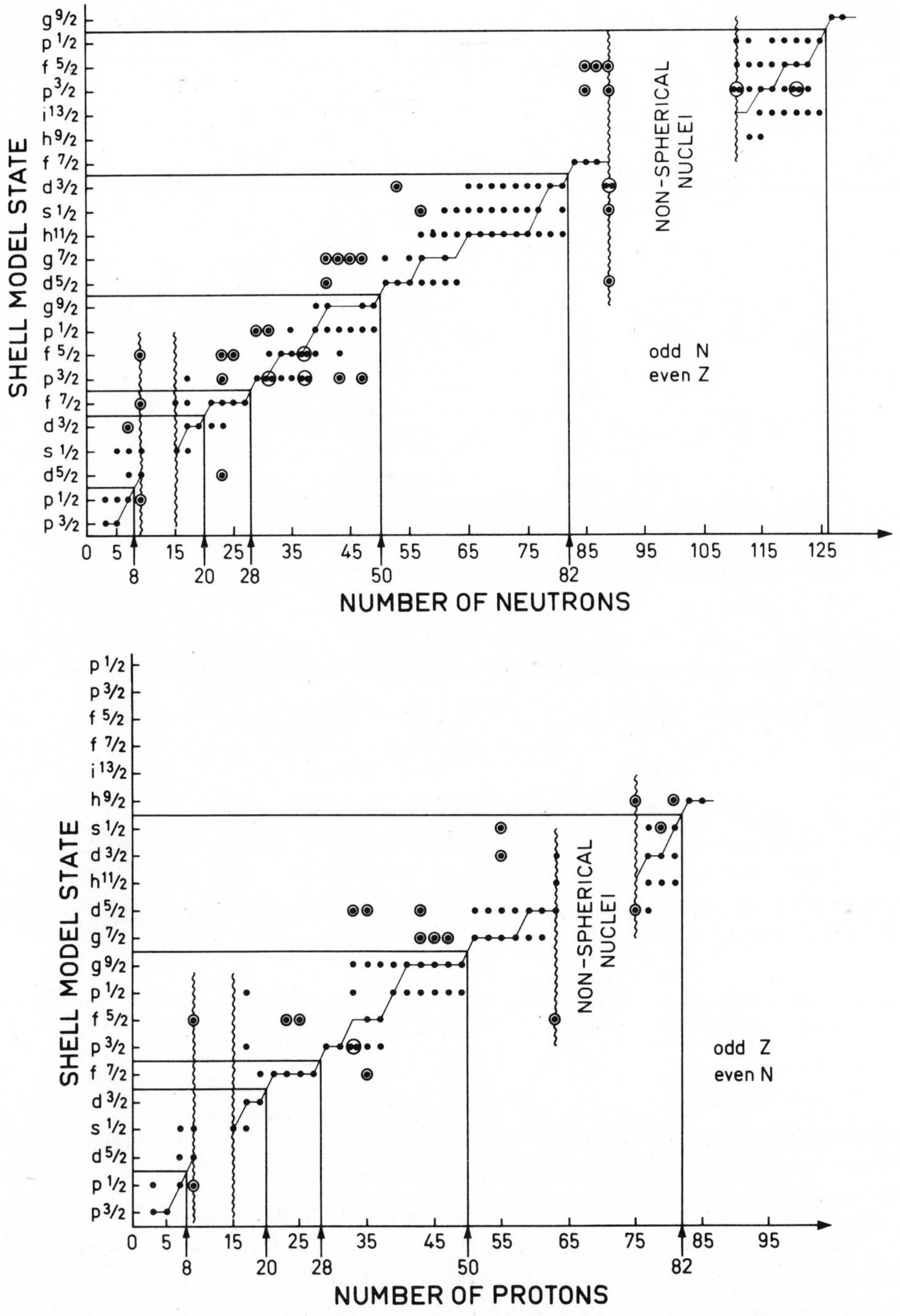

Figure 2-24 One-particle interpretation of low-energy levels in odd-A nuclei. The data for the figure are taken from Nuclear Data Sheets. The regions of stable ellipsoidal deformations are excluded, as indicated by the wavy lines. We wish to thank G. T. Ewan for help in the preparation of the figure.

▼ corresponds to $E^{(-)} + \frac{1}{2}E(2+)$, where $E^{(-)}$ is the excitation energy of the lowest state having a parity opposite to that of the ground state.

A solid mark is entered in Fig. 2-24 for each state of given spin and parity observed in any isotope (or isotone) with the given Z (or N) value. Thus, Fig. 2-24 represents a composite of data corresponding to each odd nucleon number. If two states of the same $I\pi$ are observed in a single nucleus (within the energy interval described above), two marks are entered.

The approximate sequence of single-particle orbits is indicated along the left-hand axis of Fig. 2-24 (compare with Fig. 2-23), and the broken diagonal line in the figure passes through the configurations that would represent the ground states if the orbits were filled in exactly this sequence. It is seen that the spins and parities of most of the observed low-lying states are indeed consistent with an interpretation in terms of the expected one-particle orbits.

Tests of the one-particle interpretation are provided by other known properties of the levels, such as magnetic moments and one-particle transfer cross sections. In most cases, these properties confirm the qualitative validity of the assignments. Levels for which these properties are in qualitative disagreement with the predictions have been circled in Fig. 2-24, as have also the levels with spin and parity values not expected on the basis of the one-particle spectrum. Similarly, circles have been assigned in cases where two states of the same spin and parity occur in the low-energy spectrum, since at least one must then correspond to a more complicated configuration. It should be added that, since many of the levels have been rather incompletely studied, it is possible that further investigation will reveal a somewhat larger proportion of significant disagreement with the one-particle model.

It is remarkable that so many of the low-lying states can be given a qualitative interpretation in terms of the one-particle model, despite the highly simplified nature of this description. This fact played a major role in the early development of the shell model, since it implies that the consequences of the one-particle level sequence are much more strikingly apparent than would be the case if more complicated coupling schemes prevailed for the many-particle configurations. In particular, it was possible on this basis to give the first interpretation of the ground state spins and magnetic moments (Mayer, 1950; Haxel *et al.*, 1950), the occurrence of isomerism in certain regions of nuclei (Goldhaber and Sunyar, 1951), and the data on β-decay transition rates and selection rules (Nordheim, 1951).

Since the one-particle spectrum used in this figure refers to a spherical potential, we omit from the figure the nuclei for which an appreciable deviation from spherical shape is well established. (The evidence for these nonspherical shapes is discussed in Chapter 4). For these nuclei the one-particle spectrum of Chapter 5 should be employed. It may be noted that many nuclei seem to exhibit properties suggestive of intermediate forms between spherical and nonspherical, ▲ and most of the deviations from the simple one-particle model indicated in the

▼ figure appear to be associated with these transition forms. (Methods for treating this intermediate coupling scheme are discussed in Chapter 6, but there remain important aspects of this problem that are not well understood.)

Strength functions obtained from (dp) studies (Fig. 2-25)

The cross section for the (*dp*) reaction depends on the extent to which the final state can be obtained from the target ground state by the simple addition of a single particle in an orbit with angular momentum quantum numbers lj (see Appendix 3E). Thus, from the observed yields, it is possible to obtain the one-particle parentage probability (2-133). The angular distribution of the protons resulting from the reaction is sensitive to the orbital angular momentum l of the transferred neutron, but in many cases it is not possible on this basis to distinguish between reactions with $j = l \pm \frac{1}{2}$. The reaction cross section then determines the product $(2j + 1)P_{lj}(f)$, which is the quantity plotted in Fig. 2-25.

In nuclei with configurations of approximately closed shells and at low excitation energies, the entire (*dp*) strength of given (lj) may go to a single level f, and thus the level may be identified with the corresponding one-particle configuration (see, for example, Table 3-7). However, in nuclei with several particles outside of closed shells, and quite generally at higher excitation energies, there may be many levels with the same (lj) and comparable (*dp*) yield. The distribution of the probabilities $P_{lj}(E_x)$ as a function of the excitation energy E_x is referred to as the strength function for that value of (lj).

Figure 2-25 gives the strength functions for $l = 0$, 1, and 2, as deduced from the reaction ${}^{60}_{28}\mathrm{Ni}_{32}(dp){}^{61}_{28}\mathrm{Ni}_{33}$. In the region above the neutron binding energy, $S_n({}^{61}\mathrm{Ni}) = 7.82$ MeV, the neutron resonance analysis provides additional information on the *s*-wave strength function (see Fig. 2-26). Since the target has spin zero, the j value of the transferred particle equals the total angular momentum, J, of the final state.

It is seen that the $l = 0$ strength is concentrated in a region centered at $E_x \approx 5$ MeV with a total width of $\Gamma \sim 5$ MeV. This location for the $3s_{1/2}$ orbit is in qualitative agreement with the results of calculations using the one-particle model (see Fig. 2-30). The width is a consequence of couplings between one-particle motion and other low-energy degrees of freedom in the nucleus. (See especially the particle vibration coupling discussed in Chapter 6.)

The $l = 1$ strength in Fig. 2-25 is concentrated on relatively few levels at low excitation energy in ^{61}Ni. A simple filling of the one-particle orbits would suggest the neutron configuration $(f_{7/2})^8$ $(p_{3/2})^4$ for the neutrons in excess of $N = 20$, in the ground state of ^{60}Ni, and thus one might expect all of the strong $l = 1$ transitions in ^{61}Ni to be associated with the $p_{1/2}$ orbit and to populate states with $J = 1/2$. However, the ground state of ^{61}Ni has $J = 3/2$ and is strongly populated in the (*dp*) process. Thus, one must assume an appreciable amount of configurations such as $(f_{7/2})^8$ $(p_{3/2})^2$ $(f_{5/2})^2$ in the ground state of ▲ ^{60}Ni and the corresponding configuration $(f_{7/2})^8$ $(p_{3/2})^3$ $(f_{5/2})^2$ as an important

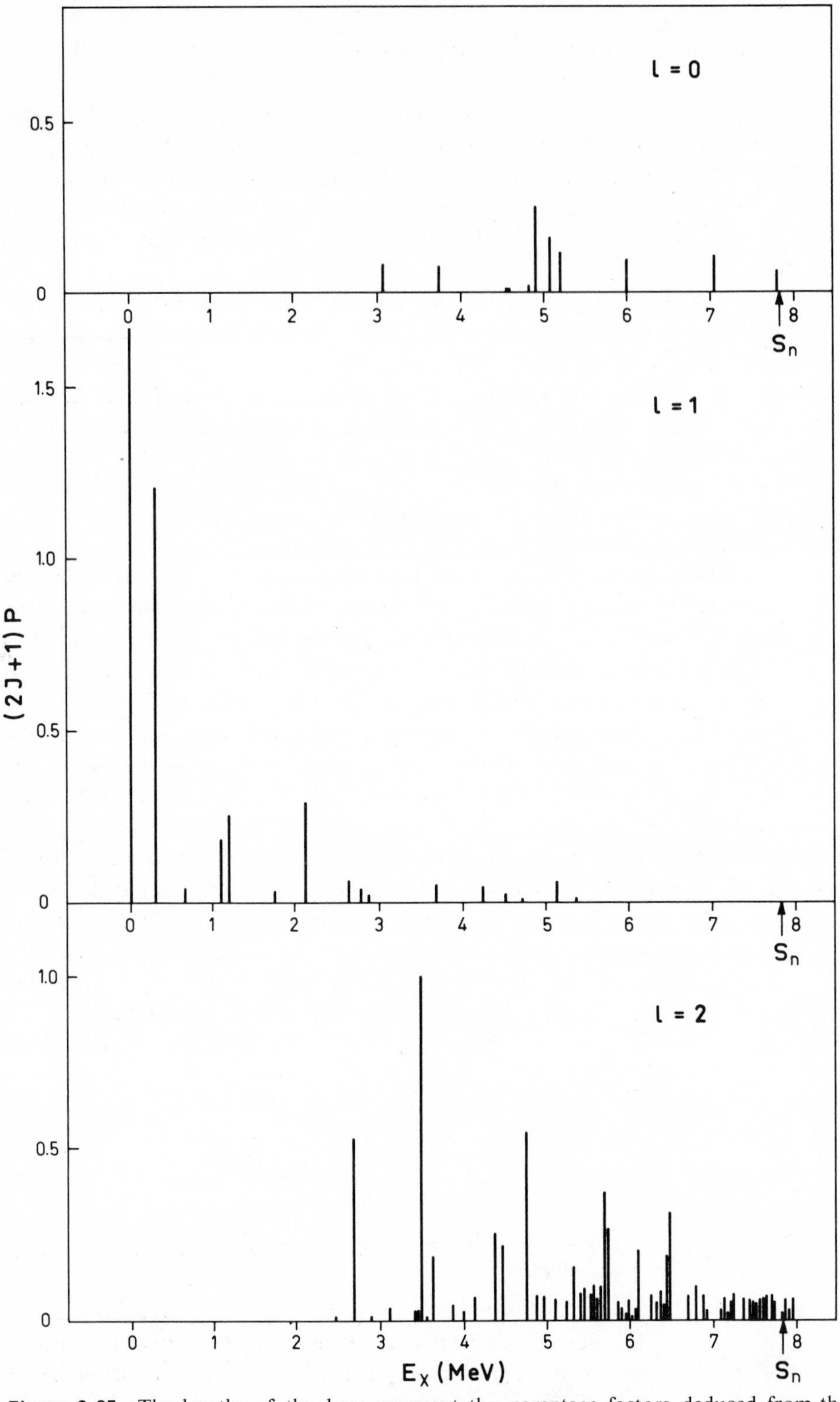

Figure 2-25 The lengths of the bars represent the parentage factors deduced from the stripping reaction $^{60}Ni(dp)^{61}Ni$. The data and analysis are from R. H. Fulmer, A. L. McCarthy, B. L. Cohen, and R. Middleton, *Phys. Rev.* **133**, B955 (1964).

▼ component in the ground state of ^{61}Ni. The cause of this type of configuration mixing is to be found in the pair correlation (see Chapter 8). Since the $p_{1/2}$ strength is expected in the region around 2 MeV above the $p_{3/2}$ level in ^{61}Ni (see Eq. (2-132)), most of the remaining strong $l = 1$ transitions may be tentatively assigned to the $p_{1/2}$ orbit. The width of the $p_{1/2}$ strength function is thus about $\Gamma \sim 2$ MeV.

The $l = 2$ strength is spread over a region starting from about $E_x \approx 3$ MeV and extending at least up to levels with $E_x \approx 8$ MeV. (It is possible that some $l = 2$ strength will be found in the region above 8 MeV, which has not yet been investigated.) Since the expected spin-orbit splitting (≈ 3 MeV) is less than the width of the strength function, it is difficult, in the absence of direct experimental assignments, to separate the $d_{5/2}$ from the $d_{3/2}$ components.

The s-wave strength function (Fig. 2-26)

The study of the resonances in the interaction of slow neutrons with nuclei has provided systematic data on the neutron widths of these resonance levels (see the example illustrated in Fig. 2-8). The reduced neutron width $\Gamma_n^{(0)}(r)$ of the resonance level r (see Eq. (2-114)) is proportional to the one-particle parentage of this level (see Appendix 3F), and thus the average of $\Gamma_n^{(0)}$ divided by the average level spacing D is a measure of the total amount of one-particle parentage per energy interval of the spectrum, that is, the strength function. The observed values of $\Gamma_n^{(0)}/D$ are plotted in Fig. 2-26 as a function of the mass number A.

The value of the strength function can be estimated from a description of the neutron-nucleus interaction that predicts the average value of the cross section for compound nucleus formation (the average of the total cross section for processes going through resonance states). In the low-energy region, the resonances are well separated ($\Gamma \ll D$), and thus we may integrate over the independent contributions of each resonance to obtain (see Eq. (3F-13))

$$\langle\sigma\rangle = \sum_{I_r = I_0 \pm \frac{1}{2}} \frac{2I_r + 1}{2(2I_0 + 1)} \frac{\pi\lambda\!\!\!^{-2}}{D} \int \frac{\Gamma_n \Gamma}{(E - E_r)^2 + (\Gamma/2)^2} \, dE$$

$$= \pi\lambda\!\!\!^{-2} \left(2\pi \frac{\Gamma_n}{D}\right) \tag{2-159}$$

where I_r and I_0 are the spins of the resonance level and the target nucleus, respectively.

The "black nucleus" estimate of Γ_n/D is obtained by assuming that the neutron wave function has an incoming, but no outgoing flux at the nuclear surface (see Blatt and Weisskopf, 1952, pp. 351 ff.) An equivalent derivation of the black nucleus result can be obtained from the fact that, in this model, the one-particle strength is uniformly distributed over the whole spectrum and, thus,

▲ Γ_n/D is equal to the value Γ_{sp}/D_{sp} corresponding to single-particle motion. For a

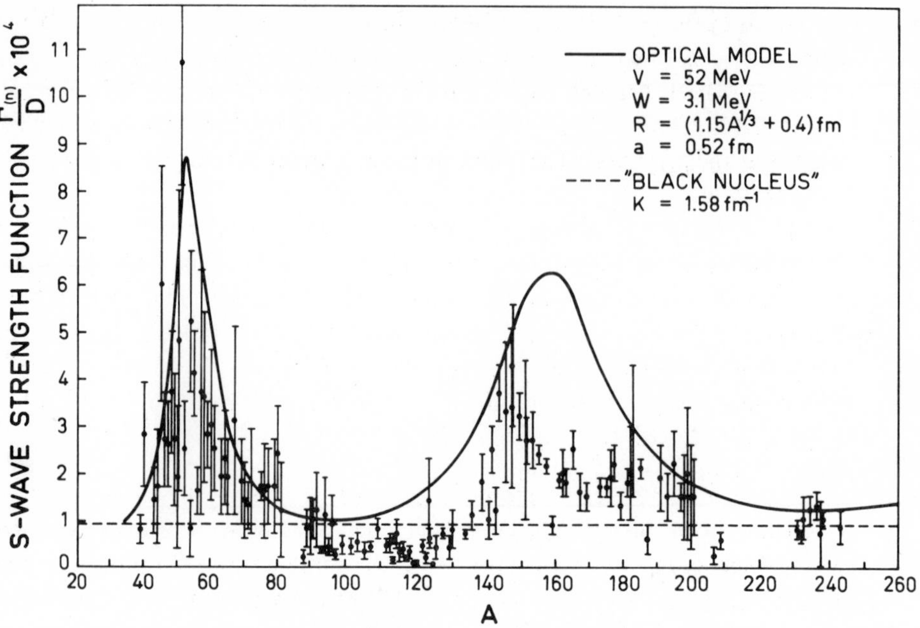

Figure 2-26 We wish to thank J. E. Lynn for a prepublication copy of his compilation of strength functions to appear in his book *The Theory of Neutron Resonance Reactions*, Clarendon Press, Oxford (1968). The optical model calculations are from E. J. Campbell, H. Feshbach, C. E. Porter, and V. F. Weisskopf, M.I.T. Tech. Rept. 73 (1960).

▼ square well potential and $l = 0$, we have (see Eqs. (3F-51) and (3F-53))

$$\Gamma_{sp} = \frac{\hbar^2}{MR^2} 2kR$$
$$D_{sp} = \frac{\hbar^2}{MR^2} \pi KR \tag{2-160}$$

and thus

$$\left(\frac{\Gamma_n}{D}\right)_{\text{black nucleus}} = \frac{\Gamma_{sp}}{D_{sp}} = \frac{2}{\pi}\left(\frac{k}{K}\right) \tag{2-161}$$

Taking $K = 1.58\ \text{fm}^{-1}$ (corresponding to a potential depth of ≈ 52 MeV) and $k = 2.19 \times 10^{-4}\ \text{fm}^{-1}$ (corresponding to a neutron energy of 1 eV), we obtain the estimate given in Fig. 2-26 (dotted line).

The solid curve in Fig. 2-26 is the estimate of Γ_n/D obtained from a calculation of the absorption cross section corresponding to an optical model potential. Both the real and imaginary potentials are assumed to have the Woods-Saxon form with the parameters given in the figure. The fact that the area under the solid curve considerably exceeds that of the "black nucleus" results from ▲ the fact that the latter estimate has been obtained from a potential with a sharp

▼ surface. (See Sec. 3F-2f for estimates of the effect of a diffuse surface on the value of Γ_{sp}.)

The maxima in the strength function at $A \approx 50$ and $A \approx 160$ correspond to the nuclei for which the 3*s* and 4*s* levels occur approximately at an excitation energy equal to the neutron binding energy (see also Fig. 2-30). The significant overestimate of Γ_n/D in the region $150 < A < 190$ can be ascribed to the major influence of the static deformations that characterize nuclei in this region (see Chapter 5).

The overestimate of Γ_n/D in the region $A \approx 110$ may in part be related to the radial distribution of the imaginary potential. In this region, which is approximately half-way between the 3*s* and 4*s* single-particle resonances, the neutron wave function has a node near the nuclear surface. Thus, if the absorption is mainly concentrated in the surface region, the resulting compound nucleus cross section is reduced.

It may be noticed that, in some cases, the *s*-wave strength function appears to exhibit considerable variations between adjacent nuclei. If confirmed, such fluctuations would be indicative of additional structure in the shape of the strength function, going beyond the picture of a simple damping mechanism represented by an imaginary potential. The possibility of such an intermediate structure ("doorway" states) in the process of compound nucleus formation is a matter of considerable current interest. (See, for example, the review by Feshbach, 1967.)

Recently, data have become available on *p*-wave resonances in the low-energy neutron interaction. Although, at the present time, these data are much less complete than for the *s*-wave strength function, it appears that there is a maximum at $A \approx 90$, as expected from the position of the 3*p* single-particle orbit (see Fig. 2-30; the experimental data on the *p*-wave strength function is reviewed by Newson, 1966).

Hole states from (p, 2p) reaction (Fig. 2-27)

While the stripping reactions give information on the strength functions for one-particle states above the Fermi energy (particle states), the knockout processes, such as $(p, 2p)$, and the pickup reactions provide the corresponding information for the states below the Fermi energy (hole states).

Figure 2-27 illustrates the study of hole states in ^{16}O by means of the $(p, 2p)$ reaction. In this experiment, the incident proton energy, E_0, is 460 MeV and the two outgoing protons are detected in a symmetrical geometry. Thus, the directions of the two protons lie in the same plane as the incident beam and make equal angles, ϑ, with it. In addition, the spectrometer selects equal energies for the two protons. In this geometry, the momentum of the recoiling nucleus is

$$p_{\text{recoil}} = p_0 - 2p_1 \cos \vartheta \tag{2-162}$$

▲ where p_0 is the incident momentum and p_1 the momentum corresponding to the

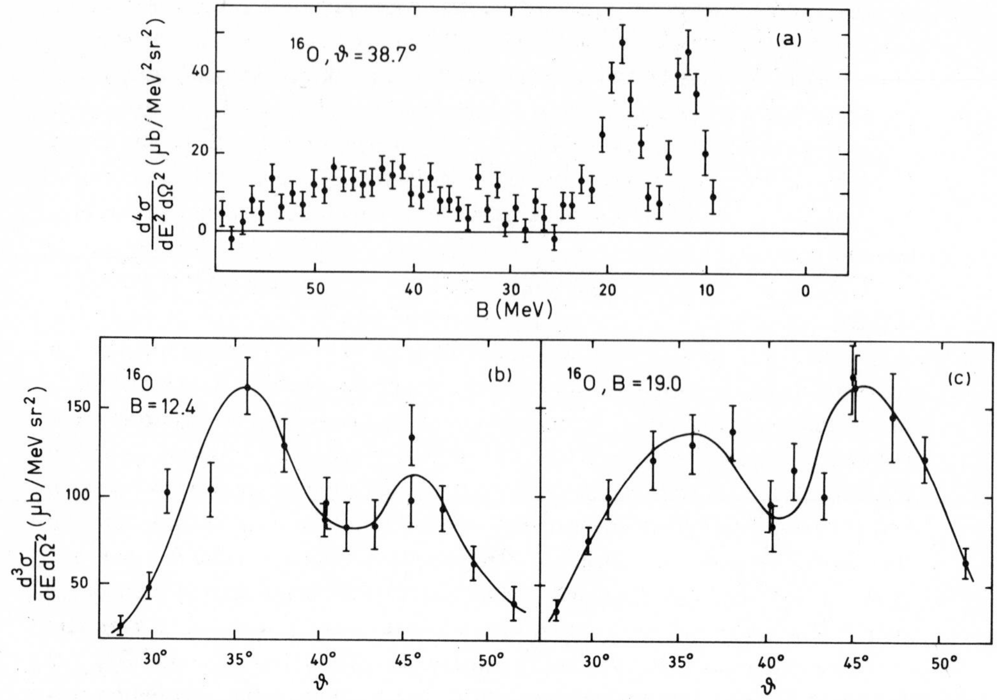

Figure 2-27 The data are taken from H. Tyrén, S. Kullander, O. Sundberg, R. Ramachandran, P. Isacsson, and T. Berggren, *Nuclear Phys.* **79**, 321 (1966); for a review of the $(p, 2p)$ reaction, see Jacob and Maris (1966).

▼ energy, E_1, selected for each of the final protons. The binding energy B of the ejected proton is obtained from the energy balance

$$B = E_0 - 2E_1 - E_{\mathrm{recoil}} \tag{2-163}$$

with

$$E_{\mathrm{recoil}} = \frac{1}{2M_r}(p_{\mathrm{recoil}})^2 \tag{2-164}$$

where M_r is the mass of the recoiling nucleus. In the upper part of Fig. 2-27, the yield of coincident protons is plotted as a function of the binding energy obtained from Eq. (2-163). The maxima in the curve correspond to the one-particle binding energies of protons in the target nucleus ^{16}O.

Protons can be ejected from the $1p_{3/2}$, $1p_{1/2}$, and $1s_{1/2}$ orbits in ^{16}O. The two highest energy peaks in Fig. 2-27 correspond to population of the ground state (1/2−) and 6.3 MeV (3/2−) state in ^{15}N. (It is possible that some part of the lower-energy peak corresponds to population of other states in the neighbor-

▲ hood of the 6.3 MeV state, but the observed intensity and angular distribution

▼ suggest that the main part of the yield corresponds to the 3/2 − state. The evidence from the pickup reaction $^{16}O(d, {}^3He)^{15}N$ further supports this conclusion (Hiebert *et al.*, 1967).) Thus, it appears that for both the $p_{1/2}$ and $p_{3/2}$ transitions, the strength is mainly contained in a single level (one-hole level).

The broad peak in Fig. 2-27a corresponding to a binding energy of about 45 MeV may be tentatively identified as the 1*s* strength function. The width of the 1*s* peak ($\Gamma \approx 15$ MeV) is considerably greater than the instrumental resolution. This width is a measure of the couplings of the 1*s* hole to other degrees of freedom of the system, which eventually damp the simple independent motion of the hole.

Figure 2-27 also illustrates the angular distribution of the protons corresponding to the two high-energy peaks ($p_{1/2}$ and $p_{3/2}$ orbits). The distribution can be interpreted in terms of the momentum distribution of the protons in the corresponding one-particle orbit. The symmetry in the detection geometry implies that the recoil momentum is directed along the beam direction (z axis), and thus the struck proton must have $p_x = p_y = 0$. The observed minimum in the yield at $\vartheta = 40°$ corresponds to the angle for $p_{\text{recoil}} = 0$. (The fact that this angle is not 45° is due, partly, to the relativistic increase in the mass of the incident proton and, partly, to the binding energy of the struck proton.) The minimum for $p_{\text{recoil}} = 0$ results from the fact that the bound proton has $l = 1$ and therefore vanishing probability for zero momentum. The maxima in the distribution correspond to the maxima in the probability distribution for p_z. Since the incident momentum is $p_0 = 1040$ MeV/c, the displacement of the peaks by $\Delta\vartheta \approx 6°$ implies $(p_z)_{\max} = p_0 \Delta\vartheta \approx 110$ MeV/c. Assuming harmonic oscillator wave functions $\varphi(p_z) \propto p_z \exp\{-p_z^2(2\hbar M\omega_0)^{-1}\}$, we obtain $(p_z)_{\max} = (\hbar M\omega_0)^{1/2}$ and, thus, the observed spacing of the maxima implies $\hbar\omega_0 \approx 13$ MeV. This is close to the value deduced from the observed charge distribution of ^{16}O (Hofstadter, 1957) and thus provides significant support for the independent-particle description of the ^{16}O ground state.

In the above discussion, we have completely ignored the deflection and attenuation of the incoming and outgoing protons resulting from their interaction with the other nucleons of the target. These distortion effects are important in a more quantitative analysis of the experiments (particularly in the interpretation of the absolute yield), but leave unaltered the main conclusions of the above discussion (Berggren and Jacob, 1963).

Optical model analysis of 30 MeV proton scattering (Fig. 2-28 and Tables 2-1 and 2-2)

An example of the optical model analysis of proton scattering is shown in Fig. 2-28. The available data include differential cross sections (Fig. 2-28a), polarization (Fig. 2-28b), and total reaction cross sections (Table 2-1) for 30 MeV

▲ protons incident on a variety of elements ranging from Ca to Pb.

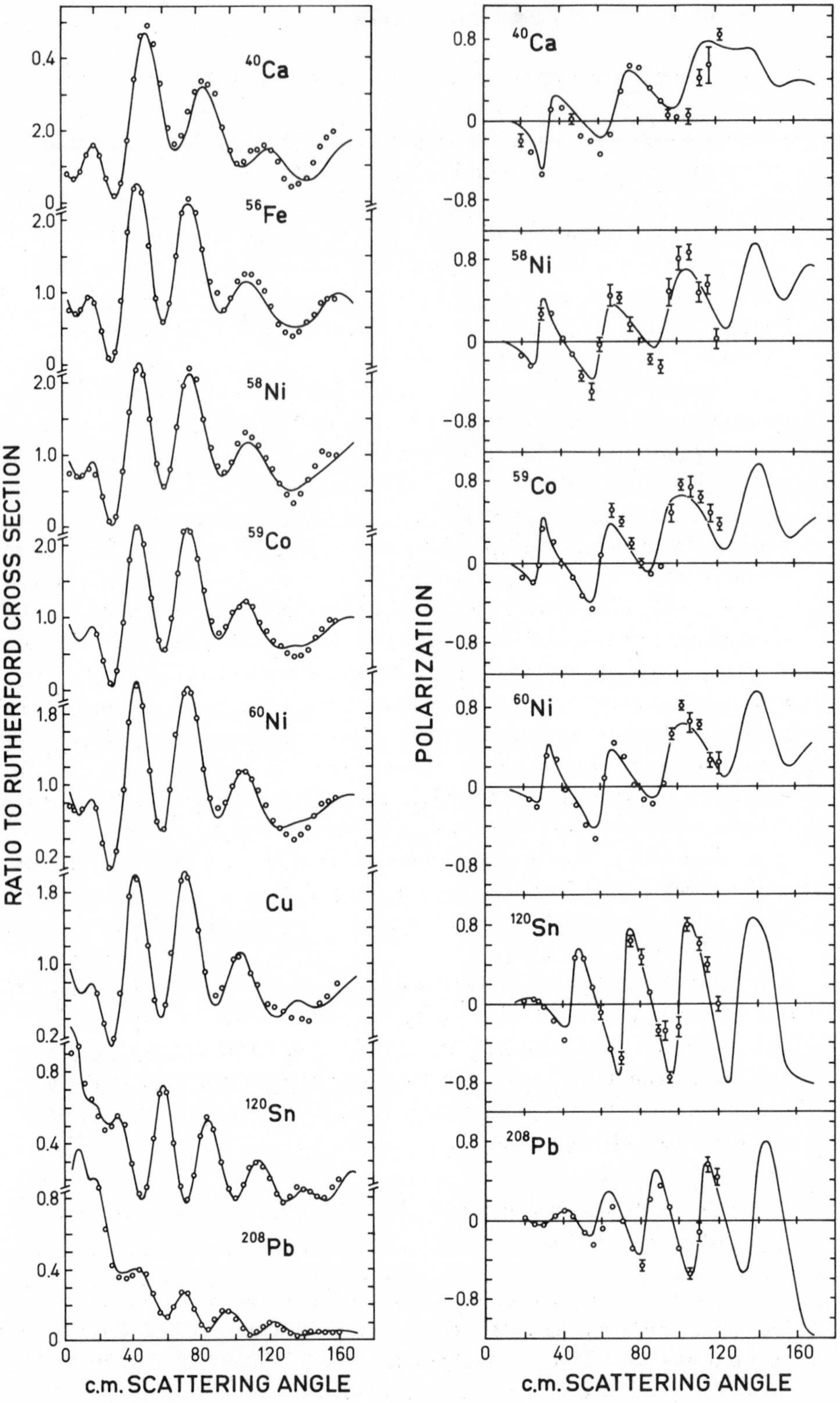
RATIO TO RUTHERFORD CROSS SECTION
^{40}Ca
^{56}Fe
^{58}Ni
^{59}Co
^{60}Ni
Cu
^{120}Sn
^{208}Pb
c.m. SCATTERING ANGLE
POLARIZATION
^{40}Ca
^{58}Ni
^{59}Co
^{60}Ni
^{120}Sn
^{208}Pb
c.m. SCATTERING ANGLE

	^{40}Ca	^{56}Fe	^{58}Ni	^{59}Co	^{60}Ni	Cu	^{120}Sn	^{208}Pb
σ_R(exp.)	915±38	1140±43	1038±32	1169±39	1053±51	1124±40	1638±68	1865±98
σ_R(calc.)	941	1137	1117	1162	1174	1215	1604	1838

Table 2-1 Reaction cross sections for 30 MeV protons. The calculated cross sections correspond to the total compound nucleus cross section obtained from the potentials listed in Table 2-2 since, for 30 MeV bombarding energy, it is expected that the compound nucleus decays predominantly to the many nonelastic channels with only a very small fraction appearing as compound-elastic scattering. The cross sections are given in millibarns (10^{-27} cm^2). The data and analysis are taken from the references given in Fig. 2-28.

▼ The curves drawn in the figure correspond to the calculated cross sections obtained from an optical potential containing the following components:

(a) Central real potential

$$Vf(r, R_V, a_V) \tag{2-165}$$

(b) Central imaginary potential with volume term W_v, and surface term W_s,

$$i\left[W_v f(r, R_W, a_W) - 4a_W W_s \frac{d}{dr} f(r, R_W, a_W)\right] \tag{2-166}$$

(c) Spin-orbit potential

$$V_{ls}(\mathbf{l}\cdot\mathbf{s})\, r^2{}_{ls} \frac{1}{r}\frac{d}{dr} f(r, R_{ls}, a_{ls}) \tag{2-167}$$

(d) Coulomb potential (corresponding to a uniformly charged sphere of radius R_C)

$$\begin{aligned} &\frac{Ze^2}{R_C}\frac{1}{2}\left[3 - \left(\frac{r}{R_C}\right)^2\right] && r \leq R_C \\ &\frac{Ze^2}{r} && r \geq R_C \end{aligned} \tag{2-168}$$

The Woods-Saxon form is chosen for the radial functions

$$f(r, R, a) = \left[1 + \exp\left(\frac{r - R}{a}\right)\right]^{-1} \tag{2-169}$$

In fitting the experimental data, it is found that the results are not very sensitive to the Coulomb radius R_C, and in the calculations this parameter has been set equal to the radius of the real potential,

$$R_C = R_V \tag{2-170}$$

The adjustment of the parameters of the potential has been carried out under ▲ the simplifying assumption that the diffuseness parameters, a, are the same for

Figure 2-28 The data for 30 MeV protons are from B. W. Ridley and J. F. Turner, *Nuclear Phys.* **58**, 497 (1964); J. F. Turner, B. W. Ridley, P. E. Cavanagh, G. A. Gard, and A. G. Hardacre, *Nuclear Phys.* **58**, 509 (1964); R. M. Craig, J. C. Dore, G. W. Greenlees, J. S. Lilley, J. Lowe, and P. C. Rowe, *Nuclear Phys.* **58**, 515 (1964). The optical model analysis is that of G. W. Greenlees and G. J. Pyle, *Phys. Rev.* **149**, 836 (1966).

▼ all nuclei, while the radius parameters, R, have a simple $A^{1/3}$ dependence,

$$R_V = r_V A^{1/3}, \quad \text{etc.} \tag{2-171}$$

The best values found for these averaged geometrical parameters are

$$\begin{aligned} r_V &= 1.2 \text{ fm} & a_V &= 0.7 \text{ fm} \\ r_W &= 1.25 \text{ fm} & a_W &= 0.7 \text{ fm} \\ r_{ls} &= 1.10 \text{ fm} & a_{ls} &= 0.7 \text{ fm} \end{aligned} \tag{2-172}$$

With these values for the geometrical parameters, the well depth parameters were adjusted for each nucleus to give an optimum fit to the observed cross ▲ sections (shown in Fig. 2-28 and Table 2-1); the resulting values of these

	^{40}Ca	^{56}Fe	^{58}Ni	^{59}Co	^{60}Ni	Cu	^{120}Sn	^{208}Pb
$-V$	46.1	46.4	47.0	47.5	47.6	47.7	51.1	53.4
$-W_v$	0.4	2.7	3.4	2.8	2.8	1.8	1.2	4.0
$-W_s$	5.96	5.2	4.4	5.7	5.5	6.1	8.7	7.6
V_{ls}	20.1	19.5	14.8	19.5	18.2	19.5	20.2	17.2

Table 2-2 Optical model parameters for 30 MeV protons. The table lists the well depth parameters (in MeV) used to generate the theoretical cross sections given in Fig. 2-28 and Table 2-1; the geometrical parameters in the potentials have the values given in Eq. (2-172). The analysis is taken from Greenlees and Pyle, *loc. cit.*, Fig. 2-28.

▼ parameters are shown in Table 2-2. Slight improvements in the fits to individual nuclei can be achieved by separate variations of the geometrical parameters for each separate nucleus. The use of a pure surface absorption ($W_v = 0$) leads to theoretical cross sections that fit the experimental data almost as well as those shown, while pure volume absorption ($W_s = 0$) leads to fits that appear to be somewhat poorer.

Systematics of optical model potential (*Fig. 2-29*)

Optical model potentials have been determined from analyses of a wide variety of data corresponding to neutron and proton interactions with many different nuclei and at different incident energies (for examples, see Figs. 2-3, 2-26, and 2-28).

Figure 2-29 contains a summary of some of the systematic features of the optical potentials determined by these analyses. In order to compare parameters corresponding to different bombarding energies, E, the figure contains only the results of analyses using especially simple and standard forms for the potentials. Thus, the central real potentials are of the Woods-Saxon type,

$$V(r) = -Vf(r) \tag{2-173}$$

with

$$f(r) = \left[1 + \exp\left(\frac{r-R}{a}\right)\right]^{-1} \tag{2-174}$$

▲

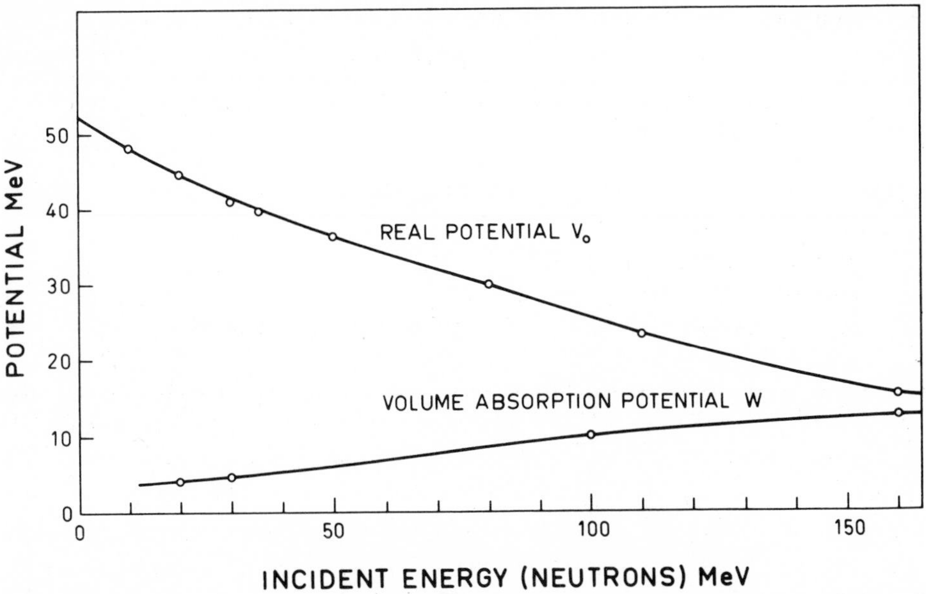

Figure 2-29 The figure is based on the optical model analyses by L. Rosen, J. G. Beery, A. S. Goldhaber, and E. H. Auerbach, *Ann. Phys.* **34**, 96 (1965) (real potential for $E_p < 22$ MeV), G. W. Greenlees and G. J. Pyle, *Phys. Rev.* **149**, 836 (1966) ($E_p = 30$ MeV), P. H. Bowen, J. P. Scanlon, G. H. Stafford, J. J. Thresher, and P. E. Hodgson, *Nuclear Phys.* **22**, 640 (1961) (15 MeV $< E_n <$ 120 MeV), P. G. Roos and N. S. Wall, *Phys. Rev.* **140**, B1237 (1965) ($E_p = 160$ MeV), and the compilation by Winner and Drisko (1965) ($E_p < 30$ MeV).
The abscissa corresponds to the bombarding energy, E_n, for neutrons; for incident protons, the corresponding bombarding energies, E_p, are larger by the Coulomb energy, since it is the kinetic energy inside the nucleus that determines the strength of the average potential.

▼ The radius and diffuseness parameters have the values

$$R = r_0 A^{1/3} \qquad r_0 = 1.25 \text{ fm}$$
$$a = 0.65 \text{ fm} \tag{2-175}$$

The values of the potential V in the figure correspond to the isoscalar part of the interaction V_0 and thus represent an average of neutron and proton potentials, where such data are available; where these data are not available, the potentials for different elements have been extrapolated to small values of Z and A, where symmetry and Coulomb energy corrections are negligible.

It is seen that the potential V_0 gradually decreases with increasing incident energy and can be approximately represented by

$$V_0 \approx 52 - 0.3E \tag{2-176}$$

in the energy region up to $E \approx 80$ MeV.

The isovector part of the real central potential has been determined from ▲ the difference of the neutron and proton potentials (for targets with $Z \neq N$),

▼ from the Z and A dependence of the potential for protons or neutrons, and from the cross section for the direct (pn) process producing the $M_T = T_0 - 1$ isobaric analog state of the target nucleus. These different analyses are consistent with a potential of the form

$$V_1(r) = \frac{\mathbf{t} \cdot \mathbf{T}_0}{A} V_1 f(r) \tag{2-177}$$

with geometrical parameters as in Eq. (2-175) and with values of V_1 ranging from 70 to 110 MeV (Hodgson, 1964; Greenlees and Pyle, 1966). The available analyses are not sufficiently accurate or consistent with each other to establish the energy dependence of the potential parameter V_1.

The available data are best fitted by an absorptive potential that is strongest in the surface region for low incident energies, while volume absorption (an imaginary potential proportional to $f(r)$) fits best at high energies. For 30 MeV protons, the potential is still dominated by surface absorption (see, for example, Table 2-2). In order to compare the variation of the absorptive potential with energy, we have somewhat simplified the description, giving in the figure the magnitude of the pure volume absorption, $-iWf(r)$, that best describes the cross sections at each energy. It is seen that the values of W increase steadily from values of a few MeV at the lowest energies to values of order 10 MeV for $E \sim 100$ MeV.

The spin-orbit potential is approximately determined for nucleons with incident energies up to 30 MeV (Rosen *et al.*, 1965; Greenlees and Pyle, 1966). In this energy range, the data can be fitted by a potential of the form

$$V_{ls}(r) = V_{ls}(\mathbf{l} \cdot \mathbf{s}) r_0^2 \frac{1}{r} \frac{d}{dr} f(r) \tag{2-178}$$

with

$$V_{ls} \approx 17 \text{ MeV} \tag{2-179}$$

The difference in radii suggested for the spin-orbit and central potentials (see Eq. (2-172)) has been interpreted (Greenlees *et al.*, 1966) in terms of the very short range of the two-body spin-orbit interaction (see Fig. 2-35).

Binding energies of single-particle orbits in a static nuclear potential (Fig. 2-30)

The systematics of the spectra obtained by solving the Schrödinger equation for one-particle motion in a spherical potential are shown in Fig. 2-30. The one-particle orbits are labeled by the quantum numbers $n_r lj$, where the number of nodes in the radial wave function is $n_r - 1$. The potential employed has the form

$$U = Vf(r) + V_{ls}(\mathbf{l} \cdot \mathbf{s}) r_0^2 \frac{1}{r} \frac{d}{dr} f(r) \tag{2-180}$$

▲ with $f(r)$ given by Eq. (2-174). The radius is assumed to vary as $A^{1/3}$, while the

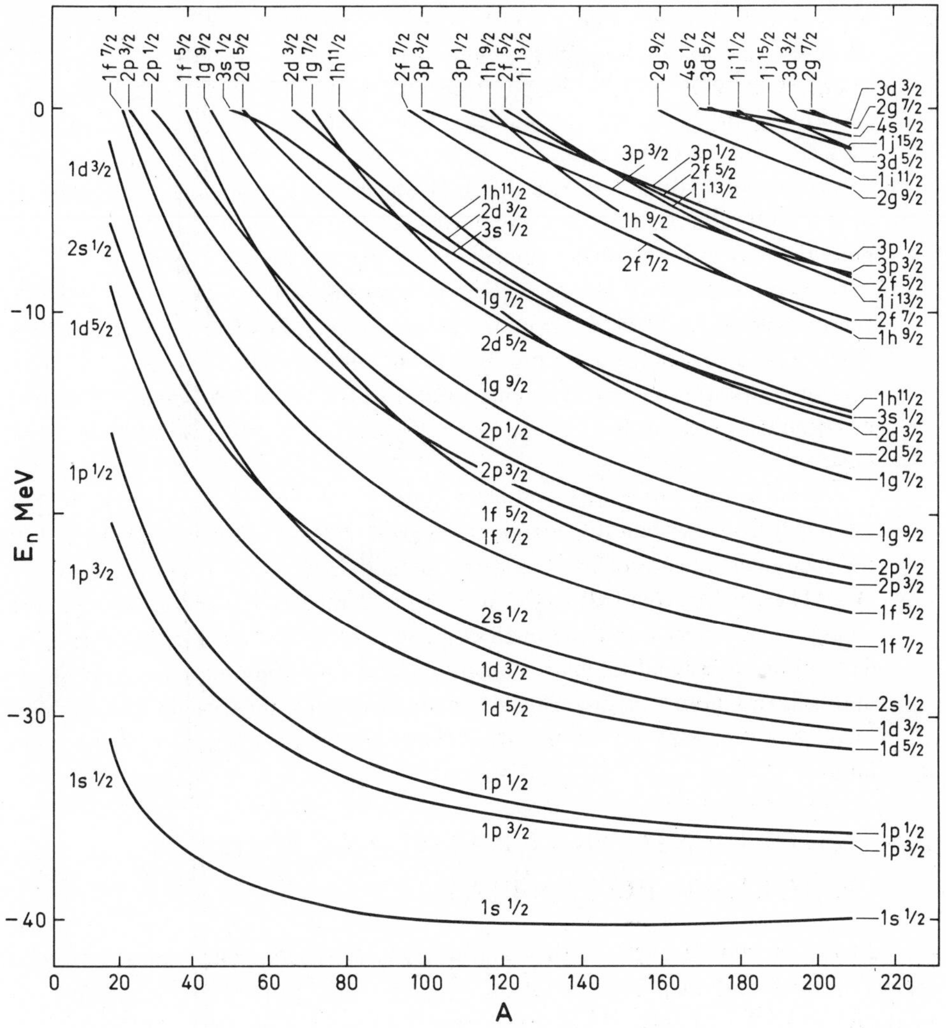

Figure 2-30 Energies of neutron orbits calculated by C. J. Veje (private communication).

▼ surface thickness parameter a is taken to be A independent.

$$R = r_0 A^{1/3} \qquad r_0 = 1.27 \text{ fm}$$
$$a = 0.67 \text{ fm} \tag{2-181}$$

The potential strengths include a term depending on the neutron excess, in order to describe approximately the potential acting on a single neutron,

$$V = \left(-51 + 33\,\frac{N-Z}{A}\right) \text{ MeV}$$
$$V_{ls} = -0.44V = \left(22 - 14\,\frac{N-Z}{A}\right) \text{ MeV} \tag{2-182}$$

▲ and the neutron excess for each A has been chosen to correspond to the

▼ minimum in the valley of β stability. (For $Z = 82$ and $A = 208$, the parameters are those used by Blomqvist and Wahlborn (1960).)

The parameters chosen give a rather good description of the overall patterns observed in the low-energy bound state spectra (see, for example, Figs. 3-3 and 3-5), and also agree with the average potentials found from the optical model analysis (see Fig. 2-29). However, no attempt has been made to obtain an optimum fit and, in any particular nucleus, small adjustments in the potential may improve the agreement. The neglect of the velocity dependence in the potential implies that one expects corrections of the order of 30% in the energy scale when comparing with the excitation energies of single-particle orbits that are far away from the Fermi surface (see, for example, Figs. 2-29 and 3-5). The description of one-particle bound states with a velocity-dependent potential has been discussed by Ross *et al.* (1956), Wyatt *et al.* (1960), and Meldner *et al.* (1965).

The magnitude of the symmetry potential is somewhat larger than that estimated from the binding energies (see Eq. 2-28)), which may possibly reflect a velocity dependence of the symmetry potential.

The general trend observed in Fig. 2-30 reflects the increasing binding energy of each orbit with the growth of the size of the binding field, as A increases. The orbits with small angular momentum and small binding energy spend an appreciable amount of time outside the nucleus and thus benefit less from an increase in the size of the potential than do the weakly bound orbits with large l. ▲

2-5 NUCLEONIC INTERACTIONS AND NUCLEAR POTENTIAL

In the preceding parts of this chapter, we have seen that a description in terms of independent-particle motion provides an appropriate basis for the analysis of many nuclear properties. We have also seen how the observed sequence of the nucleonic binding states and the nuclear scattering data can be used to determine the parameters that characterize the average nuclear potential. In this section, we consider the relationship of these parameters to the nucleonic interactions as revealed in the analysis of the two-nucleon system. The problem is one of considerable complexity and reaches into many aspects of the nuclear structure. In the present chapter, we are mainly concerned with exploring the basic physical aspects of the problem and establishing the simple qualitative features.

2-5a Main Features of Nucleonic Interaction

There has been very substantial progress in recent years in the determination of the nucleonic interaction. We shall not attempt here to present systematically the detailed methods of analysis or the varied experimental data that have contributed to this progress. Rather, the discussion will be confined to a summary of the main results of the analysis. These results provide the starting point for a comparison of nuclear properties with the two-body interaction. (For reviews of the experimental data and of the analysis see, for example, Wilson, 1963; Moravcsik, 1963; Amati, 1964.)

Low energies ($E < 5$ *MeV*)

A strongly attractive, short-range nuclear interaction can be inferred directly from the low-energy *np* and *pp* scattering experiments and from the bound state of the deuteron. Because of the centrifugal barrier, these low-energy experiments primarily give information on the *S*-wave interaction. As is well known, the low-energy experiments can be described by the effective range expansion of the phase shifts, which depends on two parameters, the scattering length a and the effective range r_e, for each spin-isospin channel. (See, for example, the textbook by Blatt and Weisskopf, 1952, pp. 56ff., and, for more details, the review article by Jackson and Blatt, 1950.) For *np* scattering, we have

$$k \cot \delta = -\frac{1}{a} + \tfrac{1}{2} r_e k^2 \qquad \text{(2-183)}$$

The observed low-energy scattering (and the deuteron binding energy) determines the parameters for the *S*-wave interaction

$$\begin{aligned} &\text{singlet state } (S = 0,\ T = 1) \quad \begin{cases} a = -23.7 \text{ fm} \\ r_e = 2.7 \text{ fm} \end{cases} \\ &\text{triplet state } (S = 1,\ T = 0) \quad \begin{cases} a = 5.39 \text{ fm} \\ r_e = 1.703 \text{ fm} \end{cases} \end{aligned} \qquad \text{(2-184)}$$

The presence of the Coulomb interaction in the *pp* scattering implies some modifications in the *pp* effective range expansion, but again the effect of the nuclear interaction is described in terms of the two parameters a and r_e. Since the phase shifts are described by two parameters, the low-energy scattering determines only two parameters of the potential, such as depth and range.

The comparison of the ^1S scattering in the *np* system with the low-energy *pp* scattering provided the first evidence for charge independence of the nuclear forces (Breit *et al.*, 1936). Because of the large scattering length, it is possible to make a very sensitive comparison of the two interactions. It is found that the *np* interaction is about 1.5% stronger than the *pp* interaction, although the exact value depends somewhat on the shape of the potential (Schwinger, 1950). More recently, evidence on the ^1S scattering length in the *nn* system has been obtained from an analysis of reactions involving two neutrons in the final state (see, for example, Baumgartner *et al.*, 1966, and the references given there). The tentative conclusion from these experiments is consistent with charge symmetry, $V_{nn} = V_{pp}$. Attempts have been made to relate the small difference between V_{np} and V_{pp} to the mass difference between charged and neutral π mesons (see, for example, Henley, 1966), but, in pressing charge independence to this level of accuracy, one is faced with a rather difficult problem resulting from the interweaving of electromagnetic and strong interaction effects.

The fact that a is negative and almost an order of magnitude larger than r_e for ^1S scattering implies that, in this channel, there is an attractive interaction with a strength slightly less than that required to give a bound state at zero energy. For rough estimates, it is often convenient to use a square well potential with strength V_0 and range b, determined so as to give the observed effective range and a bound state at zero energy,

$$b = r_e = 2.7 \text{ fm}$$

$$V_0 = \left(\frac{\pi}{2}\right)^2 \frac{\hbar^2}{Mb^2} = 14 \text{ MeV} \tag{2-185}$$

The existence of the quadrupole moment of the deuteron implies that, in the low-energy triplet interaction, the $^3S_1$ and $^3D_1$ channels are coupled, and a tensor force component must therefore be present. The expansion (2-183) now describes the "eigenphase" in the coupled channel.

If we use the parameters of Eq. (2-184) to determine an "effective" square well potential for the ^3S interaction, we find a potential with $b \approx 1.9$ fm and $V_0 \approx 35$ MeV (see, for example, Blatt and Weisskopf, 1952, Fig. 3.3, p. 64). However, it must be emphasized that the use of such an effective potential may be very hazardous in estimating interactions in the nucleus, since the tensor and central components of the force contribute very differently to the average nuclear potential and to the binding in the deuteron. Indeed, the tensor force averages to zero in the first approximation to the nuclear potential. Thus, for the estimate of the nuclear potential, it is very important to know the relative contribution of the tensor and central interactions to the observed low-energy attraction; the low-energy data alone do not provide this information.

Higher energies. Exchange potential

The investigations at low energy determine only a relatively small part of the nucleonic interaction and, in particular, are completely silent as to the nature of the repulsive element that is so important in determining the equilibrium density and average interaction in the nucleus (see Sec. 2-5b). Analysis of the high-energy scattering experiments is, therefore, essential in order to define the interaction sufficiently for it to be compared with the properties of nuclei.

Neutron-proton scattering experiments in the energy range from $E_n =$ 50 MeV to $E_n = 700$ MeV have revealed strong backward scattering and thus confirm the idea of an important exchange interaction, as originally suggested by Heisenberg (1932) and Majorana (1933) (see Fig. 2-31). In fact, since the

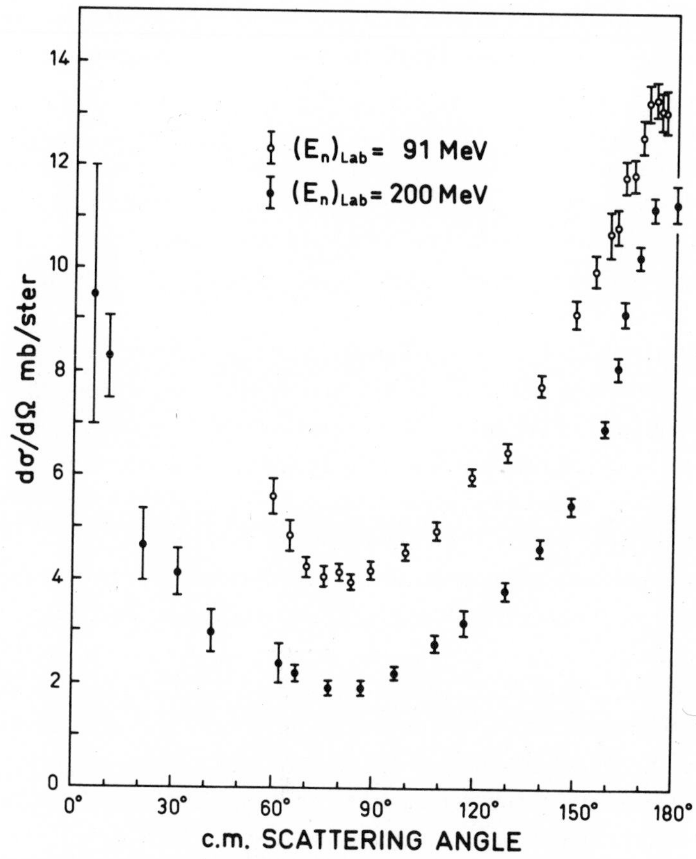

Figure 2-31 The experimental data on the *np* differential scattering cross sections are taken from R. H. Stahl and N. F. Ramsey, *Phys. Rev.* **96**, 1310 (1954) (91 MeV data) and Yu. M. Kazarinov and Yu. N. Simonov, *Exptl. Theoret. Phys. U.S.S.R.* **43**, 35 (1962) (translation *Soviet Phys. JETP* **16**, 24 (1963)) (200 MeV data). The figure gives only a small sample of the available measurements; see, for example, the compilation by Moravcsik (1963).

wavelength of the incident particle is shorter than the range of the interaction, an ordinary force would lead to a predominantly forward scattering. The observed backward scattering can, however, result from a process in which the incident neutron emits a π meson, transforming into a proton, which continues forward, while the target proton absorbs the π meson, becoming a neutron and going backward (in the center-of-mass system). Such an "exchange" scattering can be described by a potential of the form $V(r)P^r$, where P^r is an operator that exchanges the space coordinates, $\mathbf{r}_1$ and $\mathbf{r}_2$, of the two colliding particles, $P^r f(\mathbf{r}_1, \mathbf{r}_2) = f(\mathbf{r}_2, \mathbf{r}_1)$.

A pure space exchange force, $V(r)P^r$, would lead to an angular distribution strongly peaked at 180°, while a nonexchange force, $V(r)$, would lead to a maximum at 0°. It is thus possible to obtain a simple explanation of the approximately equal maxima at 0° and 180° (see Fig. 2-31) by assuming a force depending on $(1 + P^r)$ (called the Serber exchange mixture). The plus sign in this linear combination is necessary in order to obtain the strong interaction observed in S states. Such a potential acts only in states of even orbital angular momentum. The more detailed analysis has shown that this simple interpretation is only partially true; there are significant interactions in odd states (see below), but the odd-state interactions almost vanish when averaged over the relative orientations of spin and orbit, and thus it is often useful to employ the Serber mixture to obtain a rough estimate of the effect of the symmetry dependence of the central interaction between nucleons.

The Serber mixture does not contain any repulsive elements, and thus this first result of high-energy studies failed to substantiate the long favored belief that nuclear saturation would be accounted for in terms of the symmetry dependence of the nuclear force.

The systematic unraveling of high-energy nucleon-nucleon scattering has required more than a decade; the interaction has turned out to be so complicated that it has not been possible to anticipate an adequate simplifying theoretical model. In this situation, there has been no substitute for the slow accumulation of very detailed experimental data involving total cross sections and angular distributions, as well as measurements of the polarizations and spin correlations of the scattered nucleons. Even after a great wealth of data was available, many ambiguities remained in the analysis; these ambiguities were finally resolved only after it became possible to calculate a part of the scattering from meson theory (see below) and after data at different energies were combined under the assumption that the phase parameters would vary smoothly.

As a result of this work, there is now available a rather unique phase shift analysis, which describes the observed scattering up to several hundred million electron volts of energy (see Fig. 2-34, p. 264). It is also possible to find potentials that approximately reproduce these scattering cross sections, but the potentials involve a very great number of parameters, and the question of uniqueness of the description is not yet sufficiently studied (see Fig. 2-35, p. 266, for examples of such potentials). In particular, it is not yet clear to what extent the nucleonic potential contains important nonlocal elements or explicit velocity dependence; possible evidence for such terms has been presented by Giltinan and Thaler (1963).

Despite the uncertainty as to the uniqueness of the available potential fits, it is possible to deduce almost directly from the phase shifts a number of qualitative features of the interaction that are of great significance for the questions of nuclear structure.

Hard core

The fact that the ^1S phase shift becomes negative at about 200 MeV shows that the interaction in this channel, which was strongly attractive at low energies, has become effectively repulsive at the higher energies; we see here, for the first time, clear experimental evidence for a replusive component in the nucleonic interaction, which can account for the nuclear saturation. One way of introducing a repulsive interaction, which is relatively unimportant at low energies but dominates at higher energies, is in terms of a very strong repulsive potential of very short range—"the hard core".[3] From Fig. 2-34 it is seen that, at high energies, the S phases are decreasing at a rate $d\delta/dk \approx -0.6$ fm, and thus the radius of the hard core, c, must be of this magnitude. (The detailed potential fits seem to work best with values in the range $c = 0.4$ to 0.5 fm; see Fig. 2-35.)

The presence of a hard core changes somewhat the interpretation of the low-energy effective range parameters. The square well potential that gives binding at zero energy (as is approximately the case for the ^1S channel) still has $V_0 = (\frac{1}{2}\pi)^2 \hbar^2/Mb^2$, where b is the range of the attractive region extending beyond the core. The effective range, however, is considerably greater than b (see Fig. 2-32) and thus, if we use the value $c = 0.5$ fm for the hard core, the low-energy ^1S data (2-184) now imply $b = 1.7$ fm and $V_0 = 34$ MeV.

It should be emphasized that an infinite, short-range repulsion is only one, rather extreme, way of accounting for the observed change in sign of the S-wave phase shifts. Finite repulsive potentials (soft core), as well as interactions depending explicitly on the relative velocity, can also account for the observed scattering phase shifts (Rojo and Simmons, 1962; Green and Sharma, 1965; Tamagaki, 1967).

Another method of parameterizing the effect of the violent interactions at short distances is to replace the interior region by appropriate boundary conditions at some finite radius (Lomon and Feshbach, 1967). As long as the interactions responsible for these boundary conditions involve energies much greater than the bombarding energy, it may be expected that the boundary conditions will be approximately energy independent.

---

[3] Although the possibility of accounting for nuclear saturation by means of a very short-range repulsive interaction was recognized from the first discussions of the nucleonic interaction, this possibility was given rather little attention, since it conflicted with the notion of a simple structure of the nucleons. The idea was revived by Jastrow (1950) as a possible explanation of the rather low total cross section observed in high-energy *np* scattering. The first unambiguous evidence for this repulsion was provided by the detailed phase shift analysis of the extensive scattering and polarization measurements made on *pp* scattering at 310 MeV (Chamberlain *et al.*, 1957; Stapp *et al.*, 1957; Cziffra *et al.*, 1959).

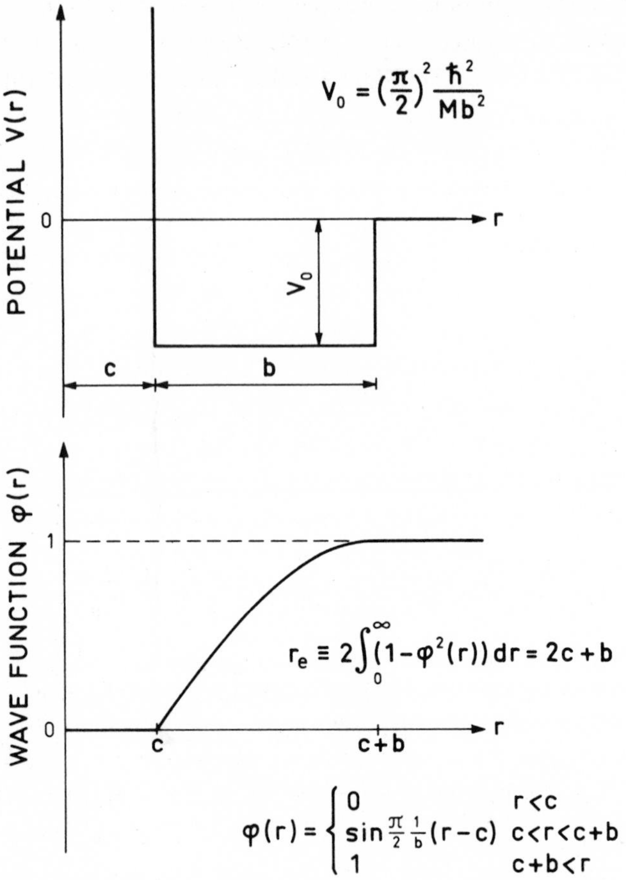

Figure 2-32 Square well potential with repulsive core and with V_0 adjusted to give a bound state at zero energy.

The ^3P phases. Spin dependence of interaction

The average of the ^3P phases

$$\langle \delta(^3P) \rangle \equiv \tfrac{1}{9}[5\delta(^3P_2) + 3\delta(^3P_1) + \delta(^3P_0)] \tag{2-186}$$

remains quite small at all energies, suggesting a relatively weak central interaction in the ^3P states, as for a Serber exchange mixture. The relative magnitude of the ^3P phases gives important information on the nature of the spin-dependent forces. Indeed, we can immediately conclude from these phase shifts that both a spin-orbit force and a tensor force are required in the nucleonic interaction.

In analyzing the effect of spin-dependent forces in the two-nucleon system, it is convenient to employ the helicity operator

$$H = \frac{1}{r}(\mathbf{S} \cdot \mathbf{r}) \qquad \mathbf{r} = \mathbf{r}_1 - \mathbf{r}_2 \tag{2-187}$$

which represents the component of the total spin in the direction of $\mathbf{r}$. The eigenvalues of the helicity are $H=0, \pm 1$. In states of given parity, opposite helicities ($H=\pm 1$) must occur with equal probability, since H changes sign under space inversion. (The helicity representation for single-nucleon motion in the nuclear potential is employed extensively in the following chapters (see Sec. 3A-1).)

The triplet states of given total angular momentum J and parity π can be labeled by the orbital angular momentum L, or by the magnitude of the helicity, $|H|$, and we have the following channels:

$$\begin{array}{llllll} J=0 & \pi=-1 & L=1 & H=0 & (^3P_0) \\ J\neq 0 & \pi=(-1)^{J+1} & L=J\mp 1 & \left\{\begin{array}{l} H=0 \\ |H|=1 \end{array}\right. & \begin{array}{l} (\sqrt{\frac{1}{3}}\,{}^3S_1+\sqrt{\frac{2}{3}}\,{}^3D_1,\ldots) \\ (\sqrt{\frac{2}{3}}\,{}^3S_1-\sqrt{\frac{1}{3}}\,{}^3D_1,\ldots) \end{array} \\ J\neq 0 & \pi=(-1)^J & L=J & |H|=1 & (^3P_1, {}^3D_2,\ldots) \end{array} \tag{2-188}$$

The transformation from the LJ to the HJ representation is given by Eq. (3A-9) and involves the vector addition coefficient $\langle L0SH|JH\rangle$ describing the coupling of the helicity to the orbital moment. Thus, for $L=J$, we have $|H|=1$, while $H=0$ for $L=1$, $J=0$. For the states with $\pi=(-1)^{J+1}$ and $J\neq 0$, there are two channels for given π and J, and one can choose as a basis either the channel with specified L or with specified $|H|$. The kinetic energy operator commutes with $\mathbf{L}$, but not with H, and for spin-independent interactions, the eigenstates therefore have definite L. The spin-orbit force also commutes with $\mathbf{L}$, and not with H. However, the tensor force operator S_{12}, given by Eq. (1-89), commutes with H, but not with L, and thus, the tensor force tends to produce states with specified $|H|$. The eigenvalues of S_{12} are seen to be

$$\begin{aligned} S_{12} &\equiv \frac{3}{r^2}(\boldsymbol{\sigma}_1\cdot\mathbf{r})(\boldsymbol{\sigma}_2\cdot\mathbf{r})-\boldsymbol{\sigma}_1\cdot\boldsymbol{\sigma}_2 \\ &= \frac{6}{r^2}(\mathbf{S}\cdot\mathbf{r})^2-2(\mathbf{S})^2 \\ &= \begin{cases} 0 & S=0 \\ -4 & S=1 \quad H=0 \\ +2 & S=1 \quad H=\pm 1 \end{cases} \end{aligned} \tag{2-189}$$

The $^3P_0$ and $^3P_1$ states have $|H|=0$ and 1 (see Eq. (2-188)) and, hence, have $S_{12}=-4$ and $+2$, respectively. Since $^3P_2$ is coupled by the tensor force to $^3F_2$, the diagonal effect of the tensor force in this channel must be intermediate between the extreme values characterizing the $^3P_0$ and $^3P_1$ channels. The observed phase shifts at high energies, however, have the relative magnitudes $\delta(^3P_2)>\delta(^3P_0)>\delta(^3P_1)$ (see Fig. 2-34) and, hence, are inconsistent with an interaction consisting only of central and tensor forces.

The spin-orbit force has an expectation value proportional to $2\langle \mathbf{L}\cdot\mathbf{S}\rangle = J(J+1)-L(L+1)-S(S+1)$ and, therefore, if this is the only spin-dependent interaction, the magnitude of the $^3P_1$ phase must be intermediate between that of $^3P_0$ and $^3P_2$. We thus conclude that both a tensor and a spin-orbit force are required to describe the observed ^3P phases.

The sign of the required spin-orbit force is seen to be attractive for the parallel alignment of spin and orbit ($^3P_2$). This spin-orbit force in the nucleonic interaction contributes in an important way to the spin-orbit force observed in the average nuclear potential (see p. 259). In a similar manner, the sign of the tensor force required by the ^3P phases is seen to be such as to give repulsion in the $^3P_1$ state ($|H|=1$) and attraction in the $^3P_0$ state ($H=0$). In the deuteron, the positive quadrupole moment shows that the helicity is predominantly $|H|=1$; for the even states, therefore, the tensor force is attractive for $|H|=1$ and repulsive for $H=0$. The overall sign of the tensor force is thus opposite for even and odd states (as in the one-pion exchange potential (2-190)).

One-pion exchange potential

The structure of the nucleonic force is intimately related to the properties and interactions of the whole family of strongly interacting particles. It has not so far been possible to derive the forces between these particles, or their masses, from simple assumptions regarding the basic structure of the strong interactions. However, certain relations between the interactions and masses of the strongly interacting particles can be established. Of particular significance is the relationship between the nucleonic force at large distances and the pion-nucleon interaction.

The force at large distances (peripheral interaction) can be described in terms of an exchange of mesons, in a similar manner as the electromagnetic interaction can be analyzed in terms of photon exchange. The special role of the pion exchange is due to the smallness of the pion mass as compared with that of other strongly interacting particles. The interaction associated with the exchange of a particle of mass m is limited to a range of the order of the Compton wavelength $\lambda_c = \hbar/mc$, as can be seen from elementary arguments. In fact, the intermediate states involved in such an exchange have an energy of at least mc^2 and so are limited to a duration of order $\hbar/mc^2$. During this time, the emitted particle cannot travel farther than $\hbar/mc$ and, thus, the interaction is expected to decrease strongly for distances greater than λ_c. If we wish to exchange n particles simultaneously, the corresponding intermediate energies are nmc^2 and the range is λ_c/n. The interaction at the largest distances is therefore determined by the exchange of single π mesons.

The asymptotic form of the one-pion exchange potential is uniquely specified by the mass and symmetry properties of the pion ($I\pi = 0-$, $T = 1$),

$$V = \frac{1}{3}\frac{f^2}{\hbar c} m_\pi c^2 (\boldsymbol{\tau}_1 \cdot \boldsymbol{\tau}_2)\left[(\boldsymbol{\sigma}_1 \cdot \boldsymbol{\sigma}_2) + \left(1 + \frac{3}{\mu r} + \frac{3}{(\mu r)^2}\right)S_{12}\right]\frac{\exp\{-\mu r\}}{\mu r}$$

$$\mu \equiv \frac{m_\pi c}{\hbar} = 0.70\ (\text{fm})^{-1} \qquad \frac{f^2}{\hbar c} = 0.081 \pm 0.002 \tag{2-190}$$

The strength of the potential is determined by the coupling constant f for the process $N \rightarrow N + \pi$. The quoted value for f has been obtained from the analysis of π-nucleon scattering (see Table 1-1, p. 4).

The π-nucleon coupling constant represents the reduced width for the process $N \rightarrow N + \pi$ and is thus a measure of the strength of the meson field surrounding a nucleon. This field is pseudoscalar, since $I\pi = 0-$, and isovector, since $T = 1$, and satisfies the field equation

$$(\nabla^2 - \mu^2)\boldsymbol{\varphi}(\mathbf{r}) = -4\pi\boldsymbol{\rho}(\mathbf{r}) \tag{2-191}$$

where the field $\boldsymbol{\varphi}$ and the nucleonic source density $\boldsymbol{\rho}$ are isobaric vectors. The nucleon, which produces the field, is considered to be at rest at the origin. (We are here exploiting the smallness of m_π as compared with the nucleon mass.)

Outside the source region, the field has the form

$$\boldsymbol{\varphi}(\mathbf{r}) = \frac{f}{\mu}\boldsymbol{\tau}(\boldsymbol{\sigma} \cdot \nabla)\frac{1}{r}\exp\{-\mu r\} \tag{2-192}$$

In fact, the only isovector that can be constructed from the nucleon variables is the nucleon isospin $\boldsymbol{\tau}$, and the only pseudoscalar is the product of the nuclear spin $\boldsymbol{\sigma}$ and the radius vector $\mathbf{r}$; the requirement that $\boldsymbol{\varphi}$ satisfies the free field equation (and decreases for large r) specifies the radial dependence in Eq. (2-192). The coupling constant f may be regarded as defined by Eq. (2-192); it is a measure of the total source strength of the nucleon. The factor μ in (2-192) has been inserted in order to give f the dimension of an electric charge.

It is seen that Eq. (2-192), apart from the isospin dependence and the factor $\exp\{-\mu r\}$, has the same form as the magnetic potential surrounding a dipole. The interaction between two nucleons, at such large separations that the overlap of their source densities can be neglected, is therefore similar to the interaction between two point dipoles,

$$V = -\frac{f^2}{\mu^2}(\boldsymbol{\tau}_1 \cdot \boldsymbol{\tau}_2)(\boldsymbol{\sigma}_1 \cdot \nabla_1)(\boldsymbol{\sigma}_2 \cdot \nabla_2)\frac{1}{r_{12}}\exp\{-\mu r_{12}\} \tag{2-193}$$

where ∇_1 and ∇_2 represent differentiations with respect to $\mathbf{r}_1$ and $\mathbf{r}_2$, respectively. (The potential (2-193) has a sign opposite to the magnetic potential between dipoles; this is a consequence of the (pseudo) scalar character of the meson field, as distinct from the vector character of the electromagnetic field.)

If the differentiations in Eq. (2-193) are carried out, one obtains the potential (2-190). (The expression (2-193) contains in addition a contact term, proportional to $\delta(\mathbf{r}_1 - \mathbf{r}_2)$, but this can be neglected, since we are considering the form of the interaction at large distances.)

Since Eq. (2-190) is only intended to describe the peripheral interaction, any tests of this term depend on isolating the small effects of the distant collisions from the stronger scattering due to the potential at shorter distances. Such a separation is usually based on the fact that the relative motion of two nucleons with angular momentum L corresponds classically to a collision with impact parameter

$$b = \frac{L}{k} \approx 9.2L\left(\frac{E_{\text{lab}}}{\text{MeV}}\right)^{-1/2} \text{fm} \tag{2-194}$$

Thus, if we choose L sufficiently large (for given E), we can be sure that the projectile has passed at a rather great distance from the target nucleon, and so only the peripheral interaction has been involved.

Many different methods of implementing this idea have been employed. For a review of the attempts to test (2-190) in the low-energy phenomena, see Taketani *et al.* (1956). Perhaps the most direct tests of the pion exchange potential are provided by phase shift analyses in which the phases with large L are calculated from Eq. (2-190), while the low phases are taken to be phenomenological parameters as in the usual phase shift description (Cziffra *et al.*, 1959). It is found that an accurate description of the experimental data is achieved in this way with fewer parameters. The range of L values adequately described by the potential (2-190) implies (see Eq. (2-194)) that this potential is the dominant interaction for $r \gtrsim 3$ fm. (See also the comparison of the one-pion exchange potential with the phenomenological potentials shown in Fig. 2-35.) In such a "modified" phase shift analysis, one can also adjust the π-nucleon coupling constant, f, to find the value that best describes the observed scattering. In this way, the analysis shown in Fig. 2-34 yields the value $f^2/\hbar c = 0.074 \pm 0.010$, which agrees well with the more accurate determination (2-190) based on pion-nucleon scattering.

Since the π-nucleon coupling constant is relatively small, the interaction (2-190) is rather weak and, in most nuclear phenomena, is overshadowed by the additional interaction effects associated with the exchange of two or more pions as well as with the virtual production of other mesonic and baryonic states. In many of these processes, the coupling constants are found to be large. The analysis of these effects presents a problem of great complexity owing to the many degrees of freedom involved and the great strength of the interactions at the shorter distances (see, for example, Fig. 2-35). (For a review of such analyses, see, for example, Bryan, 1967.)

The important role of the higher-order processes in the nucleonic interaction, together with the fact that λ_c is comparable with the average distance between particles in the nucleus, suggests some caution in the use of potentials such as those of Fig. 2-35 in the description of interactions in nuclei; it is possible that three-body forces and other higher-order effects are not completely negligible in determining the nuclear structure. Such effects have not yet been definitely identified, but the subject requires further investigation.

2-5b Relation of Nuclear Potential to Nucleonic Interactions

Saturation problem and equilibrium density

A basic property of nuclear structure is the approximate constancy of the density in the interior of all nuclei. This equilibrium density reflects a balance between attractive forces, which hold the system together, and an internal pressure, which prevents any further reduction in the volume. One source of such an internal pressure is the kinetic energy term. As a consequence of the exclusion principle, the kinetic energy per particle is proportional to $\rho^{2/3}$ (see Eq. (2-7)). Such a term, however, is not strong enough to resist the compressive effect of a purely attractive force between nucleons, since the corresponding potential energy per particle increases linearly with ρ. Thus, a system with purely attractive forces would collapse to a state with a radius of the order of the range of the interactions.

The nuclear saturation must therefore be attributed to important repulsive elements in the nucleonic interaction. The search for the expected repulsive elements has been a point of considerable interest since the first discussions of nuclear structure. For a time, the saturating feature was sought in the exchange properties of the force.[4] Indeed, the average forces in states of odd parity are appreciably weaker than those for even parity; if one weights the interactions by their statistical weights, the average odd-state potential

$$\langle V_{\text{odd}} \rangle = \frac{1}{10}({}^{1}V_{\text{odd}} + 9\,{}^{3}V_{\text{odd}}) \tag{2-195}$$

is found to almost vanish (see Fig. 2-35). To prevent collapse, however, the nuclear force must contain strong repulsive elements, and it now appears that the main effect involved is that of the "hard core", which is revealed in the S-wave phase shifts at high energy (see the discussion on p. 245).

Some of the properties of a system saturating as the result of short-range repulsions may be seen from an analysis of a simplified schematic model (Gomez *et al.*, 1958). As a first step, we consider the hard-sphere Fermi gas, a system in

---

[4] For a review of the early discussions of the saturation problem, see Rosenfeld (1948), and Blatt and Weisskopf (1952).

which the only interaction between the particles is an infinite repulsion preventing the particles from approaching closer than the distance c. The properties of this system depend on the ratio of c and the density parameter r_0 ($R = r_0 A^{1/3}$; from Eq. (2-7) we obtain $r_0 = 1.52 k_F^{-1}$). For $c \ll r_0$, the system approaches the free particle gas while, for $c \approx 2r_0$, the structure of the system approaches that of close packing of hard-spheres (close packing with a lattice distance c implies $c = (32\pi^2/9)^{1/6} r_0 \approx 1.81 r_0$). The actual nuclear force is characterized by $c \approx$ 0.5 fm, while $r_0 \approx 1.1$ fm, and thus the structure of nuclear matter is much closer to that of the free gas than to the crystalline state of closely packed spheres. The energy of a low-density hard-sphere gas can be expanded in a power series in c/r_0; the first few terms in this expansion have been evaluated, and the resulting energy function is shown in Fig. 2-33. (This expansion is further discussed in the fine print below.)

The attractive part of the nucleonic interaction has a longer range and is appreciably weaker than the repulsion. Thus, one may obtain a qualitative estimate of the binding by employing a simple first-order perturbation calculation based on undisturbed particle motion. If we first neglect the effect of exchange forces and of the two-particle correlations implied by the antisymmetrization, the binding energy per particle is simply proportional to the density, and thus varies as r_0^{-3}. Adding the kinetic energy, with inclusion of the effects of the hard cores, to the potential energy, we obtain a total energy that is schematically illustrated in Fig. 2-33. It is seen that, in order to obtain a bound system, the attractive potential must exceed a minimum value; correspondingly, the equilibrium value of r_0 has an upper bound $(r_0)_{\max}$. It follows from dimensional arguments that $(r_0)_{\max}$ is some multiple of c.

We can estimate $(r_0)_{\max}$ by employing the approximate expression for the energy $\mathscr{E}_{\text{kin}}$ of the hard-core gas given on p. 256,

$$\frac{\mathscr{E}_{\text{kin}}}{A} \approx \frac{3}{5} \varepsilon_F \left(1 - 0.8 \frac{c}{r_0}\right)^{-2} \tag{2-196}$$

The value of $(r_0)_{\max}$ is defined by the relations

$$\begin{aligned} \mathscr{E}_{\text{kin}} + \mathscr{E}_{\text{pot}} &= 0 \\ \frac{\partial}{\partial r_0}(\mathscr{E}_{\text{kin}} + \mathscr{E}_{\text{pot}}) &= 0 \end{aligned} \tag{2-197}$$

and, for $\mathscr{E}_{\text{pot}}$ proportional to r_0^{-3}, we obtain

$$\begin{aligned} \frac{r_0}{\mathscr{E}_{\text{kin}}} \frac{\partial}{\partial r_0} \mathscr{E}_{\text{kin}} &= -3 \\ (r_0)_{\max} &\approx 2.4c \end{aligned} \tag{2-198}$$

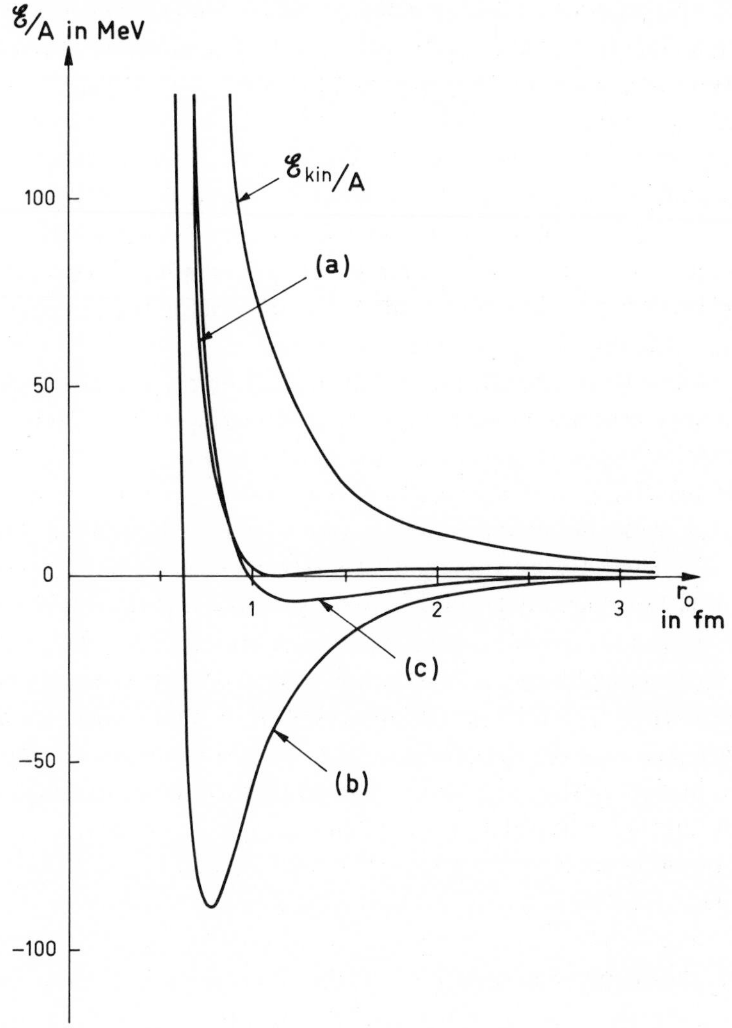

Figure 2-33 The curve $\mathscr{E}_{\text{kin}}$ represents the energy of the hard-sphere gas, Eq. (2-196). The curve (a) represents the total nuclear energy with the attractive component (2-199) adjusted to give a minimum with zero binding energy ($V_0 = 15$ MeV, $c = 0.5$ fm, $b = 1.7$ fm). The curve (b) is the same as (a), except that $V_0 = 25$ MeV. In curve (c), the attractive interaction is estimated by means of Eq. (2-200), and the parameters of the square well potential are $V_0 = 34$ MeV, $c = 0.5$ fm, $b = 1.7$ fm.

We wish to thank R. Lipperheide for assistance in the preparation of the figure.

A hard-core radius of $c = 0.5$ fm (see Eq. (2-225)) thus corresponds to $(r_0)_{\max} =$ 1.2 fm and a kinetic energy about twice the value for the noninteracting Fermi gas.

The attractive potential, $\mathscr{E}_{\text{pot}}$, employed in the above discussion can be related to the attractive part of the nucleonic interaction. To illustrate this relation, we employ the simple, central force, square well interaction of the type illustrated in Fig. 2-32, and assume the same interaction in $T=0$ and $T=1$ states. The potential energy per particle is then, in the approximation considered,

$$\frac{\mathscr{E}_{\text{pot}}}{A} = -\frac{1}{2}V_0\frac{(b+c)^3 - c^3}{r_0^3} \tag{2-199}$$

For $c=0.5$ fm and $b=1.7$ fm, corresponding to the effective range deduced from low-energy singlet scattering, the minimum value of V_0 needed to give binding is $(V_0)_{\min} \approx 15$ MeV and the corresponding total energy function is drawn as (*a*) in Fig. 2-33.

The value of the attractive potential implied by the low-energy scattering is $V_0 = 34$ MeV, and the energy function corresponding to the potential energy (2-199) with $V_0 = \frac{3}{4} \times 34$ MeV is drawn as (b) in Fig. 2-33. The factor 3/4 represents the reduction of the density at small relative distances resulting from the antisymmetrization of the wave function (see Eq. (2-36)). The increase by 70 % in the strength of the attraction as compared with (a) implies an increase in the density by a factor of 2 and a very large binding energy. The function (b), however, represents an overestimate of the potential, since the attraction is assumed to be equally strong in even and odd states. A somewhat improved evaluation is given in (*c*), where the attractive interaction is assumed to have a Serber exchange character and is thus effective only in states of even orbital symmetry. Including the correlations implied by the antisymmetrization of the wave functions, we thus obtain the contribution (see Eq. (2-41))

$$\frac{\mathscr{E}_{\text{pot}}}{A} = \frac{3}{16}\left\{-V_0\frac{(b+c)^3 - c^3}{r_0^3} + \rho\int V(r)C^2(r)\,d^3r\right\} \tag{2-200}$$

where ρ is the average density ($\rho\Omega = A$) and $C(r)$ is the two-body correlation function of the Fermi gas (see Eq. (2-37)). As is seen from the curve (c), the equilibrium density ($r_0 = 1.2$ fm, $\rho = 0.14$ (fm)$^{-3}$) in this approximation is slightly less than the experimental value, $\rho = 0.17$ fm^{-3}, as given in Eq. (2-1), and the binding energy of 7 MeV/nucleon is only about half of the observed value of b_{vol} (see Eq. (2-14)). Since the binding energy represents the small difference between the much larger kinetic energy (2-196) and attractive contribution (2-200), the discrepancy in this simple model represents only a 15% underestimate of the attractive contribution to the total energy.

The above discussion of the nuclear equilibrium density and saturation is somewhat modified by the presence of the rather strong tensor force in the nucleonic interaction (see Fig. 2-35). The expectation value of the tensor force vanishes for the uncorrelated Fermi gas owing to the spin saturation of the system ($S=0$). In second order, the tensor force contributes an attraction;

however, this attraction becomes relatively less effective with increasing density, since the exclusion principle implies that the intermediate energies in the second-order calculation must increase with increasing k_F. This density dependence of the binding due to the tensor force contributes, together with the repulsion of the hard core, to determine the equilibrium density of nuclei (Bethe, 1967).

The smallness of the total nuclear binding energy (in units of $\varepsilon_F A$) implies that the density is much lower than the critical density corresponding to close packing. Ascribing a core radius $c/2$ to each nucleon, we ensure that no pair of nucleons approaches closer than the distance c. Thus, the fraction of the total nuclear volume, Ω_{tot}, occupied by the hard cores is only

$$\frac{\Omega_{\text{core}}}{\Omega_{\text{tot}}} = \left(\frac{c}{2r_0}\right)^3 \approx 10^{-2} \tag{2-201}$$

Under such circumstances, the violent interactions produced by the singular force occur only rarely and the system can be described, to a first approximation, in terms of independent-particle motion. The hard core collisions do give an important contribution to the total energy of the system and are thereby responsible for the saturation. However, this energy is carried by a small fraction of the particles ($\sim (c/r_0)^3$), each having an energy of the order of several hundred MeV ($\sim \hbar^2/Mc^2$).

If the attractive interactions in the nucleus were stronger than those observed, the density would increase and eventually would approach the close packing limit. The characteristic parameter describing the interaction is the strength of the attraction measured in units of $\hbar^2/Mc^2$ (assuming that the range of the attraction is comparable with c). Examples of systems, where this parameter is large, are provided by aggregates of atoms, which form crystalline or rigid molecular structures (see Fig. 2-36, p. 269). The nature of the transition from independent-particle motion to the crystalline state and the associated value of the characteristic parameter present significant unsolved problems. The example of liquid ^{3}He suggests that the independent-particle description may still provide a useful approximation even for values of c/r_0 that are appreciably larger than encountered in the nuclear system. (For a discussion of the validity of the independent-particle description for ^{3}He, see, for example, Wheatley, 1966.)

The above discussion has been based on highly schematized forces, which in particular do not include the very strong attractive components that have been inferred for distances slightly greater than the hard-core radius (see Fig. 2-35). The qualitative interpretation of the saturation and the validity of the independent-particle motion can, however, be maintained for more complex interactions, since one can distinguish between the violent interactions at a short distance ($r \lesssim 1$ fm) and the much weaker and smoothly varying interactions at larger distances. The short-range components can be treated in terms of an expansion similar to that employed for the hard-sphere gas; the small parameter in this expansion represents the range of these interactions compared with typical internucleon separations. The long-range components are weak compared with the Fermi energy (see Fig. 2-35) and thus can also be treated in terms of an appropriate perturbation expansion.

Further details of the schematic model

The hard-sphere gas. If the range, c, of the hard-core interaction is sufficiently small, its effects may be obtained by means of an appropriate perturbation expansion starting from the noninteracting Fermi gas. The first term in this expansion may be obtained very simply by using the pseudopotential

$$V_{\text{core}}^{(1)} = 4\pi c \frac{\hbar^2}{M} \delta(\mathbf{r}) \tag{2-202}$$

which, when treated in Born approximation, gives, to first order in c, the same scattering amplitude as the hard-core interaction (see, for example, Blatt and Weisskopf, 1952, pp. 73ff). The expectation value of the interaction (2-202) for two nucleons in the Fermi gas is

$$\langle V_{\text{core}}^{(1)} \rangle = \frac{1}{\Omega} 4\pi c \frac{\hbar^2}{M} (1 - \delta(m_s(1), m_s(2))\delta(m_t(1), m_t(2))) \tag{2-203}$$

where Ω is the nuclear volume. The last term in Eq. (2-203) results from the antisymmetrization, which prevents two nucleons with the same spin and isobaric spin orientations from coming very close to each other. Averaging Eq. (2-203) over a Fermi gas with equal numbers of neutrons and protons, we obtain

$$\begin{aligned} \mathscr{E}_{\text{core}}^{(1)} &= \frac{3}{4} 4\pi c \frac{\hbar^2}{M} \frac{A(A-1)}{2\Omega} \\ &= \frac{2}{\pi} A \varepsilon_F c k_F \end{aligned} \tag{2-204}$$

The evaluation of the higher-order terms in the expansion in powers of $k_F c$ involves both the improvement of the simple first-order pseudopotential (2-202) and the evaluation of the higher-order perturbation effects resulting from the modifications in the wave function. The next few terms have been evaluated (Huang and Yang, 1957; de Dominicis and Martin, 1957) and yield

$$\mathscr{E}_{\text{core}} = A\varepsilon_F \left\{ \frac{2}{\pi} c k_F + \frac{12}{35\pi^2} (11 - 2 \ln 2)(c k_F)^2 + 0.78 (c k_F)^3 + \cdots \right\} \tag{2-205}$$

A convenient approximate expression for the sum of the unperturbed kinetic energy (2-10) and the contributions (2-205) is given by

$$\frac{\mathscr{E}_{\text{kin}}}{A} \approx \frac{3}{5} \left(\frac{9\pi}{8} \right)^{2/3} \frac{\hbar^2}{2M(r_0 - 0.8c)^2} \tag{2-206}$$

where r_0 is the radius parameter in the nuclear volume. The expression (2-206) reproduces the expansion (2-205) to within a few percent over the range $k_F c < 0.8$. The function (2-206) is plotted in Fig. 2-33.

Compressibility. We can also obtain an estimate of the nuclear compressibility from the simple model in which the total nuclear energy is described by the energy of the hard sphere gas (2-206) and the estimate (2-200) of the attractive interactions. The compressibility coefficient is defined by the relation

$$\begin{aligned} b_{\text{comp}} &= \rho^2 \frac{\partial^2}{\partial \rho^2}\left(\frac{\mathscr{E}}{A}\right) \\ &= \frac{1}{9} r_0^2 \frac{\partial^2}{\partial r_0^2}\left(\frac{\mathscr{E}}{A}\right) = \frac{1}{9} K \end{aligned} \tag{2-207}$$

where, in the second line, we have introduced the parameter K that is often found in the literature. From Fig. 2-33, one obtains $b_{\text{comp}} \approx 13$ MeV. There is at present little direct empirical evidence on the nuclear compressibility, but more detailed theoretical estimates give similar values. (Bethe, 1967, gives the estimate $b_{\text{comp}} \approx 15$ MeV.)

In the above discussion of the equilibrium density, we have neglected the effects of the Coulomb repulsion, which tends to increase r_0 slightly. The effect can be estimated from the compressibility

$$\frac{\delta r_0}{r_0} \approx -\frac{r_0}{KA} \frac{\partial}{\partial r_0} \mathscr{E}_{\text{Coul}} \tag{2-208}$$

and is found to amount to a few percent in heavy nuclei, assuming $b_{\text{comp}} \approx 15$ MeV. An opposite and slightly larger effect results from the surface energy, which provides a pressure tending to contract the nucleus.

Velocity dependence of the one-particle potential. The above discussion has been concerned with the relation of the nucleonic interactions to the total nuclear binding energy and density. The simple model may also be employed to illustrate features of the average nuclear potential, such as the velocity dependence. It is convenient to express the velocity dependence in terms of the effective mass M^* defined by (see p. 148)

$$\left(\frac{d\varepsilon(k)}{dk}\right)_{k=k_F} = \frac{\hbar^2}{M^*} k_F \tag{2-209}$$

for states with k in the neighborhood of k_F.

As for the total energy, we begin by considering the contribution to Eq. (2-209) implied by the hard core alone, and expand this contribution in powers of the hard-core radius c. Since the linear term (2-203) is independent of the relative momenta of the two states, the leading-order contribution to M^* is of order c^2, and the expansion yields (Bund and Wajntal, 1963)

$$\begin{aligned} \left(\frac{M}{M^*}\right)_{\text{kin}} &= 1 - 0.63(k_F c)^2 + 0.16(k_F c)^3 + \cdots \\ &\approx 0.75 \qquad \text{for} \quad k_F c = 0.69 \end{aligned} \tag{2-210}$$

The increase in M^* obtained in Eq. (2-210) implies that the repulsive core interactions contribute an energy term that decreases with increasing velocity of the particles; such a term results from the fact that particles deep in the Fermi distribution must use more highly excited components than particles near or above the Fermi surface, in establishing the correlations whereby they avoid the hard cores of the other nucleons.

The effect of the attractive Serber interaction can be evaluated in terms of an expression similar to Eq. (2-200). For the values of the attractive potential corresponding to the curve (c) in Fig. 2-33, we obtain a positive contribution

$$\delta\left(\frac{M}{M^*}\right)_{\text{pot}} \approx 0.41 \tag{2-211}$$

which, together with Eq. (2-210), implies a total effective mass at the Fermi surface about 15% smaller than the free mass.

Spin- and isospin-dependent components of nuclear potential

Some of the more detailed features of the nuclear potential can be directly related to the spin and isospin dependence of the nucleonic interactions.

An important contribution to the nuclear symmetry potential arises from the exchange character of the nuclear forces. Thus, if we assume the Serber exchange mixture for the central interaction, we can write

$$\begin{aligned} V(1,2) &= \tfrac{1}{2}(1+P^r)V(r_{12}) \\ &= \tfrac{1}{2}[1-\tfrac{1}{4}(1+\boldsymbol{\tau}_1\cdot\boldsymbol{\tau}_2)(1+\boldsymbol{\sigma}_1\cdot\boldsymbol{\sigma}_2)]V(r_{12}) \end{aligned} \tag{2-212}$$

Averaging over the coordinates of particle 2, and neglecting correlations between the particles, we obtain the average single-particle potential

$$\begin{aligned} V(\mathbf{r},\mathbf{t}) &= \left(1-\frac{4}{3A}(\mathbf{t}\cdot\mathbf{T})\right)V(\mathbf{r}) \\ V(\mathbf{r}_1) &\equiv \frac{3}{8}\int \rho(\mathbf{r}_2)V(r_{12})\,d\tau_2 \end{aligned} \tag{2-213}$$

where $\mathbf{t}=\frac{1}{2}\boldsymbol{\tau}$ is the isospin operator of the single particle and $\mathbf{T}$ the total isospin of the rest of the nucleons.

The potential (2-213) is of the form (2-29), and the ratio of $-4/3$ between isovector and isoscalar components is of the order of magnitude of, although smaller than the observed ratio of about -2 (see Eq. (2-28) and Fig. 2-29).

The result (2-213) expresses the fact that a force acting only in even orbital states is three times more effective in isosinglet states than in isotriplet states. The factor 3 corresponds to the ratio between the statistical weights $(2S+1)$, since $T=0$ states with even L have $S=1$, while $T=1$ states have $S=0$. We also note that such a force is twice as strong for unlike particles (which correspond to $T=0$ and $T=1$ with equal amplitudes) as for like particles ($T=1$). Thus, the potential (2-213) acting on a proton is proportional to $N+\frac{1}{2}Z$, while the potential acting on a neutron is proportional to $Z+\frac{1}{2}N$.

The predominance of the even-state interaction, which characterizes the Serber force, is also a feature of short-range interactions, since these are mainly effective in relative S states. Thus, for example, the leading-order effect of the hard core, which can be obtained as the expectation value of a δ-type pseudo-potential, see Eq. (2-202), gives the same ratio between isovector and isoscalar components as in Eq. (2-213). For such a force with no exchange components, the isospin dependence of the average potential derives exclusively from the correlations associated with antisymmetrization. These correlations reduce the probability for finding like particles close together (by a factor of 2 for $r_{12} \rightarrow 0$).

The occurrence of a rather strong spin-orbit force in the nucleonic interaction gives rise to a spin-orbit coupling in the average one-body potential. Writing the two-body spin-orbit force

$$V_{LS}(1, 2) = \frac{1}{\hbar} V_{LS}(r_{12})(\mathbf{r}_1 - \mathbf{r}_2) \times (\mathbf{p}_1 - \mathbf{p}_2) \cdot (\mathbf{s}_1 + \mathbf{s}_2) \tag{2-214}$$

we obtain a rough estimate of the resulting average potential acting on particle 1 by averaging over the coordinates of particle 2, neglecting correlation effects,

$$V_{ls}(1) = \frac{1}{\hbar} \int V_{LS}(r_{12})(\mathbf{r}_1 - \mathbf{r}_2) \times \mathbf{p}_1 \cdot \mathbf{s}_1 \rho(\mathbf{r}_2)\, d\tau_2 \tag{2-215}$$

Expanding the density around the point $(\mathbf{r}_2 = \mathbf{r}_1)$,

$$\rho(\mathbf{r}_2) = \rho(\mathbf{r}_1) + (\mathbf{r}_2 - \mathbf{r}_1) \cdot (\boldsymbol{\nabla}\rho)_{\mathbf{r}_2 = \mathbf{r}_1} + \cdots \tag{2-216}$$

we obtain from Eq. (2-215), assuming the range of interaction to be small compared with the surface thickness of the density distribution,

$$V_{ls}(1) = \kappa(\mathbf{l} \cdot \mathbf{s}) \frac{1}{r_1} \frac{\partial \rho(r_1)}{\partial r_1} \tag{2-217}$$

with

$$\kappa = -\tfrac{1}{3} \int V_{LS}(r) r^2 \, d^3 r \tag{2-218}$$

On account of the rather short range of the spin-orbit force, the main interaction is expected to take place in the relative P state. The potential in Eq. (2-218) should thus be the odd state spin-orbit force V_{LS}(odd). Using the potentials of Fig. 2-35, we obtain from Eqs. (2-217) and (2-218) a spin-orbit force of the type (2-144) with the coefficient $V_{ls} \approx 30$ MeV. This value is of the same sign and magnitude (but somewhat greater) than the average spin-orbit force observed in nucleon-nucleus interaction (see, for example, Table 2-2).

The estimate (2-217) is, of course, very crude. In a quantitative calculation, one must include the effect of antisymmetrization (which increases the ^3P state interaction for like particles by a factor of 2 and thus leads to an effectively stronger spin-orbit potential for neutrons than for protons in a heavy nucleus). In addition, one must take into account that the violent interactions at short distance appreciably modify the wave functions in the region where the spin-orbit force is acting. (For recent analyses, see Elliott *et al.*, 1967.) Finally, the tensor force contributes in second and higher order to the effective one-body spin-orbit potential. (See, for example, Terasawa, 1960, and references given in this article.)

Estimate of high-energy optical potential from two-body scattering amplitude

The relation of the average potential and the two-body scattering becomes especially simple for incident energies large compared to those of the particles in the bound system. If, in addition, the interactions are sufficiently weak so that the wave number in the medium differs only slightly from that of the incident wave, one can estimate the optical potential in terms of the additive effect of the collisions with each particle in the medium, considering these collisions as taking place between free particles (impulse approximation).

The propagation through a uniform medium is obtained by considering the forward scattered wave $\rho f_L(0) d\tau$ generated by each volume element $d\tau$. The density of the medium is ρ, and $f_L(0)$ is the forward scattering amplitude for a free-particle collision described in the laboratory system. The forward scattering produced by a potential V extending over the volume $d\tau$ is $-(2\pi\hbar^2)^{-1} MV\, d\tau$, and we can thus represent the scattering of the medium by the potential

$$V = -\frac{2\pi\hbar^2}{M} f_L(0)\rho \qquad (2\text{-}219)$$

We can also recognize that this expression is equivalent to the well-known expression for the index of refraction n of a gas,

$$n^2 - 1 = \frac{4\pi\rho f_L(0)}{k^2} \qquad (2\text{-}220)$$

where n is defined as the ratio of the wave number in the medium to the wave number k of the incident wave.

The imaginary part of the potential (2-219) has a very simple interpretation in terms of the connection between the total cross section for the two-particle scattering and the mean free path in the medium. The optical theorem relates the total cross section to the imaginary part of the forward scattering amplitude (see Eq. (2-90)), and thus, for the mean free path $\lambda = (\rho\sigma)^{-1}$, we obtain the relation (2-138).

The simple relation (2-219) may be expected to be approximately valid for the interaction of nuclei with nucleons having energies large compared with ε_F. The optical potentials obtained from this relation, using the measured nucleon-nucleon phase shifts, are shown in Fig. 2-37, p. 271.

Even for nucleon energies of the order of a hundred MeV, there are important corrections associated with the finite velocities of the particles in the nucleus. In particular, the exclusion principle plays a significant role in inhibiting collisions with small momentum transfers and thus reducing the imaginary part of the potential. A correction for this effect may be based on the Fermi gas model of the target nucleus. Thus, the total cross section determining λ and W may be expressed as an integral over the angular distribution for the scattering of the projectile on each of the target nucleons in the Fermi distribution. An approximate correction for the exclusion principle is obtained by omitting from this integral all contributions, in which either the projectile or the recoil nucleon has wave numbers lying within the occupied Fermi sphere $k < k_F$. As a rough approximation indicating the magnitude of this effect, we give the effective cross section, $\langle\sigma\rangle$, obtained by assuming that the elementary two-body cross section σ_0 is a constant independent of energy and angle (Clementel and Villi, 1955)

$$\begin{aligned} \langle\sigma\rangle &= \sigma_0\left[1 - \frac{7}{5}\frac{\varepsilon_F}{E} + \frac{2}{5}\frac{\varepsilon_F}{E}\left(2 - \frac{E}{\varepsilon_F}\right)^{5/2}\right] \qquad & E < 2\varepsilon_F \\ &= \sigma_0\left[1 - \frac{7}{5}\frac{\varepsilon_F}{E}\right] & E > 2\varepsilon_F \end{aligned} \tag{2-221}$$

The more detailed evaluation of this correction has been discussed by Shaw (1959).

The high-energy limit of the optical potential is also instructive in illustrating some of the assumptions underlying the use of a simple local potential. Thus, the relation (2-219) applies to the propagation through a region of uniform density. Variations in the density imply elastic scattering with finite momentum transfer. The use of the potential (2-219) with a density $\rho(r)$ leads to the correct large-angle scattering only if the two-body scattering amplitude is independent of the angle. One can take into account the dependence of f on the momentum transfer $\hbar\mathbf{q}$ by replacing $f_L(0)$ by $f_L(\mathbf{q})$ in the relation (2-219), considered as a relation between the Fourier components of density and potential. This nonlocal relation between $V(\mathbf{r})$ and $\rho(\mathbf{r})$ expresses the consequences of the finite range of the two-body interaction in regions where the density is changing. We also note that a dependence of the scattering amplitude on the incident momentum k implies that f_L in Eq. (2-219) is a momentum-dependent operator acting on the wave function, corresponding to a nonlocal velocity-dependent potential (see Eq. (2-141)). Such generalized optical potentials have been employed in the analysis of the interaction of π mesons with nuclei (see the comments on p. 219).

2-5c Theory of Nuclear Matter

The extension of the Fermi gas model to include the effects of the correlations produced by the nucleonic interactions has led to a highly developed theory of nuclear matter. Because of the simple geometry of such an infinite system, these studies have provided an important testing ground and source of invention for new tools with which to treat the quantitative relationship between the two-body forces and the nuclear properties.

The earliest studies of nuclear matter (Euler, 1937) employed nonsingular interactions, with saturation ensured through the choice of appropriate exchange mixtures. For such potentials, one may attempt a straightforward perturbation expansion in powers of the interaction. The calculations indicated a moderately rapid convergence of the power series for the ground state energy. (For a review of these early developments, see Rosenfeld, 1948, Chapter XII, and Brown, 1967, Chapter X.)

The growing evidence for independent-particle motion in the nucleus, as well as the increased knowledge of the two-nucleon interaction, provided the impetus for a reexamination of the theory. A central problem has been the development of appropriate perturbation methods applicable to a system in which the interactions contain singular elements ("hard core"). The physical basis for independent-particle motion in the presence of such interactions has been discussed in connection with the qualitative considerations in the previous section (Sec. 2-5b). The quantitative treatment has involved the development of a rather elaborate formalism (see, for example, Brueckner, 1959, and Brown, 1967, Chapters XI and XII). The problem is similar to those encountered in other many-particle systems, such as the electron gas, superfluids, and interacting quantum fields, and there has been a fruitful interplay of the efforts in these various domains. (An introduction to the formal methods of many-body theory is given in the texts by Thouless, 1961, and Nozières, 1964.)

The main applications of the theory of nuclear matter have so far concerned the nuclear binding energy and equilibrium density. At the present time, there still remains considerable uncertainty concerning the quantitative relationship of these properties as deduced from the empirical systematics of heavy nuclei and the evidence on the two-body interaction as obtained from the scattering experiments (see, for example, Bethe, 1968). Thus, it is not yet clear to what extent the remaining discrepancies are to be ascribed to the approximation methods employed, to uncertainties in the interaction, including the possible role of three- and four-body forces, or to the extrapolation of the empirical data to infinite nuclear matter.

Considerable current effort is being devoted to the study of these problems and to the further development of the methods employed in the theory of nuclear matter in order to treat the varying density and finite geometry of nuclei. It may be expected that this development will lead to important insight into many nuclear properties, such as the various components in the nuclear optical potential, the effective interactions in the nucleus, and the structure of the nuclear surface. However, the development is still in a preliminary stage, and we have not attempted to include a systematic treatment of the formalism in the present text.

▼

ILLUSTRATIVE EXAMPLES TO SECTION 2-5

Phase shift analysis for nucleon-nucleon scattering (*Fig. 2-34*)

The scattering amplitude for two spin one-half particles is a 4 × 4 matrix in the spin variables, as well as a function of the energy E and scattering angles ϑ, φ. Since the nucleon-nucleon interaction commutes with the total spin S as well as with the parity π and the total angular momentum J (see p. 68), it is convenient to expand the scattering matrix in terms of channels labeled by these quantum numbers. The channels with $S = 0$ ($J = L$, $\pi = (-1)^L$) and $S = 1$, $J = L$ ($\pi = (-1)^L$) are uncoupled and thus the scattering matrix is described by a single real parameter, the phase shift δ. The centrifugal barrier implies that, at low energies ($ka \ll L^{1/2}$, where a is a measure of the range of interaction), the phase shift $\delta(L)$ is proportional to k^{2L+1} (see, for example, Eq. (3F-37) and Table 3F-1). In the present analysis, we shall neglect the possibility of inelastic reactions, which may occur for energies above the threshold for meson production ($E_{\text{Lab}} > 280$ MeV); in practice, the meson production cross sections near threshold are sufficiently small so that the elastic scattering amplitudes remain approximately unitary up to laboratory energies of about 400 MeV (see, for example, Hama and Hoshizaki, 1964, and Azhgirey *et al.*, 1963).

The channels $S = 1$, $L = J - 1$ and $S = 1$, $L = J + 1$ are coupled by the tensor force and thus the scattering amplitude is a 2 × 2 matrix in these channels. A unitary 2 × 2 matrix requires three independent parameters. The analysis shown in Fig. 2-34 employs two real phase shifts ($\delta(L = J - 1, J)$, $\delta(L = J + 1, J)$) and a real mixing parameter ε_J. In terms of these parameters, the S matrix is

$$S^{(J)} = \begin{pmatrix} \exp\{i\delta(L = J - 1, J)\} & 0 \\ 0 & \exp\{i\delta(L = J + 1, J)\} \end{pmatrix} \begin{pmatrix} \cos 2\varepsilon_J & i \sin 2\varepsilon_J \\ i \sin 2\varepsilon_J & \cos 2\varepsilon_J \end{pmatrix} \times \begin{pmatrix} \exp\{i\delta(L = J - 1, J)\} & 0 \\ 0 & \exp\{i\delta(L = J + 1, J)\} \end{pmatrix} \quad (2\text{-}222)$$

▲

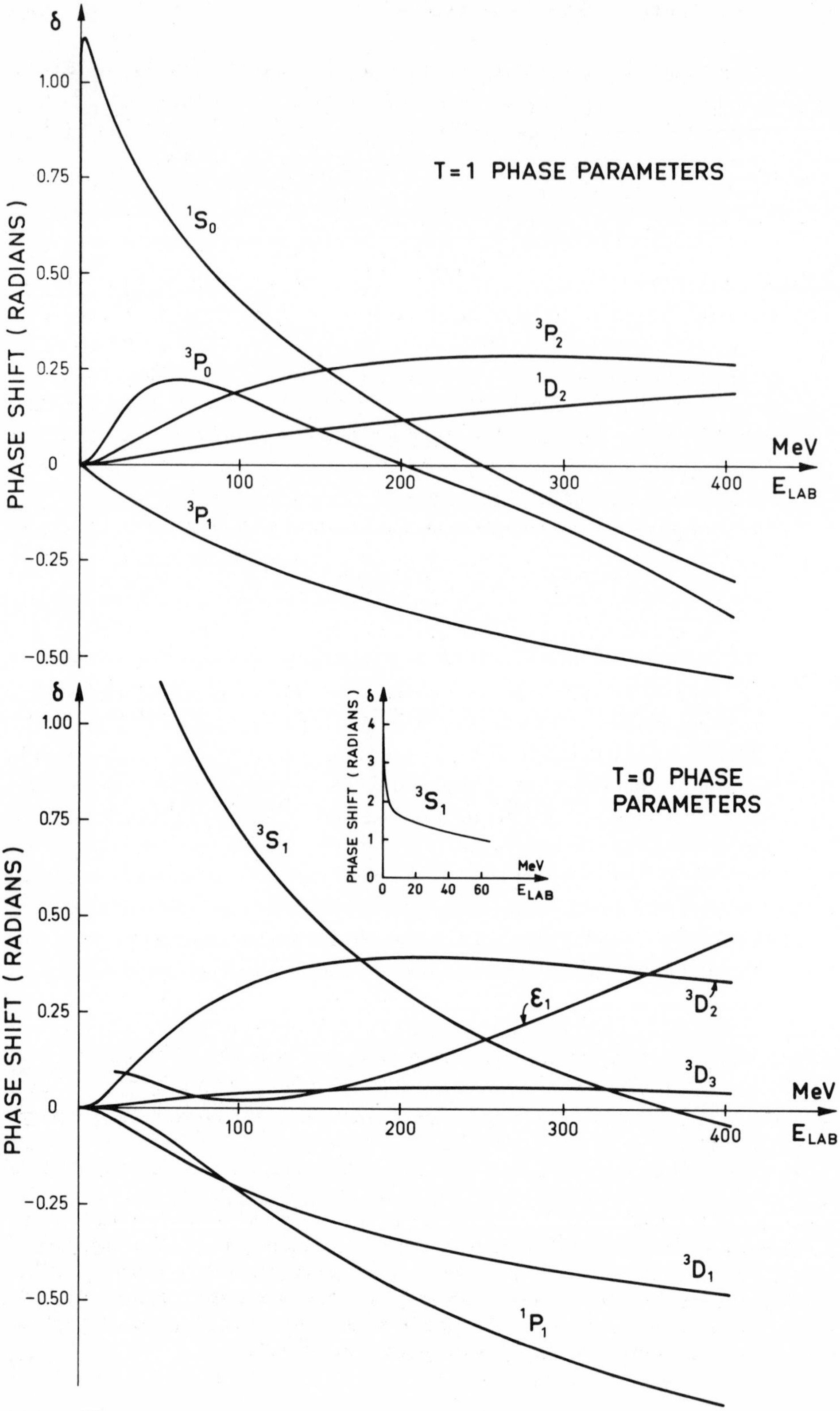
δ
1.00
0.75
0.50
0.25
0
−0.25
−0.50
PHASE SHIFT (RADIANS)
T = 1 PHASE PARAMETERS
$^1S_0$
$^3P_2$
$^3P_0$
$^1D_2$
$^3P_1$
MeV
100
200
300
400
E_{LAB}
δ
1.00
0.75
0.50
0.25
0
−0.25
−0.50
PHASE SHIFT (RADIANS)
T = 0 PHASE
PARAMETERS
$^3S_1$
ε_1
$^3D_2$
$^3D_3$
$^3D_1$
$^1P_1$
MeV
100
200
300
400
E_{LAB}
PHASE SHIFT (RADIANS)
δ
4
3
2
1
0
$^3S_1$
MeV
0
20
40
60
E_{LAB}

▼ This parameterization was introduced by Stapp *et al.* (1957), and is often referred to as the "nuclear bar" phase shifts. At low energies, $\varepsilon_J \approx \text{const}\ k^{2J}$, $\delta(L, J) \approx \text{const}\ k^{2L+1}$. In general, each of the phases $\delta(L = J - 1, J)$ and $\delta(L = J + 1, J)$ describes scattering involving both $L = J \pm 1$; only in the limit $E \to 0$, where $\varepsilon_J \to 0$, does the quantum number L have a simple significance for the wave function of the scattered particle.

The phase parameters shown in Fig. 2-34 are obtained from an analysis involving a large variety of different experimental data taken at many different energies. The phases are expanded in terms of assumed energy-dependent functions, which are chosen so that the contribution of the one-pion exchange potential (2-190) dominates at sufficiently low energies (except for the S and P wave channels). The coefficients of the energy-dependent functions are then varied to fit the experimental data; 58 adjustable parameters were employed in the analysis, which utilized 704 different pieces of experimental data. The phases fit the experimental data with a sum squared error of $\chi^2 = 646$.

The phase parameters in Fig. 2-34 describe the scattering due to the nuclear forces; to obtain the experimentally measured scattering amplitude, one must add the Coulomb phase shifts in the case of *pp* scattering.

Phenomenological nucleon-nucleon potentials (Fig. 2-35; Tables 2-3, 2-4)

The nucleon-nucleon potentials shown in Fig. 2-35 are parametrized in terms of the following functions:

$$
\begin{aligned}
V &= V_C(r) + V_T(r)S_{12} + V_{LS}(r)\mathbf{L}\cdot\mathbf{S} + V_{LL}(r)L_{12} \\
S_{12} &= \frac{3}{r^2}(\boldsymbol{\sigma}_1\cdot\mathbf{r})(\boldsymbol{\sigma}_2\cdot\mathbf{r}) - \boldsymbol{\sigma}_1\cdot\boldsymbol{\sigma}_2 \qquad\qquad (2\text{-}223) \\
L_{12} &= (\boldsymbol{\sigma}_1\cdot\boldsymbol{\sigma}_2)\mathbf{L}^2 - \tfrac{1}{2}[(\boldsymbol{\sigma}_1\cdot\mathbf{L})(\boldsymbol{\sigma}_2\cdot\mathbf{L}) + (\boldsymbol{\sigma}_2\cdot\mathbf{L})(\boldsymbol{\sigma}_1\cdot\mathbf{L})] \\
&= (\delta_{LJ} + \boldsymbol{\sigma}_1\cdot\boldsymbol{\sigma}_2)\mathbf{L}^2 - (\mathbf{L}\cdot\mathbf{S})^2
\end{aligned}
$$

and thus contain central (V_C), tensor (V_T), spin-orbit (V_{LS}), and second-order spin-orbit (V_{LL}) components. The radial functions are restricted by the condition ▲ that, at large distances, the central and tensor potentials should be described by

---

Figure 2-34 The figure illustrates the phase parameters for nucleon-nucleon scattering in the channels with $L \leq 2$. The low-energy behavior is determined by the effective range parameters (2-183); the data for $E > 24$ MeV are taken from the analysis by R. A. Arndt and M. H. MacGregor, *Phys. Rev.* **141**, 873 (1966); similar analyses have been given by Breit *et al.* (1962), Hull *et al.* (1962), and, more recently, by MacGregor *et al.* (1968). The definition of the phase parameters in terms of the scattering matrix is given by Eq. (2-222).

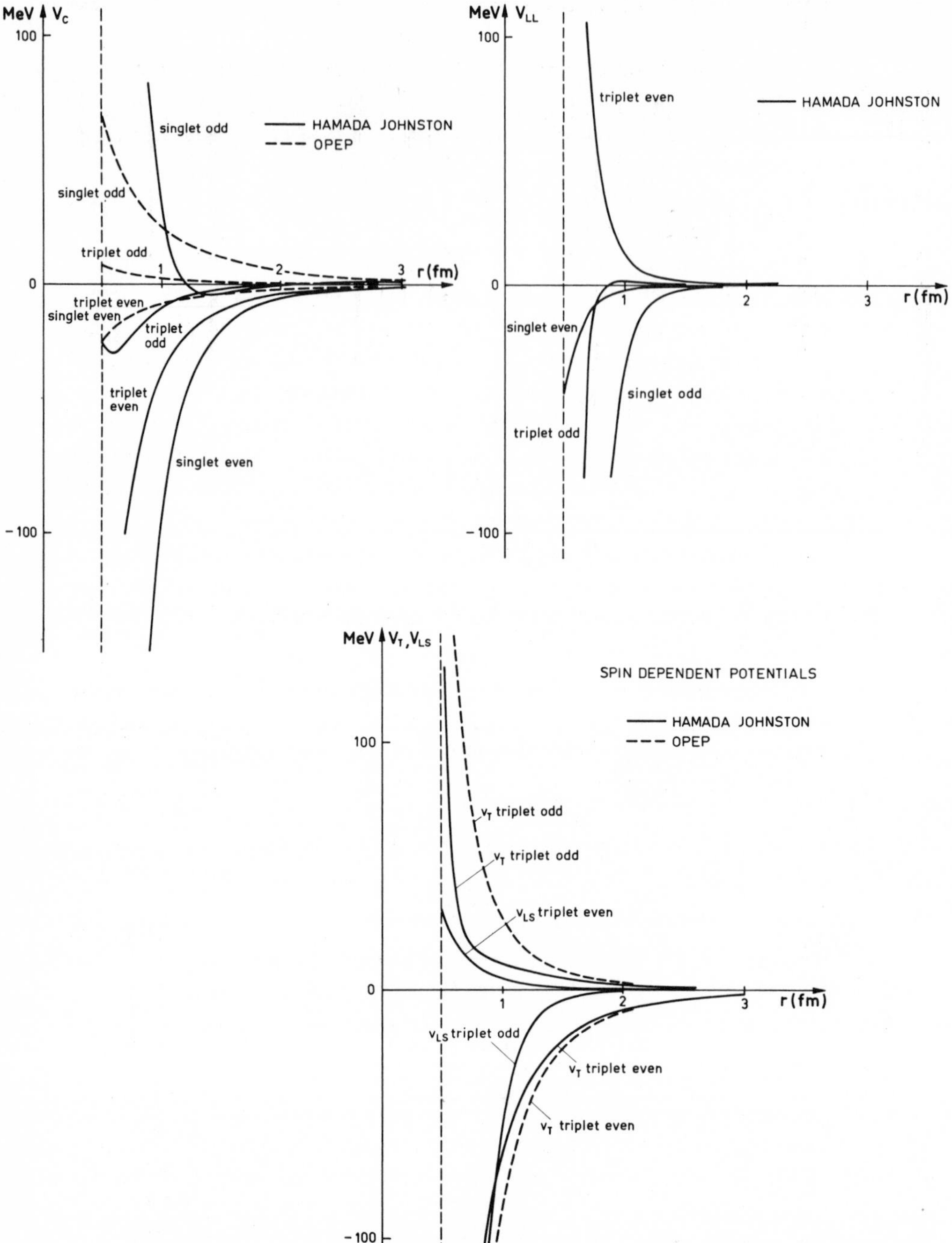

Figure 2-35 The phenomenological nucleon-nucleon potentials shown in the figure are taken from the analysis of T. Hamada and I. D. Johnston, *Nuclear Phys.* **34**, 382 (1962); similar potentials have been obtained by Lassila *et al.* (1962). The dotted potentials (OPEP) correspond to the one-pion exchange potential (Eq. (2-190)). For an example of a soft-core potential, see Reid (1968), and for a nonlocal potential, see Tabakin (1964).

▼ the one-pion exchange interaction (2-190). The assumed radial forms are

$$V_C = v_0(\boldsymbol{\tau}_1 \cdot \boldsymbol{\tau}_2)(\boldsymbol{\sigma}_1 \cdot \boldsymbol{\sigma}_2)\, Y(x)[1 + a_C Y(x) + b_C Y^2(x)]$$

$$V_T = v_0(\boldsymbol{\tau}_1 \cdot \boldsymbol{\tau}_2)(\boldsymbol{\sigma}_1 \cdot \boldsymbol{\sigma}_2) Z(x)[1 + a_T\, Y(x) + b_T\, Y^2(x)]$$

$$V_{LS} = g_{LS} v_0\, Y^2(x)[1 + b_{LS}\, Y(x)]$$

$$V_{LL} = g_{LL} v_0 \frac{Z(x)}{x^2}[1 + a_{LL}\, Y(x) + b_{LL}\, Y^2(x)]$$

$$v_0 = \frac{1}{3}\frac{f^2}{\hbar c} m_\pi c^2 = 3.65 \text{ MeV} \tag{2-224}$$

$$x = \frac{m_\pi c}{\hbar} r = \left(\frac{r}{1.43 \text{ fm}}\right)$$

$$Y(x) = \frac{1}{x} \exp\{-x\}$$

$$Z(x) = \left(1 + \frac{3}{x} + \frac{3}{x^2}\right) Y(x)$$

and, in addition, the potential has been assumed to contain a component giving rise to infinite repulsion at the radius

$$c = 0.49 \text{ fm} \qquad (x_c = 0.343) \tag{2-225}$$

The optimum adjustment of the 29 parameters in the above functions yields the parameter values given in Table 2-3 and the potentials shown in Fig. 2-35. The values of the different potential components at the hard-core radius, c, are listed in Table 2-4. ▲

	Singlet even	Triplet even	Singlet odd	Triplet odd
a_C	8.7	6.0	–8.0	–9.07
b_C	10.6	–1.0	12.0	3.48
a_T	—	–0.5	—	–1.29
b_T	—	0.2	—	0.55
g_{LS}	—	2.77	—	7.36
b_{LS}	—	–0.1	—	–7.1
g_{LL}	–0.033	0.10	–0.10	–0.033
a_{LL}	0.2	1.8	2.0	–7.3
b_{LL}	–0.2	–0.4	6.0	6.9

Table 2-3 Parameters of the Hamada-Johnston potential illustrated in Fig. 2-35.

▼ It should be emphasized that the fit to the experimental data obtained with the potential of Fig. 2-35 is appreciably poorer than the fit with the phase parameters given in Fig. 2-34, and thus there remains some uncertainty concerning ▲

▼ the correct form of the nucleonic interaction. (For a discussion of the goodness
▲ of fit of the potential models, see Amati, 1964.)

	Potentials (MeV)			
	V_C	V_T	V_{LS}	V_{LL}
Singlet even	–1460	–	–	–42
Triplet even	–207	–642	34	668
Singlet odd	2371	–	–	–6683
Triplet odd	–23	173	–1570	–1087

Table 2-4 Values of the Hamada-Johnston potential at $r = c = 0.49$ fm (see Table 2-3.)

▼ In Fig. 2-35, the one-pion exchange potentials (2-190) are also drawn. These components represent the main part of the nucleonic interaction for $r \gtrsim 3$ fm.

Comparison between atomic and nuclear binding forces (Fig. 2-36)

It is instructive to compare the nuclear two-body forces with those acting in the diatomic molecule H_2 (see Fig. 2-36). An appropriate unit of energy for such a comparison is $\hbar^2/Mc^2$, where c is the extension of the repulsive short-range potential. For molecules, c is of the order of the atomic radius $a \sim \hbar^2/e^2m$, where m is the electron mass; more precisely, we choose c to be the distance at which the potential vanishes. Figure 2-36 also shows the radial density distribution, $\varphi^2 = (r\mathscr{R}(r))^2$, for the lowest bound states.

The chemical forces between the atoms are determined by the electronic structure, and the strength of the potential is thus

$$V_{\text{mol}} \sim \frac{e^2}{a} \sim \frac{\hbar^2}{ma^2} \tag{2-226}$$

which is of order M/m on the scale considered. Such a very strong binding potential implies that the ground state wave function is strongly peaked at the minimum of the potential, and the binding energy is large compared with the zero-point kinetic energy; such a system possesses a vibrational-rotational spectrum. When more particles are added, one obtains a closely packed system with a density $\approx c^{-3}$. At low temperatures, such systems usually crystallize. (An exception is He, where the forces are relatively weak and the density relatively low; see de Boer, 1957, for a comparison of the properties of condensed systems as a function of the dimensionless interaction parameter $(MVc^2\hbar^{-2})$.)

The nuclear forces are relatively weak. The attraction close to the core, which is of order unity on the scale considered, is not sufficient to produce a
▲ bound state; the deuteron state only arises as a consequence of the tail of the

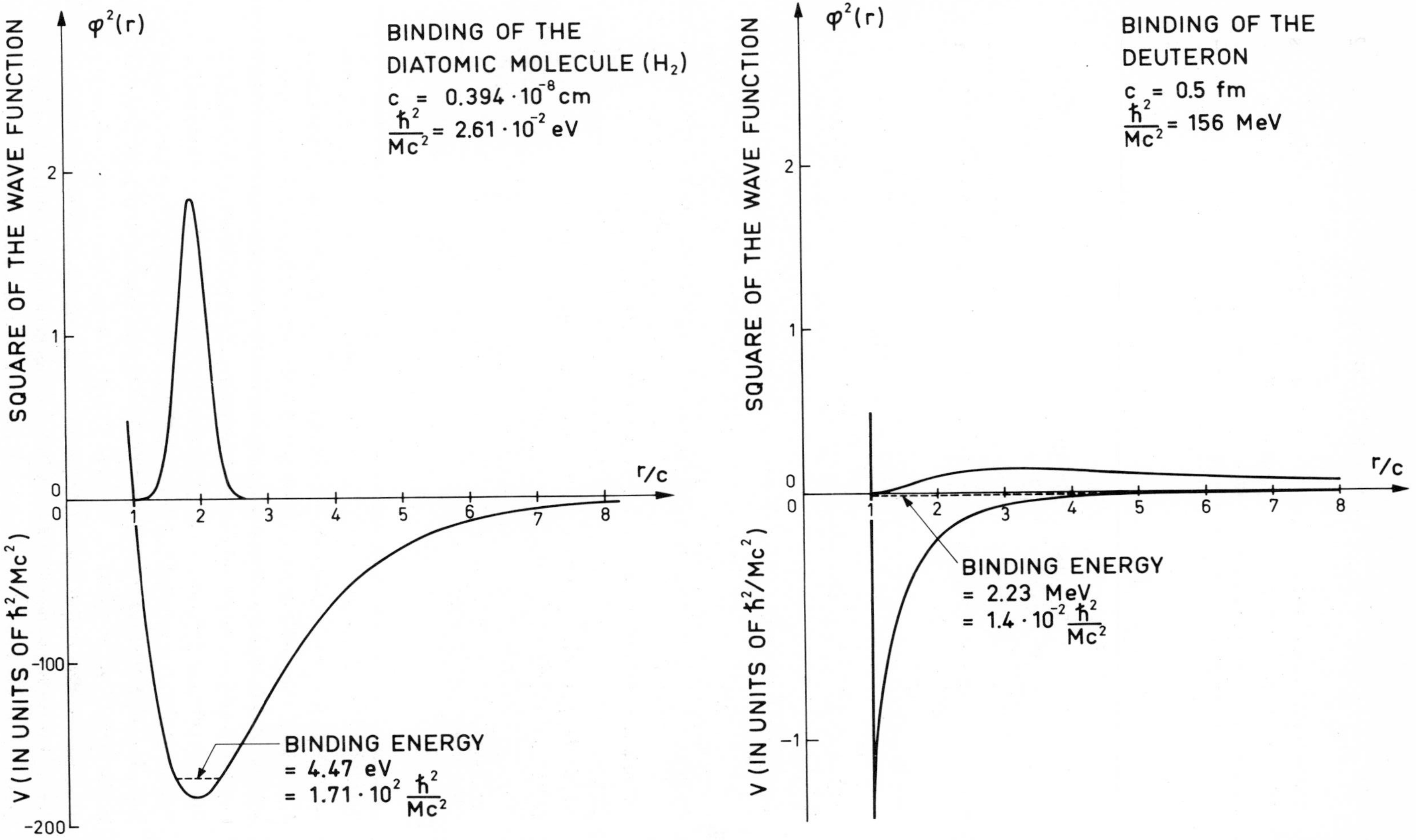

Figure 2-36 The molecular interaction corresponds to a "Morse potential," $V(r) = D\{[1 - \exp(-\gamma(r - r_e))]^2 - 1\}$, with the constants adjusted to the data on the ground state configuration, ${}^1\Sigma_g^+$, of H_2 ($r_e = 0.74 \times 10^{-8}$ cm^{-1}, $\gamma = 2.0 \times 10^8$ cm^{-1}, $D = +4.74$ eV); see G. Herzberg, *Spectra of Diatomic Molecules*, pp. 531 and 532, Van Nostrand, New York, 1950.

The nuclear interaction is the triplet even central potential from Fig 2-35; the density distribution represents the *S*-state part of the deuteron and is taken to have the simple functional form proposed by L. Hulthén and M. Sugawara, *Encyclopedia of Physics* **39**, Springer, Berlin, 1957.

▼ interaction, which is very weak, $\approx 10^{-2}$ on the scale considered. The weak attraction is barely strong enough to produce bound many-body systems, and the resulting density is $\approx 10^{-2} \times c^{-3}$; these systems can to a good approximation be described in terms of independent-particle motion.

Impulse approximation estimate of nuclear potential (*Fig. 2-37*)

For sufficiently great incident energies, the nuclear optical potential can be directly related to the nucleon-nucleon scattering amplitude (see pp. 260 ff.). Taking account of the spin and isobaric spin of the nucleons, the relation (2-219) for the central potential can be written

$$V = -\frac{2\pi\hbar^2}{M}\rho(r)\{\tfrac{1}{4}(3f_1 + f_0) + \frac{1}{A}\mathbf{t}\cdot\mathbf{T}(f_1 - f_0)\} \qquad (2\text{-}227)$$

where we have assumed that the ratio of neutron to proton density is constant throughout the nucleus; the total nucleon density is denoted $\rho(r)$, while **t** and **T** represent the isobaric spin of the projectile nucleon and the target nucleus. The amplitudes f_1 and f_0 are the "no spin-flip" nucleon-nucleon forward scattering amplitudes in the $T = 1$ and $T = 0$ channels. (The no spin-flip amplitude is obtained by taking the trace of the scattering matrix with respect to the spin polarization quantum numbers.) In terms of the "nuclear bar" phase shifts employed in Fig. 2-34, these amplitudes are

$$f_T = \frac{1}{2ik}\sum_{L,J}(2J+1)\alpha(LJT) \qquad (2\text{-}228)$$

where, for the singlet channels,

$$\alpha(LT) = \exp\{2i\delta(LT)\} - 1 \qquad (2\text{-}229)$$

and similarly for $\alpha(LLT)$, which describes the triplet channels with $L = J$; for the other triplet channels

$$\alpha(LJT) = \exp\{2i\delta(LJT)\}\cos 2\varepsilon_J - 1 \qquad L = J \pm 1 \qquad (2\text{-}230)$$

where ε_J describes the coupling of the two channels with the same J (see Eq. (2-222)). It should be noted that, as discussed in the text, the expression (2-228) represents the two-body scattering amplitude in the laboratory system and is thus twice the usual expression that refers to the center-of-mass coordinate system (compare, for example, the expression (3F-33)). The expression (2-227) has been evaluated, using the experimentally determined phase shifts as a function of the kinetic energy T of the nucleon when inside the nucleus, and the resulting potentials are plotted in Fig. 2-37 as a function of the incident energy, $E_0 = T + V(T)$. The potentials in Fig. 2-37 correspond to a density $\rho = 0.18$ nucleon fm^{-3} (corresponding to $k_F = 1.38$ fm^{-1}). In order to approximately describe the effect of the Pauli principle in reducing the magnitude of the nuclear absorption, the imaginary potentials have been multiplied by the factor given in
▲ Eq. (2-221).

▼ The impulse approximation is only expected to apply when the incident energy is large compared with the Fermi energy of the target nucleons, and thus the extent of the agreement between the potentials estimated in the present figure ▲ and those obtained from the phenomenological analyses is quite remarkable

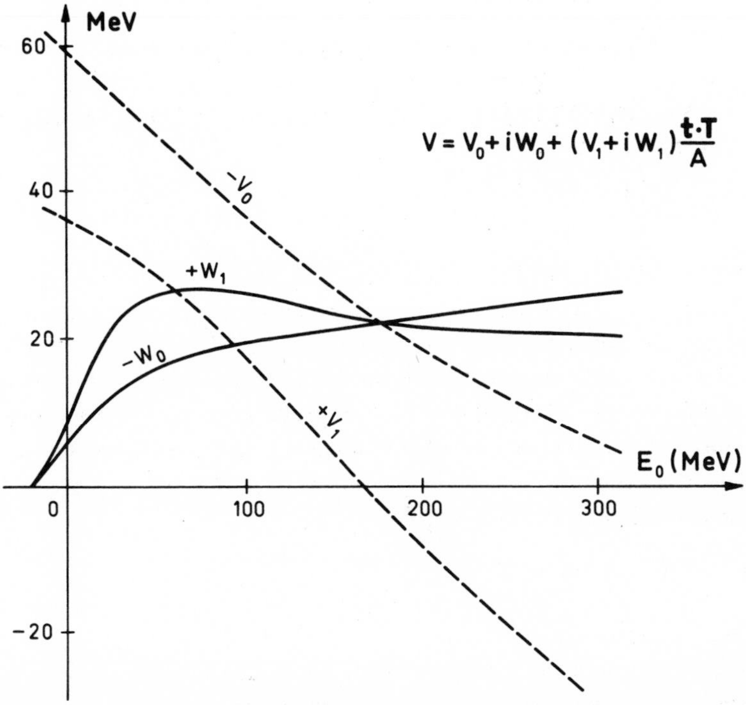

Figure 2-37 The nuclear potentials obtained by means of the impulse approximation are taken from J. Dąbrowski and A. Sobiczewski, *Phys. Letters* **5**, 87 (1963). The phase parameters used by these authors are taken from the analyses of G. Breit, M. H. Hull, Jr., K. E. Lassila, K. D. Pyatt, Jr., and H. M. Ruppel, *Phys. Rev.* **128**, 826 (1962) and of M. H. Hull, Jr., K. E. Lassila, H. M. Ruppel, F. A. MacDonald, and G. Breit, *Phys. Rev.* **128**, 830 (1962), which differ in only minor details from the values given in Fig. 2-34. We wish to thank J. Dąbrowski for discussion and correspondence concerning these potentials.

▼ (see Fig. 2-29). A critical review of the approximations involved and estimates of higher-order corrections have been given by Kerman *et al.* (1959) and, from a different point of view, by Glauber (1959).

The analysis can be extended to include the terms in the potential associated with the finite extent of the nucleus, by considering the two-body scattering amplitude for slightly nonforward directions. In this manner, estimates have been made of the nuclear spin-orbit force and of the difference between the radial extent of the optical potential and that of the density distribution (Kerman *et al.*, ▲ *loc. cit.*).

APPENDIX

2A

Antisymmetrized Product States Creation and Annihilation Operators

2A-1 Antisymmetric Wave Functions

For a system, such as a nucleus or an electron gas, which can be described in first approximation in terms of independent-particle motion, the wave function can often be conveniently expressed in terms of a linear combination of product functions of the type

$$\Phi_{\nu_1\nu_2\cdots\nu_A}(x_1\, x_2 \cdots x_A) = \varphi_{\nu_1}(x_1)\varphi_{\nu_2}(x_2)\cdots\varphi_{\nu_A}(x_A) \tag{2A-1}$$

or, in the state vector notation,

$$\langle x_1 x_2 \cdots x_A | \nu_1\nu_2 \cdots \nu_A\rangle = \langle x_1 | \nu_1\rangle\langle x_2 | \nu_2\rangle \cdots \langle x_A | \nu_A\rangle \tag{2A 2}$$

where the quantum numbers ν are a complete set of labels for the one-particle orbits, such as $nljmm_t$. The coordinates of a particle, including spin and isospin variables, are denoted by x.

Since the nucleons are fermions, the wave function must be antisymmetric under interchange of the coordinates of any pair; this implies that the component (2A-1) always occurs in a definite combination with the other components that are obtained by redistributing the A different particles among the A orbits $\nu_1\nu_2 \cdots \nu_A$. There are altogether $A!$ such components for each configuration $\nu_1\nu_2 \cdots \nu_A$ and the antisymmetrized combination can be written as a Slater determinant,

$$\Phi_{\nu_1\nu_2\cdots\nu_A}(x_1x_2\cdots x_A)_a = \langle x_1x_2 \cdots x_A | \nu_1\nu_2\cdots\nu_A\rangle_a$$

$$= \frac{1}{\sqrt{A!}}\begin{vmatrix} \varphi_{\nu_1}(x_1) & \varphi_{\nu_2}(x_1) & \cdots & \varphi_{\nu_A}(x_1) \\ \varphi_{\nu_1}(x_2) & \varphi_{\nu_2}(x_2) & \cdots & \varphi_{\nu_A}(x_2) \\ \vdots & \vdots & & \vdots \\ \varphi_{\nu_1}(x_A) & \varphi_{\nu_2}(x_A) & \cdots & \varphi_{\nu_A}(x_A) \end{vmatrix} \tag{2A-3}$$

Such determinants are thus the basic elements in any description of a many-particle system of fermions that is based on independent-particle motion.

The antisymmetrized wave function (2A-3) is completely characterized by the enumeration of the occupied orbits $\nu_1\nu_2 \cdots \nu_A$ without any reference to how the particles are distributed among these orbits. The set of antisymmetrized states $|\nu_1\nu_2 \cdots \nu_A\rangle_a$ may thus be referred to as an occupation number representation. The antisymmetry under interchange of particle coordinates implies that the state is also antisymmetric under the interchange of any two of the occupied one-particle orbits. Such an interchange amounts to a transposition of two columns in the determinant and thus multiplies the state by -1. For example, we have

$$|\nu_1\nu_2\nu_3 \cdots \nu_A\rangle_a = -|\nu_2\nu_1\nu_3 \cdots \nu_A\rangle_a \tag{2A-4}$$

2A-2 Properties of Creation Operators for Fermions

In working with the antisymmetric states, one may exploit the simple features of the occupation number representation by introducing the operators $a^\dagger(\nu)$ that create a particle moving in the one-particle orbit φ_ν. Thus, we define

$$a^\dagger(\nu)|0\rangle = |\nu\rangle \tag{2A-5}$$

where $|0\rangle$ is the vacuum, the state with no particles present. More generally, $a^\dagger(\nu)$ acting on an antisymmetric A-particle state creates an $(A+1)$-particle state, in which the orbit ν is occupied,

$$a^\dagger(\nu)|\nu_1\nu_2 \cdots \nu_A\rangle_a = \begin{cases} |\nu_1\nu_2 \cdots \nu_A\nu\rangle_a & \text{if} \quad \nu \neq \nu_1, \nu_2, \ldots, \text{and } \nu_A \\ 0 & \text{if} \quad \nu = \nu_1, \nu_2, \ldots, \text{or } \nu_A \end{cases} \tag{2A-6}$$

The relations (2A-6) define the operators $a^\dagger(\nu)$, and the algebraic properties of these operators, which we shall derive below, follow from this definition.

We can create the entire A-particle state by starting from the vacuum and adding the particles in the occupied orbits,

$$|\nu_1\nu_2 \cdots \nu_A\rangle_a = a^\dagger(\nu_A) \cdots a^\dagger(\nu_2)a^\dagger(\nu_1)|0\rangle \tag{2A-7}$$

The antisymmetry of this state thus implies (see Eq. (2A-4)) that

$$a^\dagger(\nu_i)a^\dagger(\nu_k) = -a^\dagger(\nu_k)a^\dagger(\nu_i) \tag{2A-8}$$

The Hermitian adjoint to $a^\dagger(\nu)$ is written $a(\nu)$, and thus the adjoint to the state (2A-7) is

$${}_a\langle\nu_1\nu_2 \cdots \nu_A| = \langle 0|a(\nu_1)a(\nu_2) \cdots a(\nu_A) \tag{2A-9}$$

From Eq. (2A-8), we obtain immediately

$$a(\nu_i)a(\nu_k) = -a(\nu_k)a(\nu_i) \tag{2A-10}$$

Since the operator $a^\dagger$ creates a particle, the adjoint operator a (when acting to the right) destroys a particle. Thus, the above definitions imply

$$a(\nu)|0\rangle = 0 \tag{2A-11}$$

(We can also verify the relation (2A-11) by taking matrix elements with all possible states on the left; letting the $a(\nu)$ act to the left, we obtain states in which the orbit

ν is occupied, but such states must all be orthogonal to the vacuum.) More generally, the matrix elements of $a(\nu)$ are given by the relation

$$a(\nu)|\nu_1\nu_2 \cdots \nu_A\rangle_a = \begin{cases} 0 & \text{if} \quad \nu \neq \nu_1, \nu_2, \ldots, \text{and } \nu_A \\ |\nu_1\nu_2 \cdots \nu_{A-1}\rangle_a & \text{if} \quad \nu = \nu_A \end{cases} \tag{2A-12}$$

and the additional relations obtained by interchanging the occupied orbits until the state is brought to the form (2A-12).

The operator $a^\dagger(\nu_i)a(\nu_k)$ with $\nu_i \neq \nu_k$, is nonzero only if acting on a state in which the orbit ν_k is occupied and ν_i is empty. Acting on such a state, we obtain

$$\begin{aligned} a^\dagger(\nu_A)a(\nu_{A-1})|\nu_1 \cdots \nu_{A-2}\nu_{A-1}\rangle_a &= a^\dagger(\nu_A)|\nu_1\nu_2 \cdots \nu_{A-2}\rangle_a \\ &= |\nu_1\nu_2 \cdots \nu_{A-2}\nu_A\rangle_a \end{aligned} \tag{2A-13}$$

The transposed combination acting on the same state yields

$$\begin{aligned} a(\nu_{A-1})a^\dagger(\nu_A)|\nu_1\nu_2 \cdots \nu_{A-2}\nu_{A-1}\rangle_a &= a(\nu_{A-1})|\nu_1\nu_2 \cdots \nu_{A-2}\nu_{A-1}\nu_A\rangle_a \\ &= -a(\nu_{A-1})|\nu_1\nu_2 \cdots \nu_{A-2}\nu_A\nu_{A-1}\rangle_a \\ &= -|\nu_1\nu_2 \cdots \nu_{A-2}\nu_A\rangle_a \end{aligned} \tag{2A-14}$$

It is easily verified that the change in sign in going from Eq. (2A-13) to Eq. (2A-14) is independent of the order in which we write the occupied states, and thus we have the operator relation

$$a^\dagger(\nu_i)a(\nu_k) = -a(\nu_k)a^\dagger(\nu_i) \qquad \nu_i \neq \nu_k \tag{2A-15}$$

If $\nu_i = \nu_k$, we obtain an operator with the properties

$$a^\dagger(\nu)a(\nu)|\nu_1\nu_2 \cdots \nu_A\rangle_a = \begin{cases} 0 & \text{if} \quad \nu \neq \nu_1, \nu_2, \ldots, \text{and } \nu_A \\ |\nu_1\nu_2 \cdots \nu_A\rangle_a & \text{if} \quad \nu = \nu_1, \nu_2, \ldots, \text{or } \nu_A \end{cases} \tag{2A-16}$$

For the transposed combination, the matrix elements are given by

$$a(\nu)a^\dagger(\nu)|\nu_1\nu_2 \cdots \nu_A\rangle_a = \begin{cases} 0 & \text{if} \quad \nu = \nu_1, \nu_2, \ldots, \text{or } \nu_A \\ |\nu_1\nu_2 \cdots \nu_A\rangle_a & \text{if} \quad \nu \neq \nu_1, \nu_2, \ldots, \text{and } \nu_A \end{cases} \tag{2A-17}$$

Thus,

$$a^\dagger(\nu)a(\nu) + a(\nu)a^\dagger(\nu) = 1 \tag{2A-18}$$

The rules derived above for transposition of the a and $a^\dagger$ operators are conveniently written in terms of the anticommutation relations. Defining the anticommutator of any two operators A and B,

$$\{A, B\} = AB + BA \tag{2A-19}$$

we have

$$\begin{aligned} \{a^\dagger(\nu_i), a^\dagger(\nu_k)\} &= \{a(\nu_i), a(\nu_k)\} = 0 \\ \{a^\dagger(\nu_i), a(\nu_k)\} &= \delta(\nu_i, \nu_k) \end{aligned} \tag{2A-20}$$

The algebraic properties of the $a(\nu)$ and $a^\dagger(\nu)$ operators are completely determined by the relations (2A-20), and it is possible to present a derivation of the formalism that takes these relations together with the definition (2A-5) as the starting point. The mathematical structure of this algebra was extensively studied by mathematicians in the latter half of the past century and is referred to as a Grassmann algebra. The creation operator formalism is sometimes called second quantization; however, the algebra of these operators follows directly from their relation to the antisymmetrized many-particle states and involves no new physical assumptions.

The matrix elements (2A-16) imply that the expectation value of the operator $a^\dagger(\nu)a(\nu)$ measures the probability for finding the orbit ν occupied. Thus, the operator

$$n(\nu) = a^\dagger(\nu)a(\nu) \tag{2A-21}$$

is referred to as the occupation number operator for the orbit ν, while

$$n = \sum_\nu n(\nu) \tag{2A-22}$$

is the number operator whose eigenvalue is the total number of particles.

The a and $a^\dagger$ operators can appear in the formalism in two different contexts. Above, we have mainly considered their role as the creation operators that can be used to generate a complete set of A-body wave functions. In the following, we shall exploit the fact that the a and $a^\dagger$ form a complete set of variables in terms of which any operator can be expanded. Indeed, one of the principal advantages of the creation and destruction operator formalism derives from the fact that the operators corresponding to most physical measurements act on only a few particles at a time and therefore can be expressed in terms of rather simple combinations of the a and $a^\dagger$ operators.

The description in terms of creation and annihilation operators is especially convenient for expressing the relationship between particles and holes. Since a hole state is obtained by removing a particle from closed shells, the creation operator for a hole is equal to a destruction operator for a particle, and *vice versa* (see Appendix 3B.)

2A-3 One-Particle Operators

An operator acting on the individual particles separately is referred to as a one-particle operator. For a system of identical particles, such an operator has the form

$$F = \sum_{k=1}^{A} F(x_k) \tag{2A-23}$$

Since F can change the quantum state of at most a single particle, and since F does not change the number of particles, it must be possible to express such an operator in terms of a sum of terms of the form $a^\dagger(\nu_2)a(\nu_1)$,

$$F = \sum_{\nu_1\nu_2} \langle \nu_2 | F | \nu_1 \rangle a^\dagger(\nu_2)a(\nu_1) \tag{2A-24}$$

(An operator leaving the number of particles unchanged and acting on only a single particle may also contain terms proportional to $a(\nu_2)a^\dagger(\nu_1)$. However, because of the relation (2A-20), these terms only differ from those included in Eq. (2A-24) by a constant (c number). Since most operators corresponding to physical measurements give zero when evaluated in the vacuum, this c number usually vanishes.)

The coefficients $\langle \nu_2 | F | \nu_1 \rangle$ in the expansion (2A-24) can be obtained by evaluating F for a one-particle state; we thus obtain

$$\langle \nu_2 | F | \nu_1 \rangle = \int \varphi_{\nu_2}^{\dagger}(x) F(x) \varphi_{\nu_1}(x)\, dx \tag{2A-25}$$

where the integration over x also implies a summation over the discrete variables m_s and m_t.

The matrix elements of the one-particle operator (2A-24) between states in the occupation number representation (2A-7) may be evaluated by means of the expressions (2A-13) and (2A-16); we thus obtain the nonvanishing matrix elements

$$\begin{aligned} \langle \nu_1 \nu_2 \cdots \nu_A | F | \nu_1 \nu_2 \cdots \nu_A \rangle_a &= \sum_{i=1}^{A} \langle \nu_i | F | \nu_i \rangle \\ \langle \nu_1' \nu_2 \cdots \nu_A | F | \nu_1 \nu_2 \cdots \nu_A \rangle_a &= \langle \nu_1' | F | \nu_1 \rangle \quad (\nu_1' \neq \nu_1) \end{aligned} \tag{2A-26}$$

Other nondiagonal matrix elements of F may be obtained by first permuting the order of the quantum numbers ν_k, until the matrix element is brought into the form (2A-26). The result (2A-26) can be checked by a direct evaluation of the operator (2A-23) in the states (2A-3). Indeed, these results are almost obvious and essentially express the fact that the matrix elements of a one-particle operator are unaffected by the antisymmetrization of the state.

2A-4 Two-Particle Operators

A two-particle operator acting in a system of identical particles has the form

$$G = \sum_{j<k} G(x_j, x_k) \tag{2A-27}$$

and may change the state of two particles. Since G preserves the total number of particles, the expansion in terms of the $a^{\dagger}$ and a operators can be written

$$G = \sum_{\substack{\nu_1 < \nu_2 \\ \nu_3 < \nu_4}} \langle \nu_3 \nu_4 | G | \nu_1 \nu_2 \rangle_a a^{\dagger}(\nu_4) a^{\dagger}(\nu_3) a(\nu_1) a(\nu_2) \tag{2A-28}$$

where we have assumed the states ν_i to be numbered in some (arbitrary) order, so that we can impose the restriction that each pair of levels $\nu_1 \nu_2$ (and $\nu_3 \nu_4$) is only counted once in the sum. The coefficients in Eq. (2A-28) are seen to represent the matrix elements of G between antisymmetrized two-particle states and can, therefore, be written

$$\langle \nu_3 \nu_4 | G | \nu_1 \nu_2 \rangle_a = \langle \nu_3 \nu_4 | G | \nu_1 \nu_2 \rangle - \langle \nu_4 \nu_3 | G | \nu_1 \nu_2 \rangle \tag{2A-29}$$

with

$$\langle \nu_3 \nu_4 | G | \nu_1 \nu_2 \rangle = \int \varphi_{\nu_3}^{\dagger}(x_1) \varphi_{\nu_4}^{\dagger}(x_2) G(x_1, x_2) \varphi_{\nu_1}(x_1) \varphi_{\nu_2}(x_2)\, dx_1\, dx_2 \tag{2A-30}$$

The appearance of two terms in the matrix element (2A-29) is a consequence of the antisymmetrization and is sometimes referred to as the exchange effect.

The expression (2A-28) for G can also be written in terms of an unrestricted sum over the four single-particle levels,

$$
\begin{aligned}
G &= \frac{1}{4} \sum_{\nu_1\nu_2\nu_3\nu_4} \langle \nu_3 \nu_4 | G | \nu_1 \nu_2 \rangle_a a^\dagger(\nu_4) a^\dagger(\nu_3) a(\nu_1) a(\nu_2) \\
&= \frac{1}{2} \sum_{\nu_1\nu_2\nu_3\nu_4} \langle \nu_3 \nu_4 | G | \nu_1 \nu_2 \rangle a^\dagger(\nu_4) a^\dagger(\nu_3) a(\nu_1) a(\nu_2)
\end{aligned}
\tag{2A-31}
$$

where $\langle \nu_3\nu_4 | G | \nu_1 \nu_2 \rangle_a$ changes sign under the exchange of ν_1 and ν_2 and under the exchange of ν_3 and ν_4.

From the expression (2A-28), it is simple to evaluate the matrix elements of a two-particle operator in the occupation number representation. Thus, the expectation value is given by

$$
\langle \nu_1 \nu_2 \cdots \nu_A | G | \nu_1 \nu_2 \cdots \nu_A \rangle_a = \sum_{\nu_i < \nu_j \leq \nu_A} \langle \nu_i \nu_j | G | \nu_i \nu_j \rangle_a \tag{2A-32}
$$

This result differs from that obtained for an unsymmetrized wave function by the exchange term in the matrix elements (2A-29). The nondiagonal matrix elements of G involve a change of state of one or two particles,

$$
\begin{aligned}
\langle \nu_1' \nu_2 \cdots \nu_A | G | \nu_1 \nu_2 \cdots \nu_A \rangle_a &= \sum_{\nu_i = \nu_2}^{\nu_A} \langle \nu_1' \nu_i | G | \nu_1 \nu_i \rangle_a \\
\langle \nu_1' \nu_2' \nu_3 \cdots \nu_A | G | \nu_1 \nu_2 \nu_3 \cdots \nu_A \rangle_a &= \langle \nu_1' \nu_2' | G | \nu_1 \nu_2 \rangle_a
\end{aligned}
\tag{2A-33}
$$

Other matrix elements may be obtained from these by permuting the order of the quantum numbers.

2A-5 Particle Transfer Operators

The one- and two-particle operators discussed above preserve the number of particles, but the operators measured in particle transfer reactions go between nuclear states with different numbers of particles. In the description of such processes, therefore, the creation and annihilation operator formalism is especially convenient. For example, the matrix element

$$
\langle \alpha_{A+1} | a^\dagger(\nu) | \alpha_A \rangle_a
$$

referred to as the parentage coefficient, directly measures the probability amplitude for forming the $(A+1)$-particle state specified by the quantum numbers α_{A+1} by transferring a particle in the orbit ν to the target state α_A (see Appendix 3E).

2A-6 *x* Representation

The properties of the antisymmetrized states can also be described in terms of the operators $a^\dagger(x)$ which create a particle at the point $x(=\mathbf{r}, m_s, m_t)$. The x representation is related to the ν representation by a change of basis of the one-particle states, and we thus have

$$\begin{aligned} a^\dagger(x) &= \sum_\nu \langle \nu | x \rangle a^\dagger(\nu) \\ &= \sum_\nu \varphi_\nu^\dagger(x) a^\dagger(\nu) \end{aligned} \tag{2A-34}$$

as can be verified by letting the operators in Eq. (2A-34) act on the vacuum state.

In terms of the $a^\dagger(x)$ operators, the antisymmetric state (2A-7) can be written

$$|\nu_1\nu_2 \cdots \nu_A\rangle_a = \int dx_1\, dx_2 \cdots dx_A\, \varphi_{\nu_1}(x_1)\varphi_{\nu_2}(x_2) \cdots \varphi_{\nu_A}(x_A)\, a^\dagger(x_A) \cdots a^\dagger(x_2) a^\dagger(x_1)|0\rangle \tag{2A-35}$$

where the integral sign implies a summation over spin and isospin orientations as well as an integral over $\mathbf{r}$. A one-particle operator takes the form

$$F = \iint dx_1\, dx_2 \langle x_2 | F | x_1 \rangle a^\dagger(x_2) a(x_1) \tag{2A-36}$$

and other operators can be expressed in a similar manner in the x representation.

2A-7 Density Matrices

The occupation number operator (2A-21) (and the corresponding expression in the x representation) may be viewed as the diagonal elements of the matrix operator

$$\begin{aligned} \langle \nu_1 | \rho | \nu_2 \rangle &\equiv a^\dagger(\nu_2) a(\nu_1) \\ \langle x_1 | \rho | x_2 \rangle &\equiv a^\dagger(x_2) a(x_1) \end{aligned} \tag{2A-37}$$

which is referred to as the one-particle density matrix. (We here consider the elements of the density matrices as operators; often, the density matrices are defined as the expectation value of the operator (2A-37) for the total A-particle state considered.)

The one-particle density matrix suffices to express all the properties of the many-particle system that receive additive contributions from the individual particles. Thus, the one-particle operator (2A-24) or (2A-36) can be written

$$\begin{aligned} F &= \sum_{\nu_1\nu_2} \langle \nu_2 | F | \nu_1 \rangle \langle \nu_1 | \rho | \nu_2 \rangle \\ &= \int dx_1\, dx_2 \langle x_2 | F | x_1 \rangle \langle x_1 | \rho | x_2 \rangle \\ &= \mathrm{tr}(F\rho) \end{aligned} \tag{2A-38}$$

where tr denotes the trace of the product of the two matrices F and ρ. In a similar manner, the two-particle operators can be expressed in terms of the two-particle density matrices

$$\begin{aligned} \langle \nu_1\nu_2 | \rho | \nu_3\nu_4 \rangle &\equiv a^\dagger(\nu_4) a^\dagger(\nu_3) a(\nu_1) a(\nu_2) \\ \langle x_1 x_2 | \rho | x_3 x_4 \rangle &\equiv a^\dagger(x_4) a^\dagger(x_3) a(x_1) a(x_2) \end{aligned} \tag{2A-39}$$

The local particle densities are described by matrix elements of the density operators that are diagonal in the space variables. Thus, the local one-particle density may be represented by the operator $\rho(\mathbf{r}, \mathbf{s}, \mathbf{t})$, which is a 4×4 matrix in the spin-isospin variables,

$$\langle m_s m_t | \rho(\mathbf{r}, \mathbf{s}, \mathbf{t}) | m_s' m_t' \rangle \equiv \langle \mathbf{r} m_s m_t | \rho | \mathbf{r} m_s' m_t' \rangle$$
$$= a^\dagger(\mathbf{r} m_s' m_t') a(\mathbf{r} m_s m_t) \tag{2A-40}$$

Such a matrix in m_s, m_t space can be expressed in terms of the Pauli spin and isospin matrices,

$$\rho(\mathbf{r}, \mathbf{s}, \mathbf{t}) = \frac{1}{4}\rho_{00}(\mathbf{r}) + \frac{1}{2}\sum_{i=x,y,z} \sigma_i \rho_{10,i}(\mathbf{r}) + \frac{1}{2}\sum_{j=x,y,z} \tau_j \rho_{01,j}(\mathbf{r}) + \sum_{ij} \sigma_i \tau_j \rho_{11,ij}(\mathbf{r}) \tag{2A-41}$$

where $\rho_{00}(\mathbf{r})$ is a scalar in spin space as well as in isospin space, while ρ_{10} is a vector in spin space and a scalar in isospin space, and so on.

The 16 different density components in Eq. (2A-41) represent probabilities for finding particles at the space point $\mathbf{r}$ with various specifications for the spin and isospin orientations,

$$\sum_k \delta(\mathbf{r} - \mathbf{r}_k) = \operatorname{tr} \rho(\mathbf{r}, \mathbf{s}, \mathbf{t}) \equiv \sum_{m_s m_t} \langle m_s m_t | \rho(\mathbf{r}, \mathbf{s}, \mathbf{t}) | m_s m_t \rangle = \rho_{00}(\mathbf{r})$$

$$\begin{aligned} \sum_k \sigma_i(k)\delta(\mathbf{r} - \mathbf{r}_k) &= \operatorname{tr}(\sigma_i \rho) = \rho_{10,i}(\mathbf{r}) \\ \sum_k \tau_j(k)\delta(\mathbf{r} - \mathbf{r}_k) &= \operatorname{tr}(\tau_j \rho) = \rho_{01,j}(\mathbf{r}) \\ \sum_k \sigma_i(k)\tau_j(k)\delta(\mathbf{r} - \mathbf{r}_k) &= \operatorname{tr}(\sigma_i \tau_j \rho) = \rho_{11,ij}(\mathbf{r}) \end{aligned} \tag{2A-42}$$

2A-8 Creation Operators for Bosons

The treatment of bosons in terms of creation and annihilation operators can be developed in a similar manner as the treatment of fermions considered above. Since several bosons may occupy the same one-particle state φ_ν, the basis states for the occupation number representation are specified by the number n_1 of particles or quanta in the state ν_1, the number n_2 in the state ν_2, and so on, and such a state can be written $|n_1 n_2 \ldots\rangle$. For the boson state, the normalization constant—which equals $(A\,!)^{-1/2}$ for the fermion state (see Eq. (2A-3))—depends on the individual occupation numbers $n_1 n_2 \cdots$. The magnitude of the nonvanishing matrix elements of the creation operators, $c^\dagger(\nu)$, therefore depends on the state on which they act, and the defining equation (2A-6) is replaced by

$$c^\dagger(\nu_i) | n_1 n_2 \cdots n_i \cdots \rangle = (n_i + 1)^{1/2} | n_1 n_2 \cdots n_i + 1 \cdots \rangle \tag{2A-43}$$

With the definition (2A-43), all the properties of the boson system can be expressed in terms of the creation and annihilation operators, following essentially the same line of arguments as employed above for the fermion system. The symmetry of the wave function and the normalization (2A-43) imply that the anticommutation relations (2A-20) are replaced by commutation relations for the boson operators.

It is also possible to view a system of bosons in terms of a system of quantized harmonic oscillators associated with the individual single-particle states ν. In such a description, the creation operator $c^\dagger(\nu)$ corresponds to a linear combination of the position and momentum coordinates of the νth oscillator, and the factor $(n + 1)^{1/2}$ in Eq. (2A-43) represents the familiar factor expressing the increase in the amplitudes of these coordinates with increasing excitation of the oscillators.

APPENDIX

2B

Statistical Calculation of Level Densities

2B-1 Level Density Function and its Laplace Transform

In this appendix, we consider the methods for calculating the average level density for a system described in terms of independent-particle motion.[5] The density of levels, regarded as a function of energy $\mathscr{E}$, and particle number A, is given by

$$\rho(A, \mathscr{E}) = \sum_{n,\, i} \delta(A-n)\delta(\mathscr{E} - \mathscr{E}_i(n)) \tag{2B-1}$$

where $\mathscr{E}_i(n)$ is the energy of the ith quantum state of the n-particle system. In the independent-particle approximation, we can write

$$\begin{aligned} n &= \sum_{\nu} (n(\nu))_i \\ \mathscr{E}_i &= \sum_{\nu} (n(\nu))_i \varepsilon(\nu) \end{aligned} \tag{2B-2}$$

in terms of the occupation numbers, $(n(\nu))_i$, for the one-particle state ν in the quantum state i of the n-particle system ($(n(\nu))_i = 0$ or 1 as a result of the exclusion principle).

The function (2B-1) has singularities at each of the eigenvalues (2B-2), but we are interested in the average value of this function when integrated over an interval in A and $\mathscr{E}$. Because of the additive nature of the relations (2B-2), which determine the eigenvalues of A and $\mathscr{E}$, it is convenient to work with the Laplace transform of ρ,

$$\begin{aligned} Z(\alpha, \beta) &= \int_0^\infty \int_0^\infty \rho(A, \mathscr{E}) \exp\{\alpha A - \beta \mathscr{E}\}\, dA\, d\mathscr{E} \\ &= \sum_{i,\, n} \exp\{\alpha n - \beta \mathscr{E}_i(n)\} \end{aligned} \tag{2B-3}$$

Using Eq. (2B-2) to write the sum over i and n in terms of a sum over $n(\nu)$, we express Eq. (2B-3) as a product

$$Z(\alpha, \beta) = \prod_{\nu} (1 + \exp\{\alpha - \beta\varepsilon(\nu)\}) \tag{2B-4}$$

[5] The Darwin-Fowler method employed here has been especially applied to nuclear physics problems by Strutinski (1958) and Ericson (1960). A somewhat different approach has been employed by Bloch (1954) and in Lang and Le Couteur (1954).

In each factor, the term 1 comes from $n(\nu) = 0$, and the exponential term comes from $n(\nu) = 1$. In order to evaluate the product (2B-4) in terms of a sum over the one-particle states, we take the logarithm

$$\ln Z(\alpha, \beta) = \sum_{\nu} \ln(1 + \exp\{\alpha - \beta\varepsilon(\nu)\})$$

$$= \int_0^{\infty} g(\varepsilon) \ln(1 + \exp\{\alpha - \beta\varepsilon\})\, d\varepsilon \tag{2B-5}$$

The function $g(\varepsilon)$ describes the density of one-particle states

$$g(\varepsilon) = \sum_{\nu} \delta(\varepsilon - \varepsilon(\nu)) \tag{2B-6}$$

and we use an energy scale such that $\varepsilon(\nu) \geqslant 0$ for all ν.

In the integral (2B-5), the logarithmic factor approaches zero for $\varepsilon > \alpha/\beta$, while for $\varepsilon < \alpha/\beta$ it approaches the value $(\alpha - \beta\varepsilon)$. Thus, we write the integral in the form

$$\ln Z(\alpha, \beta) = \int_0^{\alpha/\beta} g(\varepsilon)(\alpha - \beta\varepsilon)\, d\varepsilon$$

$$+ \int_0^{\alpha/\beta} g(\varepsilon)[\ln(1 + \exp\{\alpha - \beta\varepsilon\}) - (\alpha - \beta\varepsilon)]\, d\varepsilon$$

$$+ \int_{\alpha/\beta}^{\infty} g(\varepsilon) \ln(1 + \exp\{\alpha - \beta\varepsilon\})\, d\varepsilon \tag{2B-7}$$

By a change of variable we can combine the last two integrals

$$\int_0^{\alpha/\beta} g(\varepsilon) \ln(1 + \exp\{-\alpha + \beta\varepsilon\})\, d\varepsilon + \int_{\alpha/\beta}^{\infty} g(\varepsilon) \ln(1 + \exp\{\alpha - \beta\varepsilon\})\, d\varepsilon$$

$$= \int_0^{\infty} [g(\alpha/\beta + x) + g(\alpha/\beta - x)] \ln(1 + \exp\{-\beta x\})\, dx \tag{2B-8}$$

since $g(\varepsilon) = 0$ for $\varepsilon < 0$. The logarithm in this integral vanishes except in an interval of width $\sim 1/\beta$ around $x = 0$. If this interval is wide compared with the spacing of the single-particle levels $\varepsilon(\nu)$, we can treat the density functions g in Eq. (2B-8) as smooth functions equal to the average of the expression (2B-6). If, at the same time, the interval $1/\beta$ is small compared with the region over which g varies, we may expand the g functions in a power series in x and carry out the integration, term by term, to obtain

$$\ln Z(\alpha, \beta) = \int_0^{\alpha/\beta} g(\varepsilon)(\alpha - \beta\varepsilon)\, d\varepsilon + \frac{\pi^2}{6\beta} g(\alpha/\beta) + \frac{7\pi^4}{360\beta^3} g''(\alpha/\beta) + \cdots \tag{2B-9}$$

where g'' is the second derivative of g.

The integrals to be evaluated in obtaining the expansion (2B-9) are of the form

$$I_n = \int_0^{\infty} x^n \ln(1 + \exp\{-x\})\, dx \tag{2B-10a}$$

with n an even integer. Expanding the logarithm, we obtain

$$I_n = \int_0^\infty x^n \left(\sum_{m=1}^{\infty} \frac{(-1)^{m+1}}{m} \exp\{-mx\} \right) dx$$

$$= n! \sum_{m=1}^{\infty} \frac{(-1)^{m+1}}{m^{n+2}} = n! \left(1 - \frac{1}{2^{n+1}}\right) \sum_{m=1}^{\infty} \frac{1}{m^{n+2}}$$

$$= n! \left(1 - \frac{1}{2^{n+1}}\right) \zeta(n+2) \tag{2B-10b}$$

where $\zeta(x)$ is the Riemann zeta function. For even integer n, this function can be expressed in terms of the Bernoulli numbers, and thus we obtain

$$I_n = \frac{2^{n+1} - 1}{(n+1)(n+2)} \pi^{n+2} |B_{n+2}| \tag{2B-11}$$

where

$$B_2 = \frac{1}{6}, \quad B_4 = -\frac{1}{30}, \quad B_6 = \frac{1}{42}, \ldots$$

2B-2 Inversion of Laplace Transform

Having obtained an approximate expression for Z, we now invert the Laplace transform (2B-3) in order to obtain the level density

$$\rho(A, \mathscr{E}) = \left(\frac{1}{2\pi i}\right)^2 \iint_{-i\infty}^{+i\infty} Z(\alpha, \beta) \exp\{-\alpha A + \beta \mathscr{E}\}\, d\alpha\, d\beta \tag{2B-12}$$

In evaluating this expression, we shall employ the saddle-point approximation, exploiting the fact that the integrand is a rapidly varying function of α and β. Thus, the main contribution to the integral comes from a small region around the point $(\alpha_0 \beta_0)$, where the integrand is stationary. The conditions that determine this stationary point are

$$\frac{\partial \ln Z}{\partial \alpha} - A = 0$$
$$\frac{\partial \ln Z}{\partial \beta} + \mathscr{E} = 0 \tag{2B-13}$$

Expanding the exponent in the integrand to second order around the point determined by the conditions (2B-13), we obtain a Gaussian integral which can be evaluated to yield

$$\rho(A, \mathscr{E}) = \frac{Z(\alpha_0, \beta_0) \exp\{-\alpha_0 A + \beta_0 \mathscr{E}\}}{2\pi |D|^{1/2}} \tag{2B-14}$$

where the determinant D is given by

$$D = \begin{vmatrix} \dfrac{\partial^2 \ln Z}{\partial \alpha^2} & \dfrac{\partial^2 \ln Z}{\partial \alpha\, \partial \beta} \\ \dfrac{\partial^2 \ln Z}{\partial \beta\, \partial \alpha} & \dfrac{\partial^2 \ln Z}{\partial \beta^2} \end{vmatrix}_{\alpha=\alpha_0,\, \beta=\beta_0} \tag{2B-15}$$

In differentiating the function (2B-9) to obtain the stationary point determined by Eq. (2B-13), we shall consistently neglect all terms depending on derivatives of g (see, for example, the last term in Eq. (2B-9)). Thus, we obtain

$$\begin{aligned} A &= \int_0^{(\alpha/\beta)_0} g(\varepsilon)\, d\varepsilon \\ \mathscr{E} &= \int_0^{(\alpha/\beta)_0} \varepsilon g(\varepsilon)\, d\varepsilon + \frac{\pi^2}{6\beta_0^2}\, g(\alpha_0/\beta_0) \end{aligned} \tag{2B-16}$$

The relations (2B-2) imply that in the ground state

$$\begin{aligned} \int_0^{\varepsilon_F} g(\varepsilon)\, d\varepsilon &= A \\ \int_0^{\varepsilon_F} g(\varepsilon)\varepsilon\, d\varepsilon &= \mathscr{E}_0 \end{aligned} \tag{2B-17}$$

where ε_F is the Fermi energy. Thus, the conditions (2B-16) can be written

$$\alpha_0 = \beta_0\, \varepsilon_F$$

$$E \equiv \mathscr{E} - \mathscr{E}_0 = \frac{\pi^2}{6\beta_0^2}\, g(\varepsilon_F) \tag{2B-18}$$

Introducing these relations into the expression (2B-14), and carrying out the evaluation of the determinant (2B-15), we finally obtain the level density as a function of A and the excitation energy E,

$$\rho(A, E) = \frac{1}{\sqrt{48}}\,\frac{1}{E}\exp\left\{2\left(\frac{\pi^2}{6}\, g(\varepsilon_F)E\right)^{1/2}\right\} \tag{2B-19}$$

The derivation of this result has involved the following approximations:

1. *The replacement of $g(\varepsilon)$ by a smooth function in the evaluation of the integral* (2B-8). This approximation is valid, provided

$$\beta_0^{-1} g(\varepsilon_F) \gg 1 \tag{2B-20}$$

which, on account of the relation (2B-18), is equivalent to

$$g(\varepsilon_F)E \gg 1 \tag{2B-21}$$

This condition simply reflects the fact that the average level density ρ is not defined until we come to excitation energies E large compared with the energy, g^{-1}, of the first excited state.

2. *The neglect of terms depending on derivatives of g.* The last term in Eq. (2B-9) is typical of these contributions. From the relation (2B-18), we find that this term may be neglected, provided

$$\frac{(g''(\varepsilon_F))^2 E^3}{(g(\varepsilon_F))^3} \ll 1 \tag{2B-22}$$

For a Fermi gas, $g \sim A\varepsilon^{1/2}\varepsilon_F^{-3/2}$, and thus the condition (2B-22) becomes

$$E \ll \varepsilon_F A^{1/3} \tag{2B-23}$$

The neglect of the higher-order terms in β^{-1} amounts to treating the Fermi gas as "degenerate." Thus, one might have expected the much weaker condition $E < \varepsilon_F A$ which, indeed, is sufficient to ensure that the exponent in the level density is accurate to within a factor 2. However, to obtain ρ itself to such an accuracy, we must estimate the exponent with an accuracy of one unit, and then the region of validity of the expression (2B-19) is restricted by the more severe condition (2B-23).

For a system exhibiting shell structure, the one-particle level density may vary much more rapidly and irregularly than for a Fermi gas, and it may be important to improve on the present approximation.

3. *The use of the saddle-point approximation in evaluating the inverse Laplace transform* (2B-12). The accuracy of this approximation may be estimated from the magnitude of the neglected terms in the expansion of the integrand. These terms are small provided the condition (2B-20) is fulfilled.

2B-3 Average Occupation Numbers for One-Particle States

The solution to the level density problem given above can also be used to characterize the structure of the excited states in terms of the average occupation $f(\nu)$ of the one-particle states ν,

$$f(\nu) = \langle n(\nu) \rangle \tag{2B-24}$$

where the average is taken over the excited states i in a small energy interval. Since the total level density is proportional to $Z(\alpha_0, \beta_0)$, and since Z is a product of contributions from each one-particle state, the level density associated with all configurations in which the state ν is not occupied is obtained from Eq. (2B-4) by omitting the factor due to the state ν,

$$\rho(A, \mathscr{E}, n(\nu) = 0) = \rho(A, \mathscr{E})[1 + \exp\{\alpha_0 - \beta_0\, \varepsilon(\nu)\}]^{-1} \tag{2B-25}$$

The total level density is the sum of the density with $n(\nu) = 0$ and $n(\nu) = 1$, and we obtain (see Eq. (2B-18))

$$\begin{aligned} f(\nu) &= \frac{\rho(A, \mathscr{E}, n(\nu) = 1)}{\rho(A, \mathscr{E})} \\ &= [1 + \exp\{\beta_0(\varepsilon(\nu) - \varepsilon_F)\}]^{-1} \end{aligned} \tag{2B-26}$$

This distribution goes over into the ground state distribution ($n(\nu) = 1$ for $\varepsilon(\nu) < \varepsilon_F$ and $n(\nu) = 0$ for $\varepsilon(\nu) > \varepsilon_F$) as the excitation energy E goes to zero ($\beta_0 \to \infty$; see Eq. (2B-18)). In obtaining the relations (2B-25) and (2B-26), we have assumed that the occupation of the orbit ν has no effect on the stationary values α_0 and β_0 determined by Eq. (2B-13). This approximation is justified if there are many particles excited with respect to the ground state distribution, which in turn requires the condition (2B-20).

2B-4 Description of Spectrum in Terms of Quasiparticle Excitations

It is often convenient to discuss the structure of excited states in terms of the change in the occupation numbers as compared with the ground state. Thus, we may characterize a state in terms of the quantum numbers of holes (unoccupied orbits with $\varepsilon(\nu) < \varepsilon_F$) and particles (occupied orbits with $\varepsilon(\nu) > \varepsilon_F$). We refer collectively to the holes and particles as quasiparticles. The average occupation, $\hat{f}$, of the quasiparticle state is

$$\begin{aligned} \hat{f}(\nu) &= f(\nu) & \varepsilon(\nu) > \varepsilon_F \\ &= 1 - f(\nu) & \varepsilon(\nu) < \varepsilon_F \end{aligned} \tag{2B-27}$$

Employing Eq. (2B-26), we obtain

$$\hat{f}(\nu) = [1 + \exp\{\beta_0 \hat{\varepsilon}(\nu)\}]^{-1} \tag{2B-28}$$

in terms of the quasiparticle energies

$$\hat{\varepsilon}(\nu) = |\varepsilon(\nu) - \varepsilon_F| \tag{2B-29}$$

It is also possible to carry out the evaluation of the level density in terms of quasiparticle excitations. In such a description we may begin by considering the density function

$$\hat{\rho}(E) = \sum_i \delta(E - E_i) \tag{2B-30}$$

with

$$E_i = \sum_\nu (n_q(\nu))_i \, \hat{\varepsilon}(\nu) \tag{2B-31}$$

where $(n_q(\nu))_i$ are the occupation numbers for the quasiparticles in the state i. We may obtain the Laplace transform $\hat{\mathscr{Z}}(\beta)$ of the density (2B-30) and express it as a product over the quasiparticle states as above,

$$\begin{aligned} \hat{\mathscr{Z}}(\beta) &= \prod_\nu (1 + \exp\{-\beta\hat{\varepsilon}(\nu)\}) \\ \ln \hat{\mathscr{Z}}(\beta) &= \sum_\nu \ln(1 + \exp\{-\beta\hat{\varepsilon}(\nu)\}) \\ &= \frac{\pi^2}{6} g_0 \beta^{-1} + \cdots \\ g_0 &\equiv g(\varepsilon_F) \end{aligned} \tag{2B-32}$$

Inverting the Laplace transform, we now find that the level density $\hat{\rho}$ has the correct exponential dependence on E, but is greater than the value (2B-19) by a factor $(24 g_0 E)^{1/4}$. This excess of levels in the quasiparticle spectrum results from the fact that we should have restricted the excitations to those in which the number of particles is equal to the number of holes. Another way of expressing this is to say that, in the quasiparticle spectrum, there are spurious states corresponding to excitations that change the total number of particles.

We shall discuss two ways of correcting for this error in the quasiparticle level density. First, we calculate the fluctuation in the particle number associated with the occupation numbers (2B-28). Denoting the number of particles by $n(p)$ and the number of holes by $n(h)$, we have

$$\langle n(p) - n(h) \rangle = \sum_{\nu > \nu_F} [1 + \exp\{\beta_0 \hat{\varepsilon}(\nu)\}]^{-1} - \sum_{\nu < \nu_F} [1 + \exp\{\beta_0 \hat{\varepsilon}(\nu)\}]^{-1} = 0$$

$$\begin{aligned} \langle (n(p) - n(h))^2 \rangle &= \sum_\nu (\langle n_q^2(\nu) \rangle - \langle n_q(\nu) \rangle^2) = \sum_\nu \frac{\exp\{\beta_0 \hat{\varepsilon}(\nu)\}}{(1 + \exp\{\beta_0 \hat{\varepsilon}(\nu)\})^2} \\ &\approx 2\int_0^\infty g_0 \, d\hat{\varepsilon} \frac{\exp\{\beta_0 \hat{\varepsilon}\}}{(1 + \exp\{\beta_0 \hat{\varepsilon}\})^2} = g_0 \beta_0^{-1} \end{aligned} \tag{2B-33}$$

The distribution of $\Delta = n(p) - n(h)$ in the ensemble (2B-28) is Gaussian since, in any given state, Δ is the algebraic sum of many independent contributions from the different single-particle orbits. The distribution function for Δ is therefore

$$P(\Delta) = (2\pi g_0 \beta_0^{-1})^{-1/2} \exp\left\{ -\frac{\Delta^2}{2 g_0 \beta_0^{-1}} \right\} \tag{2B-34}$$

and (see Eq. (2B-18))

$$P(0) = (24 g_0 E)^{-1/4} \tag{2B-35}$$

Another method of eliminating the spurious states in the quasiparticle spectrum is to go back to the calculation in which we average over different numbers of particles in the nucleus and rewrite the expression in terms of quasiparticles. Thus Eq. (2B-4) can be written in the form

$$\begin{aligned} Z(\alpha, \beta) &= \exp\{\alpha N - \beta \mathscr{E}_0\} \prod_\nu (1 + \exp\{-\beta \hat{\varepsilon}(\nu)\}) \\ &= \exp\{\alpha N - \beta \mathscr{E}_0\} \hat{Z} \end{aligned} \tag{2B-36}$$

where N and $\mathscr{E}_0$ are functions of α and β defined by

$$\begin{aligned} N(\alpha/\beta) &= \int_0^{\alpha/\beta} g(\varepsilon) \, d\varepsilon \\ \mathscr{E}_0(\alpha/\beta) &= \int_0^{\alpha/\beta} g(\varepsilon) \varepsilon \, d\varepsilon \end{aligned} \tag{2B-37}$$

The quantity N is the number of orbits with energy less than the Fermi energy α/β, while $\mathscr{E}_0$ is the ground state energy of the system with $N(\alpha/\beta)$ nucleons. The function $\hat{Z}$ depends on β, partly through the explicit appearance of the factor β multiplying the quasiparticle energies (compare with Eq. (2B-32)), partly through the implicit dependence of the quasiparticle energies on the Fermi energy (see Eq. (2B-29)). In the approximation where we neglect the derivatives of g, the latter dependence can be ignored and the factor $\hat{Z}$ is given by Eq. (2B-32). The expressions (2B-36) and (2B-32) are thus equivalent to (2B-9) and imply the level density (2B-19).

2B-5 Thermodynamic Interpretation of Level Density Calculation

The above calculation has been performed without any of the usual references to thermodynamic concepts. We have followed this presentation in order to emphasize that no additional assumptions or approximations have been made beside those discussed above. However, it is useful to recognize that the whole calculation has been borrowed from the theory of statistical mechanics and that the function $Z(\alpha, \beta)$ has a simple interpretation in terms of the grand canonical ensemble. In such an ensemble, the probability of the n-particle nucleus in the state with the eigenvalue $\mathscr{E}_i(n)$ is proportional to $\exp\{\alpha n - \beta \mathscr{E}_i(n)\}$. The numbers α and β appear as adjustable parameters, which permit us to specify the average values of the number of particles and of the energy. The relations (2B-13) are thus recognized as the equations defining α_0 and β_0 such that $\langle n \rangle = A$ and $\langle H \rangle = \mathscr{E}$, where the expectation values mean ensemble averages. The function Z is called the partition function and Z^{-1} is recognized as the normalization constant for the probabilities (see Eq. (2B-3)).

The distribution of energies and particle numbers in the ensemble is strongly peaked around the average values, and so we can employ a Gaussian approximation in this region. The width of the Gaussian is determined by the derivatives appearing in Eq. (2B-15). Since the probability per unit area of the $\mathscr{E}$–A plane is equal to the probability per single state times the density of states, the level density is equal to the inverse probability of a single state ($= Z \exp\{-\alpha_0 A + \beta_0 \mathscr{E}\}$) divided by the effective area in the $\mathscr{E}$–A plane that contains most of the states of the ensemble. Carrying out this calculation, one comes to exactly the expression (2B-14).

The quantity $(\alpha/\beta)_0$ is called the chemical potential ($=\varepsilon_F$ for the Fermi gas) and β_0^{-1} is interpreted as the temperature. The exponent in the level density formula (2B-14), which measures the logarithm of the statistical weight, is the entropy S, which satisfies the general relation

$$dS = \beta_0 \, d\mathscr{E} \tag{2B-37a}$$

Employing Eq. (2B-13),

$$\begin{aligned} d \ln Z(\alpha_0, \beta_0) &= \frac{\partial \ln Z}{\partial \alpha_0} d\alpha_0 + \frac{\partial \ln Z}{\partial \beta_0} d\beta_0 \\ &= A \, d\alpha_0 - \mathscr{E} \, d\beta_0 \end{aligned} \tag{2B-37b}$$

and integrating Eq. (2B-37a) from zero temperature, for fixed A, we obtain

$$S = -\alpha_0 A + \beta_0 \mathscr{E} + \ln Z(\alpha_0, \beta_0) \tag{2B-37c}$$

corresponding to the exponent in Eq. (2B-14).

The temperature β_0^{-1} differs somewhat from the temperature T given on p. 154, where T^{-1} is defined as the logarithmic derivative of the level density with respect to excitation energy. The two definitions differ as a result of the energy dependence of the denominator in the level density expression (2B-14), but the difference is small in regions where the condition (2B-20) is well satisfied. The definition in the text has the advantage that it refers directly to a physical property of the system that is readily susceptible to experimental determination.

2B-6 Calculation of Level Densities Specified by Additional Quantum Numbers

The calculation of the level density given above may be generalized in order to treat level densities that are characterized by further quantum numbers, provided only that these are composed additively of contributions from each of the one-particle states.

As the simplest example of an additional quantum number, we consider the consequences of the fact that the nucleus is composed of two kinds of particles, neutrons and protons. The partition function must now depend on three parameters in order that we be able to specify the average values of the energy $\mathscr{E}$, the neutron number N, and the proton number Z,

$$\mathscr{Z}(\alpha_n, \alpha_p, \beta) = \sum_{N,Z,i} \exp\{\alpha_n N + \alpha_p Z - \beta \mathscr{E}_i(N, Z)\} \tag{2B-38}$$

Proceeding as in Eqs. (2B-4) to (2B-9), we obtain

$$\ln \mathscr{Z} = \int_0^{\alpha_n/\beta} g_n(\varepsilon)(\alpha_n - \beta\varepsilon)\, d\varepsilon + \int_0^{\alpha_p/\beta} g_p(\varepsilon)(\alpha_p - \beta\varepsilon)\, d\varepsilon + \frac{\pi^2}{6\beta}(g_n(\alpha_n/\beta) + g_p(\alpha_p/\beta)) \tag{2B-39}$$

where g_n and g_p are the one-particle level densities for neutrons and protons, respectively. The generalizations of Eqs. (2B-16) to (2B-18) are easily obtained from the expression (2B-39),

$$\begin{aligned} (\alpha_n)_0 &= \varepsilon_F^{(n)}\beta_0 \\ (\alpha_p)_0 &= \varepsilon_F^{(p)}\beta_0 \\ E &= \frac{\pi^2}{6\beta_0} g_0 \end{aligned} \tag{2B-40}$$

where

$$g_0 = g_p(\varepsilon_F^{(p)}) + g_n(\varepsilon_F^{(n)}) \tag{2B-41}$$

in terms of the Fermi energies $\varepsilon_F^{(n)}$ and $\varepsilon_F^{(p)}$ of the neutrons and protons. Since the inverse Laplace transform involves integration over three variables, the determinant of $\mathscr{Z}''$ is 3×3 and the resulting level density is

$$\rho(N, Z, E) = \frac{6^{1/4}}{12} g_0 \left(\frac{g_0^2}{4g_n(\varepsilon_F^{(n)})g_p(\varepsilon_F^{(p)})}\right)^{1/2} (g_0 E)^{-5/4} \exp\left\{2\left(\frac{\pi^2}{6} g_0 E\right)^{1/2}\right\} \tag{2B-42}$$

The expression (2B-42) has the same exponential dependence on E as does (2B-19), with $g(\varepsilon_F)$ replaced by the total density g_0, but the coefficient in front of the exponential is somewhat modified by the presence of two different kinds of particles.

A slightly more complicated calculation yields the level density as a function of the total angular momentum of the states. It is convenient first to consider the distribution as a function of the component M, which is the sum of the m values of the individual particles. We are here assuming the one-particle potential to be invariant with respect to rotations about the axis of quantization. For simplicity, we consider a

Fermi gas with only one kind of particle. Thus, the partition function must again have three parameters,

$$Z(\alpha, \beta, \gamma) = \sum_{i,n,M} \exp\{\alpha n - \beta \mathscr{E}_i(n, M) - \gamma M\} \tag{2B-43}$$

The generalization of the expressions (2B-4) to (2B-9) can be written down immediately,

$$\ln Z(\alpha, \beta, \gamma) = \iint_{\alpha - \beta\varepsilon - \gamma m > 0} g(\varepsilon, m)(\alpha - \beta\varepsilon - \gamma m)\, d\varepsilon\, dm + \frac{\pi^2}{6}\iint g(\varepsilon, m)\delta(\alpha - \beta\varepsilon - \gamma m)\, d\varepsilon\, dm + \cdots \tag{2B-44}$$

where the one-particle level density g is now a function of both ε and m. We shall find below that, except for extremely large values of M, the parameter γ is sufficiently small so that it is a good approximation to expand the expression (2B-44) in powers of γ; keeping only the terms up to γ^2 and neglecting, as above, all terms depending on the derivatives of the one-particle density, we obtain

$$\ln Z(\alpha, \beta, \gamma) \approx \int_0^{\alpha/\beta} g(\varepsilon)(\alpha - \beta\varepsilon)\, d\varepsilon + \frac{\gamma^2}{2\beta} g(\alpha/\beta)\langle m^2 \rangle + \frac{\pi^2}{6\beta} g(\alpha/\beta) \tag{2B-45}$$

where

$$g(\varepsilon) = \int_{-\infty}^{+\infty} g(\varepsilon, m)\, dm \tag{2B-46}$$

and

$$g(\varepsilon = \alpha/\beta)\langle m^2 \rangle = \int_{-\infty}^{+\infty} g(\alpha/\beta, m) m^2\, dm \tag{2B-47}$$

Thus, $\langle m^2 \rangle$ represents the average value of m^2 for the one-particle orbits at the Fermi surface. We have assumed $\langle m \rangle = 0$ as would follow, for example, from time reversal symmetry or invariance of the one-particle potential with respect to a rotation of 180° about an axis perpendicular to the symmetry axis.

The stationary point in the integrand of the inverse Laplace transform is determined from the equations

$$\begin{aligned} \frac{\partial \ln Z}{\partial \alpha} - A &= 0 \\ \frac{\partial \ln Z}{\partial \beta} + \mathscr{E} &= 0 \\ \frac{\partial \ln Z}{\partial \gamma} + M &= 0 \end{aligned} \tag{2B-48}$$

which, on employing the expression (2B-45) and neglecting derivatives of g, yields

$$A = \int_0^{(\alpha/\beta)_0} g(\varepsilon)\, d\varepsilon$$

$$\mathscr{E} = \int_0^{(\alpha/\beta)_0} g(\varepsilon)\varepsilon\, d\varepsilon + \frac{\pi^2}{6\beta_0^2} g\left(\frac{\alpha_0}{\beta_0}\right) + \frac{1}{2}\left(\frac{\gamma_0}{\beta_0}\right)^2 \langle m^2\rangle g\left(\frac{\alpha_0}{\beta_0}\right) \tag{2B-49}$$

$$M = -\frac{\gamma_0}{\beta_0} g\left(\frac{\alpha_0}{\beta_0}\right)\langle m^2\rangle$$

Using the definition of the Fermi energy, we obtain

$$\alpha_0 = \varepsilon_F \beta_0$$

$$\frac{\pi^2}{6\beta_0^2} g(\varepsilon_F) = E - \frac{M^2}{2g(\varepsilon_F)\langle m^2\rangle} \tag{2B-50}$$

$$\frac{\gamma_0}{\beta_0} g(\varepsilon_F)\langle m^2\rangle = -M$$

Introducing these expressions into the generalization of Eq. (2B-14), we obtain

$$\rho(A, E, M) = \frac{6^{1/4}}{24}\left(\frac{g_0^2}{\langle m^2\rangle}\right)^{1/2}\left[g_0 E - \frac{M^2}{2\langle m^2\rangle}\right]^{-5/4} \exp\left\{2\left[\frac{\pi^2}{6}\left(g_0 E - \frac{M^2}{2\langle m^2\rangle}\right)\right]^{1/2}\right\} \tag{2B-51}$$

$$g_0 \equiv g(\varepsilon_F)$$

In the derivation of this result, the only new approximation is that associated with the expansion of (2B-44) in powers of γ. The neglected terms in $\ln Z$ are of the magnitude

$$\left(\frac{\gamma m}{\beta}\right)^4 \beta \frac{\partial^2 g}{\partial \varepsilon^2}$$

which, on using the relations (2B-50), implies the condition

$$\frac{M^4}{g_0^4\langle m^2\rangle^2} \beta \frac{\partial^2 g}{\partial \varepsilon^2} < 1 \tag{2B-52}$$

For a Fermi gas, $g(\varepsilon) \sim A\varepsilon^{1/2}\varepsilon_F^{-3/2}$ and $g_0\langle m^2\rangle = \mathscr{I}_{\text{rig}}\hbar^{-2}$ (see below), and thus the condition (2B-52) is satisfied, provided

$$\left(\frac{\hbar^2 M^2}{2\mathscr{I}_{\text{rig}}}\right)^2 \frac{1}{\varepsilon_F^2}\left(\frac{\varepsilon_F}{AE}\right)^{1/2} < 1 \tag{2B-53}$$

The inequality is always fulfilled under the condition (2B-23), if $\hbar^2 M^2/2\mathscr{I}_{\text{rig}} \leq E$.

The above calculation may be viewed in a somewhat different light by employing the probability distribution of the quasiparticle occupation numbers. Thus, the partition function (2B-43) corresponds to an ensemble in which the probabilities are proportional to $\exp\{\alpha n - \beta\mathscr{E} - \gamma M\}$, and this, in analogy to Eq. (2B-28), implies that the probability of occupation of the quasiparticle states is given by

$$f(\nu) = (1 + \exp\{\beta_0 \hat{\varepsilon}(\nu) + \gamma_0 m(\nu)\})^{-1} \tag{2B-54}$$

Expanding f in a power series in γ_0, we obtain

$$f(\nu)=(1+\exp\{\beta_0\hat{\varepsilon}(\nu)\})^{-1}-\gamma_0 m(\nu)\frac{\exp\{\beta_0\hat{\varepsilon}(\nu)\}}{(1+\exp\{\beta_0\hat{\varepsilon}(\nu)\})^2}$$

$$+\tfrac{1}{2}(\gamma_0 m)^2\frac{\exp\{\beta_0\hat{\varepsilon}(\nu)\}(\exp\{\beta_0\hat{\varepsilon}(\nu)\}-1)}{(1+\exp\{\beta_0\hat{\varepsilon}(\nu)\})^3}+\cdots \qquad \text{(2B-55)}$$

Calculating the average value of M, we obtain to leading order

$$\langle M\rangle=-\gamma_0\sum_\nu m^2(\nu)\frac{\exp\{\beta_0\hat{\varepsilon}(\nu)\}}{(1+\exp\{\beta_0\hat{\varepsilon}(\nu)\})^2}$$

$$=-\gamma_0\langle m^2\rangle g(\varepsilon_F)\beta_0^{-1} \qquad \text{(2B-56)}$$

in agreement with the last of the equations (2B-50). Similarly, the calculation of the average excitation energy for the ensemble yields

$$\langle E\rangle=\sum f(\nu)\hat{\varepsilon}(\nu)$$

$$=g_0\frac{\pi^2}{6\beta_0^2}+\tfrac{1}{2}\gamma_0^2\langle m^2\rangle g_0\beta_0^{-2}+\cdots \qquad \text{(2B-57)}$$

in agreement with the second of the equations (2B-50). In this derivation, one sees especially clearly the role of the parameter γ as a constraint on the ensemble necessary in order to specify the average value of M. With the constrained ensemble, the average energy is higher for the same β_0, by the amount $M^2(2g_0\langle m^2\rangle)^{-1}$, which can thus be identified as an average rotational energy for the system.

To complete the calculation of the M distribution for a Fermi gas, we must now evaluate the quantity $\langle m^2\rangle$ defined by Eq. (2B-47). The distribution of the single-particle angular momenta may be obtained from a semiclassical approximation based on the function $g(\mathbf{p},\mathbf{r})$ that describes the density of one-particle states in phase space

$$g(\mathbf{p},\mathbf{r})=2\left(\frac{1}{2\pi\hbar}\right)^3 \qquad \text{(2B-58)}$$

The average $\langle m^2\rangle$ involves a sum over one-particle states with energy approximately equal to ε_F,

$$g_0\langle m^2\rangle=\int g(\mathbf{p},\mathbf{r})\delta\left(\frac{p^2}{2M_n}-\frac{(p_F(r))^2}{2M_n}\right)\frac{1}{\hbar^2}(xp_y-yp_x)^2\,d^3p\,d^3r$$

$$p_F(r)=\hbar(3\pi^2\rho(r))^{1/3} \qquad \text{(2B-59)}$$

$$g_0=g(\varepsilon_F)=\int_{-\infty}^{+\infty}g(\varepsilon_F,m)\,dm$$

where M_n is the mass of a nucleon. Since the momenta are isotropically distributed at each point in space, the cross term involving p_xp_y does not contribute, and the integral (2B-59) becomes

$$g_0\langle m^2\rangle=\frac{2}{(2\pi\hbar)^3}4\pi\frac{M_n}{3\hbar^2}\int[p_F(r)]^3(x^2+y^2)\,d^3r \qquad \text{(2B-60)}$$

Inserting the value (2B-59) for the Fermi momentum, we obtain

$$g_0\langle m^2\rangle = \frac{M_n}{\hbar^2}\int \rho(r)(x^2+y^2)\,d^3r$$
$$= \mathscr{I}_{\text{rig}}/\hbar^2 \tag{2B-61}$$

where $\mathscr{I}_{\text{rig}}$ is the moment of inertia of a rigid body with the same density distribution as the nucleus. The physical interpretation of the rigid moment of inertia for the Fermi gas model is further discussed in Sec. 9-2.

The density of states with given total angular momentum I can be obtained from a differentiation of $\rho(E, M)$,

$$\begin{aligned}\rho(E, I) &= \rho(E, M=I) - \rho(E, M=I+1)\\ &\approx -\left(\frac{\partial\rho(E, M)}{\partial M}\right)_{M=I+1/2}\\ &\approx \frac{\pi}{48}6^{-1/4}(2I+1)g_0\left(\frac{g_0\hbar^2}{\mathscr{I}_{\text{rig}}}\right)^{3/2}\left[g_0\left(E-\frac{I(I+1)\hbar^2}{2\mathscr{I}_{\text{rig}}}\right)\right]^{-7/4}\\ &\quad\times\exp\left\{2\left[\frac{\pi^2}{6}g_0\left(E-\frac{I(I+1)\hbar^2}{2\mathscr{I}_{\text{rig}}}\right)\right]^{1/2}\right\}\end{aligned} \tag{2B-62}$$

In taking the derivative, we have neglected the relatively weak M dependence of the coefficient in front of the exponential.

In order to somewhat simplify the calculation, we have considered the distribution of M values for a Fermi gas of only one kind of particle. The treatment of a system with neutrons and protons follows exactly the same lines as above; the result is quoted in the text (Eq. (2-57)).

APPENDIX

2C

Fluctuations in Terms of Random Matrices

In this appendix, we consider some features of the spectrum that results from a Hamiltonian matrix in which the individual matrix elements are assumed to have a random probability distribution.

2C-1 Random Distribution of Elements of Two-Dimensional Matrix

We start by considering the 2×2 matrix

$$H = \begin{pmatrix} H_{11} & H_{12} \\ H_{21} & H_{22} \end{pmatrix} \tag{2C-1}$$

The Hamiltonian is assumed to be Hermitian, rotationally invariant, and invariant under time reversal, and the matrix (2C-1) describes the coupling between two states with the same values of I and M (and other conserved quantum numbers, such as parity, isospin, etc.). Time reversal implies that the matrix elements of H are real in the standard basis (see Eq. (1-42)), and hermiticity adds the relation $H_{12} = H_{21}$.

We consider an ensemble of matrices of the type (2C-1), in which the probability of a given matrix is specified by some function $P(H)$. We must first characterize the function $P(H)$ so that it reflects some model of randomness for the matrix elements, and then we shall study the statistical properties of the eigenvalues and eigenfunctions corresponding to the ensemble.

The distribution $P(H)$ that we shall study below will be characterized by the following two properties[6]:

[6] Other characterizations of the distribution $P(H)$ have also been considered either because of their mathematical simplicity, or because they express a somewhat different version of randomness (see the review by Rosenzweig, 1963, and references given there). In the limit of large matrices, these other ensembles lead to the same distribution of nearest-neighbor spacings as the Gaussian ensemble considered here, provided we assume that H is Hermitian and real. The Gaussian ensembles were first considered by Wigner (1958). The derivation of the Gaussian ensemble on the basis of the two assumptions employed below is due to Porter and Rosenzweig (1960).

(1) We assume that the three matrix elements, H_{11}, H_{12}, and H_{22} are uncorrelated and, therefore,

$$P(H) = P_{11}(H_{11})P_{12}(H_{12})P_{22}(H_{22}) \tag{2C-2}$$

(2) Since the original basis states $|1\rangle$ and $|2\rangle$ employed in defining Eq. (2C-1) were arbitrarily chosen, we assume that the distribution (2C-2) is invariant under an arbitrary unitary transformation of the basis states.

Since we restrict ourselves to transformations that leave the matrix elements real, the unitary transformation becomes an orthogonal transformation in the two-dimensional vector space. It is sufficient to consider infinitesimal transformations, since a finite rotation of the basis can always be composed of a sum of infinitesimal transformations,

$$\begin{aligned} |1'\rangle &= |1\rangle + \varepsilon|2\rangle \\ |2'\rangle &= -\varepsilon|1\rangle + |2\rangle \end{aligned} \tag{2C-3}$$

The matrix elements in the new basis are to order ε,

$$\begin{aligned} H_{1'1'} &= H_{11} + 2\varepsilon H_{12} \\ H_{1'2'} &= H_{12} + \varepsilon(H_{22} - H_{11}) \\ H_{2'2'} &= H_{22} - 2\varepsilon H_{12} \end{aligned} \tag{2C-4}$$

Invariance with respect to change of basis implies

$$\begin{aligned} P(H) &= P(H') \\ &= P(H)\left\{1 + \varepsilon\left[\frac{2H_{12}}{P_{11}}\frac{dP_{11}}{dH_{11}} + \frac{H_{22} - H_{11}}{P_{12}}\frac{dP_{12}}{dH_{12}} - \frac{2H_{12}}{P_{22}}\frac{dP_{22}}{dH_{22}}\right]\right\} \end{aligned} \tag{2C-5}$$

The coefficient of ε must vanish and, hence,

$$\frac{1}{H_{12}P_{12}}\frac{dP_{12}}{dH_{12}} = -\frac{2}{H_{22} - H_{11}}\left(\frac{1}{P_{11}}\frac{dP_{11}}{dH_{11}} - \frac{1}{P_{22}}\frac{dP_{22}}{dH_{22}}\right) = -C \tag{2C-6}$$

where C is a constant, since the function on the far left depends only on H_{12}, while the function in the middle depends only on H_{11} and H_{22}. We thus obtain

$$\begin{aligned} \frac{dP_{12}}{P_{12}} &= -CH_{12}\,dH_{12} \\ P_{12} &= \left(\frac{C}{2\pi}\right)^{1/2}\exp\left\{-\frac{C}{2}H_{12}^2\right\} \end{aligned} \tag{2C-7}$$

The constant in front of the Gaussian is determined from the normalization condition. Similarly, we obtain

$$\frac{2}{P_{11}}\frac{dP_{11}}{dH_{11}} + CH_{11} = \frac{2}{P_{22}}\frac{dP_{22}}{dH_{22}} + CH_{22} = A \tag{2C-8}$$

where A is a constant. A change of A merely shifts the zero point of the energy scale. We can therefore set $A = 0$ and obtain

$$
\begin{aligned}
P_{11} &= \left(\frac{C}{4\pi}\right)^{1/2} \exp\left\{-\frac{C}{4} H_{11}^2\right\} \\
P_{22} &= \left(\frac{C}{4\pi}\right)^{1/2} \exp\left\{-\frac{C}{4} H_{22}^2\right\}
\end{aligned}
\tag{2C-9}
$$

The constant C specifies the average magnitude of the matrix elements and thus determines the average value of the level spacing.

2C-2 Distribution of Eigenvalues and Eigenvectors

The matrix (2C-1) can also be characterized by its eigenvalues

$$
\begin{aligned}
E_\alpha &= \tfrac{1}{2}(H_{11} + H_{22}) + \tfrac{1}{2}[(H_{11} - H_{22})^2 + 4H_{12}^2]^{1/2} \\
E_\beta &= \tfrac{1}{2}(H_{11} + H_{22}) - \tfrac{1}{2}[(H_{11} - H_{22})^2 + 4H_{12}]^{1/2}
\end{aligned}
\tag{2C-10}
$$

and eigenfunctions

$$
\begin{aligned}
|\alpha\rangle &= \cos\theta\,|1\rangle + \sin\theta\,|2\rangle \\
|\beta\rangle &= -\sin\theta\,|1\rangle + \cos\theta\,|2\rangle
\end{aligned}
\tag{2C-11}
$$

where

$$
\cot\theta = -\frac{1}{2H_{12}}(H_{22} - H_{11} - [(H_{22} - H_{11})^2 + 4H_{12}^2]^{1/2}) \qquad -\frac{\pi}{2} < \theta < +\frac{\pi}{2}
\tag{2C-12}
$$

We now transform the distribution function from the variables H_{11}, H_{12}, and H_{22} to the variables E_α, E_β, and θ. Since

$$
H_{11}^2 + 2H_{12}^2 + H_{22}^2 = E_\alpha^2 + E_\beta^2
\tag{2C-13}
$$

the exponent of the Gaussian is easily transformed. In order to obtain the volume element in the new variables, we must calculate the Jacobian

$$
\frac{\partial(H_{11}, H_{12}, H_{22})}{\partial(E_\alpha, E_\beta, \theta)} =
\begin{vmatrix}
\dfrac{\partial H_{11}}{\partial E_\alpha} & \dfrac{\partial H_{12}}{\partial E_\alpha} & \dfrac{\partial H_{22}}{\partial E_\alpha} \\[2ex]
\dfrac{\partial H_{11}}{\partial E_\beta} & \dfrac{\partial H_{12}}{\partial E_\beta} & \dfrac{\partial H_{22}}{\partial E_\beta} \\[2ex]
\dfrac{\partial H_{11}}{\partial \theta} & \dfrac{\partial H_{12}}{\partial \theta} & \dfrac{\partial H_{22}}{\partial \theta}
\end{vmatrix}
\tag{2C-14}
$$

which is most easily obtained from the expressions for H_{11}, H_{12}, and H_{22} in terms of E_α, E_β, and θ,

$$
\begin{aligned}
H_{11} &= E_\alpha \cos^2\theta + E_\beta \sin^2\theta \\
H_{12} &= (E_\alpha - E_\beta)\sin\theta\cos\theta \\
H_{22} &= E_\alpha \sin^2\theta + E_\beta \cos^2\theta
\end{aligned}
\tag{2C-15}
$$

Calculating the Jacobian (2C-14) from these expressions, we obtain the joint probability distribution in the new variables,

$$P(E_\alpha, E_\beta, \theta) = \frac{1}{2}\left(\frac{C}{2\pi}\right)^{3/2}(E_\alpha - E_\beta)\exp\left\{-\frac{C}{4}(E_\alpha^2 + E_\beta^2)\right\} \tag{2C-16}$$

(Notice that the definition (2C-10) implies that we have labeled the eigenvalues so that $E_\alpha > E_\beta$.) The probability of the spacing ε between the two eigenvalues may be obtained by integrating over (2C-16),

$$\begin{aligned} P(\varepsilon) &= \int P(E_\alpha, E_\beta, \theta)\delta(\varepsilon - E_\alpha + E_\beta)\, dE_\alpha\, dE_\beta\, d\theta \\ &= \frac{C}{4}\,\varepsilon \exp\left\{-\frac{C\varepsilon^2}{8}\right\} \qquad (0 < \varepsilon < \infty) \end{aligned} \tag{2C-17}$$

The constant C can be related to the mean spacing D,

$$\begin{aligned} \int_0^\infty \varepsilon P(\varepsilon)\, d\varepsilon = D &= \left(\frac{2\pi}{C}\right)^{1/2} \\ C &= \frac{2\pi}{D^2} \end{aligned} \tag{2C-18}$$

and thus the normalized distribution is

$$P(\varepsilon) = \frac{\pi}{2D^2}\,\varepsilon \exp\left\{-\frac{\pi}{4}\frac{\varepsilon^2}{D^2}\right\} \tag{2C-19}$$

The result (2C-19) is referred to as the Wigner distribution. This distribution has vanishing probability for $\varepsilon \to 0$, which reflects the fact that, in order for the matrix (2C-1) to give a degenerate pair of eigenvalues, we must satisfy both $H_{11} = H_{22}$ and $H_{12} = 0$. The probability of two such special values is vanishingly small.

From Eq. (2C-16), we see that the distribution of the eigenvectors is such that all angles θ are equally probable and that the eigenvectors are uncorrelated with the spacing. We are often interested in the probability distributions for the amplitude of a particular basis state; this can be obtained by integrating Eq. (2C-16). For example, the amplitude of the state, 1, in the eigenfunction, α, is $C_1 = \cos\theta$, and the probability distribution for this amplitude is

$$\begin{aligned} P(C_1) &= P(\theta)\left(\frac{dC_1}{d\theta}\right)^{-1} \\ &= \frac{1}{\pi}(1 - C_1^2)^{-1/2} \end{aligned} \tag{2C-20}$$

We could, indeed, have argued directly for the result (2C-20) from the fact that the original ensemble has been chosen to be invariant to a rotation of the basis vectors; this implies that the joint distribution function for the amplitudes must be

$$P(C_1, C_2) = \frac{1}{\pi}\,\delta(1 - C_1^2 - C_2^2) \tag{2C-21}$$

Integrating (2C-21) over C_2, we obtain (2C-20).

The linear dependence of $P(\varepsilon)$ on ε for small ε is a consequence of the symmetries assumed for the Hamiltonian matrix (2C-1). Somewhat different results are obtained if H has a lower symmetry (Dyson, 1962 and 1962b).

Thus, if we had not assumed time reversal invariance for the Hamiltonian, the hermiticity of H would ensure that H_{11} and H_{22} were real, but H_{12} would have a real and imaginary part, each of which would have an independent Gaussian distribution. In this case, the degeneracy of the eigenvalues would require the three conditions $H_{11} = H_{22}$, $H_{12} = H_{12}^* = 0$. We therefore obtain $P \propto \varepsilon^2$ for small values of the spacing, ε.

If H is invariant under time reversal but not rotationally invariant, one must consider separately the case of even-A and odd-A nuclei (see Sec. 1B-2). For even-A systems, we can choose a basis of eigenstates of $\mathscr{T}$ and, in this basis, the Hamiltonian is real; we therefore obtain the distribution (2C-19). For odd-A systems, the eigenstates are two-fold degenerate and one can employ a basis $|\alpha\rho\rangle$, where $\rho = \pm 1$ labels the degenerate states, which are conjugate under time reversal. In this basis, H is a matrix in α space with the symmetry properties (1B-25) and (1B-26), and the coupling between two pairs of conjugate states involves four real parameters associated with the matrices H_0, H_1, H_2, and H_3. Thus, in the absence of additional symmetries, $P(\varepsilon)$ is proportional to ε^4 for small ε. The result is modified in the presence of further symmetries. Thus, axial symmetry would imply that the degenerate levels can be labeled by $\pm M$ and that H is diagonal in ρ space ($H_1 = H_2 = 0$); hence, the coupling involves two real parameters and $P(\varepsilon) \propto \varepsilon^2$. If H is invariant with respect to a rotation $\mathscr{R}$ of π about an axis, one can employ the standard basis with $\mathscr{R}\mathscr{T} = +1$; the invariance of H with respect to $\mathscr{R}$ ($= -i\rho_2$; see Eq. (1B-22)) then implies $H_1 = H_3 = 0$, and again the coupling involves two real parameters. If both axial symmetry and $\mathscr{R}$ invariance apply, the situation is the same as for full rotational invariance.

The formulation of ensembles corresponding to Hamiltonians with partial breakdown of the various symmetries has been discussed by Dyson (1962a). The possibility of observing a small departure from time reversal invariance in terms of statistical properties of highly excited levels has been considered by Favro and MacDonald (1967) and Rosenzweig *et al.* (1968).

2C-3 Matrices of Large Dimensions

The simple 2×2 matrix discussed above illustrates the physical arguments and the type of result that can be obtained from the analysis of random matrices. However, in order to properly treat level spacings that are not small compared with the average, as well as many other questions involving correlations and distributions for properties that go beyond nearest neighbors, it is necessary to consider matrices for which the dimension N is large.

The two conditions employed above (p. 295) may be easily extended to characterize the probability distribution for the matrix elements of the general $N \times N$ random matrix. By carrying out the rotation (2C-3) successively in each of the $N(N-1)/2$ two-dimensional subspaces, we find that all the nondiagonal matrix elements have the probability distribution (2C-7), while all the diagonal elements have the distribution (2C-9). Thus, the total function $P(H)$ can be written:

$$P(H) = 2^{-N/2}\left(\frac{C}{2\pi}\right)^{N(N+1)/4} \exp\left\{-\frac{C}{4}\operatorname{tr} H^2\right\} \tag{2C-22}$$

If we diagonalize the $N \times N$ matrices, we can transform the distribution (2C-22) from the variables H_{ij} to new variables comprising the eigenvalues E_α (with $\alpha = 1$ to N) and $N(N-1)/2$ other parameters characterizing the structure of the N eigenfunctions. The exponent in Eq. (2C-22) is expressed in a form that is independent of the representation, and so we have

$$trH^2 = \sum_{\alpha=1}^{N} E_\alpha^2 \tag{2C-22a}$$

As for the 2×2 matrices, the evaluation of the volume element (the calculation of the Jacobian) is the most difficult part of the calculation. However, it is possible to determine the dependence of the Jacobian on the E_α from a dimensional argument. We first note that for degenerate eigenvalues the eigenfunctions are undetermined; the inverse transformation is therefore also undetermined and the Jacobian must vanish. Furthermore, the H_{ij} are linear functions of the E_α, and thus the Jacobian must be a symmetric polynomial of order $N(N-1)/2$ in the E_α. These conditions are sufficient to determine the joint distribution function

$$P(E_1 \cdots E_N, \theta_1 \cdots \theta_\nu)$$

$$= \mu(\theta_1 \cdots \theta_\nu) \prod_{\alpha<\beta} |E_\alpha - E_\beta| \exp\left\{-\frac{C}{4}\sum_\alpha E_\alpha^2\right\} \tag{2C-23}$$

where $\theta_1, \ldots, \theta_\nu$ are the $N(N-1)/2$ parameters describing the structures of the N eigenfunctions. The function μ will, of course, depend on how these additional parameters are chosen.

The distribution (2C-23) is by no means easy to work with and indeed the first useful information on the distribution of successive eigenvalues for the ensemble (2C-22) was obtained by employing an electronic computer to diagonalize a large number of matrices, the elements of which had been generated by a random process governed by the probability distribution (2C-22) (Rosenzweig and Porter, 1960). Later, it was found possible to give closed expressions for the distribution and correlation functions characterizing the eigenspectra of these matrices (Mehta, 1960; Mehta and Gaudin, 1960; Gaudin, 1961; Dyson, 1962; Dyson and Mehta, 1963. A systematic presentation is given in the text by Mehta, 1967.)

We shall not attempt to review the ingenious mathematical devices that have been employed in solving this problem, but shall only quote some of the most significant results obtained so far. The distribution of nearest-neighbor spacings is remarkably close to the expression (2C-19) obtained from the ensemble of 2×2 matrices; the absolute error in $P(\varepsilon)$ is nowhere greater than $0.01\ D^{-1}$ over the whole range of ε, though for large values of ε the relative error in the simple expression (2C-19) increases (Gaudin, 1961; Dyson, 1962).

A striking feature revealed by the study of random matrices of large dimensions is the tendency to long-range order in the distribution of eigenvalues (Dyson and Mehta, 1963; this feature is further discussed on p. 181).

The distribution of amplitudes in the eigenvectors may be obtained directly from the assumption that the Hamiltonian ensemble is invariant to an orthogonal change of bases. Thus, the joint distribution function for the N amplitudes is

$$P(C_1 \cdots C_N) = \frac{2}{\Omega_N}\,\delta\Big(1 - \sum_{i=1}^{N} C_i^2\Big) \tag{2C-24}$$

The normalization constant Ω_N is the total volume element of solid angle on an N-dimensional sphere

$$\Omega_N = \frac{N\pi^{N/2}}{\Gamma\left(\dfrac{N}{2}+1\right)} \tag{2C-25}$$

where Γ is the gamma function. By employing polar coordinates in the $(N-1)$-dimensional space defined by $C_2 \cdots C_N$, we can easily integrate the distribution (2C-24) over the coordinates of $C_2 \cdots C_N$ to obtain the distribution for the amplitude C_1,

$$P(C_1) = \frac{\Omega_{N-1}}{\Omega_N}\,(1 - C_1^2)^{(N-3)/2} \tag{2C-26}$$

For very large N, we can employ Sterling's formula for the gamma function and exploit the fact that, almost always, $C_1{}^2 \ll 1$,

$$P(C_1) \approx \left(\frac{N}{2\pi}\right)^{1/2} \exp\left\{-\frac{N}{2}\,C_1^2\right\} \qquad \text{for} \quad N \gg 1 \tag{2C-27}$$

An important application of the result (2C-27) occurs in the discussion of the distribution of the reduced widths for neutron or γ emission to a definite final state. Such a reduced width, $\Gamma^{(0)}$, is proportional to the probability $(C_1)^2$ of a single component $|1\rangle$ in the compound state. Thus, we obtain the distribution of $\Gamma^{(0)}$ by expressing (2C-27) in terms of $C_1{}^2$, instead of C_1,

$$\begin{aligned} P(\Gamma^{(0)})\,d\Gamma^{(0)} &= P(C_1)\left|\frac{2\,d\Gamma^{(0)}}{d\Gamma^{(0)}/dC_1}\right| \\ &= (2\pi\Gamma^{(0)}\langle\Gamma^{(0)}\rangle)^{-1/2}\exp\left\{-\frac{\Gamma^{(0)}}{2\langle\Gamma^{(0)}\rangle}\right\} d\Gamma^{(0)} \end{aligned} \tag{2C-28}$$

where $\langle\Gamma^{(0)}\rangle$ is the average value of $\Gamma^{(0)}$. The factor 2 in Eq. (2C-28) arises from the fact that both positive and negative C_1 contribute to the same value of $\Gamma^{(0)}$. The distribution (2C-28) is referred to as the Porter-Thomas distribution and is seen to imply large fluctuations in the partial widths of the individual resonances.

The very large fluctuations in the distribution (2C-28) result from the fact that only a single channel is assumed to contribute to the width. In situations where two or more channels are involved, such as in the total width for γ emission or for fission well above threshold, the distribution may be obtained by summing the contributions from each of the contributing channels. If the contributions of the ν different channels are independent and have the same average value, one obtains a χ^2 distribution with ν degrees of freedom,

$$P_\nu(\Gamma)d\Gamma = \left(\frac{\nu\Gamma}{2\langle\Gamma\rangle}\right)^{\nu/2}\left(\left(\frac{\nu}{2}-1\right)!\right)^{-1}\exp\left\{-\frac{\nu\Gamma}{2\langle\Gamma\rangle}\right\}\frac{d\Gamma}{\Gamma} \tag{2C-29}$$

The fluctuations in this distribution are

$$\langle(\Gamma-\langle\Gamma\rangle)^2\rangle = \frac{2}{\nu}\,(\langle\Gamma\rangle)^2 \tag{2C-30}$$

and thus decrease with increasing ν.

APPENDIX

2D

Model for Strength Function Phenomena[7]

We shall consider in this appendix a simple problem in quantum mechanics, which may illuminate some features of the strength function phenomena. We wish to describe how the amplitude for a particular channel a may be distributed over the many stationary states of a complicated system. The state a may, for example, describe a configuration with one nucleon in a definite orbit, while all the other nucleons form the ground state of the system with $A-1$ particles. We may also think of the state a as representing a single electron moving through a metal, a collective vibrational excitation of a nucleus or of an electron gas, etc.

2D-1 Choice of Representation

To represent the additional configurations, we shall employ a set of states α, chosen in such a manner that these states would be eigenstates of the Hamiltonian if we could neglect their coupling to the special state a. We can thus write the Hamiltonian in the form

$$H = H_0 + V \tag{2D-1}$$

where the states a and α are eigenstates of H_0,

$$\begin{aligned} H_0 |a\rangle &= E_a |a\rangle \\ H_0 |\alpha\rangle &= E_\alpha |\alpha\rangle \end{aligned} \tag{2D-2}$$

and where the coupling V only has matrix elements connecting a with α,

$$\begin{aligned} V_{a\alpha} \equiv \langle a|V|\alpha\rangle &= \langle \alpha|V|a\rangle \\ \langle a|V|a\rangle &= \langle \alpha|V|\alpha\rangle = 0 \end{aligned} \tag{2D-3}$$

(We are assuming $\mathscr{T}$ invariance and a choice of phases such that the coupling matrix elements are real; see Eq. (1-42).)

[7] The model considered in the present appendix is very similar to that discussed by Bohr and Mottelson (1953, pp. 147ff.), where the special state a is taken as a single-particle scattering resonance in the continuum. The same problem has been considered by Lane, Thomas, and Wigner (1955). Strength function phenomena of a similar type arise in connection with the photoexcitation and resonance electron scattering involving autoionizing states of atoms (Fano, 1961).

2D-2 Diagonalization

The Hamiltonian in the form (2D-1) can be easily diagonalized. If we denote the eigenvalues by E_i, the eigenvalue equation is

$$E_a - E_i = \sum_\alpha \frac{V_{a\alpha}^2}{E_\alpha - E_i} \tag{2D-4}$$

which possesses a root between each successive pair of eigenvalues E_α. The eigenstates, i, are given by

$$|i\rangle = c_a(i)\,|a\rangle + \sum_\alpha c_\alpha(i)\,|\alpha\rangle \tag{2D-5}$$

with

$$\begin{aligned} c_\alpha(i) &= -\frac{V_{a\alpha}}{E_\alpha - E_i}\, c_a(i) \\ c_a(i) &= \left(1 + \sum_\alpha \frac{V_{a\alpha}^2}{(E_\alpha - E_i)^2}\right)^{-1/2} \end{aligned} \tag{2D-6}$$

The amplitudes $c_a(i)$ describe the distribution of the properties of the state a over the spectrum i. Often this spectrum is so dense that it becomes appropriate to define a continuous strength function $P_a(E)$ representing the strength per unit energy, obtained by averaging over the states i in a small energy interval around E.

We have chosen the above representation of states, corresponding to a division of the total Hamiltonian of the form (2D-1), in order specifically to study the effect of the coupling on the state a. In order to evaluate the strength function (2D-6), however, we must have further information regarding the properties of the states α, so that we may determine the matrix elements $V_{a\alpha}$.

2D-3 Strength Function for Constant Matrix Elements

The simplest situation is that in which the coupling matrix elements $V_{a\alpha}$ are on the average independent of the energy of the state α. The matrix elements may fluctuate greatly from state to state, but their total strength over the averaging interval ΔE is assumed to be constant. Such an assumption may be employed if the width of the strength function is small compared to the characteristic energies associated with systematic variations in $V_{a\alpha}$ (see further below).

If we are not interested in investigating the fluctuations around the average, we can most conveniently introduce the assumption of a constant coupling by considering the spectrum of E_α to be uniformly spaced with a spacing constant D,

$$E_\alpha = \alpha D \qquad \alpha = 0, \pm 1, \pm 2, \tag{2D-7}$$

and assuming an exactly constant value for all the matrix elements of V,

$$V_{a\alpha} = v \tag{2D-8}$$

(We can choose phases for the states α so that $V_{a\alpha}$ is positive for all α.) With these assumptions, the sums appearing in Eqs. (2D-4) and (2D-6) may be directly evaluated to give

$$E_a - E_i = -\frac{\pi v^2}{D} \cot \frac{\pi E_i}{D}$$

$$c_a(i) = \left[1 + \left(\frac{\pi v}{D}\right)^2 \operatorname{cosec}^2 \frac{\pi E_i}{D}\right]^{-1/2} = \left[1 + \left(\frac{\pi v}{D}\right)^2 + \frac{(E_a - E_i)^2}{v^2}\right]^{-1/2} \tag{2D-9}$$

The strength function, which gives the probability of the state a per unit energy interval of the spectrum, has the simple Breit-Wigner form

$$P_a(E) = \frac{1}{D} c_a^2(E_i \approx E) = \frac{1}{2\pi} \frac{\Gamma}{(E_a - E)^2 + (\Gamma/2)^2} \tag{2D-10}$$

with the width, Γ, given by

$$\Gamma = 2\pi \frac{v^2}{D} \tag{2D-11}$$

In going from Eq. (2D-9) to Eq. (2D-10), we have assumed that $v > D$ and thus neglected the first term in the brackets; indeed, $v > D$ is necessary in order that the state a be found with appreciable probability in more than a single one of the states i, and, hence, that it be possible at all to define a strength function.

We see that the Breit-Wigner form for the strength function is an immediate consequence of the assumption of a constant coupling to the other degrees of freedom of the system. Such a situation is similar to that of an unstable particle decaying to a set of continuum states, with coupling matrix elements that do not vary appreciably over the line width. Indeed, the width Γ, given by Eq. (2D-11), has the familiar form characteristic of the width for a decay process.

2D-4 Time-Dependent Description of Coupling Process

The effect of the coupling of the state a to the other degrees of freedom can also be studied in a time-dependent description, and the assumption of constant coupling matrix elements is then seen to be equivalent to the assumption of a simple exponential decay in time. Thus, if we assume the system at time $t = 0$ to be in the state a, the probability amplitude $A_a(t)$ for finding the system in the state a at a later time t is

$$A_a(t) = \left\langle a \left| \exp\left\{-\frac{i}{\hbar} Ht\right\} \right| a \right\rangle = \sum_i c_a^2(i) \exp\left\{-\frac{i}{\hbar} E_i t\right\} \tag{2D-12}$$

where we have used the expansion of a into the set of stationary states i. In the approximation of constant energy spacings and matrix elements (Eqs. (2D-7), (2D-8), and (2D-9)), the sum over i in Eq. (2D-12) can be simply evaluated and yields

$$A_a(t) = \int_{-\infty}^{+\infty} \frac{dE}{D} \frac{\exp(-iEt/\hbar)}{(\pi v/D)^2 + ((E - E_a)/v)^2} = \exp\left\{-\frac{\Gamma}{2}|t| - \frac{i}{\hbar} E_a t\right\} \tag{2D-13}$$

where the decay probability Γ is given by Eq. (2D-11).

2D-5 Second Moment of Strength Function

Quite generally, without introducing assumptions concerning the states α, one can express the second moment W_2 of the strength function as a sum over the square of the matrix elements $V_{a\alpha}$,

$$\begin{aligned} W_2 &\equiv \sum_i (E_i - E_a)^2 [c_a(i)]^2 \\ &= \sum_i \langle a \mid i \rangle \langle i \mid (H - E_a)^2 \mid i \rangle \langle i \mid a \rangle \\ &= \langle a \mid (H - E_a)^2 \mid a \rangle \\ &= \sum_\alpha \langle a \mid H - E_a \mid \alpha \rangle \langle \alpha \mid H - E_a \mid a \rangle \\ &= \sum_\alpha (V_{a\alpha})^2 \end{aligned} \tag{2D-14}$$

If the average coupling matrix element is energy independent, the sum (2D-14) becomes infinite. Indeed, the second moment of a distribution with a Breit-Wigner line shape is infinite. Thus, the second moment does not in general determine the width of the strength function but rather reflects other features of the distribution.

2D-6 Intermediate Coupling Stages

The coupling described above in terms of the simple initial state a and the highly complex compound states α may be analyzed in more detail by considering intermediate stages in the coupling process. For example, if a represents a one-particle configuration, the initial interaction effect involves a coupling to certain rather simple configurations b (the "doorway" states), representing a particle and a vibrational (or rotational) quantum of excitation, or configurations with two particles and a hole. The matrix elements $V_{a\alpha}$ can thus be expressed in terms of the matrix elements V_{ab} and the amplitudes $c_\alpha(b)$ of the states b in the spectrum α,

$$V_{a\alpha} = \sum_b V_{ab}\, c_\alpha(b) \tag{2D-15}$$

An extreme situation giving constant average $V_{a\alpha}$ is one in which the states b are spread approximately uniformly over the spectrum and in which each α contains several components b leading to an averaging of the matrix elements V_{ab}. This situation can be described as one in which the first stage in the coupling process (the b stage) has already lost specific structure; the coupling is then equivalent to a simple damping of the channel a.

In nuclear strength function phenomena, however, one often faces situations in which it is necessary to consider explicitly the behavior of the system in intermediate stages of the coupling process (the b stage, the subsequent c stage, and so on). Examples, where such a more detailed treatment is required and where the strength function does not have the simple Breit-Wigner form, are provided by the coupling of a particle to the rotational motion (see Chapter 5) and the coupling between vibrational modes (see Chapter 6).

2D-7 Evaluation of Strength Function for Nonconstant Matrix Elements

From Eq. (2D-6), one can evaluate the strength function in terms of the quantities $V_{a\alpha}$ and E_α also in situations where the matrix elements and energy spacings are not constant. We define the strength function as the weighted average,

$$P_a(E) = \sum_i \rho(E_i - E)[c_a(i)]^2 \tag{2D-16}$$

where $\rho(x)$ is some function peaked around $x = 0$ and falling off for large $|x|$. For convenience, we choose ρ to have the form

$$\rho(x) = \frac{1}{2\pi} \frac{\Delta}{x^2 + (\Delta/2)^2} \tag{2D-17}$$

where Δ represents the energy interval around E over which the averages are taken. The weight function is so normalized that

$$\int_{-\infty}^{\infty} \rho(x)\, dx = 1 \tag{2D-18}$$

The expression (2D-16) with $c_a(i)$ given by Eq. (2D-6) and ρ by Eq. (2D-17) may be written as a contour integral,

$$P_a(E) = \frac{i\Delta}{4\pi^2} \oint_{\mathscr{C}_1} \frac{d\lambda}{(E-\lambda)^2 + (\Delta/2)^2} \left[E_a - \lambda - \sum_\alpha \frac{V_{a\alpha}^2}{E_\alpha - \lambda} \right]^{-1} \tag{2D-19}$$

with the contour given in Fig. 2D-1. The same integral extended over the contour $\mathscr{C}_2$ (see Fig. 2D-1) vanishes, since the integrand is proportional to λ^{-3} for large λ, and, therefore,

$$\begin{aligned} P_a(E) &= -\oint_{\mathscr{C}_3} - \oint_{\mathscr{C}_4} \\ &= \frac{1}{\pi} \operatorname{Im} \left[E_a - E - \frac{i\Delta}{2} - \sum_\alpha \frac{V_{a\alpha}^2}{E_\alpha - E - i\Delta/2} \right]^{-1} \\ &= \frac{1}{2\pi} \frac{\Gamma + \Delta}{(E_a + \Delta E_a - E)^2 + \frac{1}{4}(\Gamma + \Delta)^2} \end{aligned} \tag{2D-20}$$

where Γ is now the natural generalization of the expression (2D-11),

$$\Gamma = \Delta \sum_\alpha \frac{V_{a\alpha}^2}{(E - E_\alpha)^2 + (\Delta/2)^2} \tag{2D-21}$$

while the energy shift ΔE_a is defined as

$$\Delta E_a = \sum_\alpha \frac{V_{a\alpha}^2 (E - E_\alpha)}{(E - E_\alpha)^2 + (\Delta/2)^2} \tag{2D-22}$$

If the coupling $V_{a\alpha}$ is on the average about equally strong for all states α, then Γ becomes independent of E, and ΔE_a small compared to Γ, since the sum (2D-22) contains approximately equal positive and negative contributions. Thus we see that, aside from the extra width Δ introduced by the averaging, we obtain again the result (2D-10).

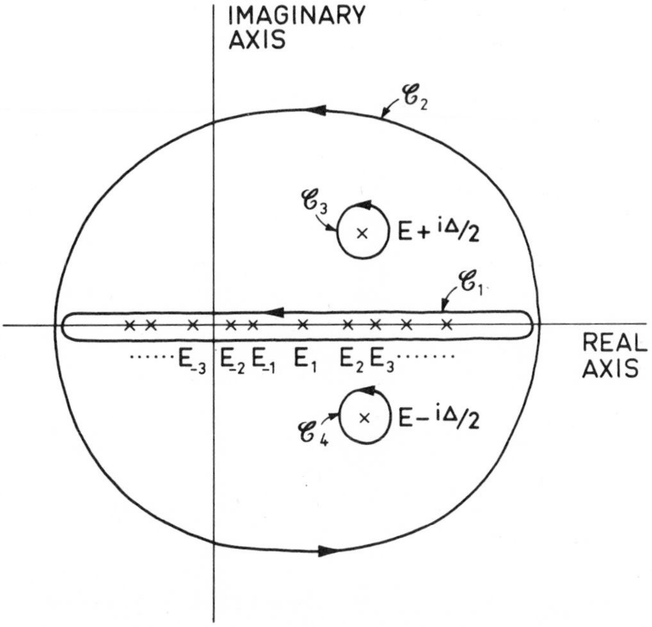

Figure 2D-1 Complex λ plane for the integrals (2D-19) and (2D-20). The integrand has poles along the real axis at $\lambda = E_i$, and at $\lambda = E \pm i\Delta/2$.

The expression (2D-20) for the strength function also applies to situations in which the average coupling matrix elements vary with energy, in which case the quantities Γ and ΔE_a become energy dependent. (Also the average level spacing D may vary with energy.) It must be emphasized, however, that in the above evaluation of the strength function (2D-20), we have assumed the matrix elements $V_{a\alpha}$ and the energy values E_α to be known quantities. If the average properties of the α states exhibit variations with energy, the determination of this structure will usually require an analysis of intermediate stages in the coupling process.

CHAPTER 3

Single-Particle Configurations

The spectra of nuclei consisting of closed shells with an additional single particle, or with a single hole, provide especially detailed and quantitative evidence on the nuclear independent-particle motion.

A closed shell contains $(2j+1)$ particles, each with an angular momentum j. Such a configuration forms only a single antisymmetric state (the Slater determinant). This state must then have total angular momentum $J=0$, since any state of total angular momentum J possesses $(2J+1)$ degenerate substates. Moreover, the parity of the closed shell is even.

Thus, for a configuration of a single particle, in addition to closed shells, one expects a number of low-lying states having angular momentum and parity determined by the quantum numbers of the orbits available to the single particle. Additional properties, such as the moments involved in electromagnetic and β transitions and the matrix elements characterizing various nuclear reaction processes, provide further information regarding the adequacy of the single-particle description of these states.

Configurations obtained by removing a particle from closed shells (single-hole configurations) are expected to have properties related in a simple manner to those of single-particle configurations.

3-1 QUANTUM NUMBERS AND WAVE FUNCTIONS PARTICLE-HOLE SYMMETRY

3-1a One-Particle States

The closed shells form a spherically symmetric density distribution and produce an isotropic nuclear potential. The motion of a particle in such a potential can be characterized by the quantum numbers $nljm$ (see Sec. 2-4), and the parity is

$$\pi = (-1)^l \tag{3-1}$$

The particle motion separates into a radial component and a component involving the angular and spin variables, which are coupled by the spin-orbit force (see Eq. (2-132)). The wave function is thus a product

$$\psi_{nljm}(\mathbf{r}, m_s(h)) = \mathscr{R}_{nlj}(r)\zeta_{ljm}(\vartheta, \varphi, m_s(h)) \tag{3-2}$$

of a radial part $\mathscr{R}$ and a spin-angular part ζ. The notation $m_s(h)$ for the spin variable refers to two different ways of expressing the spin dependence of the wave function (3-2).

In the m_s representation, the spin orientation is characterized by the component s_z along the fixed z axis, and the motion is decomposed into orbital and spin components, each specified by an m-quantum number, $m_l = l_z$ and $m_s = s_z$. Thus, the part of the state vector referring to the angular and spin degrees of freedom becomes

$$
\begin{aligned}
|ljm\rangle &= |(ls = \tfrac{1}{2})jm\rangle \\
&= \sum_{m_l m_s} |lm_l \tfrac{1}{2} m_s\rangle \langle lm_l \tfrac{1}{2} m_s | jm\rangle
\end{aligned} \tag{3-3}
$$

where $\langle lm_l\frac{1}{2}m_s | jm\rangle$ is a vector addition coefficient (see Sec. 1A-2). The angular wave function associated with the orbital state lm_l is the spherical harmonic Y_{lm_l}.

The spin orientation can also be specified by its component h (the helicity) in the direction of the radius vector of the particle

$$
h = \frac{1}{r}(\mathbf{s} \cdot \mathbf{r}) \tag{3-4}
$$

(We use the same notation, h, for the operator and its eigenvalue.) In collision problems, it is often convenient to employ a helicity referring to the projection of **s** on the momentum vector **p** (see Appendix 3F). The two helicities represent different characterizations of the spin orientation.

The helicity is a rotational invariant and hence commutes with the total angular momentum j. The spin-angular part of the one-particle state can thus be expressed in terms of components specified by the quantum numbers hjm,

$$
|ljm\rangle = \sum_{h=\pm\frac{1}{2}} |hjm\rangle \langle hjm | ljm\rangle \tag{3-5}
$$

Under spatial reflection, the helicity changes sign ($\mathbf{r} \to -\mathbf{r}$, $\mathbf{s} \to \mathbf{s}$; see Eq. (1-22)), and $\mathscr{P}$ acting on $|hjm\rangle$ therefore produces the state $|-hjm\rangle$, with a phase factor depending on the choice of relative phase for the helicity states. Thus, the states $|ljm\rangle$ with definite parity contain components with $h = +\frac{1}{2}$ and $h = -\frac{1}{2}$ in equal intensity, and the spin-angular wave functions in the states $l = j \pm \frac{1}{2}$ differ only in the relative phase of the two helicity components. The angular wave function for the helicity state hjm involves the function $\mathscr{D}^j_{mh}$, an element of the rotation matrix. The detailed form of the wave function (3-1) in the m_s and h representations, and a discussion of the phase conventions, are given in Sec. 3A-1.

The total state corresponding to a single particle outside closed shells is often conveniently expressed in the form

$$
|J = j, M = m\rangle = a^\dagger(jm)|\hat{0}\rangle \tag{3-6}
$$

where $a^\dagger(jm)$ is the operator creating a particle in the orbit $(nl)jm$. (The properties of creation and annihilation operators are discussed in Appendix 2A.)

The closed shell state denoted by $|\hat{0}\rangle$ plays the role of a generalized vacuum state.

3-1b Hole States. Particle-Hole Conjugation

The states obtained by removing a particle with angular momentum j from closed shells can be described in terms of the configuration $(j)^{2j}$ of the $2j$ particles, each having an angular momentum j. Because of the exclusion principle, there is a one-to-one correspondence between the states of this configuration (hole states) and the states of a single particle with angular momentum j. Moreover, matrix elements between hole states are related by a symmetry transformation to the matrix elements between corresponding particle states. We consider below a few simple features of the particle-hole symmetry; a more detailed discussion is given in Appendix 3B. (The particle-hole conjugation for nuclear configurations is similar to that employed in the atomic shell model; see Condon and Shortley, 1935; Racah, 1942.)

The formalism based on creation and annihilation operators is especially appropriate for expressing the symmetry between particles and holes (Bell, 1959). The creation of a hole state with quantum numbers $nljm$ is equivalent to the annihilation of a particle in the state with quantum numbers $nlj\,{-m}$ (conjugate state). It is convenient to choose the phases of the hole states such that the conjugate states are related by the time reversal operation. For the operator $b^\dagger(jm)$ creating a single hole, we then have

$$b^\dagger(jm) \equiv a(\overline{jm}) = (-1)^{j+m} a(j-m) \tag{3-7}$$

where the state $\overline{jm}$ is obtained from jm by time reversal (see Eq. (1-40)),

$$|\overline{jm}\rangle \equiv \mathcal{T}|jm\rangle = (-1)^{j+m}|j-m\rangle \tag{3-8}$$

The inclusion of the phase factor $(-1)^m$ in Eq. (3-7) implies that the operators $b^\dagger(jm)$ with different m form the components of a spherical tensor of rank j (see Sec. 1A-5e). Thus, the single-hole states

$$|j^{-1}m\rangle = b^\dagger(jm)|\hat{0}\rangle = a(\overline{jm})|\hat{0}\rangle \tag{3-9}$$

have the standard phase relations for angular momentum states.

The matrix elements for hole states are related to those for single-particle states by

$$\begin{aligned}\langle j_2^{-1}m_2|F|j_1^{-1}m_1\rangle \\ = -\langle \overline{j_1 m_1}|F|\overline{j_2 m_2}\rangle + \langle\hat{0}|F|\hat{0}\rangle\, \delta((n_1 l_1)j_1 m_1, (n_2 l_2)j_2 m_2)\end{aligned} \tag{3-10}$$

where F is an arbitrary single-particle operator. The expectation value $\langle\hat{0}|F|\hat{0}\rangle$

for the closed shells vanishes unless F is rotationally invariant (or contains scalar components). The relation (3-10) can be obtained by straightforward evaluation, using Slater determinants to describe the hole states, and follows directly if one expresses F in terms of creation and annihilation operators and introduces the equation (3-7); (see Sec. 3B-2).

The first term in Eq. (3-10) can be transformed as follows (see Eq. (1-34)):

$$\begin{aligned} -\langle \overline{j_1 m_1}|F|\overline{j_2 m_2}\rangle &= -\langle j_1 m_1|\mathcal{T}^{-1}F\mathcal{T}|j_2 m_2\rangle^* \\ &= -\langle j_2 m_2|(\mathcal{T}^{-1}F\mathcal{T})^\dagger|j_1 m_1\rangle \\ &= \langle j_2 m_2|F_c|j_1 m_1\rangle \end{aligned} \tag{3-11}$$

where the conjugate operator F_c is defined by

$$F_c = -(\mathcal{T}^{-1}F\mathcal{T})^\dagger \tag{3-12}$$

The matrix elements of F for hole states are therefore equal to the matrix elements of F_c for the corresponding particle states, if we neglect the closed shell expectation value.

An operator satisfying the relation

$$F_c = cF \qquad c = \pm 1 \tag{3-13}$$

is referred to as even ($c = +1$) or odd ($c = -1$) under particle-hole conjugation. (Any function of the one-particle variables can be divided into even and odd parts.) Examples of even and odd operators are

$$\begin{aligned} &\left.\begin{matrix} F(\mathbf{r}) \\ (\mathbf{l}\cdot\mathbf{s})F(\mathbf{r}) \end{matrix}\right\} \qquad c = -1 \\ &\left.\begin{matrix} \mathbf{s}F(\mathbf{r}) \\ \mathbf{p} \\ \mathbf{l} \end{matrix}\right\} \qquad c = +1 \end{aligned} \tag{3-14}$$

The particle-hole conjugation can also be expressed in terms of a unitary operator $\mathcal{U}_h$ which transforms $a^\dagger(jm)$ into $b^\dagger(jm)$ for the single-particle orbits contained in the closed shells (see Appendix 3B).

3-1c Isospin for Particle and Hole States

If the nucleus contains neutrons and protons filling the same shells, the resultant isospin of the closed shells is $T_0 = 0$, and the state formed by adding a particle has $T = t = \frac{1}{2}$

$$|jm, T = t = \tfrac{1}{2}, M_T = m_t\rangle = a^\dagger(jm, m_t)|\hat{0}\rangle \tag{3-15}$$

with $m_t = +\frac{1}{2}$ for a neutron and $m_t = -\frac{1}{2}$ for a proton.

The single-hole states also have $T=\frac{1}{2}$, with $M_T=\frac{1}{2}$ for a proton hole and $M_T=-\frac{1}{2}$ for a neutron hole. However, the states formed by acting with the proton-hole operator $b^\dagger(j_p m)=a(\overline{j_p m})=a(\overline{jm, m_t=-\frac{1}{2}})$ and the corresponding neutron-hole operator do not have the conventional phase relationship for an isospin doublet. For the angular momentum, the appropriate phasing of the hole states was ensured by the phase factor $(-1)^{j+m}$ in Eq. (3-7). In a similar manner, we can form hole states with the standard transformation properties in isospace,

$$\begin{aligned} |j^{-1}m, m_t\rangle &= b^\dagger(jm, m_t)|\hat{0}\rangle \\ &= \begin{cases} -b^\dagger(j_p m)|\hat{0}\rangle = -|j_p^{-1}m\rangle & m_t=+\frac{1}{2} \\ +b^\dagger(j_n m)|\hat{0}\rangle = +|j_n^{-1}m\rangle & m_t=-\frac{1}{2} \end{cases} \end{aligned} \tag{3-16}$$

In some situations, we shall find it convenient to employ the hole states labeled j_p^{-1} and j_n^{-1}. However, the hole states labeled by m_t present advantages in situations where isospin coupling and isospin transformation properties are involved.

The hole operators $b^\dagger(jm, m_t)$ are related to the a operators by

$$\begin{aligned} b^\dagger(jm, m_t) &= a(\widetilde{jm, m_t}) \\ &= (-1)^{j+m+\frac{1}{2}+m_t} a(j-m, -m_t) \\ |\widetilde{jm, m_t}\rangle &\equiv \mathscr{F}|jm, m_t\rangle \end{aligned} \tag{3-17}$$

where the transformation $\mathscr{F}$ involves the charge symmetry operation $\mathscr{R}_\tau$, given by Eq. (1-59), in addition to time reversal,

$$\begin{aligned} \mathscr{F} &= \mathscr{R}_\tau^{-1}\mathscr{T} \\ &= \exp\{i\pi T_y\}\mathscr{T} \end{aligned} \tag{3-18}$$

The transformation of operators under the $\mathscr{F}$-type particle-hole conjugation is considered in Appendix 3B.

If the nucleus contains more filled shells of neutrons than of protons, the closed shells have a resultant isospin $T_0=(M_T)_0=\frac{1}{2}(N-Z)$. The single-particle and single-hole configurations can then form states with $T=T_0\pm\frac{1}{2}$. The T structure of the various possible configurations is illustrated in Fig. 3-1, p. 315, and the associated state vectors are given in the adjoining text. It is seen that the low configurations contain only a single T value ($T=T_0+\frac{1}{2}$ for n or p^{-1} and $T=T_0-\frac{1}{2}$ for p or n^{-1}). The higher configurations of the type p and n^{-1} give rise to a T doublet ($T=T_0\pm\frac{1}{2}$), and the states involve components in which the closed shells are rotated in isospace and have $M_T=T_0-1$.

ILLUSTRATIVE EXAMPLES TO SECTION 3-1

Total nuclear isospin for single-particle and single-hole configurations (Fig. 3-1)

The ground state configuration of a nucleus with $N > Z$ is illustrated in Fig. 3-1. The shaded area refers to the occupied orbits, comprising the N lowest neutron levels and the Z lowest proton levels. The orbits are labeled by a set of quantum numbers ν (for example, $\nu = nljm$), and are ordered according to their energy. The last orbit that is occupied (the Fermi level) is denoted by $(\nu_F)_n$ and $(\nu_F)_p$ for neutrons and protons, respectively.

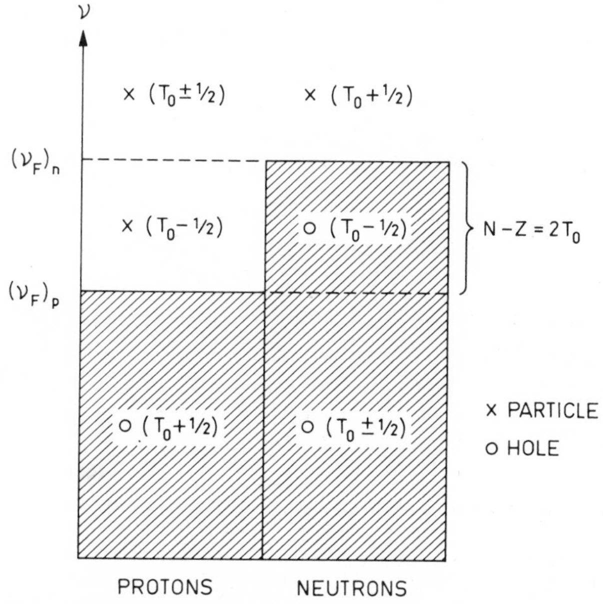

Figure 3-1 Total isospin for configurations with a single particle or a single hole outside of closed shells with $T = T_0$.

For any configuration, such as the ground state configuration, in which all the orbits occupied by protons are also occupied by neutrons, the total isospin T is equal to that of the excess neutrons, $T = T_0 = M_T = \frac{1}{2}(N - Z)$. In fact, such a state vanishes when acted upon by the total isospin component $T_+ = \sum_k (t_x + it_y)_k$ which raises M_T by one unit. The state is, therefore, fully aligned in isospace, $M_T = T$. (We are here neglecting the small difference between proton

▼ and neutron orbits caused by the Coulomb potential; the resulting isospin admixtures are discussed in connection with Fig. 2-6, p. 174).

The isospin quantum numbers associated with one-particle and one-hole configurations are shown in Fig. 3-1. The corresponding state vectors have the form

(a) n with $\nu > (\nu_F)_n$ or p^{-1} with $\nu \leqslant (\nu_F)_p$

$$T = M_T = T_0 + \tfrac{1}{2}$$

$$|\nu; T = T_0 + \tfrac{1}{2}, M_T = T_0 + \tfrac{1}{2}\rangle = a^\dagger(\nu, m_t = \tfrac{1}{2})|T = T_0, M_T = T_0\rangle \quad \text{(3-19a)}$$

$$|\nu^{-1}; T_0 + \tfrac{1}{2}, T_0 + \tfrac{1}{2}\rangle = b^\dagger(\nu, m_t = \tfrac{1}{2})|T_0, T_0\rangle$$

(b) n^{-1} or p with $(\nu_F)_p < \nu \leqslant (\nu_F)_n$

$$T = M_T = T_0 - \tfrac{1}{2}$$

$$|\nu; T = T_0 - \tfrac{1}{2}, M_T = T_0 - \tfrac{1}{2}\rangle = a^\dagger(\nu, m_t = -\tfrac{1}{2})|T = T_0, M_T = T_0\rangle \quad \text{(3-19b)}$$

$$|\nu^{-1}; T_0 - \tfrac{1}{2}, T_0 - \tfrac{1}{2}\rangle = b^\dagger(\nu, m_t = -\tfrac{1}{2})|T_0, T_0\rangle$$

(c) p with $\nu > (\nu_F)_n$ or n^{-1} with $\nu \leqslant (\nu_F)_p$

$$T = T_0 \pm \tfrac{1}{2}, \qquad M_T = T_0 - \tfrac{1}{2}$$

$$|\nu; T = T_0 - \tfrac{1}{2}, M_T = T_0 - \tfrac{1}{2}\rangle$$

$$= \left(\frac{2T_0}{2T_0 + 1}\right)^{1/2} a^\dagger(\nu, m_t = -\tfrac{1}{2})|T_0, T_0\rangle - \left(\frac{1}{2T_0 + 1}\right)^{1/2} a^\dagger(\nu, m_t = \tfrac{1}{2})|T_0, T_0 - 1\rangle$$

$$|\nu; T_0 + \tfrac{1}{2}, T_0 - \tfrac{1}{2}\rangle \quad \text{(3-19c)}$$

$$= \left(\frac{1}{2T_0 + 1}\right)^{1/2} a^\dagger(\nu, m_t = -\tfrac{1}{2})|T_0, T_0\rangle + \left(\frac{2T_0}{2T_0 + 1}\right)^{1/2} a^\dagger(\nu, m_t = \tfrac{1}{2})|T_0, T_0 - 1\rangle$$

$|\nu^{-1}; T_0 \pm \tfrac{1}{2}, T_0 - \tfrac{1}{2}\rangle$ same as $|\nu; T = T_0 \pm \tfrac{1}{2}, T_0 - \tfrac{1}{2}\rangle$ with $a^\dagger(\nu, m_t) \to b^\dagger(\nu, m_t)$

The state vectors are expressed in terms of the particle and hole creation operators, defined by Eqs. (3-15) and (3-16). The states (3-19c) contain components involving the isobaric analog state of the closed shells

$$|T_0, T_0 - 1\rangle = (2T_0)^{-1/2}(T_x - iT_y)|T_0, T_0\rangle$$

$$= \sum_{(\nu_F)_p < \nu \leqslant (\nu_F)_n} (2T_0)^{-1/2} a^\dagger(\nu_p) a(\nu_n)|T_0, T_0\rangle \quad \text{(3-20)}$$

The state (3-20) is a coherent superposition of components obtained by transforming one of the $2T_0$ excess neutrons into a proton.

Additional states with single-particle or single-hole configurations can be obtained by forming isobaric analog states of those considered above. These additional states, however, cannot be reached by adding or subtracting a nucleon from a nucleus that is fully aligned in isospace ($M_T = T_0$). ▲

3-2 ENERGY SPECTRA

The available experimental data on the energy levels of nuclei with single-particle or single-hole configurations are illustrated in Figs. 3-2 (a–f), pp. 319–324. It is seen that all the nuclei that have been sufficiently well studied do possess low-lying levels just corresponding to those expected from the single-particle level spectrum (see Figs. 2-23 and 2-30). This constitutes a decisive confirmation of the general ideas underlying the shell structure description of the nucleus.

The observed binding energies are compared in Figs. 3-3, p. 325 and 3-5, p. 328 with those calculated for a static potential with inclusion of a spin-orbit coupling. The strength and radius parameters of the potential are consistent with those deduced from the scattering experiments. The levels near the Fermi surface are rather well reproduced by such a calculation, but the observed deep-lying hole states provide evidence for a velocity dependence of similar magnitude as for the optical potential.

While the main features of the observed single-particle spectra can be well accounted for in terms of a potential with parameters smoothly varying with A and Z, one observes smaller variations in level positions, some of which may be due to detailed structure in the radial shape of the average potential, reflecting the nuclear shell structure, or to a more specific state dependence of the average potential. Moreover, the energy separation between particles and holes is found to be somewhat larger than calculated for a potential, especially for the light nuclei. Such an effect may arise from the isospin dependence of the nuclear binding energy, which implies a depression of the closed shell state ($T=0$) relative to the one-particle and one-hole configurations, which have $T=\frac{1}{2}$. (See the discussion of this and other effects that may contribute to the increased separation between particle and hole states, pp. 329 ff.)

For the closed shells with $T_0 \neq 0$, the higher-lying proton and neutron-hole configurations give rise to an isospin doublet with $T= T_0 \pm \frac{1}{2}$ (see Fig. 3-1). The energy separation is given, to a first approximation, by

$$\Delta E = E(T = T_0 + \tfrac{1}{2}) - E(T = T_0 - \tfrac{1}{2}) = \frac{T_0 + \frac{1}{2}}{A} \langle lj | V_1(r) | lj \rangle \tag{3-21}$$

in terms of the radial matrix element of the isovector potential $V_1(r)$ in Eq. (2-29). An additional effect may arise from the isovector part of the spin-orbit coupling in the nuclear potential. The empirical evidence on the separation between isospin doublets for single-particle configurations is shown in Table 3-1, p. 331, and is found to imply a strength of the isovector potential consistent with that obtained from other evidence.

The single-particle or single-hole description of the spectra of nuclei obtained by adding or removing a particle from closed shells applies only to the lowest levels. At energies comparable to those associated with the first excited states of the closed shell nuclei, one expects the occurrence of additional levels involving the degrees of freedom of the closed shell core. Such an increased complexity in the spectrum is indeed observed. In some of the lighter nuclei (such as $A = 17$, 41, 47, and 49), the onset of the spectrum involving core excitations is found to occur appreciably below the energy gap in the closed shell nuclei, indicating that the stability of the closed shells is significantly affected by the interaction with the single particle (or hole).

In the energy region above the onset of the core excitations, the level density is found to increase rapidly (see the well-studied spectra of ^{17}O and ^{41}Ca). The single-particle states occurring in this part of the spectrum may couple to neighboring levels of the same spin and parity with a resulting sharing of the single-particle properties. Illustrations of such strength function effects are provided by the spectra of ^{41}Ca and ^{49}Sc shown in Figs. 3-2c and 3-2d, by the analysis of proton resonance scattering on ^{16}O (Table 3-8), and by the hole states in ^{16}O excited in the $(p, 2p)$ reaction (Fig. 2-27).

An important area of current investigation is the relationship between the one-particle potential and the nucleonic interactions. For nonsingular interactions, this relationship is provided by the Hartree-Fock self-consistent field calculations extensively employed in atomic physics. (The equations determining the self-consistent potential are given in Sec. 3B-3b.) The preliminary investigations that have been carried out so far for nuclear systems have in particular helped to elucidate the state dependence of the one-particle potential. (For a review of these studies, see Baranger, 1966.)

▼

ILLUSTRATIVE EXAMPLES TO SECTION 3-2

Spectra of nuclei with single-particle or single-hole configurations (Figs. 3-2a to 3-2f)

The available evidence on the spectra of the nuclei obtained by removing or adding a nucleon from configurations in which the neutrons as well as the protons form closed shells is shown in Figs. 3-2a to 3-2f. We have chosen only the configurations with major closed shells (N or Z equal to one of the numbers in the sequence 2, 8, 20, 28, 50, 82, and 126).

For the observed energy levels, the excitation is given in MeV, and the available evidence on the spin and parity quantum numbers ($I\pi$) is also exhibited.

▲

▼ Uncertain values are given in parenthesis. In addition, the figures show the absolute binding energy $\mathscr{B}$ for the closed shell nuclei and the binding energy differences $\Delta\mathscr{B}$ between the neighboring nuclei and the corresponding closed shell nucleus. These binding energy differences represent separation energies for neutrons and protons in the closed shell nuclei and in the nuclei with one additional particle.

For nuclei based on closed shells with isospin $T_0 = 0$ $(N = Z)$, the low-lying states in the neighboring nuclei have $T = 1/2$. We therefore only list the T quantum number for those higher-lying levels for which the evidence indicates $T = 3/2$. For closed shells with T_0 different from zero, the addition or removal of a particle can lead to states with $T = T_0 \pm 1/2$ (see Fig. 3-1), and the spectra with different T values are shown separately. Spectra with the same values of A and T, differing only in M_T, show the expected similarity associated with isobaric ▲ invariance.

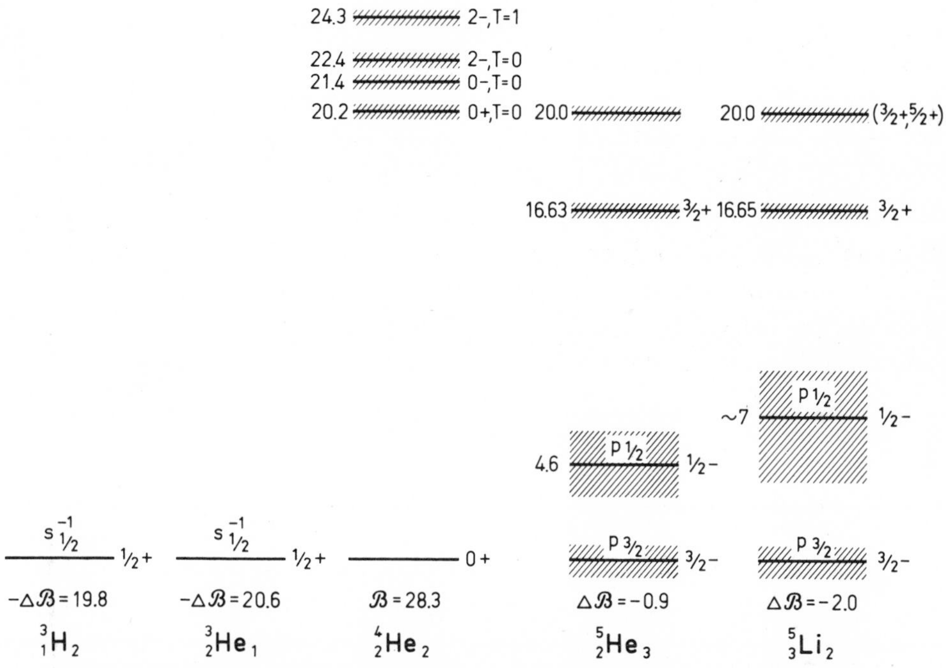

Figure 3-2a The experimental data on the spectra of ^{5}He and ^{5}Li have been summarized by T. Lauritsen and F. Ajzenberg-Selove, *Nuclear Phys.* **78**, 1 (1966). The evidence concerning the excited states of ^{4}He is taken from the review by W. E. Meyerhof and T. A. Tombrello, *Nuclear Phys.* **A109** (1968). The binding energies listed in Figs. 3-2a to 3-2f are taken from the compilation by J. H. E. Mattauch, W. Thiele, and A. H. Wapstra, *Nuclear Phys.* **67**, 1 (1965). All the excited states in the figure are unstable with respect to particle emission and have rather large widths, as indicated by the cross hatching. For the single-particle levels, $p_{3/2}$ and $p_{1/2}$, the hatched area approximately represents the width of the resonances.

▼ The levels which have properties corresponding to single-particle and single-hole configurations are labeled by the single-particle quantum numbers lj. The identification of these levels is based partly on the fact that the spin-parity values and energies correspond approximately to those expected for single particles or holes (see Fig. 2-23). Further tests of the assignments are provided by the electromagnetic moments and transition probabilities (see Tables 3-2, 3-3, and 3-4) and by the β-decay rates (see Tables 3-5 and 3-6). Additional important evidence is provided by the single-nucleon transfer reactions and by the scattering of single nucleons on closed shell nuclei. (Examples are discussed in Tables 3-7 and 3-8.)

Spectra adjacent to ^4He (Fig. 3-2a)

The $A = 5$ system contains no state that is stable with respect to particle emission. This may be seen as an especially dramatic consequence of the saturation properties of the nuclear forces. The single-particle character of the $p_{3/2}$ and $p_{1/2}$ levels is confirmed by the analysis of nucleon scattering on ^{4}He.

Spectra adjacent to ^{16}O (Fig. 3-2b)

The two lowest levels in the $A = 17$ system appear to be well described in terms of single-particle configurations (see the analysis of electromagnetic moments and β-decay rates given in Tables 3-2, 3-3, and 3-5). Starting at approximately 3 MeV, however, a rather complex level structure is observed, which must involve the excitation of the closed shells. The structure of these states has been studied by nucleon scattering on ^{16}O, which shows that only the 3/2+ states at 5.1 MeV in ^{17}O and ^{17}F can be approximately described in terms of single-particle configurations (see Table 3-8). This conclusion is confirmed by the evidence from stripping reactions leading from ^{16}O to ^{17}O and ^{17}F.

In ^{15}N and ^{15}O, the lowest excited states involve excitations of the closed shells, but the 3/2 states at 6.33 MeV and 6.16 MeV appear to be predominantly of single-hole nature, as evidenced by the pickup reactions on ^{16}O (Warburton *et al.*, 1965).

In addition to the hole states shown in Fig. 3-2b, the $(p, 2p)$ reaction has provided evidence for the occurrence of the $s_{1/2}^{-1}$ proton configuration in a broad energy region (width of about 10 MeV) centered on a mean excitation energy of about 30 MeV (see Fig. 2-27).

The rather large difference in the excitation energies of the $s_{1/2}$ levels in ^{17}O and ^{17}F can be accounted for in terms of the reduction in the Coulomb energy associated with the loose binding of the proton (Thomas-Ehrman shift).
▲ Thus, a simple calculation of neutron and proton levels in a nuclear potential

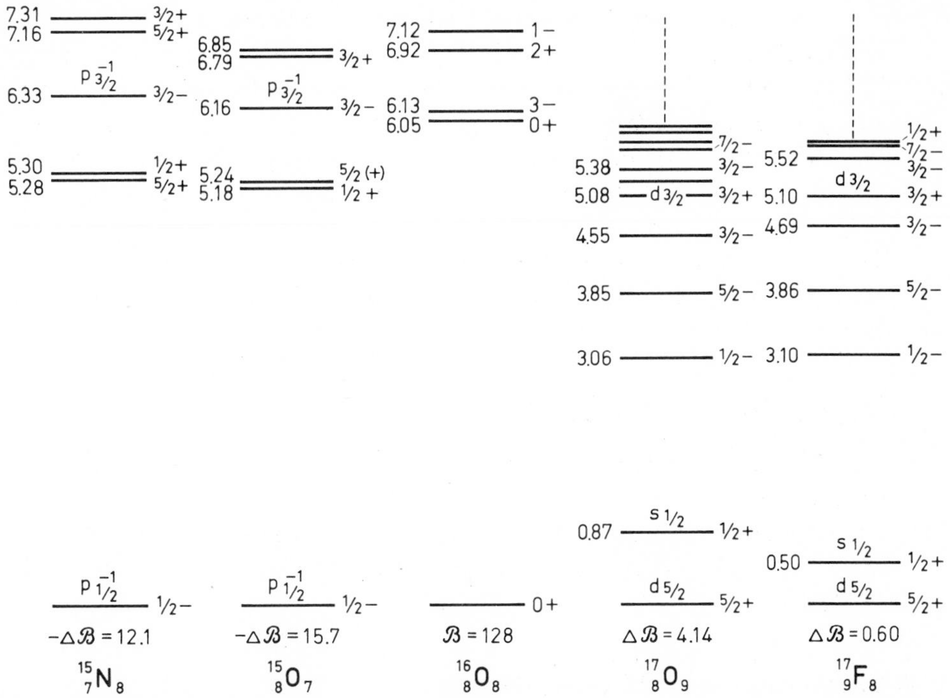

Figure 3-2b The figure is based on the syntheses of the available data given by T. Lauritsen and F. Ajzenberg-Selove in Landolt-Börnstein, *Neue Serie*, Band 1, Springer Verlag 1961, and in *Nuclear Data Sheets*, 1962, except for the revised spin assignment of the 3.8 MeV levels in ^{17}O and ^{17}F (see R. E. Segel, P. P. Singh, R. G. Allas, and S .S. Hanna, *Phys. Rev. Letters* **10**, 345, 1963). The levels in ^{17}O above 4 MeV and those in ^{17}F above 0.6 MeV are unstable with respect to particle emission and, thus, some of these levels have appreciable natural widths (see Table 3-8).

▼ with the parameters employed in Fig. 2-30 and a Coulomb potential corresponding to a uniformly charged sphere with radius $R = 3.2$ fm gives a difference in the binding energies of the $d_{5/2}$ and $s_{1/2}$ levels that is smaller for protons than for neutrons by 0.40 MeV (C. J. Veje, private communication).

Spectra adjacent to ^{40}Ca (Fig. 3-2c)

The single-particle assignments for the excited states is based on the evidence from single-nucleon transfer reactions and nucleon scattering. The results obtained from the study of the (d, p) reaction leading to ^{41}Ca are given in Table 3-7. It is found that the excited single-particle configurations are distributed over several levels, although the first excited state contains the major part (80–90%) of the $p_{3/2}$ strength. A similar structure for ^{41}Sc is exhibited by the proton scattering on ^{40}Ca. The pickup reactions leading to ^{39}Ca and ^{39}K indicate that the major $s_{1/2}^{-1}$ strength is associated with the first excited states. ▲

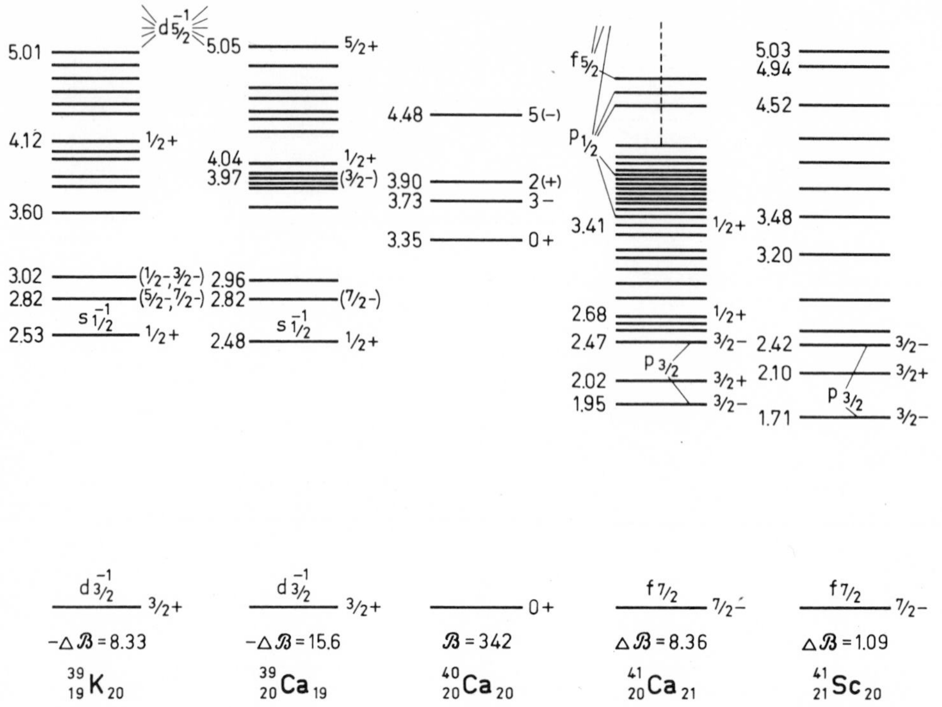

Figure 3-2c The level schemes in the figure are based on the references quoted in *Nuclear Data Sheets* and by Chen and Hurley (1966). Additional information is obtained from the study of the reactions ^{40}Ca(t, α)^{39}K (S. Hinds and R. Middleton, *Nuclear Phys.* **84**, 651, 1966) and ^{39}K(^{3}He, d)^{40}Ca (J. R. Erskine, *Phys. Rev.* **149**, 854, 1966).

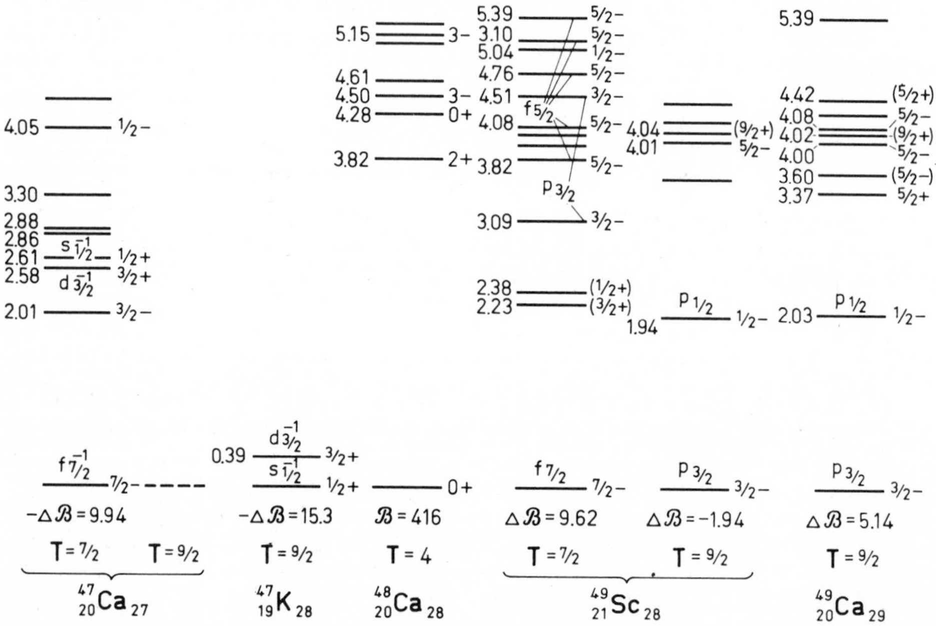

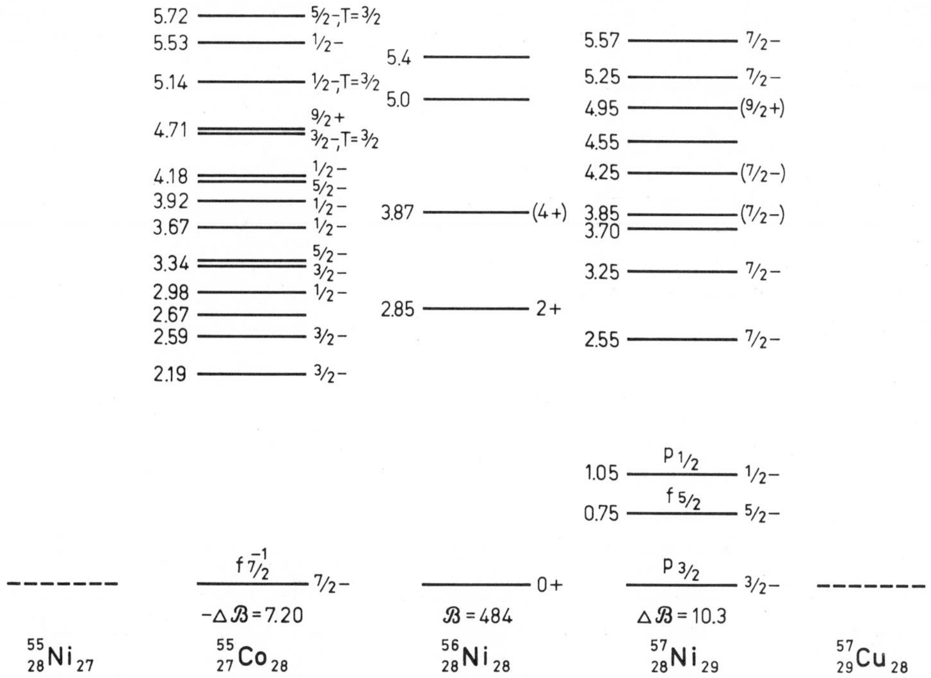

Figure 3-2e The information on the spectra shown in the figure has been obtained from the references quoted in *Nuclear Data Sheets* and by Chen and Hurley (1966).

▼ *Nuclei adjacent to* ^{48}*Ca* (*Fig. 3-2d*)

The $T = 9/2$ levels in ^{49}Sc were observed in the resonance scattering of protons on ^{48}Ca; the properties of these levels (energy separations, spin-parity quantum numbers, and single-particle parentage factors) correspond to those of the isobaric analog states in ^{49}Ca. The $T = 9/2$ levels occur at high excitation energies in ^{49}Sc ($E_{ex} \geqslant 11.5$ MeV), where the $T = 7/2$ level density is very great. The width of the $T = 9/2$ single-particle strength function is associated partly with proton emission and partly with the coupling to the $T = 7/2$ levels caused by the Coulomb interaction. (The analysis of isobaric analog states excited by proton scattering is discussed for the case of $p +$ ^{116}Sn in connection with Fig. 1-9, p. 48.) ▲

Figure 3-2d The level schemes in the figure are based on the references quoted in *Nuclear Data Sheets* and by Chen and Hurley (1966). Additional information is obtained from the study of the reactions ^{48}Ca(d, ^{3}He)^{47}K (E. Newman, J. C. Hiebert, and B. Zeidman, *Phys. Rev. Letters* **16**, 28, 1966), ^{48}Ca(p, d)^{47}Ca (T. W. Coulon, B. F. Bayman, and E. Kashy, *Phys. Rev.* **144**, 941, 1966), ^{48}Ca(p, p) (K. W. Jones, J. P. Schiffer, L. L. Lee Jr., A. Marinov, and J. L. Lerner, *Phys. Rev.* **145**, 894, 1966), and ^{48}Ca(t, α)^{47}K (J. H. Bjerregaard, O. Hansen, O. Nathan, R. Stock, R. Chapman, and S. Hinds, *Phys. Letters* **24B**, 568, 1967).

▼ From the observed single-particle and single-hole states in $A = 49$ and $A = 47$, one can obtain evidence regarding the isobaric spin dependence of the single-nucleon binding energies (see Table 3-1).

Spectra adjacent to ^{56}Ni *(Fig. 3-2e)*

The nuclei illustrated in Fig. 3-2e are all β unstable and the spectroscopic evidence is therefore as yet rather incomplete. The single-particle assignments are based mainly on the spin-parity values and the position of the levels. For the ground state of ^{55}Co, the measured magnetic moment provides additional evidence (see Table 3-3).

Spectra adjacent to ^{208}Pb *(Fig. 3-2f)*

The single-particle assignments for the low-lying levels are consistent with all the known information on these states (parentage factors from transfer reactions, see references quoted in caption to Fig. 3-2f; electromagnetic moments, see Tables 3-2, 3-3, and 3-4; β-decay rates, see Table 3-6). The only states ▲

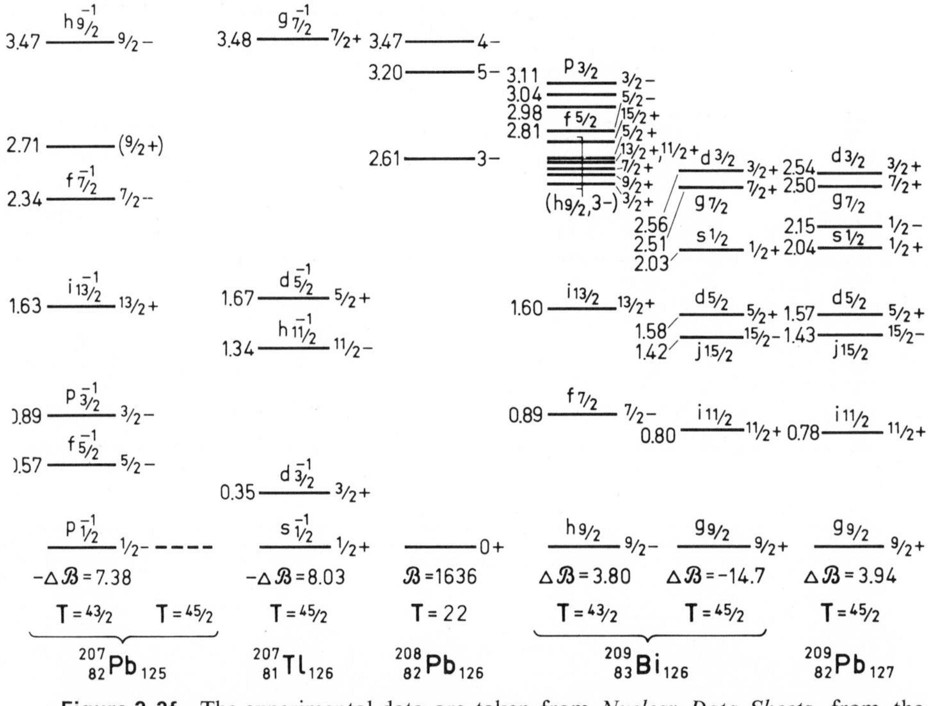

Figure 3-2f The experimental data are taken from *Nuclear Data Sheets*, from the references quoted by Chen and Hurley (1966), and from the following reaction studies: ^{208}Pb(^{3}He, *d*)^{209}Bi (C. Ellegaard and P. Vedelsby, *Phys. Letters* **26B**, 155, 1968, and the references quoted therein), ^{209}Bi(*d, d'*) (R. M. Diamond, B. Elbek, and P. O. Tjöm, priv. comm.), ^{208}Pb(α, *t*)^{209}Bi (J. S. Lilley and N. Stein, *Phys. Rev. Letters* **19**, 709, 1967), ^{208}Pb(*p, p'*) (P. von Brentano, W. K. Dawson, C. F. Mooer, P. Richard, W. Wharton, and H. Wieman, *Phys. Letters* **26B**, 666, 1968), and ^{208}Pb(*t*, α) (S. Hinds, R. Middleton, J. H. Bjerregaard, O. Hansen, and O. Nathan, *Phys. Letters* **17**, 302 1965).

▼ observed in the nuclei with $A = 207$ and $A = 209$, with energies appreciably below the energy of the first excited state of ^{208}Pb, are the single-particle and the single-hole states. Above this energy, a rather high density of levels is observed, of which only a few are included in the figure. As an example, the multiplet at about 2.6 MeV in ^{209}Bi is classified as an octupole excitation similar to that observed in ^{208}Pb, superposed on the $h_{9/2}$ ground state of ^{209}Bi. (A further discussion of this assignment will be given in Chapter 6.)

The $T = 45/2$ states of ^{209}Bi, which are observed as resonances in elastic ▲ and inelastic proton scattering on ^{208}Pb, have total widths of 2–300 keV.

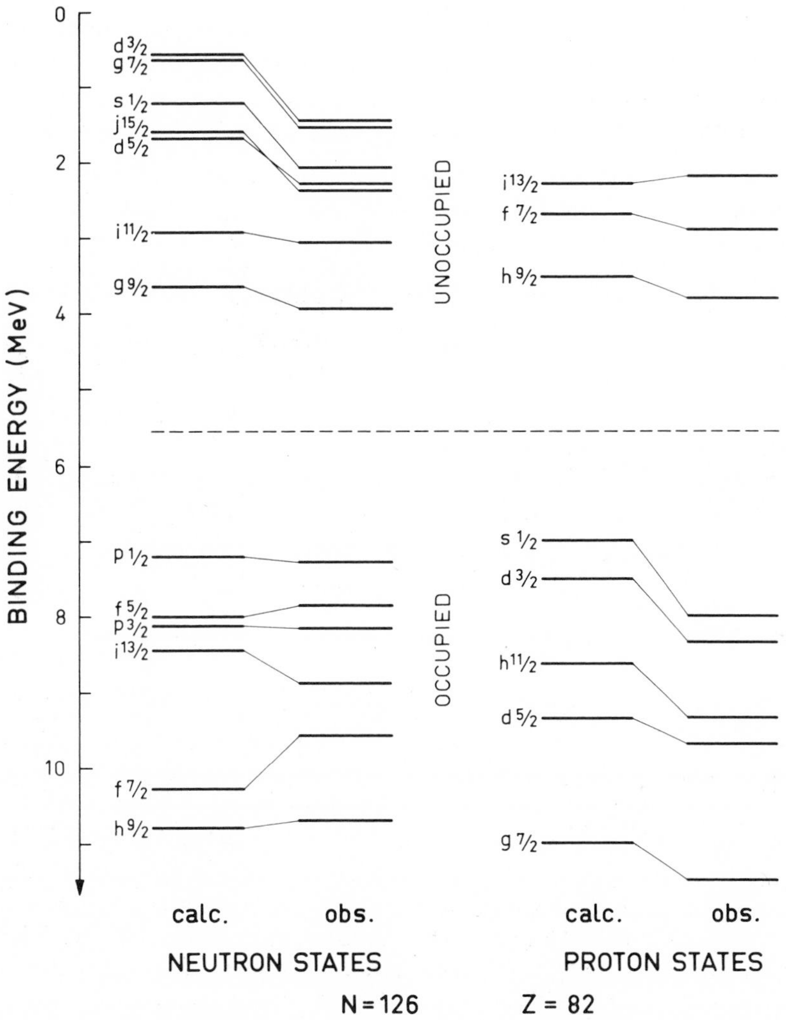

Figure 3-3 The empirical value for the binding energies of single nucleons with respect to ^{208}Pb are taken from the data shown in Fig. 3-2f. The calculated values are taken from J. Blomqvist and S. Wahlborn, *Arkiv Fysik* **16**, 545 (1960).

▼ *Energies and wave functions for single-particle states in ^{208}Pb (Figs. 3-3 and 3-4)*

The observed binding energies for neutrons and protons with respect to ^{208}Pb are compared in Fig. 3-3 with those calculated for a potential with the parameters employed in Fig. 2-30. For the protons, a symmetry potential of opposite sign to that for the neutrons, and a Coulomb potential corresponding to a uniformly charged sphere of radius $R = 1.27\ A^{1/3}$ fm have been added. (The parameters of the potential were chosen (Blomqvist and Wahlborn, 1960) to give the best fit to the then available data on the position of single-particle states for $A = 208$.)

The wave functions $\mathscr{R}_{nlj}(r)$, calculated for the neutron orbits, are illustrated in Figs. 3-4a and 3-4b. We employ a phase convention for radial wave functions that requires $\mathscr{R}_{nlj}(r)$ to be positive for large r. The radial wave functions of spin-orbit partners ($j = l \pm 1/2$) are very similar, and only for the example of the $i_{11/2}$ and $i_{13/2}$ orbits are both wave functions drawn.

Many effects depend mainly on the value of the wave functions in the region of the nuclear surface. For orbits with binding energies from a few MeV up to 10 MeV, it is seen that the radial wave function at the mean radius $R_0 = 7.5$ fm is approximately independent of nlj, and given by

$$R_0^3\, \mathscr{R}_{nlj}^2(R_0) \approx 1.4 \tag{3-22}$$

Binding energies for neutron states in ^{16}O, ^{40}Ca, ^{48}Ca, and ^{56}Ni (Fig. 3-5)

The empirical binding energies for states of a single neutron and a single-neutron hole with respect to the closed shells of $A = 16, 40, 48$, and 56 are shown in Fig. 3-5. For a few cases, the proton levels but not the neutron levels have been observed, and the neutron levels, shown by dotted lines, have been estimated by subtracting the Coulomb energy calculated for the proton orbits. For the higher-lying configurations whose properties are found to be distributed on more than a single level (strength function effects), we have plotted an average position of the single-particle (or single-hole) state, obtained by weighting the components with the observed one-particle strengths.

The calculated level positions correspond to a potential with the parameters employed in Fig. 2-30, which were chosen so as to give the best fit to the observed levels for $A = 208$. Only the bound states have been calculated. In ^{48}Ca with $T_0 = 4$, the hole states below the $f_{7/2}$ level can give rise to states with $T = 7/2$ and 9/2. The observed levels shown in Fig. 3-5 have $T = 7/2$, and their calculated position includes the effect of the charge-exchange term in the potential (see Eqs. (2-29) and (3-21)). This gives rise to an upward shift of the levels by about 1 MeV. ▲

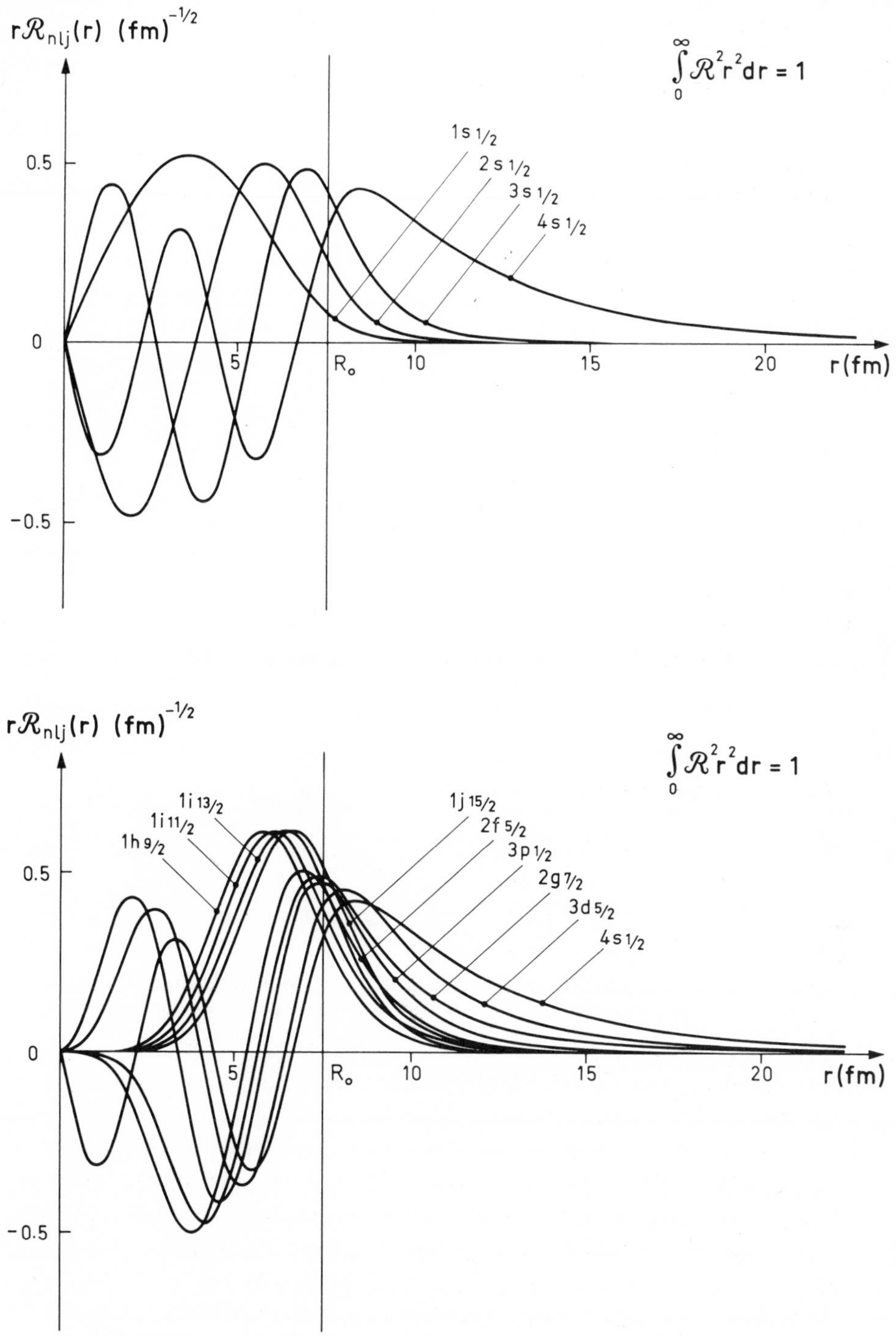

Figure 3-4 Neutron radial wave functions for $A = 208$ and $Z = 82$ (based on calculations by Blomqvist and Wahlborn, *loc. cit.*, Fig. 3-3).

The calculated spectra reproduce approximately the observed positions of the single-particle levels close to or above the Fermi surface, but underestimate the binding of deep-lying hole states (see especially the $s_{1/2}^{-1}$ level in ^{16}O). The increased binding of these states may be interpreted in terms of a velocity

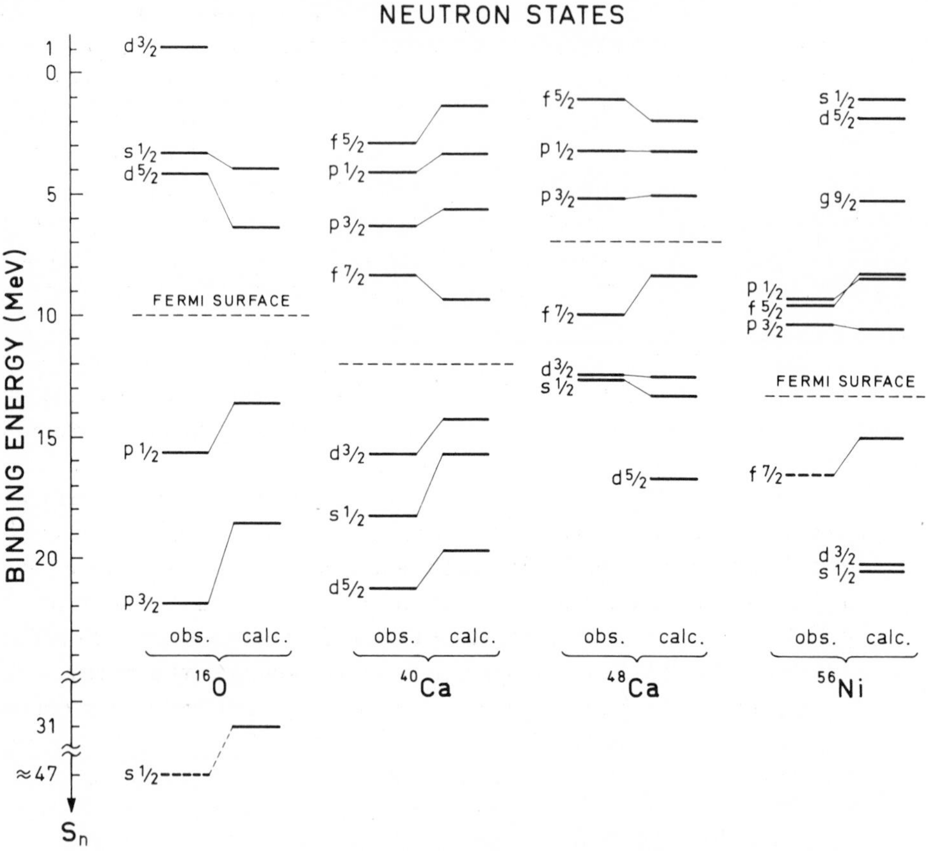

Figure 3-5 The experimental binding energies of the neutron states are derived from the spectra shown in Figs. 3-2b to 3-2e and from the references quoted there. The $s_{1/2}$ level in ^{16}O at 47 MeV is derived from the observed average position of the $s_{1/2}$ proton-hole level (see Fig. 2-27, p. 231).

dependence of the potential. We can approximately allow for this effect by considering the potential strength V_0 as a function of the energy E of the state considered. Thus, the velocity dependence observed for the optical potential (see Eq. (2–176)) accounts fairly well for the observed trend of the binding energies. The velocity dependence can also be described by a nonlocal, energy-independent potential (see references quoted in connection with Fig. 2-30).

▼ Superimposed on the smooth trend of the level positions with A and Z, one observes smaller variations that are not reproduced by the simple potential considered.

An example of such a "fine structure" in the level positions is provided by the shift of the $f_{5/2}$ level relative to the $p_{3/2}$ and $p_{1/2}$ levels as one goes from $A = 48$ to $A = 56$. In this region, the $f_{7/2}$ proton level is filling, and the depression of the $f_{5/2}$ neutron level has been interpreted in terms of the similarity of the radial wave functions of the $f_{7/2}$ and $f_{5/2}$ orbits. Thus, the contribution to the average potential from the $f_{7/2}$ protons has a radial shape favoring the $f_{5/2}$ orbits. (The empirical evidence for fine-structure effects of this type has been discussed by Cohen, 1963 and 1968. Theoretical estimates of such level shifts were considered by de-Shalit and Goldhaber, 1953, in connection with the interpretation of the systematics of isomeric transition energies pointed out by Goldhaber and Hill, 1952; for a more recent analysis, with the inclusion of pair correlations, see, for example, Silverberg, 1962 and 1964.)

An opposite but smaller effect is exhibited by the relative positions of the f and p levels for $A = 40$ and 48. In this region, the $f_{7/2}$ neutrons are filling and, on account of the symmetry (isospin dependent) part of the potential, the neutron levels are being weakly repelled.

The empirical energy separations between particle and hole states are found to be somewhat larger than those calculated for the potential. The effect is especially pronounced for the light nuclei and amounts to about 5 MeV in ^{16}O. An increase in the energy separation between occupied and unoccupied orbits is implied by the isospin dependence of the nuclear binding. Thus, a particle added to closed shells with $N = Z$ moves in a potential produced by a nucleus with $T_0 = 0$, while each of the particles in the closed shells moves in a potential produced by the rest of the particles, which form a $T_0 = 1/2$ state. We can estimate the associated extra binding ΔE of the hole state from the expression (2-29) for the nuclear symmetry potential; with $T_{A-1} = 1/2$ and the total isospin $T = 0$, and with the value (2-28) for V_1, we obtain

$$\Delta E \approx \frac{3}{4}\frac{V_1}{A} \approx 75A^{-1} \quad \text{MeV} \tag{3-23}$$

which is of the order of magnitude of the observed energy shifts. Similar effects may arise from the spin dependence of the nuclear binding and the favoring of states with high orbital symmetry (see, for example, the discussion in Chapter 7).

In a quantitative analysis of the energy separation between particle and hole states, several additional effects must be taken into account, including the velocity dependence of the potential and the increased interaction between particles in the orbits with similar radial wave functions. An increase in the ▲ binding of holes relative to particles may also arise from correlations in the

▼ ground state of the closed shell nuclei with an associated energy depression of these states. An effect in the opposite direction arises from the fact that the A value for the particle states is greater by one unit than for the hole states. The resulting increase in radius produces an energy shift of the particle states of order of magnitude $2(\delta R/R)E_{\text{kin}} \approx 25A^{-1}$ MeV. A more detailed estimate of this effect based on Fig. 2-30 yields a shift of 0.75 MeV for the particle states in ^{17}O. (The energy gap between occupied and unoccupied single-particle orbits has been discussed by Kelson and Levinson, 1964, and by Kerman *et al.*, 1966, in connection with an analysis of the self-consistent nuclear potential.)

In the comparison between the empirical separation energies and the binding energies determined from a particle in a potential, a correction must be added for the fact that, if a nucleon is suddenly removed from the nucleus A, the residual nucleus is not in a self-consistent state for the $(A-1)$ system (rearrangement energy). The effect of readjustment of the radius can be estimated from the compressibility (see Eq. (2-207))

$$\delta E = \tfrac{1}{2}(\delta r_0)^2 \frac{\partial^2}{\partial r_0{}^2}\mathscr{E} \approx \tfrac{1}{2}A^{-1}b_{\text{comp}} \tag{3-24}$$

assuming $\delta r_0 \approx r_0/3A$. For $b_{\text{comp}} \approx 20$ MeV, we thus obtain $\delta E \approx 10A^{-1}$ MeV. This simple estimate neglects the dependence of the self-consistent field in the $(A-1)$ system on the orbit of the particle that has been removed. In particular, the velocity dependence of the field may imply an especially large rearrangement energy for the deep-lying hole states (J. Svenne, private communication).

Isospin dependence of nucleonic binding states (*Table 3-1*)

If the closed shells have a nonvanishing isospin T_0, the single-particle and single-hole configurations may give rise to two different nuclear states with $T = T_0 \pm 1/2$. The energy splitting between such doublets provides a measure of the strength of the one-particle isovector potential.

The separation energies for the single-particle configurations in ^{49}Sc and for the single-hole configurations in ^{47}Ca are listed in columns two and three of Table 3-1. (For the hole configurations, S is the energy required for removal of a single particle from ^{48}Ca, leaving ^{47}Ca in the single-hole state.) For the $p_{3/2}$, $p_{1/2}$, and $f_{5/2}$ configurations, the single-particle strength is distributed over several levels and the energies listed represent weighted average energies for the strength functions determined from stripping and scattering reactions (see references quoted in caption to Fig. 3-2d). For the hole configurations with $T = 9/2$, only the $M_T = 9/2$ levels in ^{47}K have been observed, and the position of the $M_T = 7/2$ levels in ^{47}Ca was inferred by assuming a Coulomb energy of 6.8 MeV. This value was determined from the observed Coulomb energy of 7.0 MeV for $A = 49$, $T = 9/2$ by an extrapolation based on the relation (2-19).

The last column of Table 3-1 shows the calculated separation of the T ▲ doublets given by Eq. (3-21). The radial wave functions of the single-particle

▼ states are determined for a potential of the type (2-180) and the parameters employed in Fig. 2-30. While, on the average, there is rather good agreement between the empirical and theoretical values of the splitting, the $f_{5/2}$ level shows an especially large separation; this effect reflects the fact that the isovector potential results from the excess neutrons, which occupy the $f_{7/2}$ orbit, and thus we may expect this potential to act more strongly on f than on p orbits. (See the discussion in connection with Fig. 3-5.) If the average potential energy of the nucleon orbit in the field produced by the filled $f_{7/2}$ neutron shell is denoted by ▲ $U_0 + t_z U_1$, the potential energy in the field of the $f_{7/2}$ proton shell will be

Configuration	S		$(\Delta E)_{obs}$	$(\Delta E)_{cal}$
	$T=7/2$	$T=9/2$		
$f_{5/2}$	5.0	−5.9	10.9	9.4
$p_{1/2}$	3.6	−3.9	7.5	8.2
$p_{3/2}$	6.1	−1.9	8.0	8.2
$d_{3/2}^{-1}$	12.5	22.4	9.9	9.8
$s_{1/2}^{-1}$	12.6	22.1	9.5	9.0

Table 3-1 The separation energies S are taken from Fig. 3-2d and references quoted in caption to this figure. The quantity ΔE represents the energy difference between the iso-doublets, which have the quantum numbers $T=9/2$, $M_T=7/2$ and $T=7/2$, $M_T=7/2$, respectively.

▼ $U_0 - t_z U_1$. From the relative positions of the $f_{5/2}$ and $p_{1/2}$ levels in $A = 40$, 48, and 56, we may therefore estimate that $U_1(f_{5/2}) - U_1(p_{1/2}) \approx 3$ MeV, which implies a difference of $9/8 \times 3$ MeV ≈ 3.5 MeV for the T splittings in the two orbits, in agreement with the data in Table 3-1.

An additional, though less direct, estimate of the isovector potential can be obtained by comparing the binding energies for the $f_{7/2}$ and $f_{7/2}^{-1}$ configurations in ^{49}Sc and ^{47}Ca. The binding of the $f_{7/2}$ proton in ^{49}Sc and the $f_{7/2}$ neutron in ^{48}Ca involves the symmetry potential

$$(\mathbf{t}\cdot\mathbf{T}_{A-1})\frac{V_1}{A} = \begin{cases} -\dfrac{5}{2}\dfrac{V_1}{A} & {}^{49}\text{Sc} \quad T_{A-1}=4,\ T=\dfrac{7}{2} \\[2ex] \dfrac{7}{4}\dfrac{V_1}{A} & {}^{48}\text{Ca} \quad T_{A-1}=\dfrac{7}{2},\ T=4 \end{cases}$$

and we thus find

$$\Delta E = S(f_{7/2}) + E_{\text{Coul}} - S(f_{7/2}^{-1})$$
$$= \frac{17}{4A}\langle f_{7/2}|V_1(r)|f_{7/2}\rangle$$

The empirical binding energies in Fig. 3-2d and the above quoted value of ▲ 7.0 MeV for E_{Coul} give $\Delta E \approx 6.7$ MeV, while the potential $V_1(r)$ employed in

▼ Table 3-1 gives $\Delta E \approx 8.9$ MeV. It may be noted that the estimate of ΔE from the comparison of the binding energies of the $f_{7/2}$ and $f_{7/2}^{-1}$ configurations is sensitive to the energy of the closed shell state. A depression of this energy decreases $S(f_{7/2})$ and increases $S(f_{7/2}^{-1})$. In the above comparison of the binding energies we have also neglected the small increase of $S(f_{7/2})$ associated with the increase in radius resulting from the presence of an extra particle. (See the discussion of the separation between particle and hole states in connection with Fig. 3-5.) ▲

3-3 MATRIX ELEMENTS OF ELECTROMAGNETIC MOMENTS

Because of the simple and well-known structure of the electromagnetic interaction, the study of electric and magnetic moments and transition probabilities provides the opportunity for detailed tests of nuclear wave functions. In this section, we shall especially consider electric quadrupole and magnetic dipole effects, which have yielded important information regarding the properties of individual nucleons moving in the nuclear potential.

3-3a Quadrupole Moments and E2-Transition Probabilities

The electric quadrupole moment is a measure of the extent to which the nuclear charge distribution deviates from spherical symmetry. The moment is defined by

$$Q = \langle I, M = I | Q_{\text{op}} | I, M = I \rangle \tag{3-25}$$

and the quadrupole operator is given by

$$eQ_{\text{op}} = \int \rho_e(\mathbf{r}) r^2 (3\cos^2 \vartheta - 1)\, d\tau \tag{3-26}$$

in terms of the charge density $\rho_e(\mathbf{r})$.

For a single proton in an orbit $(nl)j$, one obtains (see Eqs. (3A-14) and (1A-60))

$$\begin{aligned} Q_{\text{sp}} &= \langle j, m = j | r^2 (3\cos^2 \vartheta - 1) | j, m = j \rangle \\ &= 2 \langle jj20 | jj \rangle \langle j \tfrac{1}{2} 20 | j \tfrac{1}{2} \rangle \langle j | r^2 | j \rangle \\ &= -\frac{2j-1}{2j+2} \langle j | r^2 | j \rangle \end{aligned} \tag{3-27}$$

where the radial average is given by

$$\langle j | r^2 | j \rangle = \int r^4 \mathscr{R}_{nlj}^2\, dr \tag{3-28}$$

A neutron carries no electric charge, and therefore the quadrupole moment vanishes for a single-neutron configuration.

The negative sign in Eq. (3-27) reflects the concentration of the particle density in the equatorial plane for the state $m=j$. For $j \gg 1$, the value of Q_{sp} approaches $-\langle r^2 \rangle$ characterizing a charge distribution completely concentrated in the equatorial plane.

For a single-proton hole, the quadrupole moment is $-Q_{sp}$. In fact, the state with $M=j$ represents a closed shell with the orbit $m=-j$ lacking, and this orbit has the same quadrupole moment as the one with $m=j$. The opposite signs of the quadrupole moments for a particle and a hole correspond to the fact that the quadrupole operator, being a function of the position coordinates, transforms under particle-hole conjugation with the phase $c=-1$ (see Eq. (3-14)).

If the closed shell core has a neutron excess, the particle and hole configurations may involve components with a charge exchange between the core and the particle or hole. For such states, the quadrupole moments become linear combinations of proton and neutron moments, with coefficients given by the state vectors (3-19).

The quantity Q represents the diagonal element of the quadrupole operator (the static quadrupole moment). Nondiagonal elements (transition moments) are involved in electric quadrupole ($E2$) processes (γ decay, Coulomb excitation, etc.). The amplitudes and transition rates for such processes depend on the matrix elements of the electric quadrupole tensor

$$\mathscr{M}(E2, \mu) = \int \rho_e(\mathbf{r}) r^2 Y_{2\mu}(\vartheta, \varphi)\, d\tau \tag{3-29}$$

of which the $\mu = 0$ component is proportional to Q_{op}.

The matrix elements of a spherical tensor, such as (3-29), between states with specified angular momentum quantum numbers, can be expressed in terms of reduced (double bar) matrix elements (see Sec. 1A-5). Thus, from Eqs. (3-25) and (3-26), together with (1A-60), we have

$$\begin{aligned} eQ_{\text{op}} &= \left(\frac{16\pi}{5}\right)^{1/2} \mathscr{M}(E2, \mu = 0) \\ eQ &= \left(\frac{16\pi}{5}\right)^{1/2} (2I+1)^{-1/2} \langle I\, I\, 2\, 0 | I\, I \rangle \langle I \| \mathscr{M}(E2) \| I \rangle \end{aligned} \tag{3-30}$$

The total transition rate (that is, the decay constant for a γ decay, the cross section for Coulomb excitation, etc.) involves the reduced transition probability

$$\begin{aligned} B(E2; I_1 \to I_2) &= \sum_{\mu M_2} |\langle I_2 M_2 | \mathscr{M}(E2, \mu) | I_1 M_1 \rangle|^2 \\ &= (2I_1 + 1)^{-1} |\langle I_2 \| \mathscr{M}(E2) \| I_1 \rangle|^2 \end{aligned} \tag{3-31}$$

For a transition of a single proton (or a proton hole), one obtains (see Eq. (3A-14))

$$B_{sp}(E2; j_1 \rightarrow j_2) = \frac{5}{4\pi} e^2 \langle j_1 \tfrac{1}{2} 20 | j_2 \tfrac{1}{2} \rangle^2 \langle j_2 | r^2 | j_1 \rangle^2 \tag{3-32}$$

The available experimental data on the electric quadrupole moments and transition probabilities for single-particle and single-hole configurations are listed in Table 3-2, p. 341. It is seen that the experimental values for proton configurations have the same sign (and order of magnitude) as those calculated from the one-particle wave functions. As to the quantitative comparison, some uncertainty arises from the estimate of the radial matrix element. Still, it may be concluded that the observed quadrupole effects are somewhat larger than those associated with the orbit of the single proton, indicating a significant contribution from the protons in the closed shells. Such an effect is dramatically illustrated by the electric quadrupole moments and transition probabilities associated with the single-neutron configurations. These moments have the sign and the order of magnitude to be expected for single-proton configurations.

The distortion of the closed shells by the added particle can be simply understood as a consequence of the nonspherical field generated by the extra particle.[1] The order of magnitude of the effect can be estimated by observing that the eccentricity of the density distribution is of order A^{-1} and, hence, the potential should acquire a similar shape. The orbit of each proton in the closed shell is thus slightly distorted and acquires an extra quadrupole moment of order $A^{-1} Q_{sp}$ and of the same sign as the mass quadrupole moment of the polarizing particle. The total induced quadrupole moment is of order

$$Q_{pol} \sim \frac{Z}{A} Q_{sp} \tag{3-33}$$

which roughly corresponds to the magnitude of the observed effect. (It should be emphasized that, since the induced moment is of the same order of magnitude as the polarizing single-particle moment, a quantitative estimate must also consider higher-order terms associated with the polarizing effect of the induced moment. The analysis of the self-consistent field associated with the response of the closed

---

[1] The renormalization effects for single-particle excitations are similar to the polarizability and dielectric phenomena that modify the electric and magnetic fields generated by electrons in atoms and metals. The recognition of such phenomena in the nucleus came partly from the analysis of the coupling between the particle and collective degrees of freedom (Rainwater, 1950; Bohr and Mottelson, 1953), and partly from the efforts to reconcile independent-particle motion with the strong nucleonic interactions. (See, for example, Brueckner, Eden, and Francis, 1955.) The description in terms of renormalized particle-like excitations (sometimes referred to as quasiparticles) has been formulated for infinite systems in the theory of Fermi "liquids" (Landau, 1956, 1958; for the application of this approach to nuclei, see Migdal, 1967).

shells to the presence of a single particle is discussed in Sec. 9-1. The polarization effect can also be treated in terms of the coupling between the particle and the collective oscillations associated with deformations of the core (see Chapters 6 and 9).

The polarization of the closed shells involves virtual excitations of particles into higher shells, and the associated frequencies ($\Delta E \approx 2\hbar\omega \approx 80A^{-1/3}$ MeV; see Eq. (2-131)) are therefore very high compared with the transition energies ($\Delta E \sim 1$ MeV) involved in the transitions in Table 3-2. Thus, the polarization follows adiabatically the motion involved in these transitions, and the static polarizability employed in the discussion of Q should also act in renormalizing the transition moments, as is observed.

The renormalization of the quadrupole moment of the particle represents only a small perturbation of each of the particles in the closed shells. Hence, the effects are expected to be simply additive in the case of configurations involving several particles outside of closed shells, and may conveniently be regarded as a correction to the intrinsic properties of each individual nucleon outside of the closed shells.

One often refers to the $E2$-polarization effect as giving rise to an effective charge e_{eff} associated with quadrupole processes,

$$(e_{\text{eff}})_{E2} = \frac{\langle I_2 = j_2 \| \mathscr{M}(E2) \| I_1 = j_1 \rangle}{\langle j_2 \| r^2 Y_2 \| j_1 \rangle}$$

$$= e(\tfrac{1}{2} - t_z) + (e_{\text{pol}})_{E2} \tag{3-34}$$

The difference between the effective charge and the charge of the single nucleons is referred to as the polarization charge. The effective charge values deduced from the observed static and transition moments are listed in Table 3-2. It is to be noted that the value of e_{eff} may depend somewhat on the orbit of the nucleon; in particular, the polarization effect decreases when the binding energy of the nucleon becomes small, since the nucleon, when outside the nuclear surface, is less effective in polarizing the core. (See the transition in ^{209}Pb discussed in connection with Table 3-2.)

The question also arises as to whether the polarization charge is equal for neutrons and protons, that is, whether e_{pol} is an isoscalar or whether it contains an isovector component. Such a component is expected as a consequence of the isovector nuclear potential, which implies that a neutron outside of closed shells acts more strongly on the protons of the closed shells than does an extra proton; hence, the polarization charge is expected to be somewhat larger for a neutron than for a proton. The empirical data are inconclusive on this interesting point.

3-3b Magnetic Moments

The nuclear magnetic moment provides a sensitive test of the nuclear coupling scheme, on account of the great difference between the g factors associated with the various components of the total nuclear angular momentum (orbital and spin angular momenta of neutrons and protons).

The magnetic moment is defined as

$$\mu = \langle I, M = I|\mu_z|I, M = I\rangle \tag{3-35}$$

where μ_z is the z component of the vector operator $\boldsymbol{\mu}$. For a single nucleon, we have

$$\boldsymbol{\mu} = g_l \mathbf{l} + g_s \mathbf{s} \tag{3-36}$$

in terms of the orbital and spin g factors

$$g_l = \begin{cases} 1 \\ 0 \end{cases} \qquad g_s = \begin{cases} 5.58 & \text{proton} \\ -3.82 & \text{neutron} \end{cases} \tag{3-37}$$

(in units of $e\hbar/2M_p c$). The expression (3-36) represents the magnetic dipole of a point nucleon moving in a static binding field. Corrections to this expression may arise from the nucleonic interactions, which somewhat modify the intrinsic structure of the nucleons; further, the velocity dependence of these interactions gives rise to additional terms in $\boldsymbol{\mu}$. There is little direct evidence on these interaction effects; the available, rather tentative, theoretical estimates indicate magnitudes of a few tenths of a magneton (see Sec. 3C-6).

For a nucleon in a shell model orbit, the matrix element (3-35) may be evaluated in terms of the vector model. The vectors $\mathbf{l}$ and $\mathbf{s}$ precess about the constant $\mathbf{j}$ and the average value of $\boldsymbol{\mu}$ is therefore

$$\begin{aligned} \mu_{\text{sp}} &= \frac{\langle \boldsymbol{\mu} \cdot \mathbf{j}\rangle}{j(j+1)} \langle j, m = j|j_z|j, m = j\rangle \\ &= \frac{1}{j+1} \{g_l j(j+1) + (g_s - g_l)\langle \mathbf{s} \cdot \mathbf{j}\rangle\} \\ &= j\left\{g_l \pm (g_s - g_l)\frac{1}{2l+1}\right\} \qquad j = l \pm \tfrac{1}{2} \end{aligned} \tag{3-38}$$

where the quantity $\langle \mathbf{s} \cdot \mathbf{j}\rangle$ has been evaluated by squaring the identity $\mathbf{j} - \mathbf{s} = \mathbf{l}$.

For a single-hole configuration the magnetic moment is the same as for a single particle, since the orbit $m = -j$ lacking in the closed shells has a moment opposite to the orbit with $m = j$. (We may also note that the spin and angular momentum operators transform under particle-hole conjugation with $c = +1$; see Eq. (3-14).)

The nondiagonal matrix elements of the magnetic moment operator determine the amplitudes of $M1$-transition processes. The matrix elements are usually expressed in terms of the magnetic dipole tensor

$$\mathscr{M}(M1, \mu) = \left(\frac{3}{4\pi}\right)^{1/2} \frac{e\hbar}{2Mc} (\mu)_\mu \tag{3-39}$$

where $(\mu)_\mu$ denotes the spherical component ($\mu = -1, 0, +1$) of the vector $\boldsymbol{\mu}$. Thus, the magnetic moment for a state I is related to the reduced matrix element of $\mathscr{M}(M1)$ by

$$\frac{e\hbar}{2Mc} \mu = \left(\frac{4\pi}{3}\right)^{1/2} (2I+1)^{-1/2} \langle I\, I\, 1\, 0 | I\, I \rangle \langle I \| \mathscr{M}(M1) \| I \rangle \tag{3-40}$$

For a single particle or hole, the $M1$ matrix elements have the selection rules $\Delta n = 0$, $\Delta l = 0$, $\Delta j = 0, 1$ and the only allowed transitions therefore take place between spin-orbit partners $j = l \pm \frac{1}{2}$. For such a transition we obtain (see Eq. (3C-37))

$$\begin{aligned} &\langle j_2 = l + \tfrac{1}{2} \| \mathscr{M}(M1) \| j_1 = l - \tfrac{1}{2} \rangle \\ &\quad = -\left(\frac{3}{4\pi}\right)^{1/2} \frac{e\hbar}{2Mc} (g_s - g_l)(2j_1 + 1)^{1/2} \langle j_1 \tfrac{1}{2}\, 1\, 0 | j_2 \tfrac{1}{2} \rangle \end{aligned} \tag{3-41}$$

neglecting the small difference in the radial functions for the two orbits.

The empirical moments of nuclei with single-particle or single-hole configurations are listed in Table 3-3, p. 343. For the lighter nuclei ($A \lesssim 40$), the agreement with the value (3-38) is rather good; the deviations amount to only a few tenths of a magneton. The excess moments in ^{3}H and ^{3}He are difficult to account for in terms of configuration mixing and may indicate the presence of interaction terms in the moment operators.[2] In view of this effect, the very close agreement between μ_{obs} and μ_{sp} for $A = 15$ and 17 may be somewhat fortuitous. In fact, other evidence suggests the presence of significant configuration mixings in the region of ^{16}O (see the analysis of β-decay rates in Table 3-5 and the discussion in Chapter 7).

In the heavier nuclei, the observed magnetic moments deviate appreciably from μ_{sp}. This marked difference in the behavior of the light and heavy nuclei makes it unlikely that we are dealing with a modification of the intrinsic properties of the nucleon. The observed trend, however, finds a simple explanation in terms of a polarization effect of the closed shells, somewhat similar to that discussed for the electric quadrupole moments. The polarization effect for

[2] The measurement of the moments in the $A = 3$ system led to the study of charge exchange contributions to the nuclear magnetic moments (Villars, 1947; see also references quoted in Sec. 3C-6).

magnetic moments is expected to depend decisively on the configuration of the closed shells, since the main effect is associated with the presence of unsaturated spins in the closed shells, which can be partially aligned by the interactions with the spin of the extra nucleon (Arima and Horie, 1954; Blin-Stoyle and Perks, 1954).

If the closed shells are composed of filled levels of both spin-orbit partners ($j=l\pm\frac{1}{2}$), as is the case for the closed shells up to ^{40}Ca, the nucleon spins are coupled together to a state with $S=0$. In fact, disregarding minor differences in the radial wave functions of the $j=l\pm\frac{1}{2}$ orbits, such closed shells have a wave function identical to that which would be constructed if there were no spin-orbit coupling. Therefore, L and S are, separately, constants of the motion (L-S coupling) and the uniqueness of the state ensures $L=S=0$. In such a situation, the perturbation produced by the extra nucleon to first order leaves $\langle L_z\rangle = \langle S_z\rangle = 0$ for the core, and thus leads to corrections to the magnetic moment only in higher orders.

If the closed shells contain a filled orbit with $j=l+\frac{1}{2}$, but not the partner, the unsaturated nucleon spins may be partially aligned in first order through the spin-dependent components in the nucleonic force. For simplicity, we shall consider a central force $(\boldsymbol{\sigma}_1\cdot\boldsymbol{\sigma}_2)V_\sigma(r_{12})$. The order of magnitude of the resultant spin-dependent field acting on the closed shells is $\langle V_\sigma\rangle$, which represents an average matrix element of $V_\sigma(r_{12})$ involving the particle outside closed shells and one of the particles in the filled $j=l+\frac{1}{2}$ shell. The wave function of a nucleon in a $j=l+\frac{1}{2}$ orbit will thus have admixed components with $j=l-\frac{1}{2}$,

$$\varphi_{l+\frac{1}{2},m}\rightarrow\varphi_{l+\frac{1}{2},m}-\frac{\langle V_\sigma\rangle}{\Delta\varepsilon_{ls}}\boldsymbol{\sigma}_{\text{ext}}\cdot\langle j=l-\tfrac{1}{2},m|\boldsymbol{\sigma}|j=l+\tfrac{1}{2},m\rangle\varphi_{l-\frac{1}{2},m} \tag{3-42}$$

to first order in the perturbing potential. The spin of the external polarizing nucleon is represented by $\boldsymbol{\sigma}_{\text{ext}}$, and $\Delta\varepsilon_{\text{ls}}$ is the energy difference between the $j=l\pm\frac{1}{2}$ single-particle levels (the spin-orbit splitting). The magnetic moment generated by the perturbation (3-42) is proportional to $\boldsymbol{\sigma}_{\text{ext}}$ and can thus be regarded as a renormalization of g_s by the amount

$$\begin{aligned}\delta g_s &\approx -\frac{4\langle V_\sigma\rangle}{\Delta\varepsilon_{ls}}\sum_m\langle j=l+\tfrac{1}{2},m|\mu_z|j=l-\tfrac{1}{2},m\rangle\langle j=l-\tfrac{1}{2},m|\sigma_z|j=l+\tfrac{1}{2},m\rangle\\ &=-\frac{2\langle V_\sigma\rangle}{3\Delta\varepsilon_{ls}}(g_s-g_l)\langle j=l-\tfrac{1}{2}\|\sigma\|j=l+\tfrac{1}{2}\rangle^2\\ &=-\frac{8\langle V_\sigma\rangle}{3\Delta\varepsilon_{ls}}(g_s-g_l)(l+1)\frac{2l}{2l+1}\end{aligned} \tag{3-43}$$

where g_s and g_l are the g factors of the nucleons in the closed shell. The reduced matrix element of σ occurring in Eq. (3-43) can be obtained from Eq. (3A-22).

(The spin-dependent central forces favor (LS) coupling rather than (jj) coupling, and the correlations leading to a renormalization of the spin magnetic moments constitute a partial trend away from (jj) and towards (LS) coupling (see the discussion in Sec. 9-3).)

In a heavy nucleus, there are about as many neutrons with unsaturated spin as protons and, for an isospin-independent interaction, the total polarization term (3-43) is thus rather small owing to the opposite sign of $(g_s - g_l)$ for neutrons and protons. (The magnetic moment operator is approximately an isovector; see Eq. (1-65).)

However, a force of the type $(\boldsymbol{\sigma}_1 \cdot \boldsymbol{\sigma}_2)(\boldsymbol{\tau}_1 \cdot \boldsymbol{\tau}_2)V_{\sigma\tau}(r_{12})$ will induce a polarization of neutrons and protons with opposite sign; thus, the main magnetic moment correction in heavy nuclei is expected to come from such an isospin-dependent force. (On account of the antisymmetry in the wave function, an effective isospin-dependent interaction may also result from a short-range force that does not explicitly depend on the isospin variables; see Sec. 2-5b, p. 258.)

An estimate of the order of magnitude of $\langle V_{\sigma\tau} \rangle$ can be obtained by performing an average similar to that leading to the estimate (2-213) for the symmetry potential; thus, a nucleonic force with Serber exchange mixture yields $\langle V_{\sigma\tau} \rangle \approx -\frac{1}{3}V_0 A^{-1} \approx +15A^{-1}$ MeV. The estimate (3-43) therefore gives $\delta g_s \approx 2\tau_3$ for the polarization effect in the ^{208}Pb core, which involves the $h_{11/2}$ protons and the $i_{13/2}$ neutrons with $\Delta\varepsilon_{ls} \approx 5$ MeV (see Fig. 3-3). A similar (though somewhat larger) value for δg_s is obtained for the ^{56}Ni core with the filled $f_{7/2}$ neutron and proton shells.

The observed magnetic moments in the nuclei around $A = 56$ and 208 indicate polarization effects of the estimated order of magnitude (see Table 3-3), although it hardly needs to be emphasized that the above discussion is only intended for qualitative orientation. In addition to the neglect of higher-order terms of the type mentioned in connection with the polarization effect in the quadrupole moment, the forces assumed are highly oversimplified and the exchange effects between the interacting particles have not been included.

The total polarization effect cannot be described simply in terms of a renormalized g_s factor. Not only may the effect depend somewhat on the radial distribution of the polarizing particle, but the polarization magnetic moment may also involve a "tensor component" of the form

$$(\delta\mu)_\mu = \delta g_s'(r)(Y_2\, \mathbf{s})_{\lambda=1,\mu} \tag{3-44}$$

(For small r, the leading term in $\delta g_s'(r)$ is expected to be proportional to r^2.) The expression (3-44) and a term proportional to $\mathbf{s}$ are the only axial vectors that can be constructed from the spin and position coordinates of a nucleon. Moment contributions of the type (3-44) arise when we take into account the dependence of the polarizing field on the position of the external nucleon. Such a dependence is implied by a spin-dependent central interaction as well as by noncentral nucleonic forces.

While the operator (3-44) is an effective moment, representing the contribution of the polarized core particles, each assumed to have the moment (3-36), a term of the form (3-44) may also occur in the moment operator itself, if the particles move in a velocity-dependent field such as a potential with a spin-orbit coupling (Jensen and Mayer, 1952; see also the discussion in Sec. 3C-6).

The magnetic moment contribution (3-44) has an lj dependence quite different from that of the spin magnetic moment. (The expectation value of the operator (3-44) can be obtained from the relation (3A-22).) From the measurement of two moments (or $M1$-transition rates) in the same nucleus it may thus be possible to determine the polarization factors δg_s and $\delta g_s'$ separately. (See the example in Table 3-3.) The moment operator (3-44) is also distinguished from the operator (3-36) by its ability to cause $M1$ transitions with $\Delta l = 2$ (transitions of l-forbidden type).

3-3c Other Electromagnetic Moments

The electric quadrupole ($E2$) and magnetic dipole ($M1$) moments are examples of the electric and magnetic multipole operators $\mathcal{M}(E\lambda, \mu)$ and $\mathcal{M}(M\lambda, \mu)$, which characterize the interaction of the nucleus with the radiation field. Moments of similar structure are involved in nuclear excitation processes induced by charged particles. The general expressions for these moment operators and the evaluation of single-particle matrix elements are considered in Appendix 3C.

In addition to the information on $E2$ and $M1$ moments, some evidence is available on $M4$-transition rates for single-hole configurations (see Table 3-4, p. 344). The observed rates are found to be 5 to 6 times lower than the single-particle estimate. This may indicate $M4$-polarization effects of a similar magnitude as for the $M1$ moments.

In ^{209}Pb, the strength of the $E3$ transition $j_{15/2} \rightarrow g_{9/2}$ has been measured and is found to be 50 times larger than for a single-proton transition (Ellegaard *et al.*, 1967). The large polarization charge can be understood in terms of the coupling between the single-particle motion and the octupole excitation of the ^{208}Pb closed shell configuration occurring at 2.6 MeV (see the discussion in Chapter 6). Since the octupole excitation frequency is of the same order of magnitude as the single-particle transition frequency, the polarization charge is expected to be rather strongly dependent on the transition energy.

ILLUSTRATIVE EXAMPLES TO SECTION 3-3

Electric quadrupole effects in single-particle configurations (*Table 3-2*)

The available evidence on $E2$ moments and transition probabilities for single-particle (and single-hole) configurations (j and j^{-1}) is summarized in Table 3-2. The single-particle estimates Q_{sp} and $B_{sp}(E2)$ refer to a single proton (or proton hole) and are obtained from Eqs. (3.27) and (3.32).

(a) Quadrupole moments

Nucleus	lj	$Q_{obs}(10^{-24}\ cm^2)$	$Q_{sp}(10^{-24}\ cm^2)$	e_{eff}/e
${}^{17}_{8}O$	$d_{5/2}$	-0.026	-0.066	0.40
${}^{39}_{19}K$	$d^{-1}_{3/2}$	0.09	-0.052	1.8
${}^{209}_{83}Bi$	$h_{9/2}$	-0.4	-0.26	1.6

(b) $E2$-transition probabilities

Nucleus	$(lj)_i$	$(lj)_f$	$B(E2)_{obs}(e^2fm^4)$	$B(E2)_{sp}(e^2fm^4)$	e_{eff}/e
${}^{15}_{7}N$	$p^{-1}_{3/2}$	$p^{-1}_{1/2}$	7.4	4.6	1.3
${}^{17}_{8}O$	$s_{1/2}$	$d_{5/2}$	6.3	35	0.42
${}^{17}_{9}F$	$s_{1/2}$	$d_{5/2}$	64	43	1.2
${}^{41}_{20}Ca$	$p_{3/2}$	$f_{7/2}$	66	40	1.3
${}^{41}_{21}Sc$	$p_{3/2}$	$f_{7/2}$	110	40	1.7
${}^{207}_{82}Pb$	$f^{-1}_{5/2}$	$p^{-1}_{1/2}$	70	81	0.9
${}^{207}_{82}Pb$	$p^{-1}_{3/2}$	$p^{-1}_{1/2}$	80	110	0.85
${}^{209}_{82}Pb$	$s_{1/2}$	$d_{5/2}$	150	866	0.42
${}^{209}_{83}Bi$	$f_{7/2}$	$h_{9/2}$	40 ± 20	2.3	4 ± 1.5

Table 3-2 The experimental values of the quadrupole moments are from the compilation of Lindgren (1965). The $B(E2)$ values are taken from the following references: for ^{15}N, from G. A. Beer, P. Brix, H.-G. Clerc, and B. Laube, *Phys. Letters* **26B**, 506 (1968); for ^{17}O and ^{17}F, from J. A. Becker and D. H. Wilkinson, *Phys. Rev.* **134B**, 1200 (1964); for ^{41}Ca, from P. P. Singh, R. E. Segel, R. H. Siemssen, S. Baker, and A. E. Blaugrund, *Phys. Rev.* **158**, 1063 (1967); for ^{41}Sc and ^{41}Ca, from D. H. Youngblood, J. P. Aldridge, and C. M. Class, *Phys. Letters* **18**, 291 (1965); for ^{207}Pb and ^{209}Bi, from D. S. Andreev, Ju. P. Gangrskij, I. Ch. Lemberg, and V. A. Nabičvrižvili, *Izv. Akad. Nauk.* **29**, 2231 (1965) and references quoted in this article, and from H. J. Körner, K. Auerbach, J. Braunsfurth, and E. Gerdau, *Nuclear Phys.* **86**, 395 (1966); for ^{209}Pb, from P. Salling, *Phys. Letters* **17**, 139 (1965).

▼ The radial matrix elements of r^2 have been calculated for single-particle states in the potential considered in Figs. 3-3 and 3-5. The following values are obtained:

$$
\begin{array}{ll}
^{15}\text{N} & \langle p_{3/2}|r^2|p_{1/2}\rangle = 7.6\ \text{fm}^2 \\
^{17}\text{O} & \langle d_{5/2}|r^2|d_{5/2}\rangle = 11.5\ \text{fm}^2 \\
 & \langle d_{5/2}|r^2|s_{1/2}\rangle = 12.0\ \text{fm}^2 \\
^{17}\text{F} & \langle d_{5/2}|r^2|s_{1/2}\rangle = 13.4\ \text{fm}^2 \\
^{39}\text{K} & \langle d_{3/2}|r^2|d_{3/2}\rangle = 13.0\ \text{fm}^2 \\
^{41}\text{Ca} & \langle f_{7/2}|r^2|p_{3/2}\rangle = 13.9\ \text{fm}^2 \\
^{207}\text{Pb} & \langle f_{5/2}|r^2|p_{1/2}\rangle = 32\ \text{fm}^2 \\
 & \langle p_{3/2}|r^2|p_{1/2}\rangle = 37\ \text{fm}^2 \\
^{209}\text{Pb} & \langle s_{1/2}|r^2|d_{5/2}\rangle = 60\ \text{fm}^2 \\
^{209}\text{Bi} & \langle f_{7/2}|r^2|h_{9/2}\rangle = 16.5\ \text{fm}^2 \\
 & \langle h_{9/2}|r^2|h_{9/2}\rangle = 35\ \text{fm}^2
\end{array}
$$

For ^{41}Sc, the proton $p_{3/2}$ state is unbound; we have used the same radial matrix element as for ^{41}Ca.

The effective charge found in ^{209}Pb is small as compared to that in ^{207}Pb. This appears to be a consequence of the loose binding of the last neutron in ^{209}Pb. Thus, from the wave functions in Fig. 3-4 one finds that half the radial integral is contributed by distances greater than 9.5 fm, which is already significantly larger than the mean radius (7.5 fm). The neutron is therefore less effective in generating polarizations in the closed shell core. An effect of this type is also expected for the transitions in $A = 17$ and $A = 41$.

For $A = 41$, the $p_{3/2}$ levels in Table 3-2 refer to the first excited states in ^{41}Ca and ^{41}Sc. As shown in Fig. 3-2c and Table 3-7, a part of the single-particle strength (of the order of 10–20%) is associated with higher-lying (3/2−) states. The levels considered therefore contain a corresponding amount of configurations involving the excitation of the closed shells. The observed large strength of the $E2$ transitions may possibly be associated with the magnitude of these admixtures. For the second 3/2− states at about 2.4 MeV, the $E2$ transitions to the ground state are found to be strongly hindered, with $B(E2)$ values less than $0.15\ e^2\ \text{fm}^4$ (Bearse *et al.*, 1968, and references quoted there).

The quadrupole moment of a single-particle configuration may also receive contributions from the recoil of the closed shells. Thus, the total electric quadrupole moment measured with respect to the nuclear center of mass is

$$
\begin{aligned}
Q &= \sum_p [2(z_p - Z)^2 - (x_p - X)^2 - (y_p - Y)^2] \\
&= \sum_p (2z_p^2 - x_p^2 - y_p^2) - 4Z\sum_p z_p + 2X\sum_p x_p + 2Y\sum_p y_p \\
&\quad + (A-N)(2Z^2 - X^2 - Y^2) \\
&= \sum_p (2z_p^2 - x_p^2 - y_p^2) - 2Z\left(\sum_p z_p - \sum_n z_n\right) \\
&\quad + X\left(\sum_p x_p - \sum_n x_n\right) + Y\left(\sum_p y_p - \sum_n y_n\right) - N(2Z^2 - X^2 - Y^2)
\end{aligned}
\tag{3-45}
$$

where X, Y, Z are the center-of-mass coordinates. The sums over p extend over all the $(A-N)$ protons and the sums over n over the N neutrons. ▲

▼ The matrix elements of the operator (3-45) with inclusion of the correlations due to antisymmetrization can be simply evaluated if the nucleons are assumed to move independently in a harmonic oscillator potential, since then the motion of the system separates into center-of-mass motion and intrinsic motion (see Appendix 7B). For all the states of the lowest configurations (which have the minimum number of quanta), the center of mass is in the $1s$ state and the matrix elements of the quadrupole operator (3-45) thus receive no contributions from the recoil terms. (In ^{17}O, for example, these lowest configurations comprise the $2s_{1/2}$, $1d_{5/2}$, and $1d_{3/2}$ single-neutron configurations.)

Estimates of the recoil terms for more realistic potentials would be of interest, but the vanishing of these terms for the oscillator potential suggests that they are small in most cases.

Magnetic dipole effects in single-particle configurations (*Table 3-3*)

The available evidence on magnetic dipole moments for j and j^{-1} configurations is listed in Table 3-3. The single-particle values μ_{sp} are obtained from Eqs. (3-37) and (3-38). The only directly measured $M1$ transition rate for $j^{\pm 1}$ configurations refers to the $p_{3/2}^{-1} \rightarrow p_{1/2}^{-1}$ transition in ^{15}N, determined from inelastic electron scattering (Beer *et al.*, 1968). The observed transition rate ▲ interpreted in terms of Eq. (3-41) yields a value for $g_s - g_l$, which is 0.85 ± 0.1

Nucleus	lj	μ_{obs}	μ_{sp}
^{3}H	$s_{1/2}^{-1}$	2.98	2.79
^{3}He	$s_{1/2}^{-1}$	−2.13	−1.91
^{15}N	$p_{1/2}^{-1}$	−0.28	−0.26
^{15}O	$p_{1/2}^{-1}$	0.72	0.64
^{17}O	$d_{5/2}$	−1.89	−1.91
^{17}F	$d_{5/2}$	4.72	4.79
^{39}K	$d_{3/2}^{-1}$	0.39	0.12
^{41}Ca	$f_{7/2}$	−1.59	−1.91
^{55}Co	$f_{7/2}^{-1}$	4.3 ± 0.3	5.79
^{207}Pb	$p_{1/2}^{-1}$	0.59	0.64
^{207}Pb	$f_{5/2}^{-1}$	0.65 ± 0.05	1.37
^{209}Bi	$h_{9/2}$	4.08	2.62

Table 3-3 The experimental magnetic moments are from the compilation of Lindgren (1965), except for the moments of ^{17}F (K. Sugimoto, A. Mizobuchi, K. Nakai, and K. Matuda, *Phys. Letters* **18**, 38, 1965) and of the 5/2 state in ^{207}Pb (H. J. Körner, K. Auerbach, J. Braunsfurth, and E. Gerdau, *Nuclear Phys.* **86**, 395, 1966). Where no error is given, the uncertainties are reported to be less than 0.01 magneton.

▼ times the value 4.58 for a free proton. Indirect evidence on the $M1$ component in the $f_{7/2}^{-1} \rightarrow f_{5/2}^{-1}$ transition in ^{207}Pb is provided by the observed $M1 - E2$ ratio for this transition. Assuming the $E2$ component to be given by the single-particle value with an effective charge of 0.9 (see Table 3-2), one obtains an $M1$-transition matrix element which is about a factor of two smaller than the single-particle value (see Chilosi *et al.*, 1964).

The renormalization of the magnetic moment due to the polarization of the closed shells involves two spin-polarization parameters, of which the first, δg_s, is a contribution to the spin g factor, while the second, $\delta g'_s$, is associated with the moment (3-44). From the two measured moments in ^{207}Pb and from the evidence on the $M1$ transition, one may attempt to determine the two polarization parameters. In such an analysis, one must bear in mind, however, that also additional effects, such as exchange moments and other interaction terms in the moment operator, are expected to make small contributions to the observed moments (see Sec. 3C-6). Little evidence is available concerning the magnitude of these effects, but one must reckon with a contribution amounting to one or a few tenths of a magneton. In view of this uncertainty in the interpretation of the moments, an estimate of the spin polarization parameters from the available data involves considerable latitude. A consistent tentative interpretation of the two static moments and the transition moment can be obtained by taking $\delta g_s/g_s \sim -0.5$ and the radial average $\langle \delta g'_s(r) \rangle / g_s \sim 0.4$, which implies $\mu(p_{1/2}) = 0.5$, $\mu(f_{5/2}) = 0.9$, and a reduction of 0.5 for the $M1$-matrix element for the $f_{7/2} \rightarrow f_{5/2}$ transition.

M4-transition probabilities for single-particle configurations (*Table 3-4*)

The available evidence on $M4$-transition rates for $j^{\pm 1}$ configurations is ▲ shown in Table 3-4. The single-particle transition probabilities are obtained from

Nucleus	$(lj)_i$	$(lj)_f$	$B(M4)_{obs}(e^2\text{fm}^8)$	$B(M4)_{sp}(e^2\text{fm}^8)$
$^{207}_{82}$Pb	$i_{13/2}^{-1}$	$f_{5/2}^{-1}$	2.8×10^3	1.7×10^4
$^{207}_{81}$Tl	$h_{11/2}^{-1}$	$d_{3/2}^{-1}$	3.3×10^3	1.7×10^4

Table 3-4 The experimental data are taken from the Table of Isotopes by Lederer *et al.* (1967) and include the redetermination of the lifetime for the ^{207}Pb isomer by H. P. Yule, *Nuclear Phys.* **A94**, 442 (1967).

▼ Eq. (3C-37). The radial matrix elements $\langle (lj)_f | r^3 | (lj)_i \rangle$ between initial and final states have been calculated by means of the wave functions given by Blomqvist ▲ and Wahlborn (1960).

3-4 β-DECAY MATRIX ELEMENTS

3-4a Allowed Transitions

Transition operators

The transition probabilities for β decay depend on nuclear properties similar to those involved in electromagnetic transitions. The simplest type of β processes are those in which the nucleon undergoes a β transformation as if it were at rest; the wavelengths of the emitted leptons (electron and neutrino) are usually large compared to nuclear dimensions, and the decay amplitude is therefore approximately independent of the position of the transforming nucleon.

Transitions that can be described in this lowest approximation, in which the transition operator is independent of the positions and velocities of the nucleons, are referred to as allowed transitions. These may again be divided into two types. In Fermi (F) transitions, the operator (or β moment) is independent of the nucleon spin, while in Gamow-Teller (GT) transitions, the moment is proportional to the spin operator of the decaying nucleon. Hence, in F transitions, there is no angular momentum transfer between nucleon and leptons, while in GT transitions, the decay involves a transfer of one unit of angular momentum.

The transition rates for these two types of processes can be expressed in terms of the reduced transition probabilities

$$\begin{aligned} B(\mathrm{F}; IT, M_T \rightarrow IT, M_T \pm 1) &= \frac{g_V^2}{4\pi} |\langle IMT, M_T \pm 1|\, T_\pm \,|IMT, M_T\rangle|^2 \\ B(\mathrm{GT}; I_1 T_1, M_T \rightarrow I_2 T_2, M_T \pm 1) & \\ = \frac{g_A^2}{4\pi} \sum_{\mu M_2} |\langle I_2 M_2 T_2, M_T \pm 1|& \sum_k t_\pm(k)\sigma_\mu(k)\, |I_1 M_1 T_1, M_T\rangle|^2 \end{aligned} \tag{3-46}$$

where $t_\pm = t_x \pm i t_y$ are the operators which transform a neutron into a proton, and *vice versa* ($\langle p|\, t_- \,|n\rangle = \langle n|\, t_+ \,|p\rangle = 1$), while $\sigma_\mu = 2s_\mu$ is a spherical component of the Pauli spin vector. The coupling constants for F and GT transitions are denoted by g_V and g_A (referring to the vector and axial-vector character of the β currents involved in the interactions). The empirical values of these coupling constants are given by Eq. (3D-23).

The transition operator for the Fermi processes is the component of the total isospin, and the matrix element therefore depends only on the isospin quantum numbers of the states involved (see Eq. (3D-41)). The observed F transition rates thus especially provide tests of the validity of the isospin quantum number for nuclear states (see Fig. 1-10 and Table 1-3). The Gamow-Teller matrix elements yield information regarding the coupling of the nucleon spins.

Closed shells with $N = Z$. Mirror transitions

The single-particle GT transitions have the selection rules $\Delta l = 0$ and $\Delta j = 0, 1$. For a single particle (or single hole) outside closed shells with $N = Z$, the B values are given by (see Eq. (3A-22))

$$B_{sp}(\text{GT}; lj_1 \rightarrow lj_2) = \frac{g_A^2}{4\pi} \begin{cases} \left(\dfrac{j_2+1}{j_2}\right)^{\pm 1} & j_1 = j_2 = l \pm \frac{1}{2} \\ \dfrac{2j_2+1}{l+\frac{1}{2}} & \Delta j = 1 \end{cases} \tag{3-47}$$

The main evidence on GT transitions of the type considered is derived from the mirror transitions, that is, transitions between nuclear states obtained from each other by the interchange of neutrons and protons (charge symmetry conjugates). The empirical data on these transitions are listed in Table 3-5, p. 349. The observed values of B(GT) are found to be in qualitative agreement with the single-particle values (3-47), but to be systematically smaller than this theoretical estimate, except for $A = 3$. Polarization effects similar to those discussed for the spin magnetic moments are expected to be small, since the nuclei in question have closed shells with saturated spins. The rather large reduction of the matrix elements, especially for $A = 39$ and 41, may thus indicate significant admixture of more complicated configurations or the presence of interaction terms in the GT operator.

The GT moment is related by rotational invariance in isospace to the isovector part of the spin contribution to the magnetic dipole moment. Thus, for the static dipole moment, we have

$$\frac{\langle JM, T = \frac{1}{2}\, M_T | \sum_k (\sigma_z t_z)_k \, | JM, T = \frac{1}{2}\, M_T \rangle}{\langle JM, T = \frac{1}{2}\, M_T = \frac{1}{2} \,|\, \sum_k (\sigma_z t_+)_k | JM, T = \frac{1}{2}\, M_T = -\frac{1}{2} \rangle}$$

$$= -\,2^{-1/2} \frac{\langle \frac{1}{2}\, M_T \, 1\, 0 \,|\, \frac{1}{2}\, M_T \rangle}{\langle \frac{1}{2} \, -\frac{1}{2} \, 1\, 1 \,|\, \frac{1}{2} \, \frac{1}{2} \rangle} = M_T \tag{3-48}$$

For example, the observation that B(GT) for $^{17}\text{F} \rightarrow {}^{17}\text{O}$ is about 15% smaller than the single-particle estimate (see Table 3-5) implies a reduction of about 8% in the isovector spin contribution to the magnetic moments of these nuclei. Such a reduction shifts the moments by about 0.2 of a magneton (see, for example, Eq. (3-38)). The fact that the magnetic moments of these nuclei differ from the single-particle values by less than 0.1 of a magneton (see Table 3-3) may thus indicate the presence of interaction terms in the $M1$ or GT moments, leading to an increase in the magnitude of the $M1$-matrix elements or a decrease in the magnitude of the GT-matrix elements.

Closed shells with $N > Z$

For configurations with a single particle outside closed shells with $N > Z$, the β-transition rates differ by a T-dependent factor from those of Eq. (3-47), if the proton orbit j_p is not occupied by neutrons. From Eq. (3-19), we obtain

$$B(\mathrm{GT}; j_n, T = T_0 + \tfrac{1}{2} \rightarrow j_p, T = T_0 \pm \tfrac{1}{2})$$
$$= B_{\mathrm{sp}}(\mathrm{GT}; j_n \rightarrow j_p) \begin{cases} 1 & j_p \text{ occ. by } n \quad T = T_0 - \tfrac{1}{2} \\ \dfrac{2T_0}{2T_0 + 1} & j_p \text{ unocc. by } n \begin{cases} T = T_0 - \tfrac{1}{2} \\ \\ T = T_0 + \tfrac{1}{2} \end{cases} \\ \dfrac{1}{2T_0 + 1} & \end{cases} \qquad (3\text{-}49)$$

The presence of the neutron excess is expected, however, to strongly affect the β moment for single-particle transitions, on account of the coupling of this moment to the transition moments of the excess neutrons. The effect may be compared with the renormalization of the spin magnetic moments associated with the presence of unsaturated spins in the closed shells, but new features arise from the fact that the β-transition frequencies for the particles in the closed shells may be smaller or greater than, or degenerate with the single-particle frequency, depending on the β transition considered. (The reduction of GT moments for single-particle transitions, as a result of the coupling to the particles in the closed shells, has been discussed by Fujita and Ikeda, 1965, and by Halbleib and Sorensen, 1967; see also the discussion in Sec. 9-3.)

The coupling effect becomes especially large for transitions by which a neutron transforms into a proton in the same orbit. Such a transition is degenerate with the transitions by which one of the neutrons in the closed shells transforms into a proton without change of orbit, and the nucleonic interactions therefore give rise to major correlations among the degenerate daughter states. Thus, an exchange force proportional to $(\boldsymbol{\sigma}_1 \cdot \boldsymbol{\sigma}_2)(\boldsymbol{\tau}_1 \cdot \boldsymbol{\tau}_2)$, such as considered in connection with the polarization effects in the $M1$ moments, tends to completely remove the GT strength from the single-particle transition. A perturbation estimate analogous to Eq. (3-43) would give an infinite value for the ratio of $\delta\mathscr{M}(\mathrm{GT})$ to $\mathscr{M}(\mathrm{GT})$, since $\Delta\varepsilon$ is to be replaced by a vanishing energy denominator; however, the induced moment $\delta\mathscr{M}(\mathrm{GT})$ gives rise to additional polarization effects, which can be included by replacing $\mathscr{M}(\mathrm{GT})$ by $\mathscr{M}_{\mathrm{eff}}(\mathrm{GT}) = \mathscr{M}(\mathrm{GT}) + \delta\mathscr{M}(\mathrm{GT})$. The inclusion of these higher order terms thus leads to a vanishing value for the effective single-particle moment.

Evidence on GT moments for single-particle transitions without change of orbit is provided by the decay of $^{49}\mathrm{Ca}$ (see p. 350). The transition probability

B(GT) is found to be about 30 times smaller than the value given by Eq. (3-49).

For transitions with change of orbit, the coupling to the closed shell moments may also lead to large reductions of the single-particle moments, but the magnitude of the effect is expected to depend rather sensitively on the transition frequency. There is so far no experimental evidence of β moments for single-particle (or hole) transitions of this type.

The correlation effect responsible for the quenching of the single-particle GT moments may be compared with the correlation effect that removes the Fermi strength from the single-particle transitions with $T_f = T_i - 1$. The total Fermi strength is concentrated on the isobaric analog state of the parent, which may be regarded as a coherent superposition of transitions $(jm)_n \rightarrow (jm)_p$ of all the excess neutrons (see Eq. (3-20)). In a similar manner, the interactions tend to concentrate the GT strength on a collective excitation at higher energy.

While the selection rules for the Fermi transitions are direct consequences of the isobaric symmetry, the quantitative features of the corresponding correlation effects for the GT transitions depend on the more detailed properties of the interactions. Selection rules for GT transitions would follow from symmetry considerations, if the nucleonic interactions were independent not only of the charge variables but also of the spin coordinates. The nuclear states produced by such interactions form supermultiplets (orbital permutation symmetry or U_4 symmetry; see p. 38 and Appendix 1C) and, since the GT as well as the F moments are among the generators of the U_4 symmetry group, allowed β transitions can only occur between states belonging to the same supermultiplet (Wigner, 1939).

The supermultiplet symmetry has approximate validity for the spectra of light nuclei, but the symmetry is badly broken in heavier nuclei as a consequence of the strong spin-orbit interaction in the one-particle potential, which leads to (jj) coupling. The correlations responsible for the renormalization effects for the GT moments, as well as for the spin-magnetic moments, may be viewed, however, as a trend away from the (jj) coupling scheme toward LS coupling and supermultiplet symmetry (Fujita and Ikeda, 1965; see also the discussion in Sec. 9-3).

3-4b Forbidden Transitions

In the case of transitions for which the allowed matrix elements vanish (change of parity or $\Delta I > 1$), it is necessary to take into account the dependence of the β-transition operators on the position and velocity of the nucleons. As in the case of the electromagnetic interaction, the general β interaction can be expanded in terms of a series of multipole moments. While, however, for given transfer of angular momentum and parity, the photon emission is characterized by a single moment, the β process may depend on several different moments. The structure of the β interaction and the expansion in terms of multipole moments are considered in Appendix 3D.

First-order forbidden β transitions have been studied for single-particle configurations in the region of ^{208}Pb (see Fig. 3-6, p. 351). The analysis leads to estimates of the renormalization factors for the various β moments contributing to the transitions, but the conclusions are tentative in view of the incompleteness of the experimental data.

▼

ILLUSTRATIVE EXAMPLES TO SECTION 3-4

Allowed β transitions for single-particle configurations (*Table 3-5*)

The available evidence on the β-decay rates for mirror transitions in single-particle configurations is listed in Table 3-5. The Gamow-Teller transition proba-

▲

Nuclei	lj	ft (sec)	B(GT)	B_{sp}(GT)
$n \rightarrow p$	$s_{1/2}$	1120 ± 50	3	3
$^3H \rightarrow {}^3He$	$s_{1/2}^{-1}$	1060 ± 100	3.3 ± 0.3	3
$^{15}O \rightarrow {}^{15}N$	$p_{1/2}^{-1}$	4470 ± 30	0.27 ± 0.02	1/3
$^{17}F \rightarrow {}^{17}O$	$d_{5/2}$	2370 ± 50	1.09 ± 0.1	7/5
$^{39}Ca \rightarrow {}^{39}K$	$d_{3/2}^{-1}$	4330 ± 150	0.30 ± 0.05	3/5
$^{41}Sc \rightarrow {}^{41}Ca$	$f_{7/2}$	2780 ± 100	0.83 ± 0.1	9/7

Table 3-5 The ft values are derived from measurements of lifetimes and decay energies given in the *Table of Isotopes* by Lederer *et al.* (1967). For the neutron, the half-life is from the recent measurement by C. J. Christensen, A. Nielsen, B. Bàhnsen, W. K. Brown, and B. M. Rustad, *Phys. Letters* **26B**, 11 (1967). The ft value for ^3H is based on the discussion given by J. N. Bahcall, *Nuclear Phys.* **75**, 10 (1966). The B values in the table are given in units of $(4\pi)^{-1} g_A^2$.

▼ bility B(GT) is obtained from the ft value by means of the relation (see Eqs. (3D-23) and (3D-38))

$$D = ft\left[\frac{B(\mathrm{F})}{(4\pi)^{-1}g_V^2} + \left(\frac{g_A}{g_V}\right)^2 \frac{B(\mathrm{GT})}{(4\pi)^{-1}g_A^2}\right]$$

$$D = 6260 \pm 60 \qquad \left(\frac{g_A}{g_V}\right)^2 = 1.51 \pm 0.03 \tag{3-50}$$

The Fermi transition probability B(F) is assumed to have the value one, in units of $(4\pi)^{-1}g_V^2$, as expected for transitions between isobaric analog states with $T = 1/2$ (see Eq. (3-46)).

▲

▼ While the main contribution to the transitions considered is associated with the allowed β moments ($\mathcal{M}(\rho_V, 0)$ and $\mathcal{M}(j_A, 0, 1)$), additional small contributions may arise from higher-order β moments. An estimate of the correction may be derived from the expressions for the total transition probabilities $B(\lambda\pi = 0+)$ and $B(\lambda\pi = 1+)$ that can be obtained from Eq. (3D-47) by interchanging V and A. The numerically largest correction arises from the weak magnetic moment $\mathcal{M}(j_V, \kappa = 1, \lambda = 1)$ given by Eq. (3D-37). The interference term between the weak magnetism and the Gamow-Teller moment is found to reduce the total $B(\lambda\pi = 1+)$ by the following relative amounts: -2.3% (^{15}O), -1% (^{17}F), -5% (^{39}Ca), and -1% (^{41}Sc); for $n \rightarrow p$ and ^{3}H $\rightarrow$ ^{3}He, the effect is less than $\frac{1}{2}\%$. It is to be emphasized that the present estimate is rather crude, since the ξ approximation on which Eq. (3D-47) is based is not well fulfilled for the transitions considered because of the large transition energies and low Z values. A quantitative estimate must take into account the radial dependence of the moments and the departure from the allowed shape of the β spectrum. (See, for example, the discussion of these effects in the β decay of ^{12}B and ^{12}N, pp. 414 ff.)

Additional evidence on allowed β transitions for single-particle configurations has been obtained from the study of the decay of ^{49}Ca (Chilosi *et al.*, 1965). The energy spectra of ^{49}Ca and ^{49}Sc are illustrated in Fig. 3-2d. The ground state of ^{49}Ca has $I\pi = 3/2-$ and the main β branch proceeds to the $3/2-$ level in ^{49}Sc at 3.09 MeV and has $\log ft = 5.1$. The transition involves a change of isospin ($T = 9/2 \rightarrow T = 7/2$) and the Fermi matrix element therefore vanishes. From Eq. (3-50) we thus obtain $B(\mathrm{GT}) = 0.035\ (4\pi)^{-1} g_A^2$; in comparison, the value of $B(\mathrm{GT})$ for a single-particle $p_{3/2}$ configuration is

$$B(\mathrm{GT}; p_{3/2}, T = 9/2 \rightarrow p_{3/2}, T = 7/2) = 40/27$$

in units of $(4\pi)^{-1} g_A^2$ (see Eqs. (3-47) and (3-49)).

The stripping reactions populating the states in ^{49}Ca and ^{49}Sc indicate that the $p_{3/2}$ neutron strength in ^{49}Ca is predominantly associated with the ground state, while about 60% of the $p_{3/2}$ proton strength to $T = 7/2$ levels in ^{49}Sc goes to the lowest 3/2 state at 3.09 MeV (see Erskine *et al.*, 1966). If we correct for such a dilution of the $p_{3/2}$ single-particle strength in the daughter state, the effective GT moment for the $p_{3/2}$ transition amounts to only about 20% of the single-particle value. (The moment is proportional to $(B(\mathrm{GT}))^{1/2}$.)

Forbidden β decays for single-particle configurations (Fig. 3-6 and Table 3-6)

Information on the forbidden β decays for single-particle configurations has been obtained from the study of the transitions ^{207}Tl $\rightarrow$ ^{207}Pb and ^{209}Pb $\rightarrow$ ^{209}Bi. The theoretical analysis on which the present discussion is based has been given by Damgaard and Winther (1964).

The decay of ^{207}Tl is illustrated in Fig. 3-6. The ground state decay involves matrix elements of multipolarity $\lambda\pi = 0-$ and $1-$, while the decay to the ▲

▼ excited (3/2−) state is predominantly of 1− type. The contribution from the $\lambda\pi = 2-$ transition, which is permitted by the spins of the states, is estimated to ▲ be of the order of 1%.

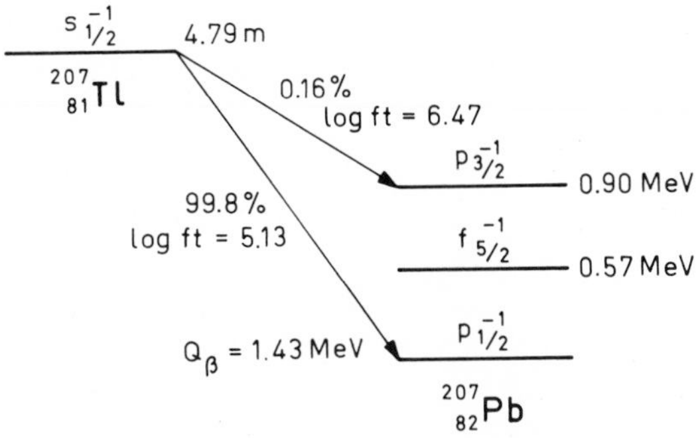

Figure 3-6 The experimental evidence on the β decay of ^{207}Tl is taken from H. D. Evans, *Proc. Phys. Soc.* (London) **63A**, 575 (1950), and from P. R. Christensen, O. B. Nielsen, and H. Nordby, *Phys. Letters* **4**, 318 (1963).

▼ In the ξ approximation, one obtains the following expressions for the *ft* values of the two transitions (see Eq. (3D-46))

$$\begin{aligned} s_{1/2} \to p_{1/2} \qquad & f_0 t = \frac{(g_V^2/4\pi)D}{B(\lambda\pi = 0-;\, s_{1/2} \to p_{1/2}) + B(\lambda\pi = 1-;\, s_{1/2} \to p_{1/2})} \\ s_{1/2} \to p_{3/2} \qquad & f_0 t = \frac{(g_V^2/4\pi)D}{B(\lambda\pi = 1-;\, s_{1/2} \to p_{3/2})} \end{aligned} \tag{3-51}$$

in terms of the reduced transition probabilities given by Eq. (3D-47). This approximation is fairly accurate for the transitions considered, but it is important in the quantitative evaluation of the multipole moments to include the corrections due to the finite nuclear size (see Eq. (3D-25)).

The $\lambda = 0-$ transitions involve two different matrix elements associated with the multipole moments $\mathscr{M}(\rho_A, \lambda = 0)$ and $\mathscr{M}(j_A, \kappa = 1, \lambda = 0)$, while the $\lambda = 1$ transitions involve the three multipole moments $\mathscr{M}(j_V, \kappa = 0, \lambda = 1)$, $\mathscr{M}(\rho_V, \lambda = 1)$, and $\mathscr{M}(j_A, \kappa = 1, \lambda = 1)$ (see Eq. (3D-47)). The two matrix elements associated with the vector interaction can be related by the continuity equation (3D-33).

In the evaluation of the matrix elements $\mathscr{M}(\rho_A, \lambda = 0)$ it is assumed that the single-particle states can be represented by motion in a central potential, which includes a spin-orbit coupling, $(\mathbf{l} \cdot \mathbf{s})\, v_{ls}(r)$, but is otherwise velocity independent. We then have the relation

$$\boldsymbol{\sigma} \cdot \mathbf{v} = \frac{\boldsymbol{\sigma} \cdot \mathbf{p}}{M} + i\hbar^{-1}(\boldsymbol{\sigma} \cdot \mathbf{r}) v_{ls}(r) \tag{3-52}$$

It is found that the term proportional to the spin-orbit potential contributes only ▲ a few percent to the matrix element.

▼ Assuming pure single-hole configurations for the states involved and employing the radial nuclear wave functions given by Blomqvist and Wahlborn (1960), one finds the matrix elements listed in Table 3-6. The coupling constant g_V was taken to have the value (3D-23), while the ratio g_A/g_V was taken to be -1.18. (The slight increase in the axial vector coupling implied by the recent neutron half-life measurement (see Eq. (3D-23)) has little effect on the present ▲ analysis.)

	$^{207}\text{Tl} \rightarrow {}^{207}\text{Pb}$		$^{209}\text{Pb} \rightarrow {}^{209}\text{Bi}$
	$s_{1/2} \rightarrow p_{1/2}$	$s_{1/2} \rightarrow p_{3/2}$	$g_{9/2} \rightarrow h_{9/2}$
$\mathscr{M}(\rho_A, \lambda = 0)$	-0.115		0.181
$-i \dfrac{m_e c}{\hbar} \xi \mathscr{M}(j_A, \kappa = 1, \lambda = 0)$	0.083		-0.022
$B(\lambda = 0)$	5.1×10^{-4}		25×10^{-4}
$\mathscr{M}(j_V, \kappa = 0, \lambda = 1)$	-0.102	0.135	-0.004
$\dfrac{i}{\sqrt{3}} \dfrac{m_e c}{\hbar} \xi \mathscr{M}(\rho_V, \lambda = 1)$	0.039	-0.053	0.002
$i \sqrt{\dfrac{2}{3}} \dfrac{m_e c}{\hbar} \xi \mathscr{M}(j_A, \kappa = 1, \lambda = 1)$	-0.080	-0.057	0.019
$B(\lambda = 1)$	102×10^{-4}	3.1×10^{-4}	0.3×10^{-4}
$(f_0 t)_{\text{cal}}$	4.6×10^4	1.6×10^6	2.0×10^5
$(f_0 t)_{\text{exp}}$	1.3×10^5	3.0×10^6	3.2×10^5

Table 3-6 The ft values for ^{207}Tl are taken from Fig. 3-6; for ^{209}Pb, from A. H. Wapstra, *Arkiv Fysik* **6**, 263 (1953). The table lists reduced matrix elements, in units of g_V, for the moments given in the first column. The reduced transition probabilities $B(\lambda)$ are in units of g_V^2, and the ft values in seconds. The table is based on the analysis by J. Damgaard and A. Winther, *Nuclear Phys.* **54**, 615 (1964) and private communication by Damgaard.

▼ From the comparison between the theoretical and the observed ft values one may attempt to estimate the renormalization factors for the β moments associated with polarization effects of the closed shells. Since both the β branches are predominantly of $\lambda = 1$ multipolarity (see Table 3-6), the ft values mainly depend on the renormalization of the two multipole moments $\mathscr{M}(\rho_V, \lambda = 1)$ and $\mathscr{M}(j_A, \kappa = 1, \lambda = 1)$. The multipole moment $\mathscr{M}(j_V, \kappa = 0, \lambda = 1)$, when expressed by means of the continuity equation, has a structure similar to $\mathscr{M}(\rho_V, \lambda = 1)$, and these two multipole moments are therefore expected to be renormalized by approximately the same factor. The two renormalization factors can thus be determined from the observed ft values, if we assume these factors to ▲ be the same for the $s_{1/2} \rightarrow p_{1/2}$ and $s_{1/2} \rightarrow p_{3/2}$ transitions.

▼ If we express the renormalization in terms of effective coupling constants $(g_V)_{\text{eff}}$ and $(g_A)_{\text{eff}}$, the experimental ft values can be fitted by the two sets of values

$$(1) \quad \left(\frac{(g_V)_{\text{eff}}}{g_V}\right)_{(\rho_V,\,\lambda=1)} = 0.6 \qquad \left(\frac{(g_A)_{\text{eff}}}{g_A}\right)_{(j_A,\,\kappa=1,\,\lambda=1)} = 0.5$$

$$(2) \quad \left(\frac{(g_V)_{\text{eff}}}{g_V}\right)_{(\rho_V,\,\lambda=1)} = 0.3 \qquad \left(\frac{(g_A)_{\text{eff}}}{g_A}\right)_{(j_A,\,\kappa=1,\,\lambda=1)} = 0.7$$

If the ξ approximation is employed, and if one neglects the energy dependence of the coefficients α_λ and $\beta_{\kappa\lambda}$ in the finite size corrections to the multipole moments (see Eq. (3D-25)), the electron spectrum has the allowed shape. When the higher-order terms are included, however, one finds small deviations from the allowed shape, associated mainly with $\mathscr{M}(j_A, \kappa = 1, \lambda = 1)$ and therefore of different magnitude for the two sets of effective coupling constants obtained above. A measurement of the spectrum shape for the ground state transition may thus make it possible to distinguish between the two interpretations of the ft values.

An important point in the present analysis is the approximate cancellation of the two $\lambda = 0$ matrix elements for the ground-state transition (see Table 3-6). This feature could in principle be tested by a measurement of the angular distribution of the electrons emitted from polarized ^{207}Tl nuclei, which would provide a measure of the relative contributions of the $\lambda = 0$ and $\lambda = 1$ matrix elements.

The β transition to the first excited state, $f_{5/2}$, has so far not been observed. It is expected to be very weak, not only because it involves the multipole order $\lambda = 2$, but also because of its l forbiddenness. In fact, assuming pure configurations, the transition involves $\Delta l = 3$, and the leading-order matrix element $\mathscr{M}(j_A, \kappa = 1, \lambda = 2)$ therefore vanishes. An analysis of such l forbidden transitions would involve an estimate of polarization terms with $\kappa = 3$, $\lambda = 2$, analogous to the tensor term (3-44) in the effective $M1$ operator.

On the basis of the analogy between the vector β interaction and the electromagnetic interaction, one expects a close similarity between the vector part of the ^{207}Tl decay and the electromagnetic decay of the isobaric analog state in ^{207}Pb ($I\pi = 1/2+$, $T = 45/2$, $M_T = 43/2$) to the low-lying $p_{1/2}$ and $p_{3/2}$ states. Thus, the $E1$ moment for the decay of the analog state (to which only the isovector component contributes, since $\Delta T = 1$) is expected to be reduced by approximately the same factor as the β moment $\mathscr{M}(\rho_V, \lambda = 1)$ in the ^{207}Tl decay. (See the comment in connection with Eq. (3D-35).)

The decay of ^{209}Pb($g_{9/2}$) may be analyzed in the same manner as the Tl decay and the results of this analysis are also shown in Table 3-6. It is found that ▲ the experimental ft value is about 50 percent greater than that obtained by

▼ assuming pure single-particle configurations and neglecting polarization effects. For this decay, the dominant transition moment is $\mathscr{M}(\rho_A,\ \lambda = 0)$, and the analysis thus indicates that this moment is renormalized by a factor of about 0.8. ▲

3-5 REACTION PROCESSES. PARENTAGE COEFFICIENTS

3-5a One-Particle Transfer Reactions

Direct tests of the single-particle interpretation of a nuclear state can be obtained from the study of one-nucleon transfer reactions (stripping and pickup processes). The amplitude for a stripping process transferring a nucleon in an orbit jm to the target nucleus is proportional to the matrix element of $a^\dagger(jm)$ between the target state and the final nuclear state; similarly, the amplitude for a pickup reaction involves the matrix element of an a (or a $b^\dagger$) operator. These matrix elements are referred to as parentage coefficients. The determination of parentage coefficients from cross sections for one-particle transfer reactions is discussed in Appendix 3E.

For processes connecting a closed shell configuration with single-particle or single-hole configurations, the reduced parentage coefficients are

$$\begin{aligned}\langle j \| a^\dagger(j) \| \hat{0} \rangle &= \langle j^{-1} \| b^\dagger(j) \| \hat{0} \rangle \\ &= \langle j^{-1} \| a(\bar{j}) \| \hat{0} \rangle = (2j+1)^{1/2}\end{aligned} \qquad T_0 = 0 \tag{3-53}$$

for closed shells with $T_0 = 0$ $(N = Z)$. If the closed shells have $T_0 \neq 0$, we must distinguish between the various configurations illustrated in Fig. 3-1,

$$j_n \text{ unoccupied} \quad j_p \text{ unoccupied}$$

$$\langle j;\, TM_T \| a^\dagger(j, m_t) \| \hat{0};\, T_0,\, M_T = T_0 \rangle = (2j+1)^{1/2} \langle T_0\, T_0\, \tfrac{1}{2} m_t \,|\, TM_T \rangle$$

$$j_n \text{ occupied} \quad j_p \text{ unoccupied}$$

$$\begin{aligned}&\langle j^{-1};\, T_0 - \tfrac{1}{2},\, M_T = T_0 - \tfrac{1}{2} \,\| b^\dagger(j, m_t = -\tfrac{1}{2}) \| \hat{0};\, T_0,\, M_T = T_0 \rangle \\ &\quad = (2j+1)^{1/2} \\ &\quad = \langle j;\, T_0 - \tfrac{1}{2},\, M_T = T_0 - \tfrac{1}{2} \| a^\dagger(j, m_t = -\tfrac{1}{2}) \| \hat{0};\, T_0\, M_T = T_0 \rangle\end{aligned} \tag{3-54}$$

$$j_n \text{ occupied} \quad j_p \text{ occupied}$$

$$\langle j^{-1};\, TM_T \| b^\dagger(j, m_t) \| \hat{0};\, T_0,\, M_T = T_0 \rangle = (2j+1)^{1/2} \langle T_0\, T_0\, \tfrac{1}{2} m_t \,|\, TM_T \rangle$$

The states identified as single-particle or single-hole configurations in the spectra in Fig. 3-2 are populated with especially large probabilities in one-nucleon transfer reactions (see references in captions). This evidence is of major significance for the interpretation of the levels. The intensities of the transfer processes are consistent with the estimate (3-54), but a quantitative test of this relation is difficult at the present time owing to the problems involved in the detailed analysis of the reaction cross sections (see Sec. 3E-1). For the higher-lying single-particle configurations, whose properties are distributed over several nuclear levels, the transfer reactions provide a determination of the strength function. As an example, the evidence obtained from the analysis of the $^{40}Ca(d, p)^{41}Ca$ process is considered in Table 3-7, p. 356.

3-5b Resonance Reactions

The spectrum above the threshold for nucleon emission can be studied by scattering processes. In the low-energy domain, one observes sharp resonances corresponding to the formation of metastable states with properties similar to the bound states. The amplitude g_{lj} for forming the resonance state by a nucleon incident on the closed shell target depends on the component in the resonance state representing the target and a single particle in an orbit with quantum numbers lj. Thus, the ratio of g_{lj} to the single-particle amplitude $(g_{lj})_{sp}$ corresponding to the scattering of a particle in a potential, is equivalent to the parentage coefficient for the bound states. The analysis of resonance reactions in terms of the amplitude for formation and decay of the resonance state, as well as simple estimates of the single-particle amplitudes, are considered in Appendix 3F. The amplitudes g_{lj} are so normalized that their absolute squares are the resonance widths Γ_{lj}.

The study of nucleon resonance reactions on closed shell nuclei has yielded important information on the location of the single-particle strength. The evidence obtained is consistent with, and supplements, that obtained from transfer reactions. An example is considered in Table 3-8, p. 358.

For the closed shells with $T \neq 0$, the main evidence on the spectra with $T = T_0 + \frac{1}{2}$ and $M_T = T_0 - \frac{1}{2}$ (isobaric analog states) has been obtained from studies of proton resonance scattering on the closed shell nuclei. The resonance widths provide information on the parentage of the levels, which can be compared with that obtained from neutron transfer reactions to the $M_T = T = T_0 + \frac{1}{2}$ components of the isobaric multiplets (see Table 1-2). By scattering protons on targets with a neutron-hole configuration, one may study the isobaric analog states ($M_T = T_0 - 1$) of the closed shell nuclei and obtain information on their parentage with respect to the neutron-hole states. (See, for example, the analysis of the $p + {}^{207}Pb$ reaction by Andersen *et al.*, 1966.)

ILLUSTRATIVE EXAMPLES TO SECTION 3-5

Parentage coefficients from $^{40}Ca(d, p)^{41}Ca$ reaction (Table 3-7)

The (d, p) stripping process on ^{40}Ca has been extensively studied with a view to determining the neutron parentage factors. A large number of proton groups are observed, corresponding to the formation of different levels in ^{41}Ca, and many of the proton groups have angular distributions with pronounced maxima, mostly in the forward hemisphere, as is characteristic of a direct transfer reaction.

In the example considered in Table 3-7, the observed angular distributions were analyzed by assuming the incident deuteron and the outgoing proton to move in an optical potential (Distorted Wave Born Approximation; see Appendix 3E). The potential assumed consists of a real central potential of the Woods-Saxon shape, an imaginary potential proportional to the radial derivative of

E_{exc} (MeV)	lj	$\langle I=j \Vert a^{\dagger}(j) \Vert 0 \rangle^2$
0	$f_{7/2}$	(8)
1.95	$p_{3/2}$	3.8
2.02	$d_{3/2}$	0.8
2.47	$p_{3/2}$	1.1
2.68	$s_{1/2}$	0.04
3.41	$s_{1/2}$	0.03
3.62	p	0.2
3.74	d	0.3
3.95	$p_{1/2}$	1.5
4.20	p	0.02
4.62	p	0.2
4.77	$p_{1/2}$	0.4
4.98	$g_{9/2}$	0.8
4.8–6.6 (4 states)	$d_{5/2}$	0.6
4.9–5.8 (3 states)	$f_{5/2}$	2.8
5.0–6.0 (4 states)	$s_{1/2}$	0.04
5.4–6.2 (8 states)	p	0.4

Table 3-7 The parentage factors, obtained from an analysis of the cross sections for the ^{40}Ca (d, p) ^{41}Ca reaction with a deuteron energy of 7 MeV, have been given by T. A. Belote, A. Sperduto, and W. W. Buechner, *Phys. Rev.* **139B**, 80 (1965). For the groups of states referred to in the last four entries in the table, the last column gives the sum of the observed parentage probabilities.

▼ the real potential (surface absorption), and the Coulomb potential. The parameters of the potential were obtained from elastic scattering data for deuterons and protons on ^{40}Ca. The effective *np* interaction was approximated by a zero-range force. The forward maxima in the observed angular distributions are rather well fitted by the analysis, and the positions of the maxima yield the l values for the transferred particle; in some cases, the j value could be deduced from the structure of the cross section at backward angles (Lee and Schiffer, 1964).

The magnitude of the observed cross section gives the parentage factor (see Eqs. (3E-2) and (3E-10)), and the values obtained are listed in Table 3-7. The absolute values have considerable uncertainty in view of the simplifying assumptions involved (such as zero range of the *np* interaction and neglect of spin-orbit coupling in the nuclear potential). The cross sections were, therefore, normalized with respect to the ground state of ^{41}Ca, which was assumed to have the full single-particle strength. For a more detailed analysis of the (d, p) cross sections leading to the ground state and lowest excited states of ^{41}Ca, see Lee *et al.* (1964).

It is seen that even for the lowest excited orbit ($p_{3/2}$), the single-particle strength is shared by two (or more) levels, although the main strength is concentrated on the 1.95 MeV level. The major part of the $p_{1/2}$ strength is also concentrated on a single level, but the remaining part is distributed over a large number of levels. The strong $l = 3$ stripping in the region of 5–6 MeV of excitation is interpreted in terms of $f_{5/2}$ transfer. Although the estimated total strength is only half of the single-particle value, the absence of other strong f levels in the region studied suggests that the main $f_{5/2}$ strength is contained in the levels listed in the table. For the still higher-lying single-particle orbits, only a fraction of the total strength appears to have been found.

The population of the positive parity states in the low-energy part of the spectrum indicates that the $2s$ and $1d$ shells in ^{40}Ca are not completely filled. Thus, the observed strength of the $d_{3/2}$ transfer to the 2.02 MeV level has been interpreted as evidence that about 20% of the $d_{3/2}$ shell is unoccupied.

The reaction was found to populate many levels in addition to those listed in Table 3-7, but the angular distribution for the additional proton groups did not show any significant component corresponding to the stripping process. It may thus be concluded that the single-particle parentage factors for these levels are small.

Reduced widths for proton resonance scattering on ^{16}O (Table 3–8)

The cross section for proton scattering on ^{16}O exhibits a number of pronounced resonances, the analysis of which yields information on the single-proton parentage factors for the resonance states in ^{17}F. The resonance parameters shown in Table 3-8 are based on differential cross section measurements ▲ for elastic proton scattering. The contribution of the separate lj channels was

▼ determined by a phase shift analysis, neglecting the minor contributions from inelastic reaction and capture processes.

To a first approximation, the scattering amplitude in the region of the resonances can be represented by the single-level formula (3F-12). The energy variation of the resonance width was taken to be of the form (see Eqs. (3F-38) and (3F-44))

$$\Gamma_r = 2kRv_l\gamma \tag{3-55}$$

with a transmission factor v_l calculated for Coulomb wave functions at an interaction radius chosen to be $R = 5.1$ fm (see p. 444). The reduced width γ obtained from Eq. (3-55) is given in Table 3-8 in percent of the unit $\hbar^2/MR^2$. ▲

E_r (MeV)	$I_r\pi$	Γ_r (MeV)	$\gamma \dfrac{MR^2}{\hbar^2} \times 10^2$
3.10	1/2−	0.020	1.3
3.86	5/2−	≤0.003	≤2.8
4.69	3/2−	0.24	6.3
5.10	3/2+	1.63	76
5.52	3/2−	0.07	1.5
5.67	7/2−	0.04	5.3
5.68	1/2+	<0.0006	<0.013
5.82	3/2+	0.19	6.8
6.04	1/2−	0.03	0.6
6.56	1/2+	0.22	3.6
6.70	3/2−	<0.003	<0.04
6.77	3/2+	0.005	0.11
7.03	3/2−	0.004	0.04
7.36		} weak levels	
7.44		} weak levels	
7.45		} weak levels	
7.47		} weak levels	
7.48	3/2+	0.85	18.8
7.55	7/2−	0.03	1.32

Table 3-8 The resonance parameters for the levels in ^{17}F are from the analysis by S. R. Salisbury and H. T. Richards, *Phys. Rev.* **126**, 2147 (1962).

▼ For some of the resonances, the width is not small compared with the distance to the nearest resonance with the same $I\pi$. For these resonances, the phase shifts were fitted in terms of a two-level formula, which includes interference effects between the resonances; the values of γ thus obtained (and listed in Table 3-8) are similar to those derived from an analysis in terms of the one-level formula. ▲

▼ The value of γ in units of $\hbar^2/MR^2$ is a measure of the single-particle strength of the levels considered (see Eq. (3F-65)), but a quantitative analysis of the one-particle parentage coefficient involves the solution of the single-particle motion in the nuclear potential. (The interaction radius assumed in the analysis seems to be rather large, and thus the estimated values of the reduced widths γ may be too small. On the other hand, the value of γ for a single-particle resonance is expected to exceed $\hbar^2/MR^2$, as a consequence of the diffuseness of the potential (see Sec. 3F-2f).

Among the levels studied, the 3/2+ state at 5.10 MeV appears to be approximately of single-particle type, although significant $d_{3/2}$ strength is also observed in the 5.82 and 7.48 MeV levels. The lowest negative parity state expected is $f_{7/2}$, but only a small fraction of the $f_{7/2}$ strength is observed in the region studied.

The analysis of neutron scattering on ^{16}O leads to conclusions similar to those from proton scattering. (For references, see Nuclear Data Sheets.) It has been found possible to reproduce the width of the $d_{3/2}$ neutron resonance at 5.1 MeV by single-particle scattering in a potential (see Kolesov *et al.*, 1963). However, the sensitivity of the width to the assumed parameters of the potential leaves considerable ambiguity in the quantitative determination of the parentage coefficient. With increased information on the nuclear potential, the resonance scattering may provide a rather precise tool for exploring the structure of the nuclear states. ▲

APPENDIX

3A

One-Particle Wave Functions and Matrix Elements

3A-1 Coupling of Spin and Orbit

3A-1a m_s representation

The wave function for a particle with spin $s = \frac{1}{2}$ moving in a spherically symmetric and parity-conserving potential can be written in the form

$$\begin{aligned}\psi_{nljm} &= \mathscr{R}_{nlj}(r)(i^l Y_l \chi)_{(l\frac{1}{2})jm} \\ &= \mathscr{R}_{nlj}(r) \sum_{m_l m_s} \langle l m_l \tfrac{1}{2} m_s | jm \rangle i^l Y_{lm_l}(\vartheta, \varphi) \chi_{m_s} \end{aligned} \qquad (3A\text{-}1)$$

where χ is the spinor wave function specified by the component m_s of the spin with respect to the fixed z axis.

The radial function may be taken to be real (for a time reversal invariant potential), and we choose the phase in such a manner that $\mathscr{R}$ is positive for large r (for r greater than the outermost nodal point),

$$\mathscr{R}_{nlj}(r) \underset{r\to\infty}{>} 0 \qquad (3A\text{-}2)$$

This phase convention is motivated by the fact that radial matrix elements are frequently dominated by the region of the nuclear surface. Examples of radial wave functions are illustrated in Fig. 3-4.

The factor i^l has been inserted in Eq. (3A-1) in order to ensure the standard transformation under time reversal (see Sec. 1B-1)

$$\mathscr{T} |nljm\rangle = (-1)^{j+m} |nlj\, -m\rangle \qquad (3A\text{-}3)$$

3A-1b h representation

In the helicity representation, the spin orientation refers to a coordinate system $\mathscr{K}'$ whose z' axis is in the direction of $\mathbf{r}$. The orientation of $\mathscr{K}'$ with respect to $\mathscr{K}$ will be denoted by $\hat{\mathbf{r}}$; the complete specification of $\mathscr{K}'$ requires three Euler angles, the polar angles ϑ, φ of $\mathbf{r}$ and a third angle ψ, which may be chosen arbitrarily. (The definition of the Euler angles is illustrated in Fig. 1A-1; the redundance of ψ will be further discussed below.)

The transformation of the spinor χ_{m_s} to the rotated frame $\mathscr{K}'$ is given by (see Eq. (1A-34))

$$\chi_{m_s} = \sum_h \mathscr{D}^{1/2}_{m_s h}(\hat{\mathbf{r}})\chi_h \tag{3A-4}$$

The wave function (3A-1) can therefore be written in the form (see Eqs. (1A-42) and (1A-43))

$$\begin{aligned}\psi_{nljm} &= \mathscr{R}_{nlj}(r) i^l \left(\frac{2j+1}{16\pi^2}\right)^{1/2} \sum_h \alpha(ljh)\mathscr{D}^j_{mh}(\hat{\mathbf{r}})\chi_h \\ &= \mathscr{R}_{nlj}(r) i^l \left(\frac{2j+1}{16\pi^2}\right)^{1/2} (\mathscr{D}^j_{m-1/2}(\hat{\mathbf{r}})\chi_{h=-1/2} + (-1)^{j-l-1/2}\mathscr{D}^j_{m1/2}(\hat{\mathbf{r}})\chi_{h=+1/2})\end{aligned} \tag{3A-5}$$

where $\alpha(ljh)$ is a phase factor,

$$\begin{aligned}\alpha(ljh) &= \left(\frac{2(2l+1)}{2j+1}\right)^{1/2} \langle l0\tfrac{1}{2}h \mid jh\rangle \\ &= (-1)^{(h+1/2)(j-l-1/2)} \\ &= \begin{cases} +1 & j = l + \frac{1}{2} \quad h = \pm\frac{1}{2} \\ \mp 1 & j = l - \frac{1}{2} \quad h = \pm\frac{1}{2} \end{cases}\end{aligned} \tag{3A-6}$$

The angular part of the wave function (3A-5) is normalized with respect to integration over all three Euler angles (φ, ϑ, ψ) specifying the orientation $\hat{\mathbf{r}}$, and we have, therefore, inserted an extra normalization factor of $(2\pi)^{-1/2}$. The wave function (3A-5) is independent of the redundant angle ψ, as follows from the derivation of ψ. It can be verified that, if $\Delta\psi$ is added to ψ, the $\mathscr{D}$ function in Eq. (3A-5) is multiplied by exp $(i\Delta\psi h)$, while χ_h is multiplied by $\exp(-i\Delta\psi h)$. (An alternative procedure would be to fix the Euler angle ψ by choosing, for example, the x' and y' axes of $\mathscr{K}'$ so that $\mathscr{K}'$ is obtained from $\mathscr{K}$ by a rotation through an angle ϑ about an axis with the direction of $\mathbf{z} \times \mathbf{z}'$; the Euler angles of $\mathscr{K}'$ would then be φ, ϑ, $\psi = -\varphi$; see Fig. 1A-1.)

We can also derive the spin angular part of the wave function (3A-5) by transforming to the "intrinsic" coordinate system $\mathscr{K}'$ with orientation $\hat{\mathbf{r}}$. An argument similar to that leading to Eq. (1A-97) gives

$$\langle \hat{\mathbf{r}}h \mid hjm\rangle = \left(\frac{2j+1}{8\pi^2}\right)^{1/2} \mathscr{D}^j_{mh}(\hat{\mathbf{r}}) \tag{3A-7}$$

Rotational symmetry specifies the $\hat{\mathbf{r}}$ and m dependence of the transformation coefficient (3A-7) but leaves open the possibility of a phase factor which may depend on j and h. Since $h \to -h$ under time reversal, we cannot employ the usual phase prescription, and the relation (3A-7) therefore involves an additional phase convention for the states $|hjm\rangle$.

For the amplitudes in the ljm representation, the transformation to the intrinsic coordinate system yields

$$\langle \hat{\mathbf{r}}m_s \mid ljm\rangle = i^l \left(\frac{2l+1}{8\pi^2}\right)^{1/2} \langle lm_l sm_s \mid jm\rangle \mathscr{D}^l_{m_l 0}(\hat{\mathbf{r}}) \tag{3A-8}$$

The phase factor i^l is here determined (apart from a factor ± 1) from the requirement that $|ljm\rangle$ has the standard transformation under time reversal. From Eqs. (3A-7) and (3A-8) together with (3A-4), we obtain the transformation coefficient

$$\langle hjm \,|\, ljm\rangle = i^l \left(\frac{2l+1}{2j+1}\right)^{1/2} \langle l0sh \,|\, jh\rangle \tag{3A-9}$$

It is seen that the relations (3A-9) and (3A-7) are equivalent to Eq. (3A-5). (The transformation coefficient (3A-9) is written in a form that is valid for particles of arbitrary spin as well as for the relative motion of two particles with total spin s and total helicity h.)

The $\mathscr{P}$ and $\mathscr{T}$ transformations of the states $|ljm\rangle$ and $|hjm\rangle$ are given by

$$\begin{aligned} \mathscr{P}\,|ljm\rangle &= (-1)^l\,|ljm\rangle \\ \mathscr{T}\,|ljm\rangle &= (-1)^{j+m}\,|lj-m\rangle \\ \mathscr{P}\,|hjm\rangle &= (-1)^{j-1/2}\,|-hjm\rangle \\ \mathscr{T}\,|hjm\rangle &= (-1)^{m+1/2}\,|-hj-m\rangle \end{aligned} \tag{3A-10}$$

The transforms of $|hjm\rangle$ can be obtained from those of $|ljm\rangle$ by means of Eq. (3A-9).

If we consider the $\mathscr{P}$ and $\mathscr{T}$ transformations in the $\hat{\mathbf{r}}h$ representation, we must choose the third Euler angle for the transformed orientations. It is convenient to make this choice such that $\hat{\mathbf{r}}$ is invariant under $\mathscr{T}$ while, under $\mathscr{P}$, $\hat{\mathbf{r}}$ transforms into $-\hat{\mathbf{r}}$, obtained from $\hat{\mathbf{r}}$ by a rotation through the angle $-\pi$ about the y' axis of $\mathscr{K}'$. We then have

$$\begin{aligned} \mathscr{T}\,|\hat{\mathbf{r}}\,h\rangle &= (-1)^{1/2+h}\,|\hat{\mathbf{r}}-h\rangle \\ \mathscr{P}\,|\hat{\mathbf{r}}\,h\rangle &= (-1)^{1/2-h}\,|-\hat{\mathbf{r}}\,-h\rangle \end{aligned} \tag{3A-11}$$

and

$$\begin{aligned} -\hat{\mathbf{r}} &= (\varphi+\pi,\, \pi-\vartheta,\, -\pi-\psi) \\ \mathscr{D}^j_{mh}(-\hat{\mathbf{r}}) &= (-1)^{j+h}\mathscr{D}^j_{m-h}(\hat{\mathbf{r}}) \end{aligned} \tag{3A-12}$$

The phase factor involved in the $\mathscr{P}$ transformation may be obtained by employing the rotation matrix (1A-47). The relation (3A-12) for the $\mathscr{D}$ function can be derived from Eq. (1A-45).

The helicity representation (3A-5) for the wave function of a particle with spin is equivalent to the representation for rotational wave functions of a system whose intrinsic shape possesses axial symmetry but not reflection symmetry (see Sec. 4-2).

3A-2 Evaluation of Matrix Elements for One-Particle Operators[3]

3A-2a Operators depending only on spatial coordinates

A tensor operator depending only on the position $\mathbf{r}$ of a particle has the general form

$$T_{\lambda\mu} = i^\lambda f(r)\, Y_{\lambda\mu}(\vartheta, \varphi) \tag{3A-13}$$

For a self-adjoint tensor (which transforms into itself under Hermitian conjugation),

[3] The one-particle matrix elements are usually evaluated employing the $(ls)j$ representation (see for example, de-Shalit and Talmi, 1963). The present section especially exploits the helicity representation, which is often useful in exhibiting simple features of the matrix elements. The helicity representation has been employed by Raynal (1967) in the evaluation of two-body interaction matrix elements.

the radial function $f(r)$ may be taken to be real. We have added the factor i^λ so as to obtain the phase factor $c_{\mathcal{T}} = c_H = 1$ for time reversal and Hermitian conjugation (see Eqs. (1A-74) and (1A-78)). In a representation with the standard phases, the matrix elements of $T_{\lambda\mu}$ are then real (see Eq. (1A-75)).

For the helicity wave functions (3A-5), the reduced matrix element defined by Eq. (1A-61) can be evaluated by means of the coupling relation (1A-43) for the $\mathcal{D}$ functions (see also Eq. (1A-42)), and we obtain

$$\begin{aligned}
&\langle n_2 l_2 j_2 \| i^\lambda f(r) Y_\lambda \| n_1 l_1 j_1 \rangle \\
&\qquad = (2j_2+1)^{1/2} \langle j_2 m_2 | T_\lambda | j_1 \rangle_{(j_1\lambda) j_2 m_2} \\
&\qquad = i^{l_1+\lambda-l_2} (-1)^{j_1+\lambda-j_2} \left(\frac{(2\lambda+1)(2j_1+1)}{4\pi} \right)^{1/2} \\
&\qquad\qquad \times \langle j_1 \tfrac{1}{2} \lambda 0 | j_2 \tfrac{1}{2} \rangle \langle j_2 | f | j_1 \rangle \begin{cases} 1 & l_1+\lambda-l_2 \text{ even} \\ 0 & l_1+\lambda-l_2 \text{ odd} \end{cases}
\end{aligned} \tag{3A-14}$$

with the radial matrix element

$$\langle j_2 | f | j_1 \rangle = \int_0^\infty \mathcal{R}_{n_2 l_2 j_2}(r) f(r) \mathcal{R}_{n_1 l_1 j_1}(r) r^2 \, dr \tag{3A-15}$$

(We employ a notation by which radial matrix elements, such as (3A-15), are distinguished from the matrix elements involving angular variables, since the latter are either labeled by magnetic quantum numbers or, in the case of the reduced matrix elements, have a double bar.) In Eq. (3A-14) we have inserted the phase factors (3A-6) and have used the symmetry relation (1A-10) for the vector addition coefficient. The parity conservation is ensured by the summation over h.

One notes that the angular matrix element in Eq. (3A-14) depends only on the j quantum numbers (not on the l values). In fact, the angular density, averaged over the spin orientation of a single-particle state, depends only on j, as follows directly from the expression (3A-5) for the wave function in the helicity representation.

We can also derive the matrix element of the tensor (3A-13) by means of the single-particle wave functions (3A-1). Performing a recoupling from the scheme $(l_1\frac{1}{2})j_1, \lambda; j_2$ to the coupling scheme $(l_1\lambda)l_2, \frac{1}{2}; j_2$ and using the relations (1A-42) and (1A-43) for the coupling of the Y functions, we obtain

$$\begin{aligned}
&\langle n_2 l_2 j_2 \| i^\lambda f(r) Y_\lambda \| n_1 l_1 j_1 \rangle \\
&\qquad = (2j_2+1)^{1/2} \langle l_2 j_2 m_2 | T_\lambda | l_1 j_1 \rangle_{(l_1\frac{1}{2})j_1,\lambda; j_2 m_2} \\
&\qquad = i^{l_1+\lambda-l_2} \left(\frac{(2\lambda+1)(2l_1+1)(2j_2+1)}{4\pi(2l_2+1)} \right)^{1/2} \langle l_1 0 \lambda 0 | l_2 0 \rangle \\
&\qquad\qquad \times \langle (l_1\lambda) l_2, \tfrac{1}{2}; j_2 | (l_1 \tfrac{1}{2}) j_1, \lambda; j_2 \rangle \langle j_2 | f | j_1 \rangle
\end{aligned} \tag{3A-16}$$

The recoupling coefficient can be expressed in terms of a $6j$ symbol (see Eq. (1A-20)). The equivalence of the expressions (3A-14) and (3A-16) exhibits the possibility of expressing a $6j$ symbol in which one of the angular momenta is 1/2 in terms of vector addition coefficients. For even values of $l_1 + \lambda - l_2$, we have

$$\begin{Bmatrix} l_1 \tfrac{1}{2} j_1 \\ j_2 \lambda l_2 \end{Bmatrix} = (-1)^{l_2+1/2+j_2}(2l_1+1)^{-1/2}(2j_2+1)^{-1/2} \frac{\langle j_1 \tfrac{1}{2} \lambda 0 \,|\, j_2 \tfrac{1}{2} \rangle}{\langle l_1 0 \lambda 0 \,|\, l_2 0 \rangle} \tag{3A-16a}$$

3A-2b Spin-dependent operators

A spin-dependent (but velocity-independent) operator can be expanded in tensors of the form

$$T_{\kappa,\lambda\mu} = i^{\kappa} f(r) (Y_\kappa(\hat{\mathbf{r}}) s)_{(\kappa 1)\lambda\mu} \tag{3A-17}$$

We can also characterize the spin dependence in terms of the (spherical) components of $\mathbf{s}$ in the intrinsic system $\mathscr{K}'$, with the orientation $\hat{\mathbf{r}}$. The basic tensors are then[4]

$$T_{\eta,\lambda\mu} = f(r) \mathscr{D}^{\lambda}_{\mu\eta}(\hat{\mathbf{r}}) s_\eta \tag{3A-18}$$

where (see Eq. (1A-52))

$$s_{\mu_s} = \sum_{\eta} \mathscr{D}^{1}_{\mu_s \eta}(\hat{\mathbf{r}}) s_\eta \tag{3A-19}$$

The transformation from Eq. (3A-17) to Eq. (3A-18) is given by

$$\begin{aligned}
(Y_\kappa s)_{(\kappa 1)\lambda\mu} &= \sum_\eta \left(\frac{2\kappa+1}{4\pi}\right)^{1/2} \langle \kappa 0 1 \eta \,|\, \lambda \eta \rangle \mathscr{D}^{\lambda}_{\mu\eta} s_\eta \\
&= \begin{cases}
-\left(\dfrac{\lambda+1}{4\pi}\right)^{1/2} \mathscr{D}_{\mu 0} s_{\eta=0} + \left(\dfrac{\lambda}{8\pi}\right)^{1/2} (\mathscr{D}^{\lambda}_{\mu 1} s_{\eta=1} + \mathscr{D}^{\lambda}_{\mu -1} s_{\eta=-1}) & \lambda = \kappa - 1 \\
-\left(\dfrac{2\lambda+1}{8\pi}\right)^{1/2} (\mathscr{D}^{\lambda}_{\mu 1} s_{\eta=1} - \mathscr{D}^{\lambda}_{\mu -1} s_{\eta=-1}) & \lambda = \kappa \\
+\left(\dfrac{\lambda}{4\pi}\right)^{1/2} \mathscr{D}^{\lambda}_{\mu 0} s_{\eta=0} + \left(\dfrac{\lambda+1}{8\pi}\right)^{1/2} (\mathscr{D}^{\lambda}_{\mu 1} s_{\eta=1} + \mathscr{D}^{\lambda}_{\mu -1} s_{\eta=-1}) & \lambda = \kappa + 1
\end{cases}
\end{aligned} \tag{3A-20}$$

In the helicity representation, we obtain the reduced matrix elements

$$\begin{aligned}
&\langle j_2 \| f(r) \mathscr{D}^{\lambda}_{\nu=0} s_{\eta=0} \| j_1 \rangle \\
&\quad = i^{l_1 - l_2} (-1)^{j_1+\lambda-j_2+1} (2j_1+1)^{1/2} \langle j_1 \tfrac{1}{2} \lambda 0 \,|\, j_2 \tfrac{1}{2} \rangle \langle j_2 | f | j_1 \rangle \tfrac{1}{2} \begin{cases} 1 & l_1 + \lambda - l_2 \ \text{odd} \\ 0 & l_1 + \lambda - l_2 \ \text{even} \end{cases} \\
&\langle j_2 \| f(r) (\mathscr{D}^{\lambda}_{\nu=1} s_{\eta=1} \pm \mathscr{D}^{\lambda}_{\nu=-1} s_{\eta=-1}) \| j_1 \rangle \\
&\quad = i^{l_1 - l_2} (-1)^{j_2 - l_2 - 1/2} (j_1 + \tfrac{1}{2})^{1/2} \langle j_1 - \tfrac{1}{2} \lambda 1 \,|\, j_2 \tfrac{1}{2} \rangle \langle j_2 | f | j_1 \rangle \tfrac{1}{2} (-1 \pm (-1)^{l_1 + l_2 - \lambda})
\end{aligned} \tag{3A-21}$$

where $\mathscr{D}^{\lambda}_{\nu}$ represents the spherical tensor of rank λ with μ component $\mathscr{D}^{\lambda}_{\mu\nu}$.

---

[4] Tensor quantum numbers are denoted by Greek letters. Since a Greek pronunciation of "helicity" presumably omits the h sound, we employ the quantum number η.

For the tensors (3A-17), the reduced matrix elements can thus be expressed in the form

$$\langle j_2 \| i^\kappa f(r)(Y_\kappa s)_{(\kappa 1)\lambda} \| j_1 \rangle$$
$$= i^{l_1 - l_2 + \kappa} \left(\frac{2j_1+1}{4\pi}\right)^{1/2} \langle j_2 | f | j_1 \rangle \tfrac{1}{2}$$
$$\times \begin{cases} (-1)^{j_1+\lambda-j_2}(\lambda+1)^{1/2}\langle j_1 \tfrac{1}{2} \lambda 0 | j_2 \tfrac{1}{2}\rangle - (-1)^{j_2 - l_2 - 1/2}(\lambda)^{1/2}\langle j_1 - \tfrac{1}{2} \lambda 1 | j_2 \tfrac{1}{2}\rangle & \lambda = \kappa - 1 \\ (-1)^{j_2 - l_2 - 1/2}(2\lambda+1)^{1/2}\langle j_1 - \tfrac{1}{2}\lambda 1 | j_2 \tfrac{1}{2}\rangle & \lambda = \kappa \\ (-1)^{j_1+\lambda+j_2}(\lambda)^{1/2}\langle j_1 \tfrac{1}{2}\lambda 0 | j_2 \tfrac{1}{2}\rangle - (-1)^{j_2 - l_2 - 1/2}(\lambda+1)^{1/2}\langle j_1 - \tfrac{1}{2}\lambda 1 | j_2 \tfrac{1}{2}\rangle & \lambda = \kappa + 1 \end{cases} \quad \text{(3A-22)}$$

assuming $l_1 - l_2 + \kappa$ to be even. (For odd $l_1 - l_2 + \kappa$, the matrix element vanishes as a consequence of parity conservation.)

The expressions (3A-22) can be further reduced by employing the recursion relation

$$\langle j_1 - \tfrac{1}{2}\lambda 1 | j_2 \tfrac{1}{2}\rangle = -\langle j_1 \tfrac{1}{2}\lambda 0 | j_2 \tfrac{1}{2}\rangle \frac{(j_1 + \tfrac{1}{2}) + (-1)^{j_1 + j_2 - \lambda}(j_2 + \tfrac{1}{2})}{(\lambda(\lambda+1))^{1/2}} \quad \text{(3A-23)}$$

The vector addition coefficients $\langle j_1 \tfrac{1}{2} \lambda 0 | j_2 \tfrac{1}{2}\rangle$ can be evaluated by means of the relations given in Appendix 7A.

In the special case of $j_1 = j_2$, the coefficient (3A-23) vanishes for even λ. Therefore, the diagonal matrix elements (3A-22) vanish for $\lambda = \kappa$. (For odd $\lambda = \kappa$, the diagonal matrix elements vanish as a consequence of parity conservation.)

If one uses $(ls)j$ coupled wave functions, the matrix elements of the operators (3A-17) can be obtained from the general formula (1A-70),

$$\langle (l_2 \tfrac{1}{2}) j_2 \| i^\kappa f (Y_\kappa s)_\lambda \| (l_1 \tfrac{1}{2}) j_1 \rangle$$
$$= ((2\lambda+1)(2j_1+1)(2j_2+1))^{1/2} \begin{Bmatrix} l_1 & \tfrac{1}{2} & j_1 \\ \kappa & 1 & \lambda \\ l_2 & \tfrac{1}{2} & j_2 \end{Bmatrix} \langle j_2 | f | j_1 \rangle \langle l_2 \| i^\kappa Y_\kappa \| l_1 \rangle \langle \tfrac{1}{2} \| s \| \tfrac{1}{2} \rangle \quad \text{(3A-24)}$$

where the angular and spin matrix elements have the values (see Eq. (1A-63))

$$\langle l_2 \| i^\kappa Y_\kappa \| l_1 \rangle = i^{l_1 - l_2 + \kappa}\left(\frac{(2\kappa+1)(2l_1+1)}{4\pi}\right)^{1/2} \langle l_1 0 \kappa 0 | l_2 0 \rangle$$
$$\langle \tfrac{1}{2} \| s \| \tfrac{1}{2} \rangle = \sqrt{\frac{3}{2}} \quad \text{(3A-25)}$$

The equivalence of the expressions (3A-22) and (3A-24) reflects special properties of the $9j$ symbols involving two $j = 1/2$ quantum numbers.

Spin-dependent tensors can also be expressed in terms of the operator $(\mathbf{s} \cdot \boldsymbol{\nabla})$ acting on a function of the coordinates. Such expressions can be written in terms of the tensors (3A-17) or (3A-18) by means of the relations

$$(\mathbf{s} \cdot \boldsymbol{\nabla}) f(r) Y_{\lambda\mu} = \left(\frac{\lambda}{2\lambda+1}\right)^{1/2}\left(f'(r) + \frac{\lambda+1}{r} f(r)\right)(Y_{\lambda-1}, s)_{(\lambda-1,1)\lambda\mu}$$
$$-\left(\frac{\lambda+1}{2\lambda+1}\right)^{1/2}\left(f'(r) - \frac{\lambda}{r} f(r)\right)(Y_{\lambda+1}, s)_{(\lambda+1,1)\lambda\mu} \quad \text{(3A-26)}$$
$$= \left(\frac{2\lambda+1}{4\pi}\right)^{1/2}\left\{ f'(r)\mathscr{D}^\lambda_{\mu 0} s_{\eta=0} + \left(\frac{\lambda(\lambda+1)}{2}\right)^{1/2} \frac{1}{r} f(r)(\mathscr{D}^\lambda_{\mu 1} s_{\eta=1} + \mathscr{D}^\lambda_{\mu -1} s_{\eta=-1})\right\}$$

3A-2c Operators involving orbital momenta

Tensors involving the orbital angular momentum **l** can be expressed in terms of **j** (=**l** + **s**) together with spin-dependent operators of the type already evaluated, and we thus consider tensors of the form

$$T_{\lambda\mu} \equiv i^{\kappa} f(r) (Y_{\kappa} j)_{(\kappa 1)\lambda\mu} \tag{3A-27}$$

The reduced matrix elements of the operator (3A-27) can be obtained by a recoupling

$$\begin{aligned}
\langle j_2 \| i^{\kappa} f(r) (Y_{\kappa} j)_{(\kappa 1)\lambda} \| j_1 \rangle
&= (2j_2+1)^{1/2} \langle j_2 m_2 | i^{\kappa} f(r) Y_{\kappa} j | j_1 \rangle_{j_1, (\kappa 1)\lambda; j_2 m_2} \\
&= (2j_2+1)^{1/2} \sum_{j'} \langle (j_1 1) j', \kappa; j_2 | j_1, (\kappa 1)\lambda; j_2 \rangle \langle j_2 m_2 | i^{\kappa} f(r) Y_{\kappa} j | j_1 \rangle_{(j_1 1) j', \kappa; j_2 m_2} \\
&= (-1)^{j_1+\lambda+j_2} ((2\lambda+1)(2j_1+1)(j_1+1)j_1)^{1/2} \begin{Bmatrix} \kappa & 1 & \lambda \\ j_1 & j_2 & j_1 \end{Bmatrix} \langle j_2 \| i^{\kappa} f(r) Y_{\kappa} \| j_1 \rangle
\end{aligned} \tag{3A-28}$$

Since **j** is diagonal in the single-particle quantum numbers nlj, only the term $j' = j_1$ contributes. We have employed the relation (1A-19) as well as the reduced matrix element (1A-63). The reduced matrix element in the last line of Eq. (3A-28) is given by Eq. (3A-14).

One can also express the angular momentum dependence in terms of the components j_η of **j** in the intrinsic coordinate system $\mathscr{K}'$ with orientation $\hat{\mathbf{r}}$. The transformation from the component j_μ in $\mathscr{K}$ to the components j_η in $\mathscr{K}'$ is given by

$$j_\mu = \sum_\eta \mathscr{D}^1_{\mu\eta}(\hat{\mathbf{r}}) j_\eta \tag{3A-29}$$

and the properties of the intrinsic components j_η are discussed in Sec. 1A-6. In particular, the action of j_η on the single-particle wave function is given by (see Eqs. (1A-90) and (1A-93))

$$j_\eta \mathscr{D}^j_{mh}(\hat{\mathbf{r}}) \chi_h = (-1)^\eta (j(j+1))^{1/2} \langle j h 1 -\eta | j h-\eta \rangle \mathscr{D}^j_{m,h-\eta}(\hat{\mathbf{r}}) \chi_h \tag{3A-30}$$

The **j**-dependent tensors can be written in terms of the j_η components by means of relations analogous to Eq. (3A-20). In this manner, the matrix elements are expressed in terms of vector addition coefficients, without involving $6j$ symbols.

APPENDIX
3B

Particle-Hole Conjugation

3B-1 Description of Fermion Systems in Terms of Particles and Holes

3B-1a Systems of identical particles

We consider a system of identical fermions (neutrons, protons, or electrons) moving independently in an average potential. The potential may have arbitrary shape, but is assumed to be time reversal invariant.

The single-particle orbits are then twofold degenerate (Kramers theorem, see p. 19), and the degenerate orbits, conjugate under time reversal, are denoted by ν and $\bar{\nu}$,

$$\begin{aligned} |\bar{\nu}\rangle &= \mathscr{T}\,|\nu\rangle \\ |\nu\rangle &= -\mathscr{T}\,|\bar{\nu}\rangle \end{aligned} \tag{3B-1}$$

since, for a single fermion, we have $\mathscr{T}^2 = -1$ (see Eq. (1-41)). If the system possesses spherical symmetry, the orbits may be labeled by $\nu = nljm$.

The particle orbits ν are numbered according to their energy ε_ν; for degenerate orbits, the numbering can be chosen arbitrarily. A state obtained by filling the first Ω pairs of orbits $(\nu, \bar{\nu})$ will be referred to as a "normal state," provided Ω is chosen such that the state is nondegenerate. For a spherical nucleus, this implies that the normal state consists of closed shells (or subshells). For a deformed nucleus, the normal state may involve an arbitrary number of paired particles. The occupancy of the single-particle levels in a normal state is referred to as a normal distribution (or Fermi distribution) and the last filled orbit as the Fermi level, ν_F.

For not too high excitation energies, the bulk of the particles remains in a normal distribution, and it is convenient to describe the system in terms of the addition or removal of particles from the normal state ("elementary excitations").

The states obtained by adding a particle in an unfilled orbit are represented by

$$|\nu\rangle = a^\dagger(\nu)\,|\hat{0}\rangle \qquad \nu > \nu_F \tag{3B-2}$$

where $a^\dagger(\nu)$ is the particle creation operator, while $|\hat{0}\rangle$ is the normal state, which plays the role of a generalized vacuum. (When there is no risk of confusion, we employ the same notation $|\nu\rangle$ for the state of a single particle as for the many-particle state (3B-2).) The states obtained by removing a particle from an occupied state, that is, by acting with an annihilation operator a on the normal state, are referred to as hole states. (The properties of creation and annihilation operators are discussed in Appendix 2A.)

The quantum numbers of a hole state are related to those of the annihilated particle by time reversal conjugation. In fact, to produce a hole state with angular momentum jm (or linear momentum $\mathbf{p}$), we must remove a particle with quantum numbers $j - m$ (or $-\mathbf{p}$). The basic relation between particles and holes can therefore be expressed in the form

$$\begin{aligned} b^\dagger(\nu) &= a(\bar{\nu}) \\ b(\nu) &= a^\dagger(\bar{\nu}) \end{aligned} \tag{3B-3}$$

where $b^\dagger$ (and its Hermitian conjugate b) are the creation (and annihilation) operators for hole states,

$$|\nu^{-1}\rangle = b^\dagger(\nu)\,|\hat{0}\rangle \tag{3B-4}$$

The inverse of Eq. (3B-3) is given by (see Eq. (3B-1))

$$\begin{aligned} a^\dagger(\nu) &= -b(\bar{\nu}) \\ a(\nu) &= -b^\dagger(\bar{\nu}) \end{aligned} \tag{3B-5}$$

In the spherical representation, the operators $b^\dagger(jm)$ form the components of a spherical tensor of rank j, as do the $a^\dagger(jm)$ (see Sec. 1A-5e).

States with two or more particles and (or) holes are obtained by acting with products of $a^\dagger$ and $b^\dagger$ operators on the normal state,

$$|\nu_1^{-1}\cdots\nu_k^{-1}\nu_{k+1}\cdots\nu_n\rangle = a^\dagger(\nu_n)\cdots a^\dagger(\nu_{k+1})b^\dagger(\nu_k)\cdots b^\dagger(\nu_1)\,|\hat{0}\rangle \tag{3B-6}$$

(In the representation of states in terms of particles and holes, all states are antisymmetrized, and the subscript a is therefore usually not needed.)

The transformation, by which the occupancy of the single-particle levels with $\nu \leqslant \nu_F$ are described in terms of ($b^\dagger$, b) operators in place of the ($a^\dagger$, a) operators, is canonical, since the commutation relations for the ($b^\dagger$, b) operators are the same as for the ($a^\dagger$, a) operators. The transformation can therefore be associated with a unitary operator $\mathscr{U}_h$, the particle-hole conjugation, with the properties

$$\begin{aligned} \mathscr{U}_h a^\dagger(\nu)\mathscr{U}_h^{-1} &= b^\dagger(\nu) = a(\bar{\nu}) \qquad && \nu \leqslant \nu_F \\ \mathscr{U}_h a^\dagger(\nu)\mathscr{U}_h^{-1} &= a^\dagger(\nu) && \nu > \nu_F \end{aligned} \tag{3B-7}$$

The vacuum state with the property $a(\nu)\,|0\rangle = 0$ for all ν is transformed into the normal state with the property $b(\nu)\,|\hat{0}\rangle = 0$ for all $\nu \leqslant \nu_F$. The phase of $\mathscr{U}_h$ is so chosen that

$$\mathscr{U}_h\,|0\rangle = |\hat{0}\rangle \tag{3B-8}$$

From this relation, together with Eqs. (3B-6) and (3B-7), follows

$$\begin{aligned} |\nu_1^{-1}\cdots\nu_k^{-1}\nu_{k+1}\cdots\nu_n\rangle &= a^\dagger(\nu_n)\cdots a^\dagger(\nu_{k+1})b^\dagger(\nu_k)\cdots b^\dagger(\nu_1)\,|\hat{0}\rangle \\ &= \mathscr{U}_h a^\dagger(\nu_n)\cdots a^\dagger(\nu_{k+1})a^\dagger(\nu_k)\cdots a^\dagger(\nu_1)\,|0\rangle \\ &= \mathscr{U}_h\,|\nu_1\cdots\nu_n\rangle_a \end{aligned} \tag{3B-9}$$

where the last state is the antisymmetrized n-particle state. Acting twice with $\mathcal{U}_h$ gives

$$\mathcal{U}_h^2 = (-1)^{\Omega - k} \qquad \text{(3B-10)}$$

where k is the number of holes and Ω the number of paired single-particle levels in the normal state.

Since the particle-hole conjugation changes a configuration with $2\Omega - k$ particles into one with k particles, the operator $\mathcal{U}_h$ commutes with the number operator only for a system with $k = \Omega$ particles. In the special case of a configuration with a half-filled j shell, $\mathcal{U}_h$ may commute with the Hamiltonian, and the stationary states may then be labeled by an additional quantum number characterizing the symmetry under particle-hole conjugation (Bell, 1959).

The particle-antiparticle conjugation (or charge conjugation), which plays a fundamental role in relativistic quantum mechanics, is a transformation from a particle state ν, with *positive* energy, to a hole state obtained by removing a particle $\bar{\nu}$, with *negative* energy, from the Dirac sea. The operation, therefore, exploits an equivalence between the particle states above and below the Fermi surface with no counterpart in the nuclear system. This symmetry makes it possible to define a particle-hole transformation which, in contrast to the operation $\mathcal{U}_h$ given by Eq. (3B-7), leaves invariant the normal state and is a constant of the motion (see the reference to $\mathscr{C}$, $\mathscr{P}\mathscr{C}$, and $\mathscr{P}\mathscr{C}\mathscr{T}$ symmetry in Chapter 1, pp. 16 and 21).

Even though the nucleonic levels $\nu_>$ and $\nu_<$ above and below the Fermi surface have different quantum numbers (such as nlj), the gross features of the single-particle spectrum, such as the level density, may in some situations be approximately the same for $\nu_>$ and $\nu_<$. This similarity may give rise to symmetry properties of the nuclear excitations analogous to those associated with charge conjugation. An operation corresponding to charge conjugation is then obtained by combining the particle-hole conjugation with a transformation $\nu_< \rightleftarrows \nu_>$ between the approximately equivalent states $(a^\dagger(\nu_>) \rightleftarrows b^\dagger(\nu_<))$. (Examples of this symmetry are discussed in Chapters 8 and 9.)

3B-1b Systems of neutrons and protons. Isospin for hole states

For a system of neutrons and protons, we can define hole states in terms of the relation (3B-3) for the neutrons and the protons, separately. We use the notation

$$\begin{aligned} |\nu_n^{-1}\rangle &= b^\dagger(\nu_n)\,|\hat{0}\rangle \\ b^\dagger(\nu_n) &= a(\bar{\nu}_n) \end{aligned} \qquad \text{(3B-11)}$$

for the neutron hole states, and a corresponding notation $(\nu_n \to \nu_p)$ for the proton hole states.

The isospin component of a hole is opposite to that of the annihilated particle ($m_t = -\frac{1}{2}$ for n^{-1}, etc.), but the creation operators $b^\dagger$ defined by Eq. (3B-11) do not transform as the components of an isospinor (a tensor of rank 1/2 in isospace). In fact, under Hermitian conjugation, a tensor component $t\ m_t$ transforms into a tensor component $t - m_t$ multiplied by a phase factor that changes sign when m_t is raised or lowered by one unit (see Eq. (1A-76)).

Hole states and hole operators with isospinor properties may be defined by

$$\begin{aligned} |\nu^{-1}, m_t\rangle &= b^\dagger(\nu, m_t)\,|\hat{0}\rangle \\ b^\dagger(\nu, m_t) &= (-1)^{1/2 + m_t} a(\bar{\nu}, -m_t) \end{aligned} \qquad \text{(3B-12)}$$

The relationship between the two sets of hole operators is given by

$$\begin{aligned} b^\dagger(\nu, m_t = \tfrac{1}{2}) &= -b^\dagger(\nu_p) = -a(\bar{\nu}_p) = -a(\bar{\nu}, m_t = -\tfrac{1}{2}) \\ b^\dagger(\nu, m_t = -\tfrac{1}{2}) &= b^\dagger(\nu_n) = a(\bar{\nu}_n) = a(\bar{\nu}, m_t = \tfrac{1}{2}) \end{aligned} \tag{3B-13}$$

The particle-hole transformation (3B-12) can be expressed in terms of the transformation

$$\mathscr{F} = \exp(i\pi T_y)\mathscr{T} = \mathscr{R}_\tau^{-1}\mathscr{T} \tag{3B-14}$$

which is the product of time reversal and a rotation through the angle $-\pi$ about the y axis in isospace (the inverse of the charge symmetry operation $\mathscr{R}_\tau$ (see Eq. (1-59)). Denoting the $\mathscr{F}$-transformed states by a tilde, we have

$$\begin{aligned} |\widetilde{\nu, m_t}\rangle &\equiv \mathscr{F}\,|\nu, m_t\rangle = (-1)^{1/2+m_t}\,|\bar{\nu}, -m_t\rangle \\ b^\dagger(\nu, m_t) &= a(\widetilde{\nu, m_t}) \end{aligned} \tag{3B-15}$$

The operator $\mathscr{F}$ is antiunitary, like $\mathscr{T}$, but obeys the relation

$$\mathscr{F}^2 = +1 \tag{3B-16}$$

for a system of nucleons. The inverse of (3B-15) is, therefore,

$$a^\dagger(\nu, m_t) = b(\widetilde{\nu, m_t}) \tag{3B-17}$$

The particle-hole conjugation $\mathscr{U}_h'$, which generates the transformation $a^\dagger(\nu, m_t) \to b^\dagger(\nu, m_t)$, has properties similar to those of $\mathscr{U}_h$; however, the relation (3B-16) implies $(\mathscr{U}_h')^2 = 1$.

If the normal state contains more neutrons than protons $((\nu_F)_n > (\nu_F)_p)$, the total isospin of the system is obtained by coupling the isospins of the extra particles and holes to the isospin of the normal state (see, for example, Eq. (3-19)).

3B-2 Matrix Elements of One-Particle Operators

3B-2a ν representation

A one-particle operator, F, can be written in terms of the $(a^\dagger, a)$ variables and the single-particle matrix elements $\langle\nu_2|F|\nu_1\rangle$ (see Eq. (2A-24)). For the states below the Fermi level, we perform the transformation (3B-3) to hole operators (replacing the summation variable ν by $\bar{\nu}$). In this manner, we obtain three different terms, corresponding to matrix elements with none, one, or two of the states having $\nu \leqslant \nu_F$

$$\begin{aligned} F &= F_0 + F_1 + F_2 \\ F_0 &= \sum_{\substack{\nu_1 > \nu_F \\ \nu_2 > \nu_F}} \langle\nu_2|F|\nu_1\rangle a^\dagger(\nu_2)a(\nu_1) && \text{(particle scattering)} \\ F_1 &= \sum_{\substack{\nu_1 \leqslant \nu_F \\ \nu_2 > \nu_F}} \{\langle\nu_2|F|\bar{\nu}_1\rangle a^\dagger(\nu_2)b^\dagger(\nu_1) && \text{(pair creation)} \\ &\quad + \langle\bar{\nu}_1|F|\nu_2\rangle b(\nu_1)a(\nu_2)\} && \text{(pair annihilation)} \\ F_2 &= -\sum_{\substack{\nu_1 \leqslant \nu_F \\ \nu_2 \leqslant \nu_F}} \langle\bar{\nu}_1|F|\bar{\nu}_2\rangle b^\dagger(\nu_2)b(\nu_1) && \text{(hole scattering)} \\ &\quad + \sum_{\nu \leqslant \nu_F} \langle\nu|F|\nu\rangle && \text{("vacuum" expectation)} \end{aligned} \tag{3B-18}$$

The last term in F_2 is the expectation value of F in the normal state. This term arises from the commutation of $b(\nu_1)$ and $b^\dagger(\nu_2)$, when the expression for F is reduced to the normal form with creation operators occurring to the left of annihilation operators.

The different matrix elements of F are illustrated by the diagrams in Fig. 3B-1. The relationship between the matrix elements for the various processes can be expressed in terms of the following simple rule (the "crossing relation"): A hole state ν^{-1} in

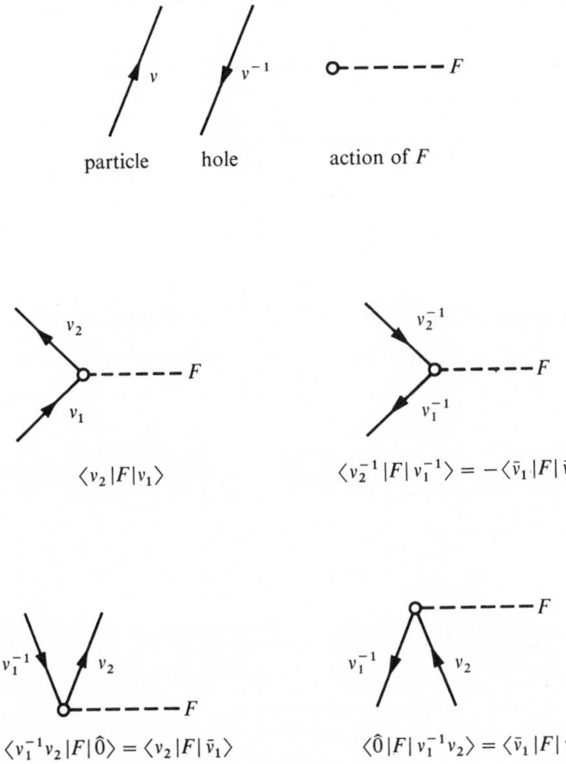

Figure 3B-1 The diagrams may be taken as a vivid notation for the matrix element, which is read from bottom (initial state) to top (final state).

initial (or final) state may be replaced by a particle state $\bar{\nu}$ in final (or initial) state; to obtain the correct sign, the state that is being transferred must first be brought all the way to the left by suitable commutations, each involving a factor of -1. For example,

$$\langle \nu_2^{-1} | F | \nu_1^{-1} \rangle = \langle \hat{0} | F | \bar{\nu}_2 \nu_1^{-1} \rangle = -\langle \hat{0} | F | \nu_1^{-1} \bar{\nu}_2 \rangle$$
$$= -\langle \bar{\nu}_1 | F | \bar{\nu}_2 \rangle \qquad \text{(3B-19)}$$

(The crossing relation leaves out a c-number term, the vacuum expectation value of F; see Eq. (3B-18).)

The matrix elements between hole states can be expressed in terms of the conjugate operator F_c with the property

$$\begin{aligned} \langle\nu_2|\,F_c\,|\nu_1\rangle_{\mathrm{sp}} &= \langle\nu_2^{-1}|\,F\,|\nu_1^{-1}\rangle - \langle\hat{0}|\,F\,|\hat{0}\rangle\delta(\nu_1,\nu_2) \\ &= -\langle\bar{\nu}_1|\,F\,|\bar{\nu}_2\rangle_{\mathrm{sp}} \\ F_c &= -(\mathscr{T}F\mathscr{T}^{-1})^\dagger \end{aligned} \tag{3B-20}$$

We have here employed Eq. (1-34) for the matrix element between time-reversed states. The subscript sp has been added to stress that the matrix elements in question refer to single-particle states (and not to configurations with a particle added to the normal state).

For self-conjugate operators, we have

$$\begin{aligned} F_c &= -(\mathscr{T}F\mathscr{T}^{-1})^\dagger = cF \\ c &= -c_{\mathscr{T}}c_H = \pm 1 \end{aligned} \tag{3B-21}$$

where the phase factors $c_{\mathscr{T}}$ and c_H characterize the transformation under time reversal and Hermitian conjugation (see Sec. 1A-5d). The quantum number c is an intrinsic property of the operator F and gives the relation between the matrix elements of F for particle and hole states. (The values of c for various operators are given in Eq. (3-14).)

One can also express the matrix elements involving hole states in terms of the transformed operator $\mathscr{U}_h^{-1}F\mathscr{U}_h$, which can be obtained from the decomposition (3B-18) by replacing all $b^\dagger$ and b operators by $a^\dagger$ and a operators. For example (see Eq. (3B-9)),

$$\begin{aligned} \langle\hat{0}|\,F\,|\nu_1^{-1}\nu_2\rangle &= \langle 0|\mathscr{U}_h^{-1}F\mathscr{U}_h\,|\nu_1\nu_2\rangle_a \\ &= \langle\bar{\nu}_1|\,F\,|\nu_2\rangle_{\mathrm{sp}} \end{aligned} \tag{3B-22}$$

(The conjugate operator F_c gives the matrix elements of $\mathscr{U}_h^{-1}F\mathscr{U}_h$ connecting states below the Fermi surface, apart from the constant expectation value term.)

The time reversal transformation affects the isospin components in an unsymmetrical manner ($t_x \to t_x$, $t_y \to -t_y$, $t_z \to t_z$, since t_x and t_z are real matrices, while t_y is imaginary). For isospin-dependent operators, we may instead employ the particle-hole conjugation based on the $\mathscr{F}$ transformation (3B-14), which inverts all three components of the isospin. The $\mathscr{F}$-type conjugate of a one-particle operator F is denoted by $F_{c'}$ and has the properties

$$\begin{aligned} \langle\nu_2 m_t(2)|\,F_{c'}\,|\nu_1 m_t(1)\rangle_{\mathrm{sp}} &= \langle\nu_2^{-1}m_t(2)|\,F\,|\nu_1^{-1}m_t(1)\rangle - \langle\hat{0}|\,F\,|\hat{0}\rangle\delta((\nu m_t)_1,(\nu m_t)_2) \\ &= -\langle\widetilde{\nu_1 m_t(1)}|\,F\,|\widetilde{\nu_2 m_t(2)}\rangle_{\mathrm{sp}} \\ F_{c'} &= -(\mathscr{F}F\mathscr{F}^{-1})^\dagger \end{aligned} \tag{3B-23}$$

For self-conjugate operators, we have

$$F_{c'} = c'F \qquad c' = (-1)^\tau c \tag{3B-24}$$

where τ is the tensorial rank of F in isospace. Thus, if F is isoscalar (isospin independent, $\tau = 0$), we have $c' = c$, while for an isovector operator ($\tau = 1$), which has the form $F = \mathbf{t}G$, we have $c'(F) = -c(G)$.

3B-2b Reduced matrix elements

In the spherical representation $\nu = (nl)jm$, we may express a tensor operator in the form (1A-86). By transforming the terms, as in Eq. (3B-18), and using the relations (1A-9) and (1A-80), we obtain

$$\begin{aligned}
\langle j_2^{-1} \| T_\lambda \| j_1^{-1} \rangle &= (-1)^{j_1+j_2-\lambda} \langle j_1 \| T_\lambda \| j_2 \rangle \\
&= c \langle j_2 \| T_\lambda \| j_1 \rangle \\
\langle (j_1^{-1} j_2) J \| T_\lambda \| \hat{0} \rangle &= (-1)^{j_1+j_2-\lambda} \langle j_2 \| T_\lambda \| j_1 \rangle \delta(J, \lambda) \\
\langle \hat{0} \| T_\lambda \| (j_1^{-1} j_2) J \rangle &= -\langle j_1 \| T_\lambda \| j_2 \rangle \delta(J, \lambda)
\end{aligned} \tag{3B-25}$$

The hole states in Eq. (3B-25) are defined in terms of the $\mathscr{T}$ transform and the particle-hole states are phased according to the definition

$$|(j_1^{-1} j_2) JM \rangle \equiv \underset{(j_1 j_2)JM}{a^\dagger(j_2) b^\dagger(j_1)} |\hat{0}\rangle \tag{3B-26}$$

The first relation in Eq. (3B-25) could also have been obtained directly from Eq. (3B-20). Monopole operators ($\lambda = 0$) of even parity may contain a constant term (the expectation value for the closed shells), which is not included in Eq. (3B-25).

For isospin-dependent operators, matrix elements reduced in isospace (see Sec. 1A-9) may be obtained from the relations involving the $\mathscr{F}$-type particle-hole conjugation.

3B-3 Matrix Elements of Two-Particle Operators

The form of a two-particle operator expressed in terms of creation and annihilation operators is given by Eq. (2A-28). We shall especially consider the nucleonic interaction V, although the relations in the first part of the present section apply to arbitrary two-particle operators. The scalar character of the interaction operator is exploited in subsequent parts of the section.

The transformation of a two-particle operator to the particle and hole variables introduces terms having the structure of a one-particle operator. An analysis of these terms, for the two-particle interaction, leads to the Hartree-Fock potential.

3B-3a ν representation

In order to obtain the form of a two-particle operator in terms of the particle and hole variables, we proceed as for the one-particle operators, replacing the $(a^\dagger, a)$ operators for the filled orbits by $(b, b^\dagger)$ operators, by means of Eq. (3B-5). After a reordering of the operators so that creation operators appear to the left of annihilation operators, the interaction takes the form (with the simplified notation 1, 2, ... for the states $\nu_1, \nu_2, \ldots$)

$$V = V_0 + V_1 + V_2 + V_3 + V_4$$

$$V_0 = \frac{1}{4} \sum \langle 34 | V | 12 \rangle_a \, a^\dagger(4) a^\dagger(3) a(1) a(2) \qquad \text{(particle-particle scattering)} \tag{3B-27a}$$

$$V_1 = \frac{1}{4}\sum \langle 34|\, V\,|1\bar{2}\rangle_a\, a^\dagger(4)a^\dagger(3)a(1)b^\dagger(2) + \frac{1}{4}\sum \langle 34|\, V\,|\bar{1}2\rangle_a a^\dagger(4)a^\dagger(3)b^\dagger(1)a(2) + \text{H.c.}$$

$$= \frac{1}{2}\sum \langle 34|\, V\,|\bar{1}2\rangle_a\, a^\dagger(4)a^\dagger(3)b^\dagger(1)a(2) + \text{H.c.}$$ (creation or annihilation of pair associated with scattering of particle) (3B-27b)

$$V_2 = -\frac{1}{4}\sum \langle 34|\, V\,|\bar{1}\bar{2}\rangle_a\, a^\dagger(4)a^\dagger(3)b^\dagger(2)b^\dagger(1) + \text{H.c.}$$ (creation or annihilation of two pairs) (3B-27c)

$$-\sum \langle \bar{1}4|\, V\,|\bar{3}2\rangle_a\, a^\dagger(4)b^\dagger(3)b(1)a(2)$$ (particle-hole scattering) (3B-27d)

$$+\sum \langle 2\bar{i}|\, V\,|1\bar{i}\rangle_a\, a^\dagger(2)a(1)$$ (single-particle potential energy) (3B-27e)

$$V_3 = \frac{1}{2}\sum \langle \bar{3}\bar{2}|\, V\,|1\bar{4}\rangle_a\, b^\dagger(4)b(3)b(2)a(1) + \text{H.c.}$$ (annihilation or creation of pair associated with scattering of hole) (3B-27f)

$$+\sum \langle \bar{2}\bar{i}|\, V\,|1\bar{i}\rangle_a\, b(2)a(1) + \text{H.c.}$$ (annihilation or creation of pair) (3B-27g)

$$V_4 = \frac{1}{4}\sum \langle \bar{1}\bar{2}|\, V\,|\bar{3}\bar{4}\rangle_a\, b^\dagger(4)b^\dagger(3)b(1)b(2)$$ (hole-hole scattering) (3B-27h)

$$-\sum \langle \bar{1}\bar{i}|\, V\,|\bar{i}\bar{2}\rangle_a\, b^\dagger(2)b(1)$$ (single-hole potential energy) (3B-27i)

$$+\frac{1}{2}\sum \langle \bar{i}\bar{k}|\, V\,|\bar{i}\bar{k}\rangle_a$$ (interaction energy of normal state) (3B-27j)

The summations extend over all occupied levels ($\nu \leqslant \nu_F$) when the state in the matrix element has a bar, otherwise over the empty levels ($\nu > \nu_F$). The factors 1/2 and 1/4 in Eq. (3B-27) would disappear if, instead of summing independently over the different states ν_i, one would restrict the sum to a definite ordering, such as, for example, $\nu_1 < \nu_2$ and $\nu_3 < \nu_4$ in Eq. (3B-27a).

If the two-particle interaction V is Hermitian and invariant under $\mathscr{T}$, we have the relation

$$\langle \bar{1}\bar{2}|\, V\,|\bar{3}\bar{4}\rangle = \langle 34|\, V\,|12\rangle \tag{3B-28}$$

It then follows from Eqs. (3B-27a) and (3B-27h) that the matrix element for the scattering of two holes is the same as for two particles (invariance of the interaction with respect to particle-hole conjugation). Moreover, with the standard phasing of the states (see Eq. (1-40)), the interaction matrix elements are real provided V is invariant under $\mathscr{R}_y(\pi)\mathscr{T}$ (see Eq. (1-42)). For a Hermitian V, the matrix elements are therefore also symmetric,

$$\langle 34|\, V\,|12\rangle = \langle 12|\, V\,|34\rangle \tag{3B-29}$$

The terms in Eq. (3B-27) involving four operators can also be arranged according to the numbers of creation and annihilation operators; thus, V_{22} represents scattering effects, while V_{13} and V_{31} are associated with the creation and annihilation of a pair, and V_{04} and V_{40} with the creation and annihilation of two pairs. Examples of such terms are illustrated by the diagrams in Fig. 3B-2.

The decomposition (3B-27) applies to the particle-hole conjugation associated with time reversal $(b^\dagger(\nu) = a(\bar{\nu}))$. If we employ the $\mathscr{F}$ transform $(b^\dagger(\nu) = a(\tilde{\nu}))$, the states $\bar{\nu}$ in Eq. (3B-27) are replaced by $\tilde{\nu}$.

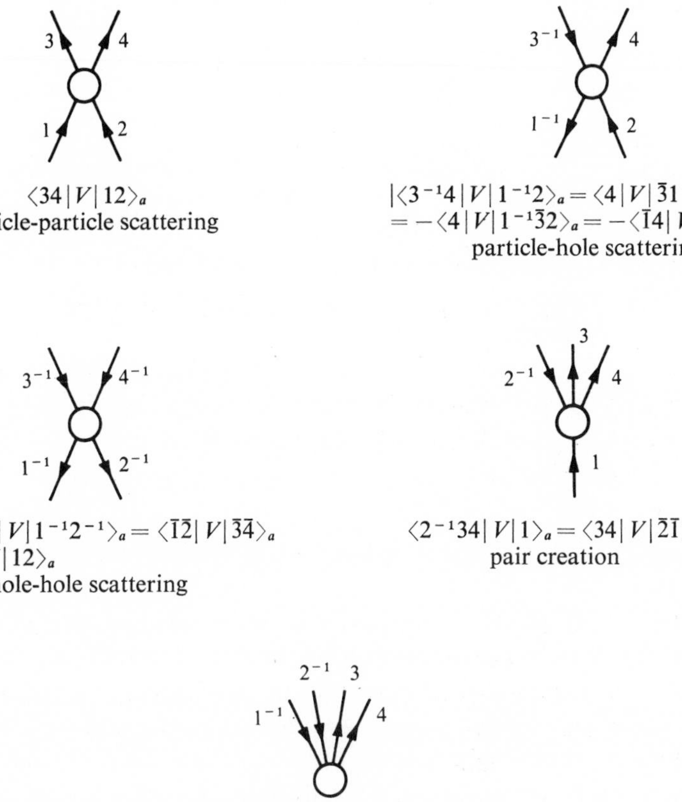

$\langle 34|V|12\rangle_a$
particle-particle scattering

$|\langle 3^{-1}4|V|1^{-1}2\rangle_a = \langle 4|V|\bar{3}1^{-1}2\rangle_a$
$= -\langle 4|V|1^{-1}\bar{3}2\rangle_a = -\langle \bar{1}4|V|\bar{3}2\rangle_a$
particle-hole scattering

$\langle 3^{-1}4^{-1}|V|1^{-1}2^{-1}\rangle_a = \langle \bar{1}\bar{2}|V|\bar{3}\bar{4}\rangle_a$
$= \langle 34|V|12\rangle_a$
hole-hole scattering

$\langle 2^{-1}34|V|1\rangle_a = \langle 34|V|\bar{2}\bar{1}\rangle_a$
pair creation

$\langle 1^{-1}2^{-1}34|V|\hat{0}\rangle_a = -\langle 34|V|\bar{1}\bar{2}\rangle_a$
creation of two pairs

Figure 3B-2 The figure illustrates the various matrix elements of a two-particle operator acting in a Fermi system. The notation is similar to that of Fig. 3B-1. The matrix elements involving hole states can be obtained from the two-particle matrix elements by means of the crossing relation given on p. 371.

3B-3b Single-particle terms. Hartree-Fock potential

The terms (*e*), (*g*), and (*i*) in the transformed operator (3B-27), which arise from the commutation of the b and $b^\dagger$ operators, represent an effective single-particle potential U, with matrix elements

$$\langle \nu_2|U|\nu_1\rangle = \sum_{\nu_i \leqslant \nu_F} \langle \nu_i \nu_2|V|\nu_i \nu_1\rangle_a \tag{3B-30}$$

(The summation over $\bar{i}$ in Eq. (3B-27) is equivalent to a summation over i.) The operator U is seen to have the particle-hole symmetry $c = -1$, assuming V to be

Hermitian and invariant under $\mathscr{T}$. If the occupied states form closed shells, the potential U is spherically symmetric, provided V is a scalar.

The potential U represents the average field produced by all the particles in the occupied orbits. In a self-consistent treatment of the interactions (the Hartree-Fock approximation), the effective single-particle Hamiltonian is

$$H_{sp} = T + U \tag{3B-31}$$

where T is the kinetic energy, and the single-particle states $|\nu\rangle$ and energies $\varepsilon(\nu)$ are determined by the relation

$$\langle \nu_2 | T | \nu_1 \rangle + \langle \nu_2 | U | \nu_1 \rangle = \langle \nu_2 | T | \nu_1 \rangle + \sum_{\nu_i \leqslant \nu_F} \langle \nu_i \nu_2 | V | \nu_i \nu_1 \rangle_a = \varepsilon(\nu_1) \delta(\nu_1, \nu_2) \tag{3B-32}$$

When the single-particle states satisfy the self-consistency relation (3B-32), it follows from Eq. (3B-27) that the total Hamiltonian takes the form

$$H = \sum_{\nu_k > \nu_F} \varepsilon(\nu_k) a^\dagger(\nu_k) a(\nu_k) - \sum_{\nu_i \leqslant \nu_F} \varepsilon(\nu_i) b^\dagger(\nu_i) b(\nu_i) + V' + \langle \hat{0} | H | \hat{0} \rangle \tag{3B-33}$$

where V' is the part of the interaction (3B-27) containing four fermion operators, while $\langle \hat{0} | H | \hat{0} \rangle$ is a constant term, representing the expectation value of H in the normal state $|\hat{0}\rangle$, in which the particles occupy the states $\nu_i \leqslant \nu_F$,

$$\begin{aligned} \langle \hat{0} | H | \hat{0} \rangle &= \sum_{\nu_i \leqslant \nu_F} \langle \nu_i | T | \nu_i \rangle + \tfrac{1}{2} \sum_{\substack{\nu_i \leqslant \nu_F \\ \nu_k \leqslant \nu_F}} \langle \nu_i \nu_k | V | \nu_i \nu_k \rangle_a \\ &= \sum_{\nu_i \leqslant \nu_F} \langle \nu_i | T + \tfrac{1}{2} U | \nu_i \rangle \end{aligned} \tag{3B-34}$$

The factor 1/2 in the last term in (3B-34) reflects the fact that the two-particle interaction contributes to the average potential for both the interacting particles and is thus counted twice, if we sum the single-particle energies for the filled orbits.

The self-consistency condition (3B-32) for the single-particle states implies that the Hamiltonian, when written in terms of the particle and hole variables, contains no terms connecting the normal state $|\hat{0}\rangle$ with states involving a single particle and a single hole,

$$\langle \nu_i^{-1} \nu_k | H | \hat{0} \rangle = 0 \qquad \nu_i \leqslant \nu_F \qquad \nu_k > \nu_F \tag{3B-35}$$

This criterion is in turn equivalent to a variational principle, which requires the expectation value of H in the normal state to be stationary with respect to variations in the single-particle states. In fact, if we vary an occupied state ν_i by admixing a component proportional to the unoccupied state ν_k, the normal state $|\hat{0}\rangle$ receives a component proportional to $|\nu_i^{-1} \nu_k\rangle$. As a consequence of Eq. (3B-35), such a variation of $|\hat{0}\rangle$ does not affect the expectation value of H to leading order. (Variations involving only linear transformations among the occupied single-particle states have no effect on the many-particle wave function for the normal state.)

3B-3c Matrix elements for angular momentum coupled states

For angular momentum coupled states, the relations between matrix elements involving particle and hole states (crossing relations) involve a recoupling of the angular momenta of the four particle states. The recoupling can be easily performed, if we write the reduced two-particle matrix element in terms of a coupling of all the four angular momenta to a resultant zero,

$$\begin{aligned}\langle (j_3 j_4)J \| V \| (j_1 j_2)J\rangle &= (2J+1)^{1/2}\langle (j_3 j_4)JM|V|(j_1 j_2)JM\rangle \\ &= \langle \bar{j}_3 \bar{j}_4|V|j_1 j_2\rangle_{(j_1j_2)J,(j_3j_4)J;0}\end{aligned} \tag{3B-36}$$

We have used the notation (compare Eq. (1A-65))

$$\begin{aligned}\langle \bar{j}_3\bar{j}_4|_{(j_3j_4)JM} &= \sum_{m_3m_4}\langle j_3 m_3 j_4 m_4|JM\rangle(-1)^{j_3+m_3+j_4+m_4}\langle j_3 -m_3\, j_4 -m_4| \\ &= (-1)^{J+M}\langle j_3 j_4|_{(j_3j_4)J-M} \equiv \langle j_3 j_4|_{(j_3j_4)\overline{JM}}\end{aligned} \tag{3B-37}$$

For example, the particle-hole matrix element is obtained as follows (see Eq. (3B-27d) and note that $|\bar{\bar{v}}\rangle = -|v\rangle$):

$$\begin{aligned}\langle (j_{\bar 3}^{-1}j_4)J\|V\|(j_{\bar 1}^{-1}j_2)J\rangle &= \langle \bar{j}_{\bar 3}^{-1}\bar{j}_4|V|j_{\bar 1}^{-1}j_2\rangle_{(j_1j_2)J,(j_3j_4)J;0} \\ &= \langle \bar{j}_1\bar{j}_4|V|j_3j_2\rangle_{a\,(j_1j_2)J,(j_3j_4)J;0} \\ &= \sum_{J'}\langle j_1j_2)J,(j_3j_4)J;0|(j_3j_2)J',(j_1j_4)J';0\rangle\langle (j_1j_4)J'\|V\|(j_3j_2)J'\rangle_a\end{aligned} \tag{3B-38}$$

For states with a definite T quantum number, we may proceed in a similar manner, employing the $\mathscr{F}$-type particle-hole conjugation. For the particle-hole matrix element we then obtain (note that $|\tilde{\bar{v}}\rangle = |v\rangle$).

$$\begin{aligned}\langle (j_{\bar 3}^{-1}j_4)JT|||V|||(j_{\bar 1}^{-1}j_2)JT\rangle &= -\sum_{J'T'}\langle (j_1j_2)J,(j_3j_4)J;0|(j_3j_2)J',(j_1j_4)J';0\rangle \\ &\times\langle (t_1t_2)T,(t_3t_4)T;0|(t_3t_2)T',(t_1t_4)T';0\rangle\langle (j_1j_4)J'T'|||V|||(j_3j_2)J'T'\rangle_a\end{aligned} \tag{3B-39}$$

The triple-bar matrix elements are reduced in isospace as well as in spin-orbital space (see Sec. 1A-9).

The interaction matrix elements for two-particle states and for particle-hole states, given by Eqs. (3B-36) and (3B-38), correspond to two different ways of coupling the four angular momenta of the single-particle states to a resultant zero. A third coupling scheme corresponds to the matrix element $V_\lambda(j_1j_2, j_3j_4)$ defined by

$$(2\lambda+1)^{1/2}V_\lambda(j_1j_2, j_3j_4) \equiv \langle \bar{j}_3\bar{j}_4|V|j_1j_2\rangle_{a\,(j_1j_3)\lambda,(j_2j_4)\lambda;0} \tag{3B-40}$$

The matrix elements V_λ may be regarded as expansion parameters for the antisymmetrized two-particle interaction matrix elements,

$$\begin{aligned}&(2J+1)^{1/2}\langle (j_3j_4)JM|V|(j_1j_2)JM\rangle_a \\ &\quad= \sum_\lambda (2\lambda+1)^{1/2}V_\lambda(j_1j_2, j_3j_4)\langle (j_1j_3)\lambda,(j_2j_4)\lambda;0|(j_1j_2)J,(j_3j_4)J;0\rangle\end{aligned} \tag{3B-41}$$

and the inverse

$$\begin{aligned}&(2\lambda+1)^{1/2}V_\lambda(j_1j_2, j_3j_4) \\ &\quad= \sum_J (2J+1)^{1/2}\langle (j_3j_4)JM|V|(j_1j_2)JM\rangle_a\langle (j_1j_2)J,(j_3j_4)J;0|(j_1j_3)\lambda,(j_2j_4)\lambda;0\rangle\end{aligned} \tag{3B-42}$$

APPENDIX

3C

Matrix Elements for Electromagnetic Interactions

3C-1 Coupling of Field and Current

The quantal theory of electromagnetic processes is based on Maxwell's equations for the propagation of the electromagnetic field and its coupling to the charge-current density. The electromagnetic interaction may be written in the form

$$\begin{aligned} H' &= -\int j_\mu(\mathbf{r}, t) A_\mu(\mathbf{r}, t)\, d^3r \\ &\equiv \int \varphi(\mathbf{r}, t)\rho(\mathbf{r}, t)\, d^3r - \frac{1}{c}\int \mathbf{j}(\mathbf{r}, t)\cdot \mathbf{A}(\mathbf{r}, t)\, d^3r \end{aligned} \tag{3C-1}$$

representing a local coupling between the four-vector potential

$$A_\mu = (\varphi, \mathbf{A}) \tag{3C-2}$$

and the four-vector charge-current density

$$j_\mu = \left(\rho, \frac{1}{c}\mathbf{j}\right) \tag{3C-3}$$

where φ and ρ represent the real parts of the time-like components of the corresponding four vectors. The conservation of electric charge is expressed by the continuity equation

$$c\frac{\partial}{\partial x_\mu} j_\mu(\mathbf{r}, t) \equiv \boldsymbol{\nabla}\cdot \mathbf{j}(\mathbf{r}, t) + \frac{\partial}{\partial t}\rho(\mathbf{r}, t) = 0 \tag{3C-4}$$

The interaction (3C-1) is invariant under continuous Lorentz transformations and is also assumed, as in classical theory, to be invariant under space reflection and time reversal. The reflection symmetry of the four-current density is given by

$$\begin{aligned} \mathscr{P}(\rho(\mathbf{r}, t), \mathbf{j}(\mathbf{r}, t))\mathscr{P}^{-1} &= (\rho(-\mathbf{r}, t), -\mathbf{j}(-\mathbf{r}, t)) \\ \mathscr{T}(\rho(\mathbf{r}, t), \mathbf{j}(\mathbf{r}, t))\mathscr{T}^{-1} &= (\rho(\mathbf{r}, -t), -\mathbf{j}(\mathbf{r}, -t)) \end{aligned} \tag{3C-5}$$

and corresponding relations hold for the potentials.

The description of the electromagnetic interaction in terms of the coupling (3C-1) with a current satisfying Eqs. (3C-4) and (3C-5) has been found to have a range of validity extending to all the atomic and nuclear systems so far studied. (See, for example, the review by Gatto, 1966; as regards the possibility of $\mathscr{T}$-violating terms in the electromagnetic current of strongly interacting particles; see also the comment in Sec. 3C-6, p. 389.)

In the present appendix, we consider the structure of the charge-current density (3C-3) for nuclear systems and the general form of the nuclear matrix elements that can be determined from transition amplitudes and cross sections for radiative processes and reactions with charged particles.

3C-2 Radiative Processes

The photons are particles with zero mass and unit spin. The spin orientation is either parallel or antiparallel to the momentum (the helicity is $h = \pm 1$), and there are thus only two photon states of given momentum, $\hbar\mathbf{q}$. The possibility of restricting the polarization states in this manner is connected with the fact that, for a massless particle, the helicity is a Lorentz invariant.

The photon states can also be specified by the angular momentum quantum numbers $\lambda\mu$ together with the magnitude q of the wave number. There are no photon states with $\lambda = 0$; for such a state, the component of angular momentum in any direction must vanish and the state would thus involve particles with helicity $h = 0$.

For each set of values $(q, \lambda\mu)$ with $\lambda \geqslant 1$, there are two photon states, which can be specified either by the helicity, $h = \pm 1$, or by the parity, $\pi = \pm 1$. States of definite π are linear combinations of states with $h = \pm 1$, occurring with equal intensity. Quanta with given λ and π are referred to as electric ($E\lambda$) and magnetic ($M\lambda$) multipole quanta

$$\pi = \begin{cases} (-1)^{\lambda} & E\lambda \quad \kappa = \lambda \pm 1 \\ (-1)^{\lambda+1} & M\lambda \quad \kappa = \lambda \end{cases} \tag{3C-6}$$

Since the photon has an intrinsic parity of -1, one can also characterize the $M\lambda$ photons as having orbital angular momentum $\kappa = \lambda$, while the $E\lambda$ quanta contain components with $\kappa = \lambda \pm 1$, with relative amplitudes $(\lambda/\lambda + 1)^{1/2}$; see Eq. (3A-9).

The vector potential $\mathbf{A}(\mathbf{r})$ is associated with the creation and annihilation of photons. The occurrence of only two polarization states for the photon corresponds to the fact that the radiation field, with a suitable choice of gauge, can be described by a purely transverse vector potential, satisfying

$$\boldsymbol{\nabla} \cdot \mathbf{A} = 0 \tag{3C-7}$$

The coupling term in Eq. (3C-1) responsible for emission and absorption of photons is seen to be of the form (1A-120). Thus, the nuclear matrix elements for emission and absorption of multipole quanta can be expressed in terms of multipole moments of the type given by Eq. (1A-127). In view of the transversality condition (3C-7), only two combinations of multipole moments (1A-127) occur for given $\lambda\mu$.

The moments associated with electric and magnetic multipole quanta can be written in the form

$$\mathscr{M}(E\lambda, \mu) = \frac{-i(2\lambda+1)!!}{cq^{\lambda+1}(\lambda+1)} \int \mathbf{j}(\mathbf{r}) \cdot \nabla \times (\mathbf{r} \times \nabla)(j_\lambda(qr) Y_{\lambda\mu}(\hat{\mathbf{r}}))\, d\tau$$

$$\mathscr{M}(M\lambda, \mu) = \frac{-(2\lambda+1)!!}{cq^{\lambda}(\lambda+1)} \int \mathbf{j}(\mathbf{r}) \cdot (\mathbf{r} \times \nabla)(j_\lambda(qr) Y_{\lambda\mu}(\hat{\mathbf{r}}))\, d\tau \qquad \text{(3C-8)}$$

where the normalization has been chosen in such a manner that the moments reduce to the usual form for $q \to 0$ (see below).

The radial function $j_\lambda(qr)$ in Eq. (3C-8) is a spherical Bessel function of order λ, which represents the radial wave function for freely propagating quanta. (See the analogous result for a scalar coupling in Sec. 1A-8a.) The radial structure of the moment (3C-8) thus reflects the fact that the propagation of the photons is not distorted during their passage through the nucleus.

The multipole fields multiplying the current $\mathbf{j}$ in the moments (3C-8) are seen to obey the condition (3C-7). While $\mathscr{M}(M\lambda)$ is of the form (1A-127) with $\kappa = \lambda$ (see Eq. (1A-125)), the relation

$$\nabla \times (\mathbf{r} \times \nabla) j_\lambda(qr) Y_{\lambda\mu}(\hat{\mathbf{r}})$$

$$= qj_{\lambda+1}(qr)\lambda\left(\frac{\lambda+1}{2\lambda+1}\right)^{1/2} \boldsymbol{\Phi}_{\kappa=\lambda+1,\lambda\mu} - qj_{\lambda-1}(qr)(\lambda+1)\left(\frac{\lambda}{2\lambda+1}\right)^{1/2} \boldsymbol{\Phi}_{\kappa=\lambda-1,\lambda\mu} \qquad \text{(3C-9)}$$

shows that $\mathscr{M}(E\lambda)$ is a sum of two terms of the type (1A-125) with $\kappa = \lambda \pm 1$, corresponding to the orbital angular momentum assignment in Eq. (3C-6).

From the relation (3C-5), it is further seen that the parity quantum numbers for the moments (3C-8) are equal to those in Eq. (3C-6), thus ensuring parity conservation, and that the time reversal phase is given by (see Eq. (1A-74))

$$c_{\mathscr{T}} = \begin{cases} (-1)^{\lambda} & E\lambda \\ (-1)^{\lambda+1} & M\lambda \end{cases} \qquad \text{(3C-10)}$$

By employing the continuity equation (3C-4) together with the identity

$$\nabla \times (\mathbf{r} \times \nabla) j_\lambda(qr) Y_{\lambda\mu}(\hat{\mathbf{r}}) = -\nabla\left(\frac{\partial}{\partial r}(rj_\lambda(qr)) Y_{\lambda\mu}(\hat{\mathbf{r}})\right) - q^2 \mathbf{r} j_\lambda(qr) Y_{\lambda\mu}(\hat{\mathbf{r}}) \qquad \text{(3C-11)}$$

one can express the electric multipole moment in the form

$$\mathscr{M}(E\lambda, \mu)$$

$$= \frac{(2\lambda+1)!!}{q^{\lambda}(\lambda+1)} \int \rho(\mathbf{r}) \frac{\partial}{\partial r}(rj_\lambda(qr)) Y_{\lambda\mu}(\hat{\mathbf{r}})\, d\tau + \frac{i(2\lambda+1)!!}{cq^{\lambda-1}(\lambda+1)} \int (\mathbf{r} \cdot \mathbf{j}(\mathbf{r})) j_\lambda(qr) Y_{\lambda\mu}(\hat{\mathbf{r}})\, d\tau \qquad \text{(3C-12)}$$

In nuclear photoprocesses, the wavelength of the photon is usually large compared to the nuclear radius,

$$qR = 6.1 \times 10^{-3} A^{1/3} E_\gamma(\text{MeV}) \qquad \text{(3C-13)}$$

$$(R = 1.2 \times A^{1/3} \quad \text{fm})$$

and, for $qr \ll 1$, one can employ the expansion of the Bessel function

$$j_\lambda(qr) = \frac{(qr)^\lambda}{(2\lambda+1)!!}\left(1 - \frac{1}{2}\frac{(qr)^2}{2\lambda+3} + \cdots\right) \tag{3C-14}$$

In most cases, it is a good approximation to retain only the leading term. The multipole moments then reduce to the simpler forms

$$\begin{aligned}\mathcal{M}(E\lambda, \mu) &= \int \rho(\mathbf{r}) r^\lambda Y_{\lambda\mu}(\hat{\mathbf{r}})\, d\tau \\ \mathcal{M}(M\lambda, \mu) &= \frac{-1}{c(\lambda+1)}\int \mathbf{j}(\mathbf{r})\cdot(\mathbf{r}\times\boldsymbol{\nabla}) r^\lambda Y_{\lambda\mu}(\hat{\mathbf{r}})\, d\tau\end{aligned} \tag{3C-15}$$

The transition amplitude for emission (or absorption) of a photon of given multipole type is proportional to the matrix element of the multipole operator. The total decay rate, summed over the magnetic substates of the photon and of the final nuclear state, is given by

$$T(E(M)\lambda; I_1 \to I_2) = \frac{8\pi(\lambda+1)}{\lambda[(2\lambda+1)!!]^2}\frac{1}{\hbar} q^{2\lambda+1} B(E(M)\lambda; I_1 \to I_2) \tag{3C-16}$$

where the reduced transition probability is

$$\begin{aligned}B(E(M)\lambda; I_1 \to I_2) &= \sum_{\mu M_2} |\langle I_2 M_2 | \mathcal{M}(E(M)\lambda, \mu) | I_1 M_1\rangle|^2 \\ &= (2I_1+1)^{-1} |\langle I_2 \| \mathcal{M}(E(M)\lambda) \| I_1\rangle|^2\end{aligned} \tag{3C-17}$$

For the first few values of λ and π, the expression (3C-16) gives, for the decay rate per second,

$$\begin{aligned}T(E1) &= 1.59 \times 10^{15} (E)^3 B(E1) \\ T(E2) &= 1.22 \times 10^{9} (E)^5 B(E2) \\ T(E3) &= 5.67 \times 10^{2} (E)^7 B(E3) \\ T(E4) &= 1.69 \times 10^{-4} (E)^9 B(E4) \\ \\ T(M1) &= 1.76 \times 10^{13} (E)^3 B(M1) \\ T(M2) &= 1.35 \times 10^{7} (E)^5 B(M2) \\ T(M3) &= 6.28 \times 10^{0} (E)^7 B(M3) \\ T(M4) &= 1.87 \times 10^{-6} (E)^9 B(M4)\end{aligned} \tag{3C-18}$$

where E is in MeV, $B(E\lambda)$ in units of $e^2(\text{fm})^{2\lambda}$, and $B(M\lambda)$ in units of $(e\hbar/2Mc)^2(\text{fm})^{2\lambda-2}$.

The form of Eq. (3C-16) can be understood from a dimensional argument. Since $B(\lambda)$ is proportional to $e^2L^{2\lambda}$, and since the factor multiplying $B(\lambda)$ can depend only on q, $\hbar$, and c, it must involve the combination $\hbar^{-1}q^{2\lambda+1}$. A derivation of Eq. (3C-16) can be found in many textbooks; see, for example, Blatt and Weisskopf (1952), Moszkowski (1965), and Rose (1955), as well as texts on quantum electrodynamics. The expression for $T(\lambda)$ can be obtained from a correspondence argument, since the electromagnetic field generated by the nucleus is the same function of the nuclear charge-current density as in classical theory. Thus, the radiated power $T(\lambda)\hbar\omega$ is the same as for a classical system of oscillating multipoles; see, for example, Jackson (1962).

The angular distribution and polarization of the emitted radiation follows from the structure of the multipole fields; see, for example, Eq. (3F-4). General expressions and tables of coefficients characterizing these distributions as well as the correlation of successive transitions can be found in the surveys given by de Groot *et al.* (1965); Frauenfelder and Steffen (1965); Dolginov (1961).

The γ-transition matrix elements can also be determined from the resonance scattering of photons as well as from nuclear reactions induced by photoabsorption. (Resonance scattering of γ rays is discussed by Malmfors, 1965, and by Mössbauer, 1965; for a review of photonuclear processes, see, for example, Levinger, 1960, and Hayward, 1964.)

3C-3 Interactions with Charged Particles

In reactions induced by the electromagnetic field of charged particles, the form of the nuclear matrix elements depends on whether or not the projectile enters the nucleus itself. If the particle remains outside the nucleus, such as in Coulomb excitation processes and, to a first approximation, in internal conversion and atomic hyperfine structure, the nuclear matrix elements are the same as those involved in radiative transitions. For example, the cross section for a first-order Coulomb excitation process can be expressed as a product of $B(E\lambda)$ and a factor that can be evaluated in terms of the motion of the projectile in the nuclear Coulomb field.

If the particle enters the nucleus, such as in electron scattering, the binding of μ mesons to heavy nuclei, and, to a minor extent, in internal conversion and hyperfine structure, two types of moments are involved. The first are similar to $\mathscr{M}(E(M)\lambda)$ with the difference, however, that $j_\lambda(qr)$ is replaced by a radial function depending on the motion of the particle inside the nucleus. (This function reduces to $j_\lambda(qr)$ with q representing the momentum transfer between the particle and the nucleus, if the particle motion is described in terms of plane waves (no distortion).) By varying the energy of the incident particle and the angle of scattering, it is thus possible to obtain detailed information on the radial distribution of the multipole moments (form factors).

In addition, the interaction with a particle inside the nucleus involves moments of the longitudinal type

$$\mathscr{M}(C\lambda, \mu) = \int \rho(\mathbf{r}) f_\lambda(r) Y_{\lambda\mu}(\hat{\mathbf{r}}) \, d\tau \tag{3C-19}$$

associated with the Coulomb field. The function $f_\lambda(r)$ depends on the radial motion of the particle inside the nucleus. The Coulomb moments (3C-19) include a monopole term ($\lambda = 0$, $\pi = +1$). If one expands $f_0(r)$ in powers of r, the leading term is a constant; to this approximation the moment is proportional to the total nuclear charge and does not give rise to intrinsic nuclear transitions. The next nonvanishing term is proportional to r^2, and the monopole operator $m(E0)$ defined by

$$m(E0) = \int \rho(\mathbf{r}) r^2 \, d\tau \tag{3C-20}$$

therefore becomes mainly responsible for transitions with $\lambda\pi = 0+$. This moment is often given in dimensionless units,

$$\rho = \frac{m(E0)}{eR^2} = \frac{1}{e} \int \rho(\mathbf{r}) \left(\frac{r}{R}\right)^2 d\tau \tag{3C-20a}$$

(see Church and Weneser, 1956).

A treatment of the various types of interactions of nuclei with charged particles may be found in the following reviews and articles (and additional references quoted there).

Coulomb excitation: Biedenharn and Brussaard (1965); Alder and Winther (reprint volume, 1966).

Electron scattering: de Forest and Walecka (1966).

Internal conversion: Listengarten (1961); Rose (1965). Effects of finite size (penetration effects) are discussed by Church and Weneser (1960) and by Gerholm and Pettersson (1965).

Hyperfine structure: Kopfermann (1958); Ramsey (1950). Penetration effects in the magnetic interaction are considered by Stroke *et al.* (1961). For a discussion of isotope (and isomer) shifts, see Wilets *et al.* (1953); Breit (1958); Shirley (1964).

μ-mesic atoms: See, for example, Wu (1967).

3C-4 Charge and Current Density for Free Nucleons

In order to evaluate the matrix elements of the multipole operators, one must express the charge and current densities in terms of the variables employed in the description of the nuclear structure. We first consider the charge and current densities for free nucleons.

The internal structure of a nucleon extends over a domain that is small compared to the size of the nucleus, for $A \gg 1$. To a first approximation, we may therefore regard the nucleons as point particles having a charge and a magnetic moment. Neglecting relativistic effects in the nucleonic motion, the charge-current density for such point particles is given by

$$\begin{aligned} \rho(\mathbf{r}) &= \sum_k e(\tfrac{1}{2} - t_z(k))\delta(\mathbf{r} - \mathbf{r}_k) \\ \mathbf{j}(\mathbf{r}) &= \sum_k e(\tfrac{1}{2} - t_z(k))\tfrac{1}{2}(\mathbf{v}_k\delta(\mathbf{r} - \mathbf{r}_k) + \delta(\mathbf{r} - \mathbf{r}_k)\mathbf{v}_k) + \frac{e\hbar}{2M}\sum_k g_s(k)\boldsymbol{\nabla} \times \mathbf{s}_k\, \delta(\mathbf{r} - \mathbf{r}_k) \end{aligned} \tag{3C-21}$$

where $t_z = +1/2$ for neutrons and $-1/2$ for protons. The spin g factor is

$$g_s = \tfrac{1}{2}(g_n + g_p) + t_z(g_n - g_p) \tag{3C-22}$$

in terms of the proton and neutron g factors.

The magnetic moment interacts with the magnetic field, which depends on the derivatives of the vector potential and so involves first-order terms in the size of the nucleon. The charge-current density (3C-21) constitutes the most general expression that includes terms at most linear in the velocity or in the nucleonic size, and that satisfies the continuity equation (3C-4) and the space reflection symmetry (3C-5). The equality of the coupling constant for the charge and for the convection current (the term proportional to $\mathbf{v}_k$) can alternatively be viewed as a consequence of the four-vector character of j_μ. (The determination of the nucleon charge and current densities from invariance arguments has been discussed by Foldy, 1953.)

In Eq. (3C-21), the only parameters, apart from the electric charge, are the magnetic moments ($\mu = \frac{1}{2}g_s$), which are found to be $\mu_p = 2.79$, $\mu_n = -1.91$ (see Table 1-1, p. 4). The moments of the nucleons differ considerably from the values ($\mu_p = 1$, $\mu_n = 0$) expected for a point particle satisfying the Dirac equation. The differences between the observed moments and the Dirac moments are referred to as the anomalous moments or the Pauli moments and are attributed to the intrinsic structure of the nucleons. The discovery of the large anomalous moment for the proton (Frisch and Stern, 1933) provided the first indication of a complex structure of the nucleons themselves, and has remained a challenge to the theory of the nucleons and the strong interactions.

The expression (3C-21) for the charge and current densities is modified by the finite extension of the nucleons and by relativistic effects. The finite size can be taken into account by replacing the δ functions in Eq. (3C-21) by electric and magnetic form factors

$$\begin{aligned} \rho(\mathbf{r}) &= e f_E(|\mathbf{r}-\mathbf{r}_k|) \\ \mathbf{j}(\mathbf{r}) &= \frac{e}{2}(\mathbf{v}_k f_E(|\mathbf{r}-\mathbf{r}_k|) + f_E(|\mathbf{r}-\mathbf{r}_k|)\mathbf{v}_k) + \frac{e\hbar}{2M} g_s \boldsymbol{\nabla} \times \mathbf{s}_k f_M(|\mathbf{r}-\mathbf{r}_k|) \end{aligned} \tag{3C-23}$$

for a single proton or neutron. One may also express the neutron and proton form factors in terms of isoscalar and isovector form factors,

$$f_0 = \tfrac{1}{2}(f_p + f_n) \qquad f_1 = \tfrac{1}{2}(f_p - f_n) \tag{3C-24}$$

To a first approximation, one may describe the size effects in terms of the electric and magnetic mean square radii of the nucleons

$$\langle r^2_{E,M} \rangle = \int r^2 f_{E,M}\, d\tau \tag{3C-25}$$

The observed values of the radii are given in Table 1-1. (For the neutron, the value of $\langle r_E^2 \rangle$ is negative, and the quantity in Table 1-1 is the square root of the absolute value of $\langle r_E^2 \rangle$.)

The relativistically invariant matrix elements of the charge-current density between states of free nucleons can be expressed in terms of electric and magnetic form factors $G_{E,M}(q^2)$, which are functions of the four-momentum transfer $\hbar q$ between the nucleon and the electromagnetic field. For $\hbar q \ll Mc$ (in the nonrelativistic limit), these form factors represent the Fourier transforms of the form factors $f_{E,M}(r)$ introduced above. With the conventional normalization, we have

$$\begin{aligned} G_E(q^2) &= \int f_E(r) \exp\{i\mathbf{q}\cdot\mathbf{r}\}\, d\tau \\ G_M(q^2) &= \mu \int f_M(r) \exp\{i\mathbf{q}\cdot\mathbf{r}\}\, d\tau \end{aligned} \tag{3C-26}$$

Thus, in the limit of small q,

$$\begin{aligned} G_{E_p}(q^2) &\approx 1 - \tfrac{1}{6}\langle r_E^2 \rangle_p q^2 \\ G_{E_n}(q^2) &\approx -\tfrac{1}{6}\langle r_E^2 \rangle_n q^2 \\ G_M(q^2) &\approx \mu(1 - \tfrac{1}{6}\langle r_M^2 \rangle q^2) \end{aligned} \tag{3C-27}$$

Alternatively, the electromagnetic structure of the nucleon can be characterized by the Dirac and Pauli form factors, associated with the charge and anomalous magnetic moment terms in the Dirac equation. The relativistic expressions for the current operator, and the connection between the different sets of form factors, can be found, for example, in the review by Hand *et al.* (1963).

The form factors $G_{E,M}(q^2)$ have been determined from electron scattering experiments for a large domain of q values ($q \lesssim 5$ to 10 fm^{-1}). (See, for example, the review by Chan *et al.*, 1966.) The present data can be approximately represented by the simple expressions

$$G_{E_p}(q^2) \approx \frac{G_{M_p}(q^2)}{\mu_p} \approx \frac{G_{M_n}(q^2)}{\mu_n} \approx \left(1+\frac{q^2}{\lambda^2}\right)^{-2} \qquad \lambda^2 = 18.1 \text{ fm}^{-2} \tag{3C-28}$$

The electric form factor for the neutron is less than 0.2 for $q > 2.5$ fm^{-1}. For smaller momentum transfers, $G_{E_n}(q^2)$ is poorly determined, but the slope for $q = 0$ is known from the neutron-electron scattering experiments (see Table 1-1). (A striking and challenging feature of the electromagnetic structure of the neutron is the vanishing of the mean square radius of the Dirac form factor (see Table 1-1).)

A number of far-reaching relations describing the electromagnetic properties of nucleons have been obtained on the basis of the extended isobaric symmetry for the hadrons (SU_3 and SU_6; see Sec. 1-3b). It is found that the electromagnetic current transforms under SU_3 as a member of an octuplet with strangeness, $S = 0$, and U spin, $U = 0$. (The invariance of the electromagnetic interactions under the U-spin transformations is discussed on p. 40 and p. 61.) The implications of SU_3 symmetry for the electromagnetic properties of the nucleons are limited by the fact that the matrix elements of an octuplet tensor between two members of an octuplet (such as the nucleons) involve two reduced matrix elements. (The product $(11) \otimes (11)$ contains the representation $(\lambda\mu) = (11)$ twice; see the similar feature encountered in the discussion of the mass splitting, p. 59.)

In the SU_6 classification, the electromagnetic current is assumed to transform as a member of the 35-dimensional representation (as a generator of the SU_6 group), with the SU_3 quantum numbers given above. Since there is only one reduced matrix element of a 35-dimensional tensor between states of a 56-dimensional representation (such as that of the nucleon), the relative magnitude of any electromagnetic moment for different members of this multiplet is given as the ratio of Clebsch-Gordan coefficients. Thus, for example, the electric neutron form factor $G_{E_n}(q^2)$ should vanish and $G_{M_p}(q^2)$ should be proportional to $G_{M_n}(q^2)$, in agreement with Eq. (3C-28).

Furthermore, one obtains the value $-2/3$ for the ratio of the magnetic moments of neutron and proton (Bég *et al.*, 1964), in remarkable agreement with the experimental values. A simple derivation of the magnetic moment ratio can be obtained on the basis of the quark model (see p. 41). In this model, we may assume the magnetic moment operator of the nucleons to be the sum of the moments of the individual quarks, each proportional to the charge of the quark, since this operator has the required transformation properties under SU_6 and SU_3. The nucleons consist of the quarks n (with charge number $-1/3$) and p (with charge number $+2/3$), each with strangeness zero, and coupled according to

$$\begin{aligned} |\text{neutron}\rangle &= |(n^2)J = 1, p; I = \tfrac{1}{2}\rangle \\ |\text{proton}\rangle &= |(p^2)J = 1, n; I = \tfrac{1}{2}\rangle \end{aligned} \tag{3C-29}$$

Since the states of the 56-dimensional representation are totally symmetric in the spin and isobaric variables, the spins of the two identical quarks must be coupled to $J = 1$. The magnetic moment ratio is then obtained from the vector coupling model

$$\frac{\mu\,(\text{neutron})}{\mu\,(\text{proton})} = \frac{-\frac{1}{3}(\mathbf{J}\cdot\mathbf{I}) + \frac{2}{3}(\frac{3}{4} - (\mathbf{J}\cdot\mathbf{I}))}{+\frac{2}{3}(\mathbf{J}\cdot\mathbf{I}) - \frac{1}{3}(\frac{3}{4} - (\mathbf{J}\cdot\mathbf{I}))} = -\frac{2}{3} \tag{3C-29a}$$

3C-5 Single-Particle Matrix Elements

If the nucleons are described as point charges with magnetic moments, the relations (3C-21) for the charge and current densities lead to the following expression for the multipole moment of a system of particles:

$$\begin{aligned}\mathcal{M}(E\lambda, \mu) &= \sum_k e(\tfrac{1}{2} - t_z(k)) r_k^\lambda Y_{\lambda\mu}(\vartheta_k, \varphi_k) \\ \mathcal{M}(M\lambda, \mu) &= \frac{e\hbar}{2Mc}\sum_k \left(g_s(k)\mathbf{s}_k + \frac{2g_l(k)}{\lambda+1}\mathbf{l}_k\right)\cdot \nabla_k(r_k^\lambda Y_{\lambda\mu}(\vartheta_k, \varphi_k))\end{aligned} \tag{3C-30}$$

The spin part of the moment (3C-30) may be obtained from Eq. (3C-15) by using the identity

$$\nabla \times (\nabla \times \mathbf{r}) r^\lambda Y_{\lambda\mu} = (\lambda + 1)\nabla r^\lambda Y_{\lambda\mu} \tag{3C-31}$$

The second term in the magnetic moment (the orbital part) is proportional to the orbital angular momentum $\hbar \mathbf{l}_k = M(\mathbf{r}_k \times \mathbf{v}_k)$ and involves the orbital g factor, $g_l = \frac{1}{2} - t_z$. One can also write the magnetic multipole moment in the form

$$\mathcal{M}(M\lambda, \mu) = \frac{e\hbar}{2Mc}(\lambda(2\lambda+1))^{1/2}\sum_k r_k^{\lambda-1}\left[\left(g_s - \frac{2g_l}{\lambda+1}\right)(Y_{\lambda-1}\, s) + \frac{2g_l}{\lambda+1}(Y_{\lambda-1}\, j)\right]_{(\lambda-1,1)\lambda\mu}^{k} \tag{3C-32}$$

where $\mathbf{j} = \mathbf{l} + \mathbf{s}$ is the total angular momentum of the nucleon. In Eq. (3C-32), the vectors $\mathbf{s}$ and $\mathbf{j}$ are represented by tensors of rank 1, coupled to the spherical harmonic $Y_{\lambda-1}$ to form tensors of rank λ.

The matrix elements of the electromagnetic multipole moments for single-particle states can be evaluated from the expressions given in Sec. 3A-2. Thus, from Eq. (3A-14), we obtain for a proton

$$\begin{aligned}&\langle j_2 \| i^\lambda \mathcal{M}(E\lambda) \| j_1\rangle \\ &= e(-1)^{j_1 - j_2 + \lambda}\, i^{l_1 - l_2 + \lambda}\left(\frac{(2\lambda+1)(2j_1+1)}{4\pi}\right)^{1/2}\langle j_2 | r^\lambda | j_1\rangle \langle j_1 \tfrac{1}{2} \lambda 0 | j_2 \tfrac{1}{2}\rangle \qquad (l_1 + \lambda - l_2 \text{ even})\end{aligned} \tag{3C-33}$$

and the reduced transition probability is given by

$$B_{\text{sp}}(E\lambda; j_1 \to j_2) = \frac{e^2}{4\pi}(2\lambda+1)\langle j_1 \tfrac{1}{2}\lambda 0 | j_2 \tfrac{1}{2}\rangle^2 \langle j_2 | r^\lambda | j_1\rangle^2 \tag{3C-34}$$

The motion of a particle is associated with a recoil of the rest of the nucleus, since the total center of mass remains at rest. This effect is of special importance for

$E1$ transitions; for these, the total moment in a one-particle transition can be obtained by replacing the charge of the particle in the expression (3C-33) by the quantity

$$(e)_{E1} = (\tfrac{1}{2} - t_z)e - \frac{Ze}{A} = \begin{cases} \dfrac{N}{A}e & \text{proton} \\ -\dfrac{Z}{A}e & \text{neutron} \end{cases} \tag{3C-35}$$

For higher electric multipoles and for magnetic multipoles, the recoil terms depend on the correlations between the particles and cannot in general be expressed as a renormalization of the single-particle moments. The effect, however, is of relative order A^{-1}, or smaller, and thus usually insignificant. (Recoil effects in $E2$ moments are discussed in connection with Table 3-2, p. 342.)

For the magnetic multipole moment, we obtain from Eq. (3C-32), employing the formulas (3A-22), (3A-23), and (3A-28),

$$\begin{aligned}
&\langle j_2 \| i^{\lambda-1}\mathscr{M}(M\lambda) \| j_1\rangle \\
&= \frac{e\hbar}{2Mc}(-1)^{j_1-j_2+\lambda-1}\, i^{l_1-l_2+\lambda-1}\left(\frac{(2j_1+1)(2\lambda+1)}{4\pi}\right)^{1/2}\langle j_2| r^{\lambda-1}|j_1\rangle \\
&\quad\times\Bigg\{\left(g_s - \frac{2}{\lambda+1}g_l\right)\frac{\lambda}{2}\langle j_1\tfrac{1}{2}\lambda 0|j_2\tfrac{1}{2}\rangle\left[1+\frac{1}{\lambda}(-1)^{l_1+1/2-j_1}\{(j_1+\tfrac{1}{2})+(-1)^{j_1+j_2-\lambda}(j_2+\tfrac{1}{2})\}\right] \\
&\quad+(-1)^{j_1+j_2+\lambda}\frac{2g_l}{\lambda+1}(\lambda(2\lambda-1)(2\lambda+1)j_1(j_1+1)(2j_1+1))^{1/2}\langle j_1\tfrac{1}{2}\,\lambda-1\,0|j_2\tfrac{1}{2}\rangle \\
&\qquad\times\begin{Bmatrix} j_1 & 1 & j_1 \\ \lambda-1 & j_2 & \lambda\end{Bmatrix}\Bigg\}
\end{aligned} \tag{3C-36}$$

with the parity selection rule that $l_1 - l_2 + \lambda - 1$ must be even.

The matrix elements for $M\lambda$ transitions with $j_2 = j_1 + \lambda$ can be given in a somewhat simpler form; in this case, the second term in Eq. (3C-36) vanishes and one obtains

$$\begin{aligned}
&\langle j_2 = j_1+\lambda \| i^{\lambda-1}\mathscr{M}(M\lambda) \| j_1\rangle \\
&\quad= -\frac{e\hbar}{2Mc}\left(g_s - \frac{2}{\lambda+1}g_l\right)\lambda\left(\frac{2\lambda+1}{4\pi}\right)^{1/2}(2j_1+1)^{1/2}\langle j_1\tfrac{1}{2}\lambda 0|j_2\tfrac{1}{2}\rangle\langle j_2|r^{\lambda-1}|j_1\rangle \\
&B_{\text{sp}}(M\lambda; j_1\to j_2=\lambda+j_1) \\
&\quad=\left(\frac{e\hbar}{2Mc}\right)^2\left(g_s-\frac{2}{\lambda+1}g_l\right)^2\lambda^2\,\frac{2\lambda+1}{4\pi}\langle j_1\tfrac{1}{2}\lambda 0|j_2\tfrac{1}{2}\rangle^2\langle j_2|r^{\lambda-1}|j_1\rangle^2
\end{aligned} \tag{3C-37}$$

with the selection rule $l_2 = l_1 + \lambda - 1$.

In order to have a somewhat simpler unit for comparison with observed electromagnetic transition rates, one often uses an approximate version of the expressions (3C-34) and (3C-37) referred to as the Weisskopf units. First, the radial integrals $< j_2|r^\lambda|j_1 >$ are approximated by the values $3(\lambda + 3)^{-1} R^\lambda$, as would be appropriate for a constant wave function extending out to the radius R. Second, the vector addition coefficients are evaluated for the transition $j_1 = \lambda + 1/2, j_2 = 1/2$. Third, for $M\lambda$ transitions, the factor $\lambda^2(g_s - 2(\lambda+1)^{-1}g_l)^2$ is replaced by the value 10. Employing a radius of $R = 1.2\ A^{1/3}$ fm, we obtain

$$B_W(E\lambda) = \frac{(1.2)^{2\lambda}}{4\pi}\left(\frac{3}{\lambda+3}\right)^2 A^{2\lambda/3}e^2(\text{fm})^{2\lambda}$$

$$B_W(M\lambda) = \frac{10}{\pi}(1.2)^{2\lambda-2}\left(\frac{3}{\lambda+3}\right)^2 A^{(2\lambda-2)/3}\left(\frac{e\hbar}{2Mc}\right)^2(\text{fm})^{2\lambda-2} \qquad (3C\text{-}38)$$

3C-6 Interaction Effects in the Current

For a system of interacting nucleons, the expression for the charge-current density may differ from the corresponding expression for free nucleons. This is connected with the composite structure of the nucleons, which may be affected by their interaction, and the related fact that the nuclear forces are transmitted by charged quanta which themselves generate electromagnetic effects.

If we restrict ourselves to electromagnetic matrix elements between nuclear states (excluding processes involving real mesons, hyperons, etc.), it is possible to consider the effects of the virtual degrees of freedom associated with the nucleonic structure in terms of operators depending only on the variables of the nucleons themselves (positions, momenta, spins, and isospins). In fact, the matrix elements of any operator, between nuclear states, can be expressed in this manner if we include terms depending on the variables of two or more nucleons. (It is to be emphasized that we are considering the electromagnetic moments of a nucleus, expressed in terms of the coordinates of *all* the nucleons. If, instead, one wishes to express the moments for configurations of one or more nucleons outside of closed shells in terms of the degrees of freedom of these nucleons only, the effective single-particle moments include polarization terms associated with the virtual excitation of the particles in the closed shells (see Sec. 3-3).)

3C-6a Symmetry properties

The part of the electromagnetic current associated with the interaction between the nucleons (the "interaction current") may comprise a great variety of different contributions, and only limited guidance can be obtained from invariance arguments associated with the transformation of j_μ under space-time reflections, Lorentz transformations, and rotations in isospace (Osborne and Foldy, 1960).

While the experimental evidence establishes the $\mathscr{P}$ conservation and Lorentz invariance of the electromagnetic interaction of nuclear systems with very high accuracy, the evidence for $\mathscr{T}$ conservation is much less precise (see Sec. 1-2, p. 21). In this connection, it is of significance that the transformation (3C-5) under time reversal, for the part of the current associated with an isolated nucleon, is a consequence of the continuity equation together with $\mathscr{P}$ invariance (Bernstein *et al.*, 1965), as can be seen from the fact that in the derivation of Eq. (3C-21) no assumptions were made regarding $\mathscr{T}$ invariance. For a nuclear system, therefore, a violation of time reversal invariance in electromagnetic processes would have to be associated with the interaction terms in the current; the present experimental data are hardly accurate enough to test the $\mathscr{T}$ invariance of this part of the current.

The electromagnetic current for a single nucleon consists of an isoscalar and an isovector part (see, for example, Eq. (3C-21)), and it is usually assumed that this is a general property of the electromagnetic current for strongly interacting particles, connected with the SU_3 symmetry of the current (see p. 386). There is so far little evidence, however, concerning the possible existence of current components with higher tensorial rank in isospace, which might occur in the interaction terms in the nucleonic current.

3C-6b Electric multipole moments

The interactions are expected to have a relatively minor effect on the nuclear charge distribution, and thus on the electric multipole moments. When two (or more) nucleons interact, their charge may become redistributed over the interaction volume, but on account of the conservation of their total charge and the rather small distances over which the displacement of charge takes place, the low Fourier components of the charge distribution are almost unaffected. Thus, if we consider electric multipoles of not too high order ($\lambda < A^{1/3}$) and restrict ourselves to wave numbers small compared to the inverse range of interaction and frequencies less than the average duration of the collision between two nucleons, we may to a good approximation employ the expression (3C-21) for the nuclear charge density, derived for point nucleons. (The insensitivity of the electric moments to exchange interactions was first noted by Siegert, 1937.)

3C-6c Magnetic multipole moments

The nuclear current distribution is more sensitive to the interactions. The large anomalous magnetic moments indicate the importance of the internal dynamics (meson couplings, quark structure, etc.) in determining the magnetic properties of nucleons. Since there is no conservation law for magnetic moments, one may expect the total moment for a pair of nucleons to be significantly modified when the particles are within the range of interaction. Still, the smallness of the nucleonic kinetic energies compared with the characteristic energies for exciting nucleons ($\sim$200 MeV, see Fig. 1-11) may suggest that the interaction terms in the nucleonic magnetic moments may be treated as corrections to the predominantly one-particle moments.

An estimate of the additional terms in the nuclear current operator involves an analysis of the mesonic currents associated with the interactions in nuclei. An interesting specific effect, which has received much attention, is the possibility of a reduction in the anomalous nucleonic moments caused by the presence of neighboring nucleons, which inhibit certain virtual meson emission and absorption processes, as a consequence of the exclusion principle (Miazawa, 1951). An estimate of the effect, based on available information on the interactions in pion nucleon systems and on the electromagnetic form factors of nucleons and mesons, has suggested a " quenching " of the nucleon anomalous moments by about a tenth of a magneton (Drell and Walecka, 1960). The current rapid growth in the exploration of the nucleonic structure may be expected to further elucidate the many interesting effects that may be associated with interaction currents in the nucleus.

The structural effects involved in the interaction moments are also responsible for the charge exchange and velocity dependence of the nucleonic forces. The relationship between the phenomenologically determined interactions and the exchange currents has been the subject of extensive discussion (see, for example, the review by Sachs, 1953), and in the following sections we consider some of the qualitative features of this relationship. As we shall see, only rather limited guidance can be obtained from an analysis at this level of phenomenology.

3C-6d Effect of charge exchange interactions

An important feature of the nucleonic interaction is the possibility of a charge exchange between the colliding particles (see pp. 242 ff.). Phenomenologically, the effect can be described in terms of charge exchange potentials. In the presence of such a potential, the charge and current density operators (3C-21) do not satisfy the local conservation law (3C-4), since charge can be displaced without being transmitted by particles. The actual processes involve the transfer of charge by quanta, such as π and ρ mesons, but can also be expressed in terms of an exchange current $\mathbf{j}_{\text{exch}}(\mathbf{r})$ depending on the variables of the interacting nucleons. In order that the total current, which is the sum of (3C-21) and $\mathbf{j}_{\text{exch}}(\mathbf{r})$, satisfy the continuity equation, the divergence of $\mathbf{j}_{\text{exch}}$ must obey the condition

$$\begin{aligned} \nabla \cdot \mathbf{j}_{\text{exch}}(\mathbf{r}) &= -\frac{i}{\hbar}[V_{\text{exch}}, \rho(\mathbf{r})] \\ &= -\frac{ie}{\hbar}\sum_{i<k}(t_z(i) - t_z(k))\,V_\tau(ik)P^\tau(ik)(\delta(\mathbf{r}-\mathbf{r}_i) - \delta(\mathbf{r}-\mathbf{r}_k)) \end{aligned} \tag{3C-39}$$

We are assuming the charge exchange interaction to be a function $V_\tau(ik)$ of space and spin coordinates of the interacting particles multiplied by the charge exchange operator $P^\tau(ik)$ (see Eq. (1-57)) and the charge density is taken to have the form (3C-21).

In order to estimate the magnetic moment contributions from the exchange current, it is necessary to make further assumptions regarding the structure of the process, since Eq. (3C-39) determines only the divergence of $\mathbf{j}_{\text{exch}}$, but not its rotation $(\nabla \times \mathbf{j}_{\text{exch}})$.

A simple, semiclassical picture describes the exchange current as concentrated on the straight line connecting the two interacting point charges; the strength J of this current (the product of current density and the area of the current filament) is then equal to the factor multiplying $(\delta(\mathbf{r} - \mathbf{r}_i) - \delta(\mathbf{r} - \mathbf{r}_k))$ in Eq. (3C-39). The associated magnetic multipole moment is given by (see Eq. (3C-15))

$$\delta\mathscr{M}(M\lambda, \mu) = \frac{J}{2c(\lambda+1)} \sum_{i<k} (\mathbf{r}_i + \mathbf{r}_k) \cdot \int_{\mathbf{r}_i}^{\mathbf{r}_k} (d\mathbf{s} \times \nabla) r^{\lambda} Y_{\lambda\mu}(\hat{\mathbf{r}}) \tag{3C-40}$$

where $d\mathbf{s}$ is the line element on the straight path from $\mathbf{r}_i$ to $\mathbf{r}_k$.

The result (3C-40) may also be derived by expressing the charge exchange interaction in terms of the space exchange operator $P^r(ik)$, which can be written in the form

$$P^{\mathbf{r}}(ik) = \exp\left\{\frac{i}{\hbar}\left(\int_{S_1} d\mathbf{s} \cdot \mathbf{p}_i + \int_{S_2} d\mathbf{s} \cdot \mathbf{p}_k\right)\right\} \tag{3C-41}$$

where the exponential operators are defined by

$$\exp\left\{\frac{i}{\hbar}\int_S d\mathbf{s} \cdot \mathbf{p}\right\} = \prod_r \left(1 + \frac{i}{\hbar} d\mathbf{s}_r \cdot \mathbf{p}\right) \tag{3C-42}$$

$$\int_S d\mathbf{s} \to \sum_r d\mathbf{s}_r$$

In these equations, S_1 and S_2 are arbitrary paths leading from $\mathbf{r}_i$ to $\mathbf{r}_k$, and vice versa. In the presence of an electromagnetic field, $\mathbf{p}$ is to be replaced by $\mathbf{p} - ec^{-1}(\frac{1}{2} - t_z)\,\mathbf{A}(\mathbf{r})$ (gauge invariant derivative), and we obtain a coupling to the electromagnetic field associated with the current J passing from one particle to another. Assuming S_1 and S_2 to coincide with the straight line connecting $\mathbf{r}_i$ and $\mathbf{r}_k$, the resulting multipole moment has the value (3C-40). (This derivation is essentially the one given by Sachs, 1948; see also Sachs, 1953, pp. 60 ff.) It is seen that the condition of charge conservation leaves the choice of the paths S_1 and S_2 ambiguous, corresponding to the possibility of additional divergence-free currents.

For the $M1$ moment, the expression (3C-40) can be written

$$\delta\mathscr{M}(M1, \mu) = \left(\frac{3}{4\pi}\right)^{1/2} \frac{ie}{4\hbar c} \sum_{i<k} (t_z(i) - t_z(k)) V_\tau(ik) P^{\mathbf{r}}(ik)((\mathbf{r}_i + \mathbf{r}_k) \times (\mathbf{r}_i - \mathbf{r}_k))_\mu \tag{3C-43}$$

For most cases so far considered, the effect of the additional moment (3C-43) appears to be small (see Spruch, 1950). Thus, for the two-particle system (np), the moment with respect to the center of mass vanishes and, for $A = 3$, the contribution of $\delta\mathscr{M}$ to the static moments vanishes in first approximation, since the orbital motion is predominantly in an S state. In heavier nuclei, one may attempt to derive an effective single-particle moment by averaging the part of the expression (3C-43) associated with a definite nucleon k over the other particles in the nucleus; however, if one neglects the correlation between space and spin coordinates, such an average vanishes. The above schematic description of the exchange effect will be modified in a significant way owing to the fact that the extension of the charge-current distribution around the individual nucleons is comparable to the separation between the interacting nucleons (both are of the order of the Compton wavelength for mesons). Hence, the ambiguity associated with the choice of the path for the transmission of the charge can only be resolved by a more detailed analysis of the meson processes responsible for the charge exchange.

3C-6e *Effect of velocity-dependent interactions*

In the presence of velocity-dependent nucleonic forces, the relationship between velocity and momentum of a particle is modified. In particular, if the interaction contains a two-body spin-orbit interaction of the form (1-92), we have

$$\begin{aligned} \mathbf{v}_k &= \frac{i}{\hbar}[H, \mathbf{r}_k] \\ &= \frac{\mathbf{p}_k}{M} - \frac{1}{\hbar}\sum_i ((\mathbf{r}_k - \mathbf{r}_i) \times (\mathbf{s}_k + \mathbf{s}_i)) V_{\mathrm{LS}}(r_{ik}) \end{aligned} \tag{3C-44}$$

For simplicity, we shall consider an isospin-independent interaction; the inclusion of charge exchange would modify the isospin dependence of the resulting moments and, in addition, would imply exchange terms of the type considered above.

The nucleonic current is proportional to $\mathbf{v}_k$ rather than to $\mathbf{p}_k$, as is required by the conservation law for the charge-current density. If one expresses $\mathbf{j}(\mathbf{r})$ in terms of the momentum variables, the current therefore contains two-particle terms obtained by inserting the expression (3C-44) into Eq. (3C-21). In particular, in the orbital magnetic moment in Eq. (3C-30), the quantity $\hbar \mathbf{l}_k$ is to be replaced by $M(\mathbf{r}_k \times \mathbf{v}_k)$, and we thus obtain the additional magnetic dipole moment (in units of $e\hbar/2Mc$)

$$\begin{aligned} \delta\boldsymbol{\mu} &= \frac{M}{\hbar}\sum_k (\tfrac{1}{2} - t_z(k))(\mathbf{r}_k \times \delta\mathbf{v}_k) \\ &= \frac{M}{2\hbar^2}\sum_{i<k} (t_z(k) - t_z(i))(\mathbf{r}_k + \mathbf{r}_i) \times ((\mathbf{r}_k - \mathbf{r}_i) \times (\mathbf{s}_k + \mathbf{s}_i)) V_{\mathrm{LS}}(r_{ik}) \\ &\quad - \frac{M}{2\hbar^2}\sum_{i<k} (1 - (t_z(i) + t_z(k)))(\mathbf{r}_k - \mathbf{r}_i) \times ((\mathbf{r}_k - \mathbf{r}_i) \times (\mathbf{s}_k + \mathbf{s}_i)) V_{\mathrm{LS}}(r_{ik}) \end{aligned} \tag{3C-45}$$

If one averages the terms in Eq. (3C-45) involving a particular nucleon k, and assumes the particles i to form a spherically symmetric core (see the similar estimate (2-215) of the single-particle potential produced by a two-body spin-orbit force), one obtains

$$\delta\boldsymbol{\mu} = \delta\boldsymbol{\mu}^{(1)} + \delta\boldsymbol{\mu}^{(2)} \tag{3C-46}$$

with

$$\begin{aligned} \delta\boldsymbol{\mu}^{(1)} &= -\frac{M}{\hbar^2}\frac{2Z}{A}\kappa\rho\mathbf{s} \\ \delta\boldsymbol{\mu}^{(2)} &= \frac{M}{\hbar^2}\left(t_z - \frac{N-Z}{2A}\right)\kappa\frac{1}{r}\frac{\partial\rho}{\partial r}(\mathbf{r} \times (\mathbf{r} \times \mathbf{s})) \end{aligned} \tag{3C-47}$$

where κ is the average of the spin-orbit interaction given by Eq. (2-218). One thus gets partly a renormalization of the one-particle g_s factor and partly a term proportional to the tensor $(Y_2 s)_1$. The latter term has a magnitude that can be directly related to the one-particle spin-orbit potential $V_{ls}(r)$

$$\delta\boldsymbol{\mu}^{(2)} \approx \frac{M}{\hbar^2}\left(t_z - \frac{N-Z}{2A}\right) v_{ls}(r)(\mathbf{r} \times (\mathbf{r} \times \mathbf{s}))$$

$$V_{ls}(r) = (\mathbf{l} \cdot \mathbf{s}) v_{ls}(r) \tag{3C-48}$$

$$(\mathbf{r} \times (\mathbf{r} \times \mathbf{s}))_\mu = -\left(\frac{8\pi}{9}\right)^{1/2} r^2 (Y_2 s)_{(21)1\mu} - \tfrac{2}{3} r^2 s_\mu$$

The estimate (3C-48) gives a contribution to the magnetic moments of the order of a tenth of a magneton, but cannot claim quantitative significance on account of the simplified averaging employed and the neglect of the isospin dependence of the two-particle spin-orbit force, which is not expected to have the same effect on the interaction moment as on the average single-particle potential.

One may attempt to estimate the magnitude of the interaction moment (3C-45) directly from the single-particle spin-orbit potential by inserting this potential into the Hamiltonian giving the relation between $\mathbf{v}_k$ and $\mathbf{p}_k$, as in Eq. (3C-44) (Jensen and Mayer, 1952). The moment obtained in this manner differs from the expression (3C-46), which includes additional contributions from the particles in the closed shells. For closed shells consisting entirely of neutrons ($N = A$), these additional terms vanish and the moment (3C-46) equals that derived from the one-body Hamiltonian. However, for $N \simeq \frac{1}{2}A$, the moment $\delta\boldsymbol{\mu}^{(2)}$ is purely isovector and, in addition, one obtains an isoscalar moment $\delta\boldsymbol{\mu}^{(1)}$. The difficulty of deriving the nuclear magnetic moment operator from the effective one-particle potential may also suggest caution in deriving conclusions from the phenomenological two-particle interaction, without a more detailed analysis of the associated additional degrees of freedom.

The absence of a general relationship between interaction moments and the velocity dependence of the effective one-particle potential is evident from the fact that such a velocity dependence can be produced by velocity-independent two-particle interactions. For example, a tensor force acting to second order can give rise to a spin-orbit coupling, and a velocity-dependent central field can result from a short-range repulsion together with a long-range attraction (see Sec. 2-5b). A treatment of such a velocity-dependent central potential on the basis of Eq. (3C-44) would suggest an orbital magnetic moment with the effective mass M^* replacing M. The spurious character of this effect may be seen by considering a model in which all the particles have the same g_l and $g_s = g_l = g$. For such a system, the magnetic moment equals $\boldsymbol{\mu} = g\mathbf{J}$ for all states, provided the basic two-particle interactions are velocity independent.

APPENDIX

3D

Beta Interaction

3D-1 Weak Interaction Processes and Weak Current

For many years, the nuclear β decay appeared to occupy an isolated position among the known reactions of atomic particles, but more recent developments have revealed a great variety of elementary particle processes that are intimately related to the β-decay phenomenon. The associated interaction is characterized by a coupling strength many orders of magnitude smaller than for electromagnetic forces and is referred to as the weak interaction.

3D-1a Classification of weak interaction processes

One can divide the observed weak interaction processes into the following groups:

(*i*) PROCESSES INVOLVING ONLY LEPTONS. The only process of this type so far studied is the μ decay ($\mu^- \to e^- + \bar{\nu}_e + \nu_\mu$ and the charge conjugate process). Intimately related processes are the inelastic neutrino scatterings, $\bar{\nu}_e + e^- \to \bar{\nu}_\mu + \mu^-$ and $\nu_\mu + e^- \to \nu_e + \mu^-$.

(*ii*) PROCESSES INVOLVING HADRONS AND LEPTONS. These processes may be subdivided into strangeness-conserving processes and strangeness-violating processes. Examples of strangeness-conserving processes involving the lepton pair (e, ν_e) are

$$(Z, A) \to (Z+1, A) + e^- + \bar{\nu}_e \qquad \beta^- \text{ decay}$$

$$(Z, A) \to (Z-1, A) + e^+ + \nu_e \qquad \beta^+ \text{ decay}$$

$$e^- + (Z, A) \to (Z-1, A) + \nu_e \qquad \text{electron capture}$$

$$\left.\begin{array}{l} \nu_e + (Z, A) \to (Z+1, A) + e^- \\ \bar{\nu}_e + (Z, A) \to (Z-1, A) + e^+ \end{array}\right\} \qquad \text{inverse } \beta \text{ decay (charge exchange scattering of neutrinos)}$$

$$\pi^+ \to \pi^0 + e^+ + \nu_e$$

$$\Sigma^+ \to \Lambda + e^+ + \nu_e$$

$$\pi^+ \to e^+ + \nu_e$$

In addition, corresponding processes involving the lepton pair (μ, ν_μ) are found to occur, when sufficient energy is available.

Examples of strangeness-violating processes are

$$\Lambda \rightarrow p + e^- + \bar{\nu}_e$$
$$\Xi^- \rightarrow \Lambda + e^- + \bar{\nu}_e$$
$$K^+ \rightarrow \pi^0 + e^+ + \nu_e$$

and corresponding reactions involving muons.

(*iii*) PROCESSES INVOLVING ONLY HADRONS. Among the best studied processes of this type are

$$\Lambda \rightarrow p + \pi^-$$
$$K^+ \rightarrow \pi^+ + \pi^0$$
$$K^+ \rightarrow \pi^+ + \pi^+ + \pi^-$$
$${}^4_\Lambda H \rightarrow {}^4He + \pi^-$$

which are all characterized by unit change of strangeness ($\Delta S = 1$). One also expects strangeness-conserving weak interactions of the purely hadronic type (see p. 397).

3D-1b Current coupling

A comprehensive description of all the weak interaction processes can be based on the four-vector current

$$j_\mu(\mathbf{r}) = (j_\mu(\mathbf{r}))_{\text{hadr}} + (j_\mu(\mathbf{r}))_{\text{lept}} \tag{3D-1}$$

consisting of a hadronic and a leptonic part. The assumption of a coupling of this current to itself

$$\begin{aligned} H' &= k \int j_\mu^\dagger(\mathbf{r}) j_\mu(\mathbf{r})\, d^3\mathrm{r} \\ &= k \left\{ \int (j_\mu^\dagger(\mathbf{r}))_{\text{lept}} (j_\mu(\mathbf{r}))_{\text{lept}}\, d^3\mathrm{r} + \left(\int (j_\mu^\dagger(\mathbf{r}))_{\text{hadr}} (j_\mu(\mathbf{r}))_{\text{lept}} d^3\mathrm{r} + \text{H.c.} \right) \right. \\ &\quad \left. + \int (j_\mu^\dagger(\mathbf{r}))_{\text{hadr}} (j_\mu(\mathbf{r}))_{\text{hadr}}\, d^3\mathrm{r} \right\} \end{aligned} \tag{3D-2}$$

is found to be compatible with all the evidence on the three different types of processes listed above. The constant factor k in Eq. (3D-2) depends on the normalization of the current and equals $2^{-1/2} g_V^{-1}$ for the normalization employed below.

The fact that the weak interactions are generated by a four-current implies an analogy to electromagnetic interactions. Thus, in the β-decay process, the hadronic current corresponds to the nuclear charge-current density, while the leptonic current is formally analogous to the electromagnetic 4-vector potential (see Eq. (3C-1)); this analogy was the original basis for the theory of β decay (Fermi, 1934).

The analogy between weak and electromagnetic interactions may go still deeper. It has been suggested that the coupling (3D-2) is transmitted by a vector field corresponding to the photon field, though with a nonvanishing rest mass. There is no simple argument pointing to a particular value for the mass M_W of such "intermediate bosons," and present experimental evidence only allows the conclusion that these quanta, if they exist, must have $M_W > 2M_{\text{nucleon}}$. (For a review of the theory of intermediate bosons and reference to the experimental evidence, see Lee and Wu, 1965.) The presence of an intermediate field would imply a finite range of order $\hbar/M_W c$ for the interaction between nucleons and leptons, but would not significantly affect the nuclear β-decay matrix elements, since the momentum transfer in such processes is very small compared with $M_W c$.

3D-1c Hadronic current. Parity-violating nuclear forces

The hadronic part of the current consists of a strangeness-conserving as well as a strangeness-violating part, and the last coupling term in Eq. (3D-2) therefore involves a strangeness-conserving interaction as well as the strangeness-violating interaction of which examples are quoted under (iii) in Sec. 3D-1a. For example, the expression (3D-2) implies a contribution to the force acting between two nucleons. Although this force is very weak ($\sim 10^{-6}$) compared with the main components in the nucleonic interaction, it has the special property that it violates $\mathscr{P}$ symmetry and hence produces a small parity admixture of nuclear states.

The β-decay interaction (second term in expression (3D-2)), when taken to second order, also produces parity-violating nucleonic forces, but these are of order 10^{-12} as compared with the strong interactions, and therefore of negligible significance in the present context (although one should bear in mind that the second-order coupling diverges for a leptonic current with point structure). The detection of parity admixtures of order 10^{-6} therefore provides a significant test of the assumption underlying Eq. (3D-2). Evidence for such parity admixtures is discussed on pp. 23 ff.

3D-1d Leptonic current. Lepton conservation

The main evidence for the four-vector character of the weak interactions is provided by the study of leptonic processes, in particular of nuclear β decay. The analysis of the angular and spin correlations of the emitted lepton pair (e, ν_e) shows that the leptons are coupled, at least to first approximation, through a four-vector current constructed as a bilinear form in the lepton fields, taken at the same space-time point. The coupling involves predominantly, and perhaps only, neutrinos with negative helicity ($h = \mathbf{s} \cdot \hat{\mathbf{p}} = -1/2$) and antineutrinos with positive helicity (two-component neutrino theory). The leptonic current is thus a combination of polar vector and axial vector currents. (The experimental evidence defining the leptonic coupling is reviewed, for example, by Lee and Wu, 1965.)

The assumption of the coupling (3D-2) implies the occurrence of a number of so far unobserved leptonic weak interaction processes, such as elastic neutrino-electron scattering ($\bar{\nu}_e + e^- \rightarrow \bar{\nu}_e + e^-$) and the related electron-positron annihilation ($e^- + e^+ \rightarrow \nu_e + \bar{\nu}_e$), which may play a significant role in determining the time scale for evolution of very hot stars. (See, for example, Fowler and Hoyle, 1964.)

The leptonic current is governed by the laws of lepton conservation expressing the constancy of the number of electronic leptons $N(e^-) + N(\nu_e) - N(e^+) - N(\bar{\nu}_e)$ and of muonic leptons $N(\mu^-) + N(\nu_\mu) - N(\mu^+) - N(\bar{\nu}_\mu)$.

Evidence for the conservation law for electronic leptons comes from the failure to observe certain neutrino-induced processes, such as $\bar{\nu}_e + n \rightarrow p + e^-$ or double β-decay processes with no emission of neutrinos, $(Z, A) \rightarrow (Z + 2, A) + e^- + e^-$. Double β decay may proceed by the much slower channel $(Z, A) \rightarrow (Z + 2, A) + e^- + e^- + \bar{\nu}_e + \bar{\nu}_e$, for which the rate is expected to be below the present limit of direct observations. A review of the experimental evidence favoring lepton conservation, together with a discussion of the relation between this conservation law and the two-neutrino theory, is given by Lee and Wu (1965); see also the more recent search for double β decay of ^{48}Ca by Bardin *et al.* (1967). Experimental evidence for the occurrence of double β decay of ^{130}Te with a half life of about 10^{21} years has been obtained from the content of ^{130}Xe in tellurium ore (Kirsten *et al.*, 1968). A half life of this magnitude is of the order of that expected for double β decay with emission of two neutrinos, implying conservation of leptons to a high accuracy.

The study of processes involving high-energy muonic neutrinos (produced by π-μ decay) places a low upper limit on the cross section for reactions such as $\bar{\nu}_\mu + n \rightarrow p + \mu^-$ and thereby tests the law of muonic lepton conservation (see the survey by Bernardini, 1966).

The existence of two different types of neutrinos, associated with electrons and muons, respectively, was deduced from the observation that neutrinos from π-μ decay, interacting with nuclei, give rise to μ particles, but not to electrons. (For a review of these experiments, see, for example, Wu and Moszkowski, 1966, p. 291.)

The separate conservation of electronic and muonic leptons implies that the leptonic current is a sum of two parts involving (e, ν_e) and (μ, ν_μ) separately. The two parts are found to have identical structure. Experimental evidence for this equivalence is provided by the comparison between μ capture and β-decay processes, and from the study of decay processes that proceed by emission of (e, ν_e) and (μ, ν_μ) pairs, in competition. (See, for example, the determination of the branching ratio for the processes $\pi^+ \rightarrow e^+ + \nu_e$ and $\pi^+ \rightarrow \mu^+ + \nu_\mu$ (Di Capua *et al.*, 1964).)

The expected large production of neutrinos in the interior of stars, together with the very small cross section for interaction of neutrinos with matter, has led to the suggestion (Pontecorvo and Smorodinski, 1961) of a significant neutrino density in the universe. These neutrinos may induce reactions (such as $\nu_e + n \rightarrow p + e^-$) affecting the lifetime and spectra of the β-radioactive nuclei. Since no effects of this type have yet been observed, an upper limit can be placed on the cosmic neutrino flux. The cosmological significance of this evidence has been discussed by Weinberg (1962 and 1962a).

3D-2 Symmetry Properties of β Current

The study of the weak interaction processes has indicated a number of symmetry relations, which partly define the structure of the β current. The development in this field in recent years has been very rapid and has indicated a variety of intriguing connections. It must be stressed, however, that many of the relations considered below, though compatible with the available evidence, have not yet been subjected to accurate experimental tests.

The part of the current responsible for the nuclear transmutations (the strangeness-conserving part of the hadronic current) is denoted by

$$j_\mu^\beta(\mathbf{r}) = (\rho^\beta(\mathbf{r}), \mathbf{j}^\beta(\mathbf{r})) \tag{3D-3}$$

The four-vector current is expressed in terms of a charge density and a three-vector current, as in the electromagnetic case. (Following the conventional notation, we omit in Eq. (3D-3) the factor c which appears in the analogous expression (3C-3).)

3D-2a Reflection symmetry

The weak interactions are found to violate $\mathscr{P}$ invariance (see Sec. 1-2b). The current (3D-3) is therefore a combination of polar and axial vector parts

$$(\rho^\beta, \mathbf{j}^\beta) = (\rho_V, \mathbf{j}_V) + (\rho_A, \mathbf{j}_A) \tag{3D-4}$$

with opposite reflection symmetries (see Eq. (1A-108)),

$$\begin{aligned} \mathscr{P}(\rho_V(\mathbf{r}), \mathbf{j}_V(\mathbf{r}))\mathscr{P}^{-1} &= (\rho_V(-\mathbf{r}), -\mathbf{j}_V(-\mathbf{r})) \\ \mathscr{P}(\rho_A(\mathbf{r}), \mathbf{j}_A(\mathbf{r}))\mathscr{P}^{-1} &= (-\rho_A(-\mathbf{r}), \mathbf{j}_A(-\mathbf{r})) \end{aligned} \tag{3D-5}$$

The experimental data on β decay are consistent with the assumption that the weak interactions are invariant under time reversal (see Sec. 1-2c) with the β current transforming as

$$\mathscr{T}(\rho^\beta(\mathbf{r}), \mathbf{j}^\beta(\mathbf{r}))\mathscr{T}^{-1} = (\rho^\beta(\mathbf{r}), -\mathbf{j}^\beta(\mathbf{r})) \tag{3D-6}$$

in analogy to the relation (3C-5) for the electromagnetic current. (See, however, the evidence on K° decay (p. 21), which may indicate a partial violation of time reversal in weak decay processes.)

3D-2b Charge symmetry

The operator j_μ^β transforms a neutron into a proton, and has the quantum number $\mu_\tau = -1$ with respect to rotations about the z axis in isospace; similarly, the Hermitian conjugate $(j_\mu^\beta)^\dagger$ has $\mu_\tau = +1$.[4] The sign of μ_τ can also be inverted by the charge symmetry operation $\mathscr{R}_\tau$ and we can, therefore, characterize the β current by its transformation under the combination of $\mathscr{R}_\tau$ and Hermitian conjugation. The available evidence is compatible with the assumption that j_μ^β is odd under this transformation

$$\begin{aligned} \mathscr{R}_\tau(\rho^\beta, \mathbf{j}^\beta)\mathscr{R}_\tau^{-1} &= -(\rho^\beta, \mathbf{j}^\beta)^\dagger \\ \mathscr{R}_\tau &= \exp\{-i\pi T_y\} \end{aligned} \tag{3D-7}$$

As will be discussed below, components in j_μ^β with opposite transformation would not contribute to allowed β decay and the present data are not very specific as regards the possible magnitude of such components (see Sec. 3D-3).

One can also combine the relations (3D-6) and (3D-7) into the transformation under the operation $\mathscr{F} = \mathscr{R}_\tau\mathscr{T}$ (see Eq. (1B-15))

[4] We consistently employ the assignment $m_t = +1/2$ for neutrons and $m_t = -1/2$ for protons, which is opposite to that conventionally used in elementary particle physics.

$$\mathscr{T}(\rho^\beta, \mathbf{j}^\beta)\mathscr{T}^{-1} = (-\rho^\beta, \mathbf{j}^\beta)^\dagger \tag{3D-8}$$

The symmetry property (3D-7) or (3D-8) is usually discussed in terms of the transformation G, which is the product of the charge symmetry operation $\mathscr{R}_\tau$ and the particle-antiparticle conjugation $\mathscr{C}$ (see, for example, Weinberg, 1958). The G invariance provides a relation between the matrix elements of the β current for nucleons and antinucleons, but if, in addition, one assumes the $\mathscr{P}\mathscr{C}\mathscr{T}$ invariance, which is implied by a local relativistic theory (see Chapter 1, p. 21), one obtains restrictions on the nucleonic matrix elements themselves. Thus, the $\mathscr{P}\mathscr{C}\mathscr{T}$ invariance implies that any vector field $F_\mu(\mathbf{r})$ transforms under $\mathscr{P}\mathscr{C}\mathscr{T}$ into $-F_\mu^\dagger(-\mathbf{r})$ and the relations (3D-8) and (3D-5) together with the $\mathscr{P}\mathscr{C}\mathscr{T}$ symmetry are therefore equivalent to the assumption that $(j_V)_\mu$ is invariant under the G transformation, while $(j_A)_\mu$ changes sign.

3D-2c Conservation of vector current

It is a remarkable feature of the vector current in β decay that the total vector transition "charge" for the decay of the nucleon (neutron → proton)

$$\begin{aligned} \langle p|Q_V|n\rangle &= g_V \\ Q_V &\equiv \int \rho_V(\mathbf{r})\, d\tau \end{aligned} \tag{3D-9}$$

is very close to the corresponding quantity for the μ decay. (The quantitative comparison is given below.) In view of the complex intrinsic structure of the particles involved, the constancy of the transition charges suggests the operation of invariance principles.

A similar relationship is well known to apply to the electromagnetic interactions, and corresponds to the equality of the electric charge Q^{el} for the different charged particles. This fact is usually attributed to two basic properties of the electromagnetic interaction. One is the continuity equation (3C-4). On account of this conservation law, the total charge of a particle is unaffected by complexities in its internal structure. For example, the presence of virtual mesons in the nucleon leaves the total charge unchanged. (The electromagnetic interactions themselves, on account of their long-range character, can shift charge to infinity, and thus give rise to a charge renormalization similar to that of a charged particle in a dielectric medium. The renormalization factor, however, is the same for all charged particles and, hence, does not affect the present argument.)

In addition, the electromagnetic phenomena appear to be governed by a universality principle that requires all the primordial particles to have the same charge (or multiples thereof).

The observed equality of the β-transition charges thus suggests that the vector current in β decay is subject to a continuity equation and a universality principle. An intriguing hypothesis, which encompasses these relations, envisages an intimate connection between the vector currents in the beta and electromagnetic interactions (Feynman and Gell-Mann, 1958). The hadronic part of the electromagnetic current consists of an isoscalar and an isovector component. Apart from normalization factors, these components represent the charge-current densities of hypercharge Y and isospin T_z. (The charge Q equals $\frac{1}{2}Y - T_z$, multiplied by the electric coupling constant e

(see Eq. (1-62).) Similarly, the vector β current (and its Hermitian conjugate) may be viewed as the charge-current densities of the isospin components $T_{\mp}$ multiplied by the vector coupling constant g_V. The suggested relationship can be expressed in the form

$$(j_V)_\mu = -\frac{g_V}{e}[T_x - iT_y, j_\mu^{\text{el}}] \tag{3D-10}$$

The isoscalar part of j^{el} (and the leptonic part) commutes with T and thus does not contribute to the expression (3D-10). (We have ignored a factor c in the three-current part of Eq. (3D-10) arising from the different conventions in the normalization of the currents.) For the total transition charge Q_V we obtain, from Eqs. (3D-9) and (3D-10),

$$\begin{aligned} Q_V &= -\frac{g_V}{e}[T_x - iT_y, Q^{\text{el}}] \\ &= g_V(T_x - iT_y) \end{aligned} \tag{3D-11}$$

The connection between the transition charge Q_V and the isospin has been tested for widely different $T = 1$ triplets with $I = 0$ in the hadronic spectrum (nuclear isobaric transitions and $\pi^+ \rightarrow \pi^\circ + e^+ + \nu_e$; see Fig. 1-10). The value obtained for g_V is found to agree to within a few percent with the coupling constant in μ decay; $((g_V)_\mu - (g_V)_{\text{nucl}} \approx 0.02 g_V$, see Freeman, 1965; for an interpretation of the small difference, see p. 402.) Further evidence for the relation (3D-10) is obtained from a determination of the β-transition moment that corresponds to the $M1$ moment (weak magnetism, see pp. 414 ff.).

For the axial vector decay of the nucleon, the coupling constant g_A is found to differ by about 20% from the corresponding transition charge in μ decay. The difference in the axial vector transition charges may be attributed to renormalization effects caused by the strong interactions and can be related to other processes involving these interactions (Adler, 1965; Weisberger, 1965).

3D-2d Violation of continuity equation by electromagnetic interactions

If we neglect the effect of the electromagnetic interactions on the hadronic systems (and assume isospin invariance of the strong interactions), we obtain from Eqs. (3D-10) and (3C-4) the continuity equation

$$\frac{\partial}{\partial x_\mu}(j_V)_\mu = \nabla \cdot \mathbf{j}_V + \frac{1}{c}\frac{\partial \rho_V}{\partial t} = 0 \tag{3D-12}$$

This conservation law, however, is violated by the electromagnetic interactions. A modified continuity equation can be obtained if we assume the general validity of the relation (3D-10). If the Hamiltonian (with the neglect of the weak interactions) is written in the form $H = H^0 + H^{\text{el}}$, where H^0 commutes with $\mathbf{T}$, we find

$$\begin{aligned} \nabla \cdot \mathbf{j}_V + \frac{1}{c}\frac{\partial \rho_V}{\partial t} &= -\frac{g_V}{e}[T_x - iT_y, \nabla \cdot \mathbf{j}^{\text{el}}] - \frac{g_V}{ec}\frac{\partial}{\partial t}[T_x - iT_y, \rho^{\text{el}}] \\ &= \frac{ig_V}{e\hbar c}[[T_x - iT_y, H^{\text{el}}], \rho^{\text{el}}] \end{aligned} \tag{3D-13}$$

3D-2e Strangeness-violating current (SU_3 symmetry)

One may attempt to relate the strangeness-violating and strangeness-conserving parts of the hadronic weak current within the framework of the SU_3 symmetry scheme for the strong interactions.

The strangeness-conserving current and its Hermitian conjugate are characterized by the same quantum numbers (T, M_T, S, and A) as the π^+ and π^- mesons. One may therefore envisage an octuplet of weak currents corresponding to the octuplet of the pseudoscalar mesons $(\pi^\pm, \pi^0)$, (K^+, K^0), $(K^-, \bar{K}^0)$, and η. Such an octuplet current also comprises strangeness-violating charged components with the same quantum numbers as the K^+ and K^- mesons. (There is so far no empirical evidence for the existence of the neutral currents.)

In the application of the principle of universality of the hadronic current, the question arises as to whether each octuplet member has the full universal strength or whether it is some measure of the total hadronic current that should be equated to the strength of the leptonic current as observed in the μ decay.

The experimental evidence indicates an appreciably weaker coupling for the strangeness-violating leptonic decays, as compared with the strangeness-conserving transitions. For example, the ft value for the leptonic Λ decay $(\Lambda \rightarrow p + e^- + \bar{\nu}_e)$ is observed to be an order of magnitude larger than the ft value for the neutron decay. Therefore, it has been suggested (Cabibbo, 1963) that it is the sum of the squares of the hadronic coupling constants that equals the universal value. Thus, we write for the total hadronic current

$$(j_\mu)_{\text{hadr}} = j_\mu(\Delta S = 0)\cos\vartheta + j_\mu(\Delta S = 1)\sin\vartheta \tag{3D-14}$$

where the components $j(\Delta S = 0)$ and $j(\Delta S = 1)$ (and their Hermitian conjugates) behave under SU_3 transformations as the π^+ and K^+ (and π^- and K^-) components of a unitary octuplet. With a current of the form (3D-14), an approximate description of all the leptonic decays of the baryons and mesons can be obtained. The best fit to the empirical data is obtained by taking the angular parameter ϑ to have the values $\vartheta_V = 0.21$ and $\vartheta_A = 0.27$ for the vector and axial vector currents, respectively. (See, for example, Brene *et al.*, 1966.)

The formulation of the universality principle leading to the expression (3D-14) implies that the vector transition charge for the neutron decay denoted by g_V in Eq. (3D-9) is to be compared with the quantity $\cos\vartheta_V(g_V)_\mu = 0.98\ (g_V)_\mu$, where $(g_V)_\mu$ is the vector coupling constant in μ decay. This correction is seen to be of the right sign and magnitude to account for the small discrepancy mentioned above. It should be noted, however, that some uncertainty attaches to the estimates of the radiative corrections to β decay, which have been applied in the determination of $(g_V)_{\text{nucl}}$. These corrections amount to a few percent. (For a discussion of this point, see, for example, Lee and Wu, 1965. The possibility of estimating these corrections from experimentally measurable form factors has been discussed by Källén, 1967.)

3D-3 Nonrelativistic Form of β Current

In the present section, we consider the form of the β current for individual nucleons; as in the case of the electromagnetic current, we restrict ourselves to a nonrelativistic approximation, valid to first order in the nucleonic velocity, and include only terms linear in the size of the nucleon. For a system of nucleons, the interactions may modify the properties of the particles and thus give rise to interaction terms in the β current depending on the coordinates of two or more nucleons. (See the discussion in Sec. 3C-6 of similar terms in the electromagnetic current.) There is so far little evidence regarding the structure and significance of these interaction terms in the β current, and we shall therefore confine ourselves to a discussion of the β current for free nucleons. (The general form of the nonrelativistic β current, for free nucleons as well as for nucleons moving in nuclear matter, has been discussed, on the basis of invariance arguments, by Winther, 1962; see also the formulation by Stech and Schülke, 1964.)

As a first step, we consider the most general form of the velocity-independent terms describing the charge and current densities associated with a single nucleon. The leading terms that do not involve the size of the nucleon are

$$\begin{aligned} \rho_V &= g_V\, t_-(k)\delta(\mathbf{r}-\mathbf{r}_k) \\ \mathbf{j}_A &= g_A\, t_-(k)\boldsymbol{\sigma}_k\,\delta(\mathbf{r}-\mathbf{r}_k) \end{aligned} \tag{3D-15}$$

where g_V and g_A are the vector and axial vector coupling constants. The coordinates of the nucleon are labeled by k. The operator $t_- = t_x - it_y = \frac{1}{2}\tau_-$ transforms a neutron into a proton with the matrix element $\langle p|t_-|n\rangle = 1$. (We express the nucleon spin in terms of the Pauli spin vector $\boldsymbol{\sigma} = 2\mathbf{s}$, as is conventional in β-decay theory.)

The $\mathscr{T}$ invariance (Eq. (3D-6)) requires g_V and g_A to be real quantities. The terms in Eq. (3D-15) then also satisfy $\mathscr{F}$ invariance, as defined by Eq. (3D-8). (The $\mathscr{F}$ transformation is a combination of charge symmetry and time reversal, and we have $\mathscr{T}t_-\mathscr{T}^{-1} = t_-$ since t_y is a purely imaginary matrix, and $\mathscr{R}_\tau(t_x - it_y)\mathscr{R}_\tau^{-1} = -t_x - it_y = -t_+ = -t_-^\dagger$).

The possible terms that are linear in the nucleonic size and independent of velocity are

$$\begin{aligned} \rho_A &= i\,\frac{g_A\hbar}{2Mc}\, t_-(k)\alpha_1\boldsymbol{\sigma}_k\cdot\nabla\delta(\mathbf{r}-\mathbf{r}_k) \\ \mathbf{j}_V &= \frac{g_V\hbar}{2Mc}\, t_-(k)\{\mu_\beta(\nabla\times\boldsymbol{\sigma}_k)\delta(\mathbf{r}-\mathbf{r}_k) + i\alpha_2\,\nabla\delta(\mathbf{r}-\mathbf{r}_k)\} \end{aligned} \tag{3D-16}$$

involving three new dimensionless quantities, α_1, α_2, and μ_β. The term proportional to μ_β is the analog of the magnetic moment term in Eq. (3C-21). With the choice of phase factors in Eq. (3D-16), the $\mathscr{T}$ invariance requires all three parameters α_1, α_2, and μ_β to be real. The $\mathscr{R}_\tau$ transformation (3D-7), however, is seen to imply that the charge-current densities are Hermitian, apart from the factor t_-, and hence requires α_1 and α_2 to be imaginary (and μ_β to be real); the assumption of both $\mathscr{T}$ and $\mathscr{R}_\tau$(or $\mathscr{F}$) invariance thus implies $\alpha_1 = \alpha_2 = 0$. The terms in Eq. (3D-16) proportional to α_1 and α_2 are therefore usually omitted, although there is little direct experimental information on their magnitude.

From the velocity-independent terms in the charge-current density, we can obtain the terms proportional to $\mathbf{v}_k$ by using the four-vector character of $j_\mu = (\rho, \mathbf{j})$. If we transform to a coordinate system $\mathscr{K}'$ moving with a velocity $\mathbf{u} = \mathbf{v}_k$ with respect to the laboratory system, so that the nucleon is at rest in $\mathscr{K}'$, we have, to first order in u/c,

$$\begin{aligned} \rho(\mathbf{v}_k = \mathbf{u}) &= \rho(\mathbf{v}_k = 0) + \frac{\mathbf{u}}{c}\cdot\mathbf{j}(\mathbf{v}_k = 0) \\ \mathbf{j}(\mathbf{v}_k = \mathbf{u}) &= \mathbf{j}(\mathbf{v}_k = 0) + \frac{\mathbf{u}}{c}\,\rho(\mathbf{v}_k = 0) \end{aligned} \tag{3D-17}$$

Neglecting terms involving both $\mathbf{v}_k$ and the derivative $\boldsymbol{\nabla}$, and omitting the α_1 and α_2 terms in Eq. (3D-16), we obtain for a system of free nucleons

$$\begin{aligned}
\rho_V &= g_V \sum_k t_-(k)\delta(\mathbf{r}-\mathbf{r}_k) \\
\rho_A &= g_A \sum_k t_-(k)\frac{1}{2c}(\boldsymbol{\sigma}_k\cdot\mathbf{v}_k\delta(\mathbf{r}-\mathbf{r}_k)+\delta(\mathbf{r}-\mathbf{r}_k)\boldsymbol{\sigma}_k\cdot\mathbf{v}_k) \\
\mathbf{j}_V &= g_V \sum_k t_-(k)\left\{\frac{1}{2c}(\mathbf{v}_k\delta(\mathbf{r}-\mathbf{r}_k)+\delta(\mathbf{r}-\mathbf{r}_k)\mathbf{v}_k)+\frac{\hbar}{2Mc}\mu_\beta\boldsymbol{\nabla}\times\boldsymbol{\sigma}_k\delta(\mathbf{r}-\mathbf{r}_k)\right\} \\
\mathbf{j}_A &= g_A \sum_k t_-(k)\boldsymbol{\sigma}_k\delta(\mathbf{r}-\mathbf{r}_k)
\end{aligned} \tag{3D-18}$$

We have symmetrized the terms in $\mathbf{v}_k$, as in Eq. (3C-21), to ensure the relation (3D-7) for the Hermitian conjugation. (The difference between the symmetrized and unsymmetrized terms is equivalent to a derivative term independent of $\mathbf{v}_k$ and thus to the addition of terms of the type proportional to α_1 and α_2 in Eq. (3D-16).)

In order to make clear the distinction between the operator $\mathbf{v}_k$ (whose eigenvalue changes somewhat in the β process) and the transformation velocity $\mathbf{u}$, which is a c number, we shall consider the transformation (3D-17) in more precise terms. The charge and current densities ρ and $\mathbf{j}$ are operators depending on the space point, $\mathbf{r}$, as well as on the nucleonic variables, and translational invariance implies $\rho = \rho(\mathbf{r}-\mathbf{r}_k, \mathbf{v}_k, \mathbf{s}_k)$ and similarly for $\mathbf{j}$. If we perform a Lorentz transformation to a coordinate system $\mathscr{K}'$ moving with a velocity $\mathbf{u}$ with respect to $\mathscr{K}$, we may think of ρ, $\mathbf{j}$ as a four-vector field with the transformation (see the corresponding expression (1A-106) for rotations)

$$\begin{aligned}
\mathscr{U}^{-1}\rho(\mathbf{r})\mathscr{U} &= \rho(\mathbf{r})+\frac{\mathbf{u}}{c}\cdot\mathbf{j}(\mathbf{r}) \\
\mathscr{U}^{-1}\mathbf{j}(\mathbf{r})\mathscr{U} &= \mathbf{j}(\mathbf{r})+\frac{\mathbf{u}}{c}\rho(\mathbf{r})
\end{aligned} \tag{3D-19}$$

to first order in $\mathbf{u}/c$. (It is sufficient to consider the situation for $t=0$ at which $\mathscr{K}$ and $\mathscr{K}'$ momentarily coincide.) Alternatively, we may regard ρ and $\mathbf{j}$ as functions of the particle variables and, thus,

$$\begin{aligned}
\mathscr{U}\rho(\mathbf{r}-\mathbf{r}_k, \mathbf{v}_k, \mathbf{s}_k)\mathscr{U}^{-1} &= \rho(\mathbf{r}-\mathbf{r}_k, \mathbf{v}_k-\mathbf{u}, \mathbf{s}_k) \\
\mathscr{U}\mathbf{j}(\mathbf{r}-\mathbf{r}_k, \mathbf{v}_k, \mathbf{s}_k)\mathscr{U}^{-1} &= \mathbf{j}(\mathbf{r}-\mathbf{r}_k, \mathbf{v}_k-\mathbf{u}, \mathbf{s}_k)
\end{aligned} \tag{3D-20}$$

since, to first order in $\mathbf{u}$, the particle coordinates transform as in a Galilean transformation (see Eq. (1-13)). Performing the two transformations (3D-19) and (3D-20) in succession, we obtain

$$\begin{aligned}
\rho(\mathbf{r}-\mathbf{r}_k, \mathbf{v}_k, \mathbf{s}_k) &= \rho(\mathbf{r}-\mathbf{r}_k, \mathbf{v}_k-\mathbf{u}, \mathbf{s}_k)+\frac{\mathbf{u}}{c}\cdot\mathbf{j}(\mathbf{r}-\mathbf{r}_k, \mathbf{v}_k-\mathbf{u}, \mathbf{s}_k) \\
\mathbf{j}(\mathbf{r}-\mathbf{r}_k, \mathbf{v}_k, \mathbf{s}_k) &= \mathbf{j}(\mathbf{r}-\mathbf{r}_k, \mathbf{v}_k-\mathbf{u}, \mathbf{s}_k)+\frac{\mathbf{u}}{c}\rho(\mathbf{r}-\mathbf{r}_k, \mathbf{v}_k-\mathbf{u}, \mathbf{s}_k)
\end{aligned} \tag{3D-21}$$

which yields the desired relations. (A somewhat similar argument would be involved in a derivation of the expression $M\mathbf{v}$ for the momentum $\mathbf{P}$ from the four-vector character of $(E, c\mathbf{P})$ and the fact that, for $\mathbf{v}\rightarrow 0$, we have $E = Mc^2$ and $\mathbf{P}=0$.)

The vector charge-current density in Eq. (3D-18) is seen to obey the continuity equation (3D-12), provided $t_-(k)$ is time independent, as for a system of free nucleons. Conversely, the form (3D-18) for $\mathbf{j}_V$ follows from the continuity equation, since the term proportional to α_2 in Eq. (3D-16) violates this relation. For the vector current, one cannot therefore, to the approximation considered, distinguish between the consequences of $(\mathscr{T}, \mathscr{F})$ invariance and of the continuity relation. (For a system of interacting nucleons with isospin-dependent forces, the time variation of $t_-(k)$ must be compensated by interaction terms in the current (see p. 409).)

The suggested relationship between $(j_V)_\mu$ and the electromagnetic four-vector current, implied by Eq. (3D-10), is fulfilled by the expression (3D-18), provided the parameter μ_β takes the value (see Eq. (3C-21))

$$\mu_\beta = \tfrac{1}{2}((g_s)_p - (g_s))_n = 4.7 \tag{3D-22}$$

Experimental support for this value of μ_β has been obtained from the analysis of the decays of ^{12}B and ^{12}N (see pp. 414 ff.).

The coupling constants g_V and g_A are found to be

$$\begin{aligned} g_V &= (1.40 \pm 0.02)10^{-49} \text{ erg cm}^3 \\ &= (1.36 \pm 0.02)10^{-3} \frac{e^2\hbar^2}{M_p^2 c^2} \\ \frac{g_A}{g_V} &= -1.23 \pm 0.01 \end{aligned} \tag{3D-23}$$

These values are obtained from the measured half-life of the neutron (Christensen *et al.*, 1967), which depends on the combination $g_V^2 + 3g_A^2$ (see Eq. (3D-38)), together with the observed transition rate for $0+ \rightarrow 0+$ decays within $T = 1$ triplets, which is proportional to g_V^2 (see Fig. 1-10). Moreover, the analysis of polarizations and angular correlations for the decay of polarized neutrons establishes the ratio g_A/g_V to be approximately real (which provides evidence for the assumed time reversal invariance), and to have a negative sign. (For a review of the evidence on the β-decay coupling constants, see Kofoed-Hansen, 1965; Lee and Wu, 1965.)

The β current discussed in the present section is expected to apply not only to processes involving (e, ν_e) but also to processes involving (μ, ν_μ), although there is so far little evidence to test this consequence of the assumed coupling (3B-2). In muonic nuclear processes, such as μ capture, the momentum transfer is usually much larger than in the β-decay processes, and it may therefore be necessary in the expression for the current to include higher-order terms in the nucleon initial and final velocities (that is, in $\mathbf{v}$ and $\mathbf{V}$) than those contained in Eq. (3D-18). Among these terms is the so-called induced pseudoscalar coupling. (For a review of the evidence on the coupling of muons to nucleons, see Lee and Wu, 1965. See also the surveys by Rood, 1966; Balashov and Eramzhyan, 1967, and the article by Foldy and Walecka, 1965).

With inclusion of higher-order terms in the size of the nucleon, the β current can be expressed in terms of form factors similar to those characterizing the electromagnetic structure of nucleons. The relationship (3D-10) implies that the form factors of the vector β current are the same as the isovector form factors for the electromagnetic current, discussed in Sec. 3C-4.

3D-4 Multipole Moments

The coupling (3D-2) contains a scalar and a vector part (in the sense of spatial rotations) and can be expanded in multipole components, as described in Sec. 1A-8. The nuclear multipole matrix elements have the form

$$\begin{aligned}\mathscr{M}(\rho_{V,A}, \lambda\mu) &= \int a_\lambda(r)\, Y_{\lambda\mu}(\hat{\mathbf{r}})\rho_{V,A}(\mathbf{r})\, d\tau \\ \mathscr{M}(j_{V,A}, \kappa\lambda\mu) &= \int b_{\kappa\lambda}(r)(Y_\kappa(\hat{\mathbf{r}})\, j_{V,A}(\mathbf{r}))_{(\kappa 1)\lambda\mu}\, d\tau\end{aligned} \tag{3D-24}$$

where the radial functions $a_\lambda(r)$ and $b_{\kappa\lambda}(r)$ depend on the momenta and polarization of the emitted (or absorbed) leptons. If one neglects the effect of the nuclear Coulomb field on the electron motion, the functions a_λ and $b_{\kappa\lambda}$ reduce to spherical Bessel functions (j_λ and j_κ), as in the electromagnetic case (see Eq. (3C-18)).

The functions $a_\lambda(r)$ and $b_{\kappa\lambda}(r)$ can be obtained from a solution of the Dirac equation in the Coulomb field of the nucleus. To a first approximation, one may employ an expansion of a_λ and $b_{\kappa\lambda}$ for small r,

$$\begin{aligned}a_\lambda(r) &= r^\lambda\left(1 + \alpha_\lambda \frac{r^2}{R^2} + \cdots\right) \\ b_{\kappa\lambda}(r) &= r^\kappa\left(1 + \beta_{\kappa\lambda} \frac{r^2}{R^2} + \cdots\right)\end{aligned} \tag{3D-25}$$

We have here chosen a normalization of the radial functions, which gives the coefficient unity for the leading terms. The expansion (3D-25) is the analog of Eq. (3C-14). However, the Coulomb field may greatly increase the wave number of the electron in the nuclear region, and the values of α and β may amount to as much as 0.2 in the heaviest nuclei. (See the example discussed on p. 350 and the reference quoted there.)

The moments (3D-24) refer to β^- processes; for β^+ processes and electron capture, the corresponding moments involve the Hermitian conjugate charge and current densities, obtained by replacing t_- by t_+ in the current j^β. The radial factors are different for β^-, β^+, and electron capture processes.

If we retain only the leading term in Eq. (3D-25), the multipole moments (3D-24) take the form

$$\begin{aligned}\mathscr{M}(\rho_{V,A}, \lambda\mu) &= \int r^\lambda Y_{\lambda\mu}(\hat{\mathbf{r}})\rho_{V,A}(\mathbf{r})\, d\tau \\ \mathscr{M}(j_{V,A}, \kappa\lambda\mu) &= \int r^\kappa (Y_\kappa(\hat{\mathbf{r}}) j_{V,A}(\mathbf{r}))_{(\kappa 1)\lambda\mu}\, d\tau\end{aligned} \tag{3D-26}$$

From Eqs. (3D-5) and (3D-6) it is seen that the moments have the parity quantum numbers

$$\pi = \begin{cases} (-1)^{\lambda} & \rho_V \\ (-1)^{\lambda+1} & \rho_A \\ (-1)^{\kappa+1} & j_V \\ (-1)^{\kappa} & j_A \end{cases} \tag{3D-27}$$

and the time reversal phases (see Eq. (1A-74))

$$c_{\mathscr{T}} = \begin{cases} (-1)^{\lambda} & \rho_{V,A} \\ (-1)^{\kappa+1} & j_{V,A} \end{cases} \tag{3D-28}$$

Although a large number of moments may contribute to a given transition, the main effects usually arise from a small number of terms. The relative contribution of the different moments depends on the leptonic matrix elements as well as on the nuclear matrix elements. The magnitude of the transition matrix element associated with a given multipole moment is partly characterized by the leading power of r in the multipole density (λ for $\mathscr{M}(\rho, \lambda)$ and κ for $\mathscr{M}(j, \kappa\lambda)$); each extra factor r reduces the total matrix element by a factor of the order of the nuclear radius R multiplied by the wave number of the leptons (inside the nucleus). Moreover, the nuclear moments associated with ρ_A and $\mathbf{j}_V$ involve a factor v/c relative to those of ρ_V and $\mathbf{j}_A$ or, in the case of the spin magnetic moment term in $\mathbf{j}_V$, a factor of order $\mu_\beta\, v/c$ (see Eq. (3D-18)).

It is customary to classify the transitions according to the order of forbiddenness n, defined as the sum of powers with which r and v occur in the moment (considering the spin part of $\mathbf{j}_V$ comparable to the orbital part). Thus, the parity change is always $\pi = (-1)^n$. For given π and $\Delta I = I_i - I_f$, the moments of leading order are

$$\begin{aligned}
&\pi = (-1)^{\Delta I} \\
&\left.\begin{aligned}
&\rho_V;\ \lambda = \Delta I \\
&j_V;\ \kappa = \Delta I - 1,\ \lambda = \Delta I \quad (\Delta I \neq 0) \\
&j_A;\ \kappa = \Delta I,\ \lambda = \Delta I \qquad\quad (\Delta I \neq 0) \\
&j_A;\ \kappa = \Delta I,\ \lambda = \Delta I + 1
\end{aligned}\right\} n = \Delta I \\
&\pi = (-1)^{\Delta I + 1}\ (\Delta I \neq 0) \\
&j_A;\ \kappa = \Delta I - 1,\ \lambda = \Delta I \qquad\qquad n = \Delta I - 1 \\
&\pi = -1,\ \Delta I = 0 \\
&\left.\begin{aligned}
&\rho_A;\ \lambda = 0 \\
&\rho_V;\ \lambda = 1 \\
&j_V;\ \kappa = 0,\ \lambda = 1 \\
&j_A;\ \kappa = 1,\ \lambda = 0, 1, \text{and } 2
\end{aligned}\right\} n = 1
\end{aligned} \tag{3D-29}$$

Although the listed terms are usually responsible for the main transition strength, additional terms may contribute significantly, in particular in cases where the leading-order nuclear matrix elements are small because of special features in the structure of the states. If we employ the charge current operators (3D-18), the multipole moments in the approximate form (3D-26) become

$$\begin{aligned}
\mathscr{M}(\rho_V, \lambda\mu) &= g_V \sum_k t_-(k) r_k^{\lambda} Y_{\lambda\mu}(\hat{\mathbf{r}}_k) \\
\mathscr{M}(j_A, \kappa\lambda\mu) &= g_A \sum_k t_-(k) r_k^{\kappa} (Y_{\kappa}(\hat{\mathbf{r}}_k)\boldsymbol{\sigma}_k)_{\lambda\mu} \\
\mathscr{M}(\rho_A, \kappa\lambda\mu) &= \frac{g_A}{c} \sum_k t_-(k)(\boldsymbol{\sigma}_k \cdot \mathbf{v}_k) r_k^{\lambda} Y_{\lambda\mu}(\hat{\mathbf{r}}_k)
\end{aligned} \tag{3D-30}$$

In the evaluation of the j_V moments with $\kappa = \lambda - 1$ one may exploit the continuity equation (Fujita, 1962; Eichler, 1963; Damgaard and Winther, 1966). Using the spherical tensor relation (1A-125), we obtain

$$\begin{aligned}\mathcal{M}(j_V, \kappa=\lambda-1, \lambda\mu) &= (\lambda(2\lambda+1))^{-1/2}\int(\mathbf{j}_V\cdot\nabla)r^\lambda Y_{\lambda\mu}\,d\tau \\ &= -(\lambda(2\lambda+1))^{-1/2}\int(\nabla\cdot\mathbf{j}_V)r^\lambda Y_{\lambda\mu}\,d\tau\end{aligned} \tag{3D-31}$$

where the divergence of $\mathbf{j}_V$ can be expressed in terms of ρ_V by means of the continuity equation (3D-13). If we approximate H^{el} by the Coulomb interaction between the protons in the nucleus, we obtain (since H^{el} commutes with ρ^{el}),

$$\begin{aligned}\nabla\cdot\mathbf{j}_V &= -\frac{1}{c}\frac{\partial\rho_V}{\partial t} + \frac{ig_V}{e\hbar c}[[T_x - iT_y, \rho^{\mathrm{el}}], H^{\mathrm{el}}] \\ &= -\frac{1}{c}\frac{\partial\rho_V}{\partial t} + \frac{i}{\hbar c}[H^{\mathrm{el}}, \rho_V] \\ &= -\frac{1}{c}\frac{\partial\rho_V}{\partial t} + \frac{ieg_V}{\hbar c}\sum_k t_-(k)\varphi_{\mathrm{Coul}}(\mathbf{r}_k)\delta(\mathbf{r}-\mathbf{r}_k)\end{aligned} \tag{3D-32}$$

In the last step, we have employed the expression (3D-18) for ρ_V and have assumed that the main effect of H^{el} is associated with the average Coulomb field φ_{Coul}. The modified continuity equation (3D-32) can also be obtained (Veltman, 1966) from the principle of minimality, which assumes that the electromagnetic coupling can be derived by replacing derivatives in the dynamical equations, such as (3D-12), which are valid in the absence of electromagnetism, by the gauge invariant derivative,

$$\frac{\partial}{\partial x_\mu} \to \frac{\partial}{\partial x_\mu} - \frac{ie}{\hbar c}A_\mu$$

where A_μ is the four-vector potential. From Eqs. (3D-31) and (3D-32), we obtain

$$\mathcal{M}(j_V, \kappa=\lambda-1, \lambda\mu) = -\frac{ig_V}{c\hbar}(\lambda(2\lambda+1))^{-1/2}\sum_k t_-(k)(e\varphi_{\mathrm{Coul}}(\mathbf{r}_k) + \Delta E)r_k^\lambda Y_{\lambda\mu}(\hat{\mathbf{r}}_k) \tag{3D-33}$$

where $\Delta E = E_i - E_f$ is the transition energy representing the mass difference between the initial state, i, and the final state, f. The relation (3D-33) refers to β^- decay. For β^+ decay, the moment is obtained by inverting the sign of φ_{Coul} and replacing t_- by t_+.

If the Coulomb potential energy is replaced by its average value ΔE_{Coul}, the relation (3D-33) can be written

$$\mathcal{M}(j_V, \kappa=\lambda-1, \lambda\mu) = -\frac{i}{\hbar c}(\lambda(2\lambda+1))^{-1/2}(\Delta E_{\mathrm{Coul}} + E_i - E_f)\mathcal{M}(\rho_V, \lambda\mu) \tag{3D-34}$$

It must be noted, however, that the radial variation of the Coulomb field may be important especially in cases where the overlap of the radial wave functions in the initial and final state is small due to oscillations in sign. For example, in the cases considered in Table 3-6, the term involving the Coulomb potential was found to be decreased, as a consequence of the radial variation of φ_{Coul}, by factors of 0.9 and 0.3 for ^{207}Tl and ^{209}Pb, respectively.

The matrix elements of $\mathcal{M}(j_V, \kappa=\lambda-1, \lambda\mu)$ and $\mathcal{M}(\rho_V, \lambda\mu)$ for the transition $i \to f$

are related by isobaric symmetry to the matrix elements of corresponding electromagnetic moments for the transition $i' \rightarrow f$, where i' is the isobaric analog of i. From the relation (3D-10) it follows that the ratio of the two β-matrix elements is equal to the ratio of the matrix elements of the electromagnetic moments obtained by replacing ρ_V, $\mathbf{j}_V$ by ρ^{el}, $\mathbf{j}^{\text{el}}$ (and g_V by e), provided the states i and i' are exact isobaric analog states. We then have

$$\begin{aligned}\langle f \,|\, \mathscr{M}^{\beta} \,|\, i\rangle &= -\frac{g_V}{e} \langle f \,|[T_-, \mathscr{M}^{\text{el}}]|\, i\rangle \\ &= \frac{g_V}{e} (2T_i)^{1/2} \langle f \,|\, \mathscr{M}^{\text{el}} \,|\, i'\rangle\end{aligned} \tag{3D-35}$$

assuming $(M_T)_i = T_i$ and $(M_T)_f = T_f$. The electromagnetic moments involving $\mathbf{j}^{\text{el}}$ and ρ^{el} are connected by the continuity equation for the electromagnetic current, and we therefore obtain a relation for β moments, which corresponds to Eq. (3D-34) with the energy factor $E_{\text{Coul}} + E_i - E_f$ replaced by $E_i' - E_f$. The two energies are equal, if E_{Coul} is taken to be the Coulomb energy difference $E_i' - E_i$ between the isobaric analog states. In order to obtain the more general relation (3D-33), one must include the effect of the Coulomb field in violating the isobaric relationship between the states i and i'. Indeed, the difference between $e\varphi_{\text{Coul}}(\mathbf{r})$ and its average value represents the nondiagonal effect of H^{el}, which distorts the nuclear wave functions.

One may also attempt to derive the expression (3D-33) directly from the expression (3D-18) for the current $\mathbf{j}_V$. The magnetic moment term in $\mathbf{j}_V$ does not contribute to the moment (3D-31), and the term in $\mathbf{v}_k$ can be transformed by employing the relation

$$\begin{aligned}t_-(k)(\mathbf{v}_k \cdot \boldsymbol{\nabla}_k r_k^\lambda Y_{\lambda\mu}(\hat{\mathbf{r}}_k))_{\text{sym}} &= t_-(k) \frac{d}{dt} r_k^\lambda Y_{\lambda\mu}(\hat{\mathbf{r}}_k) \\ &= \frac{d}{dt}(t_-(k) r_k^\lambda Y_{\lambda\mu}(\hat{\mathbf{r}}_k)) - r_k^\lambda Y_{\lambda\mu}(\hat{\mathbf{r}}_k) \frac{d}{dt} t_-(k)\end{aligned} \tag{3D-36}$$

If the time derivative of $t_-(k)$ results only from the Coulomb forces acting on the nucleon, the relation (3D-36) leads again to the result (3D-33), corresponding to the fact that the continuity relation (3D-13) is implied by the expression (3D-18), if we are dealing with free nucleons or if only electromagnetic forces act on $t_-(k)$. However, if charge exchange forces are present, $(d/dt)t_-(k)$ receives additional contributions, and the relation (3D-36) is then no longer equivalent to Eq. (3D-33). For example, if the nuclear states are described in terms of one-particle motion, the isovector term in the average potential (symmetry term; see Eq. (2-29)) gives a contribution to the time derivative of t_-, which may be as large as that of the Coulomb potential. In such a situation, the continuity relation implies the presence of interaction terms in $\mathbf{j}_V$, depending on the coordinates of two nucleons, and of such a magnitude as to account for the difference between the relations (3D-33) and (3D-36). (See the analogous interaction term in the electromagnetic current associated with charge exchange interactions and velocity-dependent forces (Sec. 3C-6).)

The j_V moments with $\kappa = \lambda$ are the analogs of the magnetic multipole moments, and can be written in a form corresponding to Eq. (3C-30),

$$\begin{aligned}\mathscr{M}(j_V, \kappa = \lambda, \lambda\mu) &= i\left(\frac{\lambda+1}{\lambda}\right)^{1/2} \frac{g_V \hbar}{2Mc} \sum_k t_-(k)\left\{\mu_\beta \boldsymbol{\sigma}_k + \frac{2}{\lambda+1}\mathbf{l}_k\right\} \cdot \boldsymbol{\nabla}_k(r_k^\lambda Y_{\lambda\mu}(\hat{\mathbf{r}}_k)) \\ &= -i\left(\frac{\lambda+1}{\lambda}\right)^{1/2} \frac{g_V}{e} [T_-, \mathscr{M}(M\lambda\mu)]\end{aligned} \tag{3D-37}$$

The j_V moments with $\kappa = \lambda + 1$ are usually too small to be of significance.

Many different notations have been used for the nuclear matrix elements in β decay. In Table 3D-1, we compare the multipole moments as defined above with some of the notations that are employed in the literature.

Present notation	Konopinski and Uhlenbeck	Konopinski and Rose
$\mathcal{M}(\rho_V, \lambda=0)$	$C_V \int 1$	$C_V\langle 1\rangle$
$\mathcal{M}(j_A, \kappa=0, \lambda=1)$	$C_A \int \boldsymbol{\sigma}$	$C_A\langle \sigma\rangle$
$\mathcal{M}(j_A, \kappa=1, \lambda=0)$	$-C_A \int \boldsymbol{\sigma}\cdot\mathbf{r}$	$-iRC_A\langle i\boldsymbol{\sigma}\cdot\hat{\mathbf{r}}\rangle$
$\mathcal{M}(\rho_A, \lambda=0)$	$-C_A \int \gamma_5$	$-C_A\langle\gamma_5\rangle$
$\mathcal{M}(\rho_V, \lambda=1)$	$\sqrt{3}C_V \int \mathbf{r}$	$i\sqrt{3}RC_V\langle i\hat{\mathbf{r}}\rangle$
$\mathcal{M}(j_V, \kappa=0, \lambda=1)$	$-C_V \int \boldsymbol{\alpha}$	$C_V\langle\boldsymbol{\alpha}\rangle$
$\mathcal{M}(j_A, \kappa=1, \lambda=1)$	$-i(3/2)^{1/2}\, C_A \int \boldsymbol{\sigma}\times\mathbf{r}$	$-i(3/2)^{1/2}\, RC_A\langle\boldsymbol{\sigma}\times\hat{\mathbf{r}}\rangle$
$\mathcal{M}(j_A, \kappa=1, \lambda=2)$	$\frac{1}{2}\sqrt{3}\, C_A \int B_{ij}$	$i\sqrt{4\pi}\, RC_A\langle\boldsymbol{\sigma}\cdot\mathbf{T}_2^1\rangle$

Table 3D-1 Notations for β moments. Column 2 gives the notation for β-matrix elements (E. J. Konopinski and G. E. Uhlenbeck, *Phys. Rev.* **60**, 308, 1941), which is most frequently used in the current literature. Column 3 shows the notation introduced by E. J. Konopinski and M. E. Rose in *Alpha-, Beta- and Gamma-Ray Spectroscopy*, K. Siegbahn, ed., vol. 2, p. 1327, North-Holland, Amsterdam, 1965. The quantities in columns 2 and 3 represent reduced matrix elements of the operators in column 1, multiplied by the factor $(4\pi/(2I_i+1))^{1/2}$, where I_i is the spin of the initial state. (Notations used by different authors often differ by an overall phase factor.) It is further to be noted that the matrix elements in columns 2 and 3 represent the leading-order moments with the radial dependence (3D-30).

3D-5 *ft* Values

The absolute transition rates of a β process, as well as the energy spectrum, polarization, and angular correlations of the emitted leptons, depend on the leptonic matrix elements of the current $(j_\mu)_{\text{lept}}$ in Eq. (3D-2). We here confine ourselves to listing the expressions for the transition probabilities for some of the relatively simple types of β processes. (For a general survey of the theory of β radioactivity, including tabulations of the various spectral and correlation functions, see Chapters 19, 22, 23, and 24 in Siegbahn, 1965, and the texts by Konopinski, 1966; Schopper, 1966; Wu and Moszkowski, 1966.)

In order to compensate for the dependence of the decay rate on the transition energy, it is customary to express the transition probability for a β process in terms of the product ft, where t is the half life while f is a dimensionless quantity depending on the charge of the nucleus and the energy and multipolarity of the transition. This quantity represents the phase space for the leptons and is thus analogous to the factor $(\Delta E)^{2\lambda+1}$ in the electromagnetic transition rate (see Eq. (3C-16)). The f functions are obtained as integrals over the electron spectra and their evaluation involves the treatment of the electron motion in the Coulomb field of the nucleus and the atomic electrons. (For a detailed discussion of the effect of the screening by the atomic electrons, see, for example, Durand, 1964; Bühring, 1965.)

For the allowed transitions ($n = 0$), the only moments that contribute are $\mathscr{M}(\rho_V, \lambda = 0)$ and $\mathscr{M}(j_A, \kappa = 0, \lambda = 1)$ referred to as Fermi and Gamow-Teller moments, respectively. The transition rate can be expressed in the form

$$f_0\, t(B(\mathrm{F}) + B(\mathrm{GT})) = \frac{\pi^2 \hbar^7 \ln 2}{2 m_e^5 c^4} = D \frac{g_V^2}{4\pi} \qquad \text{(3D-38)}$$

$$D \equiv \frac{2\pi^3 \hbar^7 \ln 2}{g_V^2 m_e^5 c^4} = 6250 \text{ sec}$$

where f_0 is the f function for allowed transitions. (The index 0 for f_0 is often omitted if it is clear from the context that one is dealing with the allowed f function.) The reduced transition probabilities in Eq. (3D-38) are given by

$$B(\mathrm{F}) = \frac{1}{2I+1} |\langle I \| \mathscr{M}(\rho_V, \lambda = 0) \| I \rangle|^2$$
$$B(\mathrm{GT}) = \frac{1}{2I_i+1} |\langle I_f \| \mathscr{M}(j_A, \kappa = 0, \lambda = 1) \| I_i \rangle|^2 \qquad \text{(3D-39)}$$

The Fermi moment is proportional to the total transition charge and can thus be obtained directly from Eq. (3D-11) without any assumptions concerning the more detailed structure of the system,

$$\mathscr{M}(\rho_V, \lambda = 0) = \frac{1}{(4\pi)^{1/2}} Q_V = \frac{g_V}{(4\pi)^{1/2}} (T_x - iT_y) \qquad \text{(3D-40)}$$

The matrix element of Q_V is nonvanishing only for transitions between isobaric analog states, for which we obtain

$$B(\mathrm{F}; TM_T \to TM_T \pm 1) = \frac{g_V^2}{4\pi} (T \mp M_T)(T \pm M_T + 1) \qquad \text{(3D-41)}$$

The Gamow-Teller moment is given by

$$\mathscr{M}(j_A, \kappa = 0, \lambda = 1, \mu) = \frac{g_A}{(4\pi)^{1/2}} \sum_k t_-(k) \sigma_\mu(k) \qquad \text{(3D-42)}$$

Since the allowed transitions represent an approximation that neglects the variation of the lepton wave functions inside the nucleus, the allowed β moments are independent of the positions of the nucleons.

The first forbidden transitions ($n = 1$) are governed by the matrix elements of the moments

$$\left.\begin{aligned}\mathscr{M}(\rho_A, \lambda=0) &= (4\pi)^{-1/2}\frac{g_A}{c}\sum_k t_-(k)(\boldsymbol{\sigma}(k)\cdot\mathbf{v}_k)\\ \mathscr{M}(j_A, \kappa=1, \lambda=0) &= g_A\sum_k t_-(k)r_k(Y_1(\hat{\mathbf{r}}_k)\sigma(k))_0\end{aligned}\right\}\lambda\pi = 0-$$

$$\left.\begin{aligned}\mathscr{M}(\rho_V, \lambda=1, \mu) &= g_V\sum_k t_-(k)r_k Y_{1\mu}(\hat{\mathbf{r}}_k)\\ \mathscr{M}(j_V, \kappa=0, \lambda=1, \mu) &= (4\pi)^{-1/2}\frac{g_V}{c}\sum_k t_-(k)(v_k)_{1\mu}\\ \mathscr{M}(j_A, \kappa=1, \lambda=1, \mu) &= g_A\sum_k t_-(k)r_k(Y_1(\hat{\mathbf{r}}_k)\sigma(k))_{1\mu}\end{aligned}\right\}\lambda\pi = 1- \tag{3D-43}$$

$$\mathscr{M}(j_A, \kappa=1, \lambda=2, \mu) = g_A\sum_k t_-(k)r_k(Y_1(\hat{\mathbf{r}}_k)\sigma(k))_{2\mu} \qquad \lambda\pi = 2-$$

The moments that are independent of the position of the nucleons are coupled to the part of the lepton current that is constant over the nuclear volume. The leptonic matrix elements for these moments are exactly the same as for the corresponding $0+$ and $1+$ moments (with A and V interchanged) since, for the parity-violating β interaction (3D-2), the coupling to the leptons is independent of the parity of the nuclear moments.

The $0-$ and $1-$ moments that are linear in r are coupled to the leptons through the derivative of the lepton wave functions and are thus multiplied by the factor ik, where k is the lepton wave number inside the nucleus. The dependence of k on the energy of the emitted leptons implies a deviation of the electron spectrum from that of allowed transitions.

In nuclear transitions, however, the Coulomb energy of the electron inside the nucleus is often rather large compared with the transition energy as well as with the electronic rest mass. Under these conditions, the electron spectra as well as polarizations and angular correlations for the transitions considered depend only on the multipole order. In fact, if we can disregard the effect of the rest mass on the motion of the electrons inside the nucleus, the leptonic current creates electrons as well as neutrinos in a state of definite helicity ($h = -1/2$ for e^- and ν_e; $h = +1/2$ for e^+ and $\bar{\nu}_e$). For the transitions of multipole order $\lambda = 0$ and 1, the leptons are predominantly created in states of angular momentum $j = 1/2$; for $j = 3/2$, the leptons must penetrate the centrifugal barrier, which reduces the amplitude by a factor of order pR, where p is the momentum of the lepton measured at infinity. The total state of the lepton pair is therefore uniquely specified by the quantum numbers $j_e = j_\nu = 1/2$, h_e, h_ν, $\lambda\mu$, together with the energy of the emitted electron; hence, polarizations and angular correlations depend only on λ and are the same for first forbidden as for allowed transitions. Moreover, when the transition energy is small compared with the Coulomb energy, the wave number of the electron inside the nucleus is large compared with that of the neutrino, and is approximately independent of the total energy of the electron. The main contribution to the coupling of the r-dependent moments therefore involves the electron wave number, and the energy dependence of the spectrum remains the same as for the allowed transitions.

The magnitude of the Coulomb energy may be represented by the dimensionless parameter

$$\xi \equiv \frac{Ze^2}{2R}\frac{1}{m_e c^2} \approx 1.2\, ZA^{-1/3} \tag{3D-44}$$

involving the nuclear charge Z and radius $R \approx 1.2\, A^{1/3}$ fm, and the conditions stated above correspond to

$$\xi \gg \frac{\Delta E}{m_e c^2} \quad \text{and} \quad \xi \gg 1 \tag{3D-45}$$

In the "ξ approximation", terms of relative order $\xi^{-1}\Delta E/m_e c^2$ and ξ^{-1} are neglected, and the decay rates for $0-$ and $1-$ transitions can be expressed in terms of the f function for allowed transitions,

$$f_0\, t(B(\lambda\pi = 0-) + B(\lambda\pi = 1-)) = \frac{Dg_V^2}{4\pi} \tag{3D-46}$$

where

$$B(\lambda\pi = 0-) = \frac{1}{2I_i + 1}\,|\langle I_f \,\|\, \pm\mathscr{M}(\rho_A, \lambda = 0) - i\frac{m_e c}{\hbar}\,\xi\mathscr{M}(j_A, \kappa = 1, \lambda = 0)\| I_i\rangle|^2$$

$$\begin{aligned} B(\lambda\pi = 1-) = \frac{1}{2I_i + 1}\,|\langle I_f \,\|\, &\mathscr{M}(j_V, \kappa = 0, \lambda = 1) \\ &\pm \frac{i}{\sqrt{3}}\frac{m_e c}{\hbar}\,\xi\,\mathscr{M}(\rho_V, \lambda = 1) + i\sqrt{\frac{2}{3}}\frac{m_e c}{\hbar}\,\xi\mathscr{M}(j_A, \kappa = 1, \lambda = 1)\| I_i\rangle|^2 \end{aligned} \tag{3D-47}$$

It must be emphasized that, even if the conditions (3D-45) are fulfilled, there may be significant corrections to the ξ approximation, especially if the different terms in Eq. (3D-47) tend to cancel each other.

In Eq. (3D-47), the upper and lower signs refer to β^- and β^+ decays, respectively. The different behavior of the various terms with respect to interchange of β^- and β^+ is related to the G parity of the β current (see p. 400). Thus, we first note that, as a consequence of $\mathscr{PC}$ symmetry, the β^- decay $I_i \to I_f + e^- + \bar{\nu}_e$ has the same energy spectrum and decay rate as the β^+ decay of the antinucleus $(I_i)_{\text{anti}} \to (I_f)_{\text{anti}} + e^+ + \nu_e$. Next, the nuclear matrix elements for antinuclear β^+ decay can be related to matrix elements for nuclear β^+ decay by the transformation $G = \mathscr{C}\mathscr{R}_\tau$, under which the nuclear vector β current $(j_V)_\mu$ is invariant while the axial vector current $(j_A)_\mu$ changes sign. For the matrix elements of the β moments, we therefore have

$$\begin{aligned} \langle (T_f M_f)_{\text{anti}}\,|\mathscr{M}(V, A)|(T_i M_i)_{\text{anti}}\rangle &\equiv \langle T_f M_f|\mathscr{C}^{-1}\mathscr{M}(V, A)\mathscr{C}|T_i M_i\rangle \\ &= \pm\langle T_f M_f|\mathscr{R}_\tau \mathscr{M}(V, A)\mathscr{R}_\tau^{-1}|T_i M_i\rangle \\ &= \pm(-1)^{T_i + M_i + T_f + M_f}\langle T_f - M_f\,|\mathscr{M}(V, A)|\, T_i - M_i\rangle \end{aligned} \tag{3D-48}$$

where the upper and lower signs refer to vector and axial vector moments, respectively. In addition, we must take into account that the Coulomb potentials for antinuclear and nuclear β^+ decay have opposite signs. Hence, the terms in Eq. (3D-47) that are independent of ξ change sign for A, but not for V, while the terms proportional to ξ change sign for V, but not for A, when β^- decay is replaced by β^+ decay.

If A and V are interchanged in Eq. (3D-47), one obtains an expression for $\lambda\pi = 0+$ and $1+$ transitions, which includes the higher-order terms neglected in Eq. (3D-39). Among these, the transition moment $\mathscr{M}(j_V, \kappa = 1, \lambda = 1)$ is the analog of the magnetic dipole moment; see Eq. (3D-37).

For $\lambda\pi = 2-$ first forbidden transitions and for transitions with $n \geqslant 2$, the electron spectra deviate considerably from those of allowed processes. Transitions with $\lambda = n + 1$ are referred to as unique n-forbidden transitions, and their decay rate can be expressed in the form

$$f_n t B(\lambda = n+1) = \frac{D g_V^2}{4\pi}\left[\frac{(2n+1)!!}{[(n+1)!]^2 n!}\right] \tag{3D-49}$$

with

$$B(\lambda = n+1) = \frac{1}{2I_i+1}\left|\langle I_f \| \mathscr{M}(j_A, \kappa = n, \lambda = n+1) \| I_i \rangle\right|^2 \tag{3D-50}$$

Expressions for and tabulations of the Fermi functions f_n are given by Zyryanova (1963) and in the references quoted on p. 410.

When the conditions (3D-45) are fulfilled, the decay rate for transitions with $\lambda = n$ (and $n > 1$) can be expressed in terms of f_{n-1}, as in the case of $\lambda = n = 1$.

▼

ILLUSTRATIVE EXAMPLES TO APPENDIX 3D

Test of relation between β decay moments (weak magnetism) and electromagnetic transition moments (Fig. 3D–1).

As discussed in Section 3D-2c, the observed equality between the total vector charge Q_V as determined in nuclear β decay and in the decay of the μ meson has led to the suggestion that the vector part of the strangeness-conserving hadronic β current can be obtained by a rotation in isospace of the electromagnetic current (see Eq. (3D-10)). A significant test of this hypothesis is provided by a comparison of the moment $\mathscr{M}(j_V, \kappa = 1, \lambda = 1)$ and the magnetic dipole operator $\mathscr{M}(M1)$ (Gell-Mann, 1958).

A measurement of the matrix elements of the weak magnetic moment $\mathscr{M}(j_V, \kappa = 1, \lambda = 1)$ is rather difficult, since the transitions with $\lambda = 1$ and $\pi = +1$ are usually dominated by the Gamow-Teller moment $\mathscr{M}(j_A, 0, 1)$, which is of allowed type ($n = 0$), while $\mathscr{M}(j_V, 1, 1)$ is of second forbidden type ($n = 2$). However, the energy dependence of the electron spectrum is different for the two moments, and a contribution from the weak magnetic moment therefore implies a deviation from the

▲

▼ allowed spectrum. Conditions for determining the moment $\mathcal{M}(j_V, 1, 1)$ are favorable if the β transition has a large Q value and if the isobaric analog γ transition has a large $M1$ moment. Such a case is provided by the decay of the ($I\pi = 1+$) isobaric
▲ triplet in $A = 12$, illustrated in Fig. 3D-1.

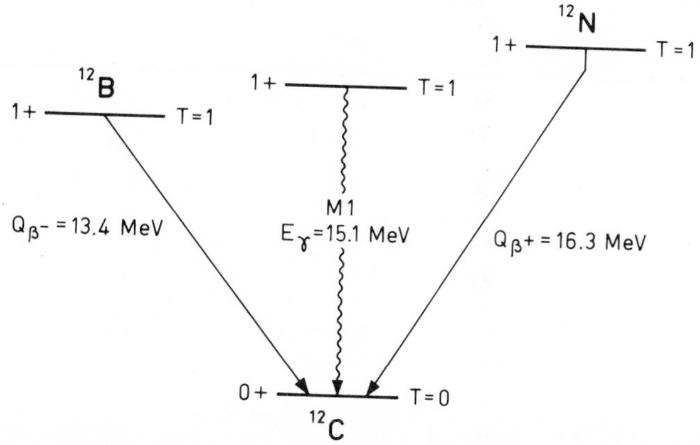

Figure 3D-1 Comparison between β and γ transitions from analogous $T = 1$ states in $A = 12$ nuclei. Both the β and γ transitions have other branches (not shown), which populate exited states in ^{12}C (see, for example, Ajzenberg and Lauritsen, 1968).

▼ The γ width for the ground state decay of the 15.1 MeV level in ^{12}C is found to be $\Gamma_\gamma = 39.4 \pm 1.5$ eV (see the compilation by Ajzenberg-Selove and Lauritsen, 1968), and we therefore obtain, by means of Eq. (3C-18),

$$B(M1; 1+ \rightarrow 0+) = 1.0 \left(\frac{e\hbar}{2Mc}\right)^2$$
$$|\langle 0+ \| \mathcal{M}(M1) \| 1+ \rangle| = 1.72 \frac{e\hbar}{2Mc} \tag{3D-51}$$

The relation (3D-37) gives, for $\lambda = 1$,

$$\langle 0+, T=0 \| \mathcal{M}(j_V, 1, 1) \| 1+, T=1, M_T=1 \rangle$$
$$= 2i \frac{g_V}{e} \langle 0+, T=0 \| \mathcal{M}(M1) \| 1+, T=1, M_T=0 \rangle \tag{3D-52}$$

and, hence,

$$|\langle 0+ \| i\mathcal{M}(j_V, 1, 1) \| 1+ \rangle| = 3.44 \frac{g_V \hbar}{2Mc} \tag{3D-53}$$

In the analysis of the β spectrum with the accuracy required to determine the $\mathcal{M}(j_V, 1, 1)$ moment, we must also include the other $n = 2$ moments contributing to the transition (Gell-Mann and Berman, 1959; see also the recent analysis by Huffaker and Laird, 1967). These comprise the moments $\mathcal{M}(\rho_A, \lambda = 1)$ and $\mathcal{M}(j_A, \kappa = 2, \lambda = 1)$, and, to the same order, we must consider the modification in the allowed
▲ moment $\mathcal{M}(j_A, 0, 1)$ associated with the variation of the lepton wave functions inside

▼ the nucleus; the leading-order variation is proportional to r^2 (see the expansion (3D-25)) and can be expressed in terms of the moment

$$\begin{aligned}\mathscr{M}'(j_A, \kappa=0, \lambda=1, \mu) &= (4\pi)^{-1/2}\int r^2(j_A(\mathbf{r}))_\mu\, d\tau \\ &= (4\pi)^{-1/2} g_A \sum_k t_-(k) r_k{}^2 \sigma_\mu(k)\end{aligned} \tag{3D-54}$$

The electron spectrum is obtained by evaluating the lepton matrix elements and averaging over the direction of the neutrino and the polarization of the electron (see the references quoted on p. 410). The correction factor to the allowed spectrum is found to be (J. Damgaard, private communication)

$$\begin{aligned}P(E_e) = \langle 0+\|\mathscr{M}(j_A, 0, 1)\|1+\rangle^{-2}\Bigg\{&\left(1 \mp \frac{13}{30}\frac{Ze^2}{R} E_e R^2\right)\langle 0+\|\mathscr{M}(j_A, 0, 1)\|1+\rangle \\ &- \left(\frac{1}{6}(E_e{}^2 + E_\nu{}^2) \pm \frac{1}{2}\frac{Ze^2}{R} E_e\right)\langle 0+\|\mathscr{M}'(j_A, 0, 1)\|1+\rangle \\ &+ \frac{1}{3\sqrt{3}}(E_e + E_\nu)\langle 0+\|i\mathscr{M}(\rho_A, 1)\|1+\rangle \\ &\pm \frac{\sqrt{6}}{9}(E_e - E_\nu)\langle 0+\|i\mathscr{M}(j_V, 1, 1)\|1+\rangle \\ &+ \frac{2\sqrt{2}}{27} E_e E_\nu \langle 0+\|\mathscr{M}(j_A, 2, 1)\|1+\rangle\Bigg\}^2\end{aligned} \tag{3D-55}$$

where the upper sign refers to β^- and the lower sign to β^+ decay. The expression (3D-55) represents an approximation appropriate for a transition with large energy and small nuclear charge (which is an opposite extreme to the ξ approximation discussed on p. 413). Thus, we have neglected terms proportional to the electron rest mass, and in the radial expansion of the lepton wave functions we have included only the leading terms, except for the allowed moment.

In Eq. (3D-55), we have used relativistic units ($m_e = c = \hbar = 1$). The electron and neutrino energies are denoted by E_e and E_ν, and we have

$$E_e + E_\nu = W_0 = \begin{cases} 27.2\ m_e c^2 & {}^{12}\mathrm{B}(\beta^-) \\ 32.9\ m_e c^2 & {}^{12}\mathrm{N}(\beta^+) \end{cases} \tag{3D-56}$$

where W_0 is the transition energy.

The first correction term in Eq. (3D-55) arises from the difference between the electron wave function at the nuclear center and the wave function conventionally employed in the evaluation of the allowed spectrum. (For a detailed derivation, see Huffaker and Laird, *loc. cit.*) The Coulomb potential has been assumed to be that of a homogeneously charged sphere of radius R, and we employ the value

$$R = 1.22\, A^{1/3}\ \mathrm{fm} = 2.8\ \mathrm{fm} = 0.72 \times 10^{-2}\frac{\hbar}{m_e c} \tag{3D-57}$$

which implies

▲
$$R\, W_0 = \begin{cases} 0.20 & {}^{12}\mathrm{B}(\beta^-) \\ 0.24 & {}^{12}\mathrm{N}(\beta^+) \end{cases} \tag{3D-58}$$

▼ The behavior of the terms in Eq. (3D-55) with respect to interchange of β^- and β^+ is related to the G parity of the β current, as discussed on p. 413. Thus, the interference between vector and axial vector contributions has opposite sign for β^- and β^+, while the axial vector correction terms are the same for β^- and β^+, except for the contributions from the Coulomb field. The symmetry of the terms with respect to interchange of electron and neutrino energies can be understood from the same argument. In fact, apart from the Coulomb effects, the emitted leptons are only distinguished by their opposite helicity; the helicities are also inverted when β^- decay is replaced by β^+ decay and, hence, the Z-independent terms must have the same symmetry with respect to interchange of E_e and E_ν as for interchange of β^- and β^+.

The correction factor (3D-55), with $E_\nu = W_0 - E_e$, involves terms independent of the electron energy (which will be neglected), terms linear in E_e, as well as quadratic terms in E_e. The experiments are not sufficiently accurate to detect the quadratic dependence, and we therefore represent the quadratic terms by their slope at the mean energy $\langle E_e \rangle$ for the measured part of the energy spectrum. One then obtains

$$P(E_e) = 1 + aE_e \tag{3D-58a}$$

with

$$\begin{aligned} a = &\pm \frac{4\sqrt{6}}{9} \frac{\langle 0+ \| i\mathscr{M}(j_V, 1, 1) \| 1+ \rangle}{\langle 0+ \| \mathscr{M}(j_A, 0, 1) \| 1+ \rangle} \mp \frac{13}{15} R^2 \frac{Ze^2}{R} \\ &+ \left(\frac{2}{3} (W_0 - 2\langle E_e \rangle) \mp \frac{Ze^2}{R} \right) \frac{\langle 0+ \| \mathscr{M}'(j_A, 0, 1) \| 1+ \rangle}{\langle 0+ \| \mathscr{M}(j_A, 0, 1) \| 1+ \rangle} \\ &+ \frac{4\sqrt{2}}{27} (W_0 - 2\langle E_e \rangle) \frac{\langle 0+ \| \mathscr{M}(j_A, 2, 1) \| 1+ \rangle}{\langle 0+ \| \mathscr{M}(j_A, 0, 1) \| 1+ \rangle} \end{aligned} \tag{3D-59}$$

In order to estimate the various contributions to a, we first note that the matrix element of $\mathscr{M}(j_A, 0, 1)$ can be obtained from the ft values (Kavanagh, 1964)

$$\begin{aligned} ft\,(^{12}\text{B}) &= (1.180 \pm 0.007) \times 10^4 \text{ sec} \\ ft\,(^{12}\text{N}) &= (1.306 \pm 0.009) \times 10^4 \text{ sec} \end{aligned} \tag{3D-60}$$

Taking the average value, $ft = 1.24 \times 10^4$ sec, we obtain the GT matrix element (see Eqs. (3D-38) and (3D-39))

$$|\langle 0+ \| \mathscr{M}(j_A, 0, 1) \| 1+ \rangle| = 0.345\, g_V \tag{3D-61}$$

and, hence, from the estimate (3D-53),

$$\begin{aligned} \frac{4\sqrt{6}}{9} \frac{\langle 0+ \| i\mathscr{M}(j_V, 1, 1) \| 1+ \rangle}{\langle 0+ \| \mathscr{M}(j_A, 0, 1) \| 1+ \rangle} &= \pm 0.296 \times 10^{-2} (m_e c^2)^{-1} \\ &= \pm 0.58 \times 10^{-2} (\text{MeV})^{-1} \end{aligned} \tag{3D-62}$$

The observed 10% difference between the ft values for ^{12}B and ^{12}N presents an interesting problem. The difference cannot be attributed to the contribution of $\mathscr{M}(j_V, 1, 1)$ in Eq. (3D-55), since the factor $(E_e - E_\nu)$ approximately vanishes when integrated over the electron spectrum. Moreover, the Coulomb correction terms in the spectrum are too small by an order of magnitude. The difference in ft values must therefore be attributed to a violation of charge symmetry in the nuclear states involved, possibly connected with the rather large difference in the nucleonic binding energies.
▲ (For a discussion of the ft-value difference in terms of a small violation of isospin

symmetry, see for example, Eichler *et al.*, 1964, and Mafethe and Hodgson, 1966. The possibility of attributing the effect to a violation of G invariance has been discussed by Blin-Stoyle and Rosina, 1965.)

The sign of the ratio (3D-62), although not directly determined by the Γ_γ and ft values, can be inferred from the magnitude of these transition rates. The matrix elements of the $M1$ and $\mathscr{M}(j_V, 1, 1)$ transition moments involve an orbital and a spin part (see Eq. (3D-37)), and from the value (3D-53) we obtain

$$|\langle 0+ \| \sum_k t_-(k)(\sigma_k + \frac{1}{4.7} l_k) \| 1+ \rangle| = 1.1 \tag{3D-63}$$

The spin part of this matrix element is determined by the moment (3D-61), which gives

$$|\langle 0+ \| \sum_k t_-(k)\sigma_k \| 1+ \rangle| = 1.0 \tag{3D-64}$$

The approximate equality of these two matrix elements implies that the orbital contribution to the weak magnetism is either small compared to the spin contribution, in which case the two matrix elements (3D-63) and (3D-64) have the same sign, or approximately twice as large as the spin contribution, with negative sign for the ratio (3D-62). However, the latter assumption would imply an orbital matrix element $L_- \equiv |\langle 0+ \| \sum_k t_-(k) l_k \| 1+ \rangle| \approx 10$ and can therefore be rejected. (For example, jj-coupling wave functions, which imply enhanced orbital matrix elements, give a value of about 1.15 for L_-; calculations based on wave functions representing a coupling intermediate between (jj) and (LS) give smaller values for L_- (see, for example, Weidenmüller, 1960).) We may therefore conclude that the ratio (3D-62) is positive.

The contributions to the shape factor (3D-59) involving the moment $\mathscr{M}'(j_A, 0, 1)$ are rather small compared with those involving $\mathscr{M}(j_V, 1, 1)$. If we can assume $\mathscr{M}(j_A', 0, 1)$ as well as the leading-order moment $\mathscr{M}(j_A, 0, 1)$ to be mainly associated with the nucleons in the p shell, we have

$$\frac{\langle 0+ \| \mathscr{M}'(j_A, 0, 1) \| 1+ \rangle}{\langle 0+ \| \mathscr{M}(j_A, 0, 1) \| 1+ \rangle} \approx \langle r^2 \rangle_{l=1} \approx 0.44 \times 10^{-4} \left(\frac{\hbar}{m_e c}\right)^2 \tag{3D-65}$$

using the value $\langle r^2 \rangle^{1/2} = 2.40 \text{ fm} = 0.62 \times 10^{-2} \, \hbar/m_e c$, obtained from the electron scattering data (see, for example, Ajzenberg-Selove and Lauritsen, 1968), together with the estimate

$$\langle r^2 \rangle \approx \frac{1}{3} \langle r^2 \rangle_{l=0} + \frac{2}{3} \langle r^2 \rangle_{l=1} \approx \frac{13}{15} \langle r^2 \rangle_{l=1} \tag{3D-66}$$

based on the value of $\langle r^2 \rangle_{l=1} : \langle r^2 \rangle_{l=0} = 5/3$ for the harmonic oscillator potential (see Eq. (2-153)). The experimental daat referred to below are based on measurements in an energy range with mean values $\langle E_e \rangle \approx 9$ MeV (^{12}B) and $\langle E_e \rangle \approx 10$ MeV (^{12}N). For the contribution to a from the moment $\mathscr{M}'(j_A, 0, 1)$, we thus obtain the values -0.10×10^{-2} (MeV)$^{-1}$ and $+0.02 \times 10^{-2}$ (MeV)$^{-1}$ for ^{12}B and ^{12}N, respectively. The second term in Eq. (3D-59), which is independent of the higher moments, amounts to $\mp 0.054 \times 10^{-2}$ (MeV)$^{-1}$.

The matrix element $\langle 0+ \| \mathscr{M}(j_A, 2, 1) \| 1+ \rangle$ is expected to be comparable with, or smaller than, $\langle 0+ \| \mathscr{M}'(j_A, 0, 1) \| 1+ \rangle$. (For example, if the 0+ state is represented by a filled $p_{3/2}$ subshell and the 1+ state by a $p_{3/2}^{-1} p_{1/2}$ configuration, Eq. (3A-22) yields $\langle 0+ \| \mathscr{M}(j_A, 2, 1) \| 1+ \rangle : \langle 0+ \| \mathscr{M}'(j_A, 0, 1) \| 1+ \rangle = -2^{-3/2}$.) If the matrix elements of $\mathscr{M}(j_A, 2, 1)$ and $\mathscr{M}'(j_A, 0, 1)$ are taken to be equal, the magnitude of

▼ the last term in Eq. (3D-59) is less than $0.02 \times 10^{-2}\ (\text{MeV})^{-1}$, and we shall therefore neglect this term.

For the shape correction factors, we finally obtain

$$(a)_{\text{calc}} = \begin{cases} +0.43 \times 10^{-2}\ (\text{MeV})^{-1} & {}^{12}\text{B}(\beta^-) \\ -0.51 \times 10^{-2}\ (\text{MeV})^{-1} & {}^{12}\text{N}(\beta^+) \end{cases} \tag{3D-67}$$

The measurements of the spectral shapes (corrected for electromagnetic radiative effects) have given the correction factors (Wu, 1964)

$$(a)_{\text{exp}} = \begin{cases} (+0.55 \pm 0.10) \times 10^{-2}\ (\text{MeV})^{-1} & {}^{12}\text{B}(\beta^-) \\ (-0.52 \pm 0.06) \times 10^{-2}\ (\text{MeV})^{-1} & {}^{12}\text{N}(\beta^+) \end{cases} \tag{3D-68}$$

and are thus consistent with the theoretical prediction.

In view of the small orbital contribution to the moment $\mathcal{M}(j_V, 1, 1)$, the agreement between the experimental and theoretical values of the shape correction factor primarily constitutes a test of the predicted value 4.7 for the spin coupling constant μ_β. For point nucleons obeying the Dirac equation with no anomalous moments, one would expect the value $\mu_\beta = 1$, but the structural effects revealed by the anomalous magnetic moments lead to an increase of μ_β by almost a factor of 5. ▲

APPENDIX

3E

Nucleon Transfer Reactions

The electromagnetic and beta interactions are weak compared with typical nuclear energies, and the effects of these couplings on nuclear structure may be treated as perturbations. Nuclear processes induced by these interactions can therefore be described in a straightforward manner in terms of definite, often fairly simple, nuclear matrix elements (see Appendices 3C and 3D). When strongly interacting particles collide with nuclei, however, they may become temporarily integrated into the nuclear structure in such a manner that the collision is best described as a scattering state of the compound system, involving the many degrees of freedom needed to describe the complexity of the states at the rather high excitation involved.

In certain nuclear processes, however, the projectile may directly excite some simple degree of freedom of the target, or transfer one or more nucleons, without interacting significantly with the other internal degrees of freedom of the target. Such direct processes may represent either peripheral interactions, in which the projectile passes just at the nuclear surface, or reactions involving single nucleons, which have an appreciable probability for traversing the nucleus without becoming absorbed. In the analysis of nuclear reactions, the direct processes have been identified by means of their characteristic angular distributions and excitation functions.

There is a great variety of different possible types of direct reaction processes corresponding to the freedom in the choice of projectiles and in the choice of outgoing subunits detected. Each of these processes is expected to provide a tool for specifically exploring certain aspects of the nuclear structure. So far, only a few of the simplest of the direct reactions have been extensively studied, but these have already contributed in an essential manner to our knowledge of nuclear properties.

The direct inelastic excitation of collective nuclear states can be described by a natural generalization of the concept of the average nuclear field, and these processes are discussed in connection with the consideration of the fields associated with the different collective modes. (See, for example, Chapter 6 (vibrational excitations), Appendix 5A (rotations), and the charge exchange potential (2-29) for excitation of isobaric analog states.) In the present appendix, we consider the matrix elements determined from nucleon transfer reactions.

3E-1 Single-Nucleon Transfer

3E-1a Factorization of amplitude. Parentage factors

A great variety of processes has been studied, in which the projectile loses or gains a single nucleon as a result of the interaction with the target. It is found that many of these reactions $((d, p), (p, d), (^3\text{He}, \alpha)$, etc.) lead with appreciable probability to the formation of definite states in the final nucleus and that the angular distributions of the outgoing particle often show pronounced maxima and minima, especially in the forward direction. These features of the reaction suggest that a process, such as (d, p), can be viewed as a direct transfer of a neutron from the projectile to a one-particle orbit in the final nucleus, while the proton proceeds without exciting the internal degrees of freedom of the target (Butler, 1951).

Even such a simplified view of the reaction leads in general to a three-body scattering problem involving the coordinates of the target, the neutron, and the proton. However, in the interpretation of nucleon transfer reactions, it has been found possible to achieve a remarkable degree of success by employing a simple approximate description in which the process is considered as proceeding in three stages:

(a) the projectile moves in the average field of the target, as in an elastic scattering process;

(b) a nucleon is transferred from the projectile to an orbit in the target;

(c) the outgoing particle proceeds in the average field of the final nucleus.

The essential point in this description is the assumption that the scattering processes, defined by (a) and (c), are separated by a single action (b) in which the final state of the residual nucleus is created by the addition of the transferred nucleon to the initial state of the target. In stages (a) and (c), only the average properties of the target are involved; the detailed structure of the nuclear states enters only in stage (b).

The total scattering amplitude for a stripping reaction is the sum of the amplitudes for depositing a nucleon with specified values of the quantum numbers jm,

$$f^{(+1)}(I_1M_1\mathbf{p}_1h_1 \rightarrow I_2M_2\mathbf{p}_2h_2) = \sum_{jm} f^{(+1)}(jm; I_1M_1\mathbf{p}_1h_1 \rightarrow I_2M_2\mathbf{p}_2h_2) \qquad \text{(3E-1)}$$

The superscript $(+1)$ indicates a transfer process in which a single nucleon is added to the target, while the quantum numbers of the target and final state are indicated by I_1 and I_2, respectively. The momentum and helicity of the incident projectile are denoted by $\mathbf{p}_1$ and h_1, and the corresponding specification for the outgoing particle is $\mathbf{p}_2h_2$. (The helicity quantum numbers refer to the component of the spin in the direction of the momentum; some general properties of scattering amplitudes in the helicity representation are considered in Sec. 3F–1a.)

If we assume that the transferred particle enters an orbit specified by definite radial quantum number, the partial amplitude in Eq. (3E-1) can be expressed in factored form

$$f^{(+1)}(jm; I_1M_1\mathbf{p}_1h_1 \rightarrow I_2M_2\mathbf{p}_2h_2) = \langle I_2M_2|a^\dagger(jm)|I_1M_1\rangle f_{\text{sp}}^{(+1)}(jm; \mathbf{p}_1h_1 \rightarrow \mathbf{p}_2h_2) \quad \text{(3E-2)}$$

The amplitude $f_{\text{sp}}^{(+1)}(jm)$ describes the stripping process for the idealized situation in which the final nuclear state corresponds to a simple one-particle motion of the transferred nucleon in the binding field of the target. The factor multiplying $f_{\text{sp}}^{(+1)}(jm)$ is the parentage coefficient and is expressed as a matrix element of the operator $a^\dagger(jm)$, which creates a nucleon in the one-particle orbit jm (the properties of creation operators are discussed in Appendix 2A). In the amplitude (3E-2), the detailed structure of the nuclear states I_1 and I_2 is reflected only in the parentage factor.

The amplitude $f^{(-1)}$ for the inverse reaction (pickup) can be expressed in a manner similar to the relation (3E-2),

$$f^{(-1)}(jm; I_1M_1 \to I_2M_2) = \langle I_2M_2 | a(jm) | I_1M_1 \rangle f_{\text{sp}}^{(-1)}(jm) \tag{3E-3}$$

where $a(jm)$ is the annihilation operator and $f_{\text{sp}}^{(-1)}(jm)$ the amplitude for picking up a nucleon initially occupying the one-particle orbital jm. Since pickup and stripping processes are related by time reversal, we have (see Eq. (1B-35))

$$\begin{aligned} f_{\text{sp}}^{(+1)}(jm; \mathbf{p}_1h_1 \to \mathbf{p}_2h_2) &= f_{\text{sp}}^{(-1)}(\overline{jm}; \overline{\mathbf{p}_2h_2} \to \overline{\mathbf{p}_1h_1}) \\ &= (-1)^{j+m} f_{\text{sp}}^{(-1)}(j\,-m; -\mathbf{p}_2h_2 \to -\mathbf{p}_1h_1) \end{aligned} \tag{3E-4}$$

(The transformation of helicity states under time reversal is given by Eq. (3F-6).)

In general, the radial motion of the deposited particle will not correspond to that of a single shell model orbit $nljm$. One may then employ a description in which the nucleon is deposited at the radial distance r, with the angular momentum quantum numbers ljm,

$$f^{(+1)}(ljm, I_1M_1 \to I_2M_2) = \int \mathbf{r}^2\, dr \langle I_2M_2 | a^\dagger(rljm) | I_1M_1 \rangle f_{\text{sp}}^{(+1)}(rljm) \tag{3E-5}$$

The operator $a^\dagger(rljm)$ creates a nucleon with the coordinates $rljm$ (compare the operator $a^\dagger(x)$ considered in Sec. 2A-6). The matrix element $\langle I_2M_2 | a^\dagger(rljm) | I_1M_1 \rangle$ represents the radial wave function of the transferred nucleon and in situations, such as that considered above, where this wave function is approximately proportional to the one-particle radial wave function $\mathscr{R}_{nlj}$, we have

$$\langle I_2M_2 | a^\dagger(rljm) | I_1M_1 \rangle \approx \langle I_2M_2 | a^\dagger(nljm) | I_1M_1 \rangle \mathscr{R}_{nlj}(r) \tag{3E-6}$$

corresponding to Eq. (3E-2). However, especially when the binding energy of the nucleon differs appreciably from those of the shell model orbits, the radial wave function of the transferred particle may depend on the more detailed structure of the nuclear states involved, and the approximation (3E-6) may not be justified.

The matrix elements of the tensor operators $a^\dagger(jm)$ can be written

$$\begin{aligned} \langle I_2M_2 | a^\dagger(jm) | I_1M_1 \rangle &= \langle I_1M_1 | a(jm) | I_2M_2 \rangle \\ &= (2I_2+1)^{-1/2} \langle I_1M_1 jm | I_2M_2 \rangle \langle I_2 \| a^\dagger(j) \| I_1 \rangle \end{aligned} \tag{3E-7}$$

We are assuming the standard phases which imply real matrix elements for $a^\dagger(jm)$ and $a(jm)$; see Sec. 1A-5e.

For deformed nuclei, the parentage factor may be evaluated by a transformation to the intrinsic frame (see Eq. (1A-98))

$$\begin{aligned} a^\dagger(jm) &= \sum_{\Omega} \mathscr{D}^j_{m\Omega}(\omega) a^\dagger(j\Omega) \\ &= \sum_{\Omega,\nu} \mathscr{D}^j_{m\Omega}(\omega) \langle \nu | j\Omega \rangle a^\dagger(\nu) \end{aligned} \tag{3E-8}$$

where Ω represents the component of angular momentum along the intrinsic axis, while ν specifies the one-particle states in the deformed potential.

The simple factorization (3E-2) of the transfer amplitude is only valid if the entrance (and exit) channels are not strongly coupled to any simple excitation of the target (and final nucleus). Considerable success has been obtained on the basis of this approximation, but efforts have also been made to extend the treatment to include the coupling to the rotational and vibrational degrees of freedom in the entrance and exit channels.

3E-1b Cross sections and sum rules

In the approximations (3E-2) and (3E-3), the stripping and pickup cross sections for unpolarized targets, summed over m and over the orientation M_2 of the final state, are given by (see Eq. (3E-7))

$$\begin{aligned} d\sigma^{(+1)}(j; I_1 \rightarrow I_2) &= (2I_1+1)^{-1} \sum_{M_1 M_2 m} d\sigma^{(+1)}(jm; I_1 M_1 \rightarrow I_2 M_2) \\ &= (2j+1)^{-1}(2I_1+1)^{-1}\langle I_2 \| a^\dagger(j) \| I_1\rangle^2 \, d\sigma_{\text{sp}}^{(+1)}(j) \\ d\sigma_{\text{sp}}^{(+1)}(j) &= \sum_m d\sigma_{\text{sp}}^{(+1)}(jm) \\ d\sigma^{(-1)}(j; I_1 \rightarrow I_2) &= (2I_1+1)^{-1} \sum_{M_1 M_2 m} d\sigma^{(-1)}(jm; I_1 M_1 \rightarrow I_2 M_2) \\ &= (2j+1)^{-1}(2I_1+1)^{-1}\langle I_1 \| a^\dagger(j) \| I_2\rangle^2 \, d\sigma_{\text{sp}}^{(-1)}(j) \\ d\sigma_{\text{sp}}^{(-1)}(j) &= \sum_m d\sigma_{\text{sp}}^{(-1)}(jm) \end{aligned} \tag{3E-9}$$

(The cross sections are related to the scattering amplitudes by Eq. (1B-34) and may be taken for specified values of $\mathbf{p}_1 h_1$, $\mathbf{p}_2 h_2$ or may be summed (or averaged) over the polarization values.) In the definition of the single-particle cross sections $d\sigma_{\text{sp}}^{(\pm 1)}(j)$, it has been assumed that the target nucleus has $I_1 = 0$, and the product nucleus $I_2 = j$. For stripping, the single-particle cross section corresponds to a target with no nucleons in the orbits jm while, for pickup, the single-particle unit refers to a closed shell target containing $2j+1$ nucleons in the orbits jm. (In the literature, a single-particle transfer cross section is sometimes employed, which represents an average rather than a sum over m, and which is therefore smaller than that defined in Eq. (3E-9) by a factor $(2j+1)$.

If several j values contribute to the same transition, the transfer cross sections summed over M_1, M_2, and m are obtained as the sum over the partial cross section (3E-9) for the various values of j. In correlation experiments, involving, for example, the angular correlation between the outgoing particle and a γ ray resulting from the decay of the product state, the amplitudes for the transfer with different j must be added coherently.

The nuclear matrix elements involved in the one-particle transfer reactions are often expressed in terms of the spectroscopic factor $\mathcal{S}$ (Macfarlane and French, 1960), which is related to the parentage coefficient by

$$\mathcal{S} = (2I_2+1)^{-1}\langle I_2 \| a^\dagger(j) \| I_1\rangle^2 \tag{3E-10}$$

If the coupling of the isospins is included, the spectroscopic factor is defined by

$$\begin{aligned}\mathcal{S} &= (2T_2+1)^{-1}(2I_2+1)^{-1}\langle I_2 T_2 |||\, a^\dagger(jt)\, ||| I_1 T_1\rangle^2 \\ &= (2I_2+1)^{-1}\langle T_1(M_T)_1 t = \tfrac{1}{2}m_t \,|\, T_2(M_T)_2\rangle^{-2}\langle T_2(M_T)_2 I_2 \,||\, a^\dagger(jt, m_t)\,||\, T_1(M_T)_1 I_1\rangle^2\end{aligned} \qquad \text{(3E-11)}$$

For completely parallel coupling of isospins (as in the case of (d, p) reactions on target nuclei with $M_T = T$), the vector addition coefficient in Eq. (3E-11) is unity and the spectroscopic factors defined by Eqs. (3E-10) and (3E-11) are identical.

The simple commutation rules and tensor properties of the operators $a^\dagger(jm)$ and $a(jm)$ can be exploited to obtain sum rules for the parentage coefficients and the stripping cross sections (Macfarlane and French, 1960). For example, when summing over all the final states αI_2 in a pickup reaction, we can use the completeness relation to express the result in terms of the number operator

$$\begin{aligned}\sum_{\alpha I_2}\langle I_1 \,||\, a^\dagger(j) \,||\, \alpha I_2\rangle^2 &= (2I_1+1)\langle I_1 M_1 \,|\, \sum_m a^\dagger(jm)a(jm) \,|\, I_1 M_1\rangle \\ &= (2I_1+1)n(j)\end{aligned} \qquad \text{(3E-12)}$$

where $n(j)$ is the number of nucleons occupying the shell model orbital j in the initial state I_1 (see Eq. (2A-21)). Similarly, for the parentage coefficient appearing in the stripping reaction, we may use the anticommutation relations (2A-20) for $a, a^\dagger$

$$\begin{aligned}\sum_{\alpha I_2}\langle \alpha I_2 \,||\, a^\dagger(j) \,||\, I_1\rangle^2 &= (2I_1+1)\langle I_1 M_1 \,|\, \sum_m a(jm)a^\dagger(jm) \,|\, I_1 M_1\rangle \\ &= (2I_1+1)(2j+1-n(j))\end{aligned} \qquad \text{(3E-13)}$$

Combining Eqs. (3E-12) and (3E-13), we obtain a sum rule involving both stripping and pickup cross sections, which is independent of the structure of the state I_1 and therefore may be useful in testing the consistency of the analysis of the empirical cross sections.

The above sum rules are especially simple because they depend only on the scalar combination of $a^\dagger(jm)$ and $a(jm)$, which is proportional to the number operator for particles in the orbit j. More general tensor operators of the form $(a^\dagger(j')a(\bar{j}))_{\lambda\mu}$ (see Eq. (1A-85)) can be evaluated by means of a recoupling (French, 1964)

$$\begin{aligned}\langle I_1' \,||\, (a^\dagger(j')a(\bar{j}))_{(jj')\lambda} \,||\, I_1\rangle &= (-1)^{j+j'-\lambda}\sum_{\alpha I_2}(2I_2+1)^{-1/2} \\ &\quad \times \langle (jj')\lambda, (I_1 I_1')\lambda; 0 \,|\, (jI_1)I_2, (j'I_1')I_2; 0\rangle \langle \alpha I_2 \,||\, a(\bar{j}') \,||\, I_1'\rangle \langle \alpha I_2 \,||\, a(\bar{j}) \,||\, I_1\rangle \\ &= \sum_{\alpha I_2}(-1)^{I_1+I_2-j}(2\lambda+1)^{1/2}\begin{Bmatrix} j & j' & \lambda \\ I_1' & I_1 & I_2\end{Bmatrix}\langle \alpha I_2 \,||\, a(\bar{j}') \,||\, I_1'\rangle\langle \alpha I_2 \,||\, a(\bar{j}) \,||\, I_1\rangle\end{aligned} \qquad \text{(3E-14)}$$

Thus, for example, taking $I_1' = I_1$ and $j' = j$, we obtain the contribution of the nucleons in the orbit j to the 2^λ-pole moment of the initial state I_1 in terms of a sum over pickup cross sections, in which each transition is weighted by a recoupling factor that depends on the spin I_2 of the final state.

3E-1c Single-particle amplitude

The factorization of the amplitude, as expressed by Eq. (3E-2), represents the main result of the present section and makes possible the interpretation of the measured transfer cross sections in terms of the parentage factors, provided the single-particle amplitudes are known. These may often be approximately obtained from measurements involving states that have relatively simple configurations, or from sum rules. Even in the absence of such measurements, the relative transfer cross sections may provide important information on the structure of the states involved.

Considerable progress has also been made in the theoretical calculation of the absolute values of the single-particle transfer amplitudes $f_{\mathrm{sp}}^{(\pm 1)}$ as well as the dependence of these amplitudes on the lj quantum numbers, the Q value, and so on. The most extensively studied approximation is based on the success of the optical model in treating elastic scattering processes not only of single nucleons but also of composite particles, such as deuterons. Thus, in the distorted wave Born approximation, it is assumed that the initial and final stages of the reaction can be described in terms of the motion of the projectile and outgoing particle in the optical potentials. The use of first-order perturbation theory corresponds to the assumption that the transfer takes place as a single action (see p. 421). The transfer process itself is caused by the effective interaction responsible for the dissociation of the projectile into transferred nucleon and outgoing particle (in the case of stripping). The effective interaction to be employed in such a calculation may be affected in an important manner by the distortion of the composite particles moving in the nuclear potential.

The treatment of nuclear transfer reactions by means of the distorted wave Born approximation has been reviewed, for example, by Austern (1963) and Satchler (1966). (See also the detailed analysis of the ^{40}Ca(d, p) reaction by Lee *et al.*, 1964.) Similar approximation methods have been used to describe atomic rearrangement collisions (see, for example, Bransden, 1965.) The estimates of $f_{\mathrm{sp}}^{(\pm 1)}$, which have been given on the basis of the distorted wave Born treatment, involve a considerable number of approximations, and the critical examination of these approximations as well as efforts to provide improved treatments are subjects of active current interest.

3E-2 Two-Particle Transfer

In processes involving the transfer of two nucleons, a great variety of different reaction mechanisms may be involved and, at the present time, rather little is known about the possible contributions of these different mechanisms. The available data, however, seem to indicate that, especially for low-lying states, an important contribution arises from processes in which the two nucleons are transferred as a single entity. Such a process can be formulated in close analogy to the one-particle transfer reactions discussed above (see, for example, Glendenning, 1965).

For definiteness, we consider the (t, p) process, in which case the transferred entity is a dineutron in a ^1S state of relative motion, corresponding approximately to the internal motion of the neutrons in the triton. Expanding the reaction amplitude in terms of components corresponding to the insertion of the dineutron at the point $\mathbf{r}$, we have

$$f^{(+2)}(I_1 M_1 \rightarrow I_2 M_2) = \int \langle I_2 M_2 | A^\dagger(\mathbf{r}) | I_1 M_1 \rangle f_{\mathrm{sp}}^{(+2)}(\mathbf{r})\, d^3 r \tag{3E-15}$$

where the operator $A^\dagger(\mathbf{r})$ creates a dineutron at the point $\mathbf{r}$ and can be written

$$A^\dagger(\mathbf{r}) = \frac{1}{\sqrt{2}} \sum_{\substack{m_s(1)\\ m_s(2)}} \int d^3r_1\, d^3r_2\, \delta(\mathbf{r} - \tfrac{1}{2}(\mathbf{r}_1 + \mathbf{r}_2))\varphi_{2_n}(r_{12})$$
$$\times \chi_{S=0}(m_s(1), m_s(2))a^\dagger(\mathbf{r}_2\, m_s(2))a^\dagger(\mathbf{r}_1\, m_s(1)) \qquad \text{(3E-16)}$$

in terms of the wave function $\varphi_{2_n}(r_{12})\chi_{S=0}$ describing the relative motion of the two neutrons in the triton. (We are here neglecting the fact that the relative motion of the two neutrons may depend on their position with respect to the proton and target nucleus; such effects would imply a dependence of the wave function of the dineutron on the coordinate $\mathbf{r}$.)

The operator $A^\dagger(\mathbf{r})$ may be expanded in terms of the operators $a^\dagger(\nu)$, which describe the transfer into specified single-particle orbits in the nuclear potential

$$A^\dagger(\mathbf{r}) = \frac{1}{2} \sum_{\nu_1\nu_2} \langle \nu_1\nu_2 | {}^2n, \mathbf{r}\rangle_a a^\dagger(\nu_2)a^\dagger(\nu_1) \qquad \text{(3E-17)}$$

The specification ν may, for example, refer to the set of quantum numbers $nljm$. The coefficient $\langle \nu_1\nu_2 | {}^2n, \mathbf{r}\rangle_a$ gives the overlap between the dineutron at point $\mathbf{r}$ and the antisymmetrized two-particle state $|\nu_1\nu_2\rangle_a$. Since the dineutron state is antisymmetric $({}^1S)$, we can write

$$\langle \nu_1\nu_2 | {}^2n, \mathbf{r}\rangle_a = \sqrt{2}\langle \nu_1\nu_2 | {}^2n, \mathbf{r}\rangle \qquad \text{(3E-18)}$$

where the overlap factor without the subscript a refers to the unsymmetrized two-particle state $|\nu_1\nu_2\rangle$.

The transition amplitude for transfer of a dineutron with specified angular momentum JM is obtained by expanding the amplitude for transfer at the point $\mathbf{r}$ in spherical harmonics. Thus, we write

$$f^{(+2)}(rJM; I_1M_1 \rightarrow I_2M_2) = \langle I_2M_2 | A^\dagger(rJM) | I_1M_1\rangle f_{\text{sp}}^{(+2)}(rJM) \qquad \text{(3E-19)}$$

where

$$\begin{aligned} f_{\text{sp}}^{(+2)}(rJM) &= \int d\Omega\, i^{-J} Y_{JM}^*(\hat{\mathbf{r}}) f_{\text{sp}}^{(+2)}(\mathbf{r}) \\ A^\dagger(rJM) &= \int d\Omega\, i^J Y_{JM}(\hat{\mathbf{r}}) A^\dagger(\mathbf{r}) \end{aligned} \qquad \text{(3E-20)}$$

In terms of the shell-model orbits, we have

$$A^\dagger(rJM) = \frac{1}{2} \sum_{\nu_1\nu_2} \langle \nu_1\nu_2 | {}^2n, rJM\rangle_a a^\dagger(\nu_2)a^\dagger(\nu_1) \qquad \text{(3E-21)}$$

For a deformed nucleus, the transformation to the intrinsic frame yields

$$\begin{aligned} A^\dagger(rJM) &= \sum_{M'} \mathscr{D}^J_{MM'}(\omega)A^\dagger(rJM') \\ A^\dagger(rJM') &= \frac{1}{2} \sum_{\nu_1\nu_2} \langle \nu_1\nu_2 | {}^2n, rJM'\rangle_a a^\dagger(\nu_2)a^\dagger(\nu_1) \end{aligned} \qquad \text{(3E-22)}$$

where M' is the component of angular momentum with respect to the intrinsic 3-axis, and where ν specifies the single-particle orbits in the deformed field (intrinsic states). The component M' is equal to the sum of the Ω values for the orbits ν_1 and ν_2.

Additional discussion of the transition operator for two-particle transfer reactions is given in Chapter 8, in connection with the analysis of experiments testing the pair coupling scheme.

APPENDIX

3F

Resonance Reactions

In a variety of nuclear scattering and reaction processes involving projectiles of not too large energy, the cross sections exhibit sharp resonances. These resonances can be associated with the formation of metastable compound systems with a lifetime long compared with typical periods of the internal motion. The stability of the resonance states may be due to centrifugal or Coulomb barriers impeding the disintegration process, or to a complexity in the intrinsic structure implying a small amplitude for the configurations associated with the decay channels. Such resonance structure is a characteristic feature of most many-body systems and has been observed, for example, in electron-atom scattering and in the interactions of "elementary" particles.

In the first section of this appendix, we consider the general structure of resonance cross sections and the relationship between the resonance parameters and the properties of the metastable compound states. The discussion also includes an analysis of resonance effects in averaged cross sections. In the following section, we study in some detail a simple potential scattering model illustrating some of the significant features of nuclear resonance reactions and providing estimates of the single-particle units for the resonance widths.

3F-1 General Features of Resonance Scattering

3F-1a Decay amplitudes

The decay of a nuclear resonance state, like decay of an unstable particle, can be characterized by the amplitudes for transitions into the various open channels. We shall consider the decay as a two-body process by which a particle is emitted leaving the residual nucleus in a definite state. The particle may be a nucleon, a photon, a composite particle (d, α, etc.), or may represent a system with a continuous mass spectrum (pair of nucleons, electron-neutrino pair, etc.)

The resonance state will be labeled by the angular momentum quantum numbers $I_r\ M_r$, and the decay channels may, for example, be specified by the quantum numbers I, l, and j referring to the spin of the residual nucleus, the orbital angular momentum of relative motion, and the total angular momentum obtained by coupling l and the spin s of the emitted particle. The decay amplitude will be denoted by $g(I_r \rightarrow Ilj)$ and is so normalized that the absolute square is the partial width

$$\Gamma(I_r \to Ilj) = |g(I_r \to Ilj)|^2 \tag{3F-1}$$

which gives the probability per unit time (multiplied by $\hbar$) for decay into the channel considered. The total width Γ_r is the sum over all partial widths

$$\Gamma_r = \sum_{Ilj} \Gamma(I_r \to Ilj) \tag{3F-2}$$

and gives the lifetime of the metastable state. The exponential decay implies that the time dependence of the wave function is the same as for a stationary state with complex energy $E_r - \frac{1}{2}i\Gamma_r$.

We can also describe the decay in terms of amplitudes specifying the direction $\hat{\mathbf{p}}$ of the emitted particle and the orientations M and m_s of the spins I and s,

$$g(I_r M_r \to IM\hat{\mathbf{p}}m_s) = \sum_{lj} \langle lm_l s m_s | jm\rangle \langle IMjm | I_r M_r\rangle Y_{lm_l}(\hat{\mathbf{p}})\, g(I_r \to Ilj) \tag{3F-3}$$

If the polarization of the emitted particle is specified by the helicity $h = \mathbf{s}\cdot\hat{\mathbf{p}}$, we obtain, with a normalization of the helicity amplitudes to solid angle $8\pi^2$ (see below),

$$\begin{aligned} g(I_r M_r \to IM\hat{\mathbf{p}}h) &= \sum_{lj} \langle l0sh | jh\rangle \langle IMjm | I_r M_r\rangle \left(\frac{2l+1}{8\pi^2}\right)^{1/2} \mathscr{D}^j_{mh}(\hat{\mathbf{p}}) g(I_r \to Ilj) \\ &= \sum_{hj} \langle IMjm | I_r M_r\rangle \left(\frac{2j+1}{8\pi^2}\right)^{1/2} \mathscr{D}^j_{mh}(\hat{\mathbf{p}}) g(I_r \to Ihj) \end{aligned} \tag{3F-4}$$

The latter expression, in which the decay channels are labeled by h instead of l, is especially appropriate to γ emission. For given multipolarity and parity ($E\lambda$ or $M\lambda$), the decay involves a combination of the two amplitudes $g(I_r \to I, h = \pm 1, j = \lambda)$ with equal magnitude.

The relation (3F-4) can be obtained by the same procedure as employed in the derivation of the helicity wave functions in coordinate space (see Sec. 3A-1). It is to be emphasized that the helicities referring to the directions of $\mathbf{p}$ and $\mathbf{r}$ are distinct quantities, although we employ the same notation h when there is no possibility of confusion. (The scattering formalism in the helicity representation was developed by Jacob and Wick, 1959; the notation of this reference differs from that employed here by a complex conjugation of the $\mathscr{D}$ functions (see footnote on p. 77) and by the choice of a fixed value for the third Euler angle ($\psi = -\varphi$; see Sec. 3A-1b).)

In analogy to Eqs. (3A-4) and (3A-5), we have

$$\begin{aligned} |\mathbf{p}\, m_s\rangle &= \sum_h \mathscr{D}^s_{m_s h}(\hat{\mathbf{p}}) |\mathbf{p}\, h\rangle \\ \langle \mathbf{p}\, h | pljm\rangle &= \langle l0sh | jh\rangle \left(\frac{2l+1}{8\pi^2}\right)^{1/2} \mathscr{D}^j_{mh}(\hat{\mathbf{p}}) \end{aligned} \tag{3F-5}$$

where $\hat{\mathbf{p}}$ represents three Euler angles of which the third, ψ, is redundant. The angular parts of the amplitudes (3F-4) and (3F-5) are thus normalized with respect to integration over $8\pi^2$. We note that transformation coefficients, such as that in Eq. (3F-4), referring to momentum space, do not contain the phase factor i^l appearing in Eq. (3A-5) (see comment on p. 97).

The transformation of the momentum states under space reflection and time reversal is

$$\begin{aligned}
\mathscr{P}\,|\mathbf{p}\, m_s\rangle &= |-\mathbf{p}\, m_s\rangle \\
\mathscr{T}\,|\mathbf{p}\, m_s\rangle &= (-1)^{s+m_s}|-\mathbf{p}\, -m_s\rangle \\
\mathscr{P}\,|\mathbf{p}\, h\rangle &= (-1)^{s-h}|-\mathbf{p}\, -h\rangle \\
\mathscr{T}\,|\mathbf{p}\, h\rangle &= |-\mathbf{p}\, h\rangle
\end{aligned} \tag{3F-6}$$

where $-\mathbf{p}$ denotes the orientation obtained by rotating $\mathbf{p}$ about the intrinsic y' axis through the angle $-\pi$. (The corresponding transformation of the helicity states in the space representation is given by Eq. (3A-11)).

The time reverse of the decay process $I_r \rightarrow I + s$ is a process by which the state I_r is formed in a collision between the particles I and s. Hence, time reversal invariance relates the decay and formation amplitudes (see Sec. 1B-4),

$$\begin{aligned}
g(Ilj \rightarrow I_r) &= g(I_r \rightarrow Ilj) \\
g(IM\hat{\mathbf{p}}h \rightarrow I_r M_r) &= g(\overline{I_r M_r \rightarrow IM\hat{\mathbf{p}}h}) \\
&= (-1)^{I_r + M_r + I + M} g(I_r\, -M_r \rightarrow I\, -M\, -\hat{\mathbf{p}}\, h)
\end{aligned} \tag{3F-7}$$

It is often convenient to view the decay (and formation) of the metastable state, r, as caused by a perturbation H', a small part of the Hamiltonian, in the absence of which the state r would be completely stable (see also the discussion in Sec. 1B-4). The decay amplitude is then given by the matrix element of H' coupling the unperturbed state r to the out-state describing the scattering of the products in the absence of H' (nonresonant scattering),

$$g(I_r \rightarrow Ilj) = (2\pi)^{1/2}\langle (Ilj)I_r \text{ out}|H'|\, I_r\rangle \tag{3F-8}$$

The proportionality factor corresponds to a normalization of the continuum states per unit energy.

For photon or lepton emission, the interaction H' can be expressed as an integral over a local interaction density proportional to the electromagnetic and weak currents (see Appendices 3C and 3D). For nuclear reactions, the quantity H' has a more complicated nonlocal structure. We shall not need the explicit form of H', however, since we only wish to exploit the possibility, implied by the metastability of the resonance state, of describing the decay and formation processes as first-order perturbation effects.

The question has been raised (Dirac, 1935, p. 201) whether it is justifiable, in the case of nuclear processes as distinct from photoprocesses, to treat the system in terms of independent sets of states for the bound levels and the decay products. The problem of overcompleteness in the total degrees of freedom, however, does not seem to present serious difficulties in the present context; for example, one may quantize the continuum states in a volume excluding that occupied by the nucleus. It may also be remarked that, at the present time, it may be difficult to maintain a sharp distinction between photoprocesses involving the creation of a particle and processes involving the emission of a particle already present in the system.

3F-1b Resonance scattering

The resonance reaction may be viewed as a two-stage process, $1 \rightarrow r \rightarrow 2$, involving the formation and subsequent decay of the resonance state r. The entrance and exit channels, 1 and 2, will be specified by the direction $\hat{\mathbf{p}}$ of relative motion and the polarizations of the particles involved. The resonance scattering amplitude $f_{\rm res}(1 \to r \to 2)$ involves the product of the formation and decay amplitudes $g(1 \to r)$ and $g(r \to 2)$ and can be obtained by a second-order perturbation treatment.

The transition matrix element for the second-order process is (see Eq. (3F-8))

$$\begin{aligned} \langle 2\text{ out}\,|V|\,1\text{ in}\rangle &= \sum_{M_r} \frac{\langle 2\text{ out}\,|H'|\,I_r M_r\rangle\,\langle I_r M_r\,|H'|\,1\text{ in}\rangle}{E - E_r + \frac{1}{2}i\Gamma_r} \\ &= \frac{1}{2\pi}\sum_{M_r}\frac{g(1\to I_r M_r)g(I_r M_r \to 2)}{E - E_r + \frac{1}{2}i\Gamma_r} \end{aligned} \tag{3F-9}$$

By using the complex energy $E_r - \frac{1}{2}i\Gamma_r$ for the intermediate state in the second-order perturbation treatment, we have taken into account the damping of the resonance state caused by the coupling to all the different decay channels; the virtual transitions associated with this coupling also produce a small energy shift of the resonance state (self-energy effect) which is included in E_r. In the perturbation calculation leading to Eq. (3F-9), we are therefore using a representation in which the effects of the coupling H', apart from the infinitesimal parts that couple to the selected exit and entrance channels 1 and 2, are incorporated in the properties of the resonance state. (For an explicit treatment of the coupling H' acting between a sharp intermediate state with real energy and the complete set of decay channels, see, for example, Dirac, 1935, pp. 203 ff., and Heitler, 1954, pp. 196 ff.)

The total scattering amplitude can be written

$$f(1\to 2) = f_{\rm nr}(1\to 2) + f_{\rm res}(1\to 2) \tag{3F-10}$$

where the first term (the nonresonant amplitude) describes the scattering in the absence of the coupling H', while the resonant term represents the effect of the perturbation H'. In the neighborhood of a sharp resonance, the nonresonant amplitude is expected to be approximately constant. In some situations, the nonresonant scattering may be associated with potential scattering or with direct reaction processes.

The resonant amplitude is proportional to the transition matrix element (3F-9). With f normalized according to Eq. (1B-31), we have

$$f_{\rm res}(1\to 2) = -4\pi^2\hbar(p_1 p_2)^{-1/2}\langle 2\text{ out}\,|V|\,1\text{ in}\rangle \tag{3F-11}$$

(The proportionality factor can be obtained from the familiar expression for the transition probability per unit time, $2\pi\hbar^{-1}|\langle 2\text{ out}|V|\ 1\text{ in}\rangle|^2 d\Omega$, together with the relations (1B-33) and (1B-34). From Eqs. (3F-9) and (3F-11), we thus obtain the general form of the resonance scattering amplitude (Breit and Wigner, 1936),

$$\begin{aligned} &f_{\rm res}((IM\hat{\mathbf{p}}h)_1 \to (IM\hat{\mathbf{p}}h)_2) \\ &\quad = -2\pi\hbar(p_1 p_2)^{-1/2}\sum_{M_r}\frac{g((IM\hat{\mathbf{p}}h)_1 \to I_r M_r)g(I_r M_r \to (IM\hat{\mathbf{p}}h)_2)}{E - E_r + \frac{1}{2}i\Gamma_r} \end{aligned} \tag{3F-12}$$

For definiteness, we have employed the helicity representation for the incoming and outgoing particles. The cross section is related to the scattering amplitude by Eq. (1B-34). (Note the extra factor 2π in the helicity representation with normalization (3F-4).)

In the absence of nonresonant scattering, the total resonance cross section for unpolarized target and projectile becomes

$$\frac{1}{(2s_1+1)(2I_1+1)}\sum_{h_1M_1h_2M_2}\int_{\Omega_2} d\sigma(1\rightarrow 2)$$
$$=\frac{2I_r+1}{(2s_1+1)(2I_1+1)}\pi\lambda_1^2\frac{\Gamma(r\rightarrow 1)\Gamma(r\rightarrow 2)}{(E-E_r)^2+\frac{1}{4}\Gamma_r^2} \qquad \text{(3F-13)}$$

where $\Gamma(r \rightarrow 1)$ is the width for decay of the resonance state into channel 1, specified by the nuclear state I_1 and the projectile with spin s_1, and, correspondingly, for $\Gamma(r \rightarrow 2)$.

The interference between resonant and nonresonant scattering depends on the phases of the decay amplitudes, which can be related to the phase shifts in the nonresonant scattering through the unitarity of the scattering amplitude together with the time reversal condition for the decay and formation amplitudes (see Sec. 1B-4). The result has an especially simple form in the representation B, that diagonalizes the amplitude for the nonresonant scattering (the eigenchannels of the nonresonant scattering). From Eq. (1B-39) we then have

$$g(I_r \rightarrow B) = \exp(i\delta_B)(\Gamma(I_r \rightarrow B))^{1/2} \qquad \text{(3F-13a)}$$

where δ_B is the phase shift of the nonresonant scattering in the eigenchannel B.

The general form (3F-12) of the resonance scattering amplitude is seen to follow directly from the assumed existence of a metastable state with a lifetime large compared with the characteristic periods of the internal motion. Such a metastability implies that the state could be made stationary by a small perturbation. One can therefore employ the general results of perturbation theory, even though the form of the perturbation is not specified and may have a complex structure. In fact, the explicit construction of the appropriate perturbation operator for metastable nuclear states, in terms of the coordinates of the emitted particle, appears to be an as yet unsolved problem.

One can also formulate the relationship between the resonance scattering amplitude and the properties of the decaying state in terms of the analytic properties of the scattering amplitude, considered as a function of a complex energy variable E.[5] The existence of a decaying state with only outgoing waves implies a pole in the scattering amplitude at the energy $E_r - \frac{1}{2}i\Gamma_r$ of the decaying state (see, for example, Eq. (1B-27) defining the scattering matrix); in a similar manner, the bound states correspond to poles in the scattering amplitude for real values of the energy. The residue of the pole must have the factored form as in Eq. (3F-12), since each pole, if assumed to be single, occurs in a definite eigenchannel, α, of the scattering matrix; hence, the residue for the amplitude $f(1 \rightarrow 2)$ involves the product $\langle 2 \text{ out} | \alpha \rangle \langle \alpha | 1 \text{ in} \rangle$.

In the neighborhood of a pole, the general expression for the scattering matrix

[5] Such a formulation of the theory of nuclear resonance reactions has especially been exploited by Humblet and Rosenfeld; see, for example, the survey by Humblet (1967). See also the review by McVoy (1967).

consists of an approximately constant term and a pole term. In the eigenchannels B for the constant term, the S matrix can therefore be written in the form

$$\langle B'|S|B\rangle = \exp(2i\delta_B)\delta(B, B') - i\frac{g(B')g(B)}{E - E_r + \frac{1}{2}i\Gamma_r} \tag{3F-14}$$

The formation and decay amplitudes are equal, as a consequence of $\mathscr{R}\mathscr{T}$ invariance. In fact, time reversal symmetry implies $\langle B'|S|B\rangle = \langle \bar{B}|S|\bar{B}'\rangle$ (see Eq. (1B-29)) and, with the standard phasing, we have $\mathscr{R}|\bar{B}$ in (out)$\rangle = |B$ in (out)$\rangle$; see Eq. (1-39)). Hence, $\langle B'|S|B\rangle$ is a symmetric matrix. Further, the unitary condition

$$\langle B''|SS^\dagger|B\rangle = \sum_{B'} \langle B''|S|B'\rangle \langle B|S|B'\rangle^* = \delta(B'', B) \tag{3F-15}$$

which is to be satisfied for all E with energy-independent parameters $g(B)$, E_r, and Γ_r, implies that $g(B)$ has the phase δ_B and satisfies the relation

$$\sum_B |g(B)|^2 = \Gamma_r \tag{3F-16}$$

corresponding to the phase relation (3F-13a) for the decay amplitude and the relation (3F-2) equating the total width with the sum of the partial widths. The arguments based on the pole structure and unitarity thus lead to the same form of the resonance scattering amplitude as that derived above.

The crucial point in both the above derivations of the resonance formula is the existence of a long-lived metastable state. One can also express this metastability in terms of the operator that gives the time delay in the scattering process and in this manner derive the general expression for resonance scattering (Goldberger and Watson, 1964).

While the resonance amplitude can always be cast in the form (3F-12), different parametrizations of the cross sections for resonance reactions are frequently used in the literature. Thus, in the Kapur-Peierls and Wigner-Eisenbud formulations of nuclear reaction theory, the response of the nucleus to the incident radiation is analyzed in terms of the formation of discrete compound states defined by boundary conditions at some suitable radius R representing the nuclear surface. (See the reviews by Brown, 1959, and by Lane and Thomas, 1958.)

The description of the resonance reaction in terms of energy-independent decay amplitudes is valid in the limit of sharp and well-isolated resonances, where the only energy dependence of the cross section in the region of the resonance is that implied by the denominator in Eq. (3F-12). Even for rather narrow resonances, however, it may be necessary to take into account the energy dependence of the amplitudes g, especially when the formation and decay involve the transmission through a large potential barrier, associated with centrifugal or Coulomb forces. To a first approximation, one can write g as the product of a constant factor (the reduced amplitude) containing the information about the structure of the resonance state, and an energy-dependent transmission coefficient whose square represents the probability for the particle to penetrate through the potential barrier from the nuclear surface to infinity, with an additional factor proportional to the relative velocity v, which determines the flux at infinity. Such a description also applies if the state r is a weakly bound state (negative energy resonance) or if it is unbound but with an energy E_r in the threshold region for the channel considered. Estimates of the transmission coefficient will be considered in Sec. 3F-2.

It must be recognized that, in situations where it is important to take into account the energy variation of the resonance parameters, the separation of the total scattering amplitude into resonance and direct terms is no longer unambiguous. This is a reflection of the fact that, in such circumstances, the properties of the decaying state are a function of the energy with which it is formed.

The problem of the interference of nearby resonances is another question that goes beyond the simple treatment discussed above, since it involves the coupling of the decaying states; moreover, the unitarity condition implies more complicated expressions for the phase of the decay amplitudes and for the relation of the total and partial widths (see, for example, the treatment of the two-level model in the R-matrix theory, discussed by Lane and Thomas, 1958). The problem associated with interfering resonances becomes especially acute in the region of high excitation, where the widths become comparable with or larger than the spacings of the levels. Indeed, the choice of appropriate physical concepts for the description of the highly excited region of the spectrum, where the levels are strongly overlapping, presents important questions for future investigations.

3F-1c Resonances in average cross section. Gross structure[6]

The resonances considered above are associated with metastable states of the compound system, which decay into the various open channels. A somewhat different type of resonance phenomena may occur when a metastable state is formed in the initial stage of the reaction ("door-way" state), representing, for example, the motion of the projectile in the average potential generated by the target. Such metastable states may decay partly into the open channels (direct reactions), and partly through the coupling to the internal degrees of freedom of the colliding particles (compound nucleus formation).

The direct and compound reactions are distinguished by the time scales involved. Resonance effects associated with the direct reactions can therefore be studied by considering wave packets that define the duration of the collision with a latitude Δt small compared with the periods and lifetimes of the compound states, but sufficiently large to permit the occurrence of resonance in the direct stage of the reaction. The analysis in terms of such wave packets corresponds to averaging the cross sections over energy domains ΔE small compared with the width of the direct resonance, but large compared with the spacings D and widths Γ of the compound states. Thus, the direct resonances are associated with the gross structure of the cross sections; with higher

[6] Resonance effects in energy-averaged nuclear cross sections were considered by Feshbach, Porter, and Weisskopf (1954). The physical significance of the averaging was further elucidated by Friedman and Weisskopf (1955).

resolution, the cross sections exhibit fine structure, the nature of which depends on the relative magnitude of D and Γ. For $D \gg \Gamma$, the cross sections have well-isolated resonances of the form discussed above. For $D \lesssim \Gamma$, there is strong interference between resonances, and the cross sections show fluctuations associated with the superposition of the compound states and characterized by energy intervals of the order of Γ. (For a review of such fluctuation effects, see Ericson and Mayer-Kuckuk, 1966.)

The cross sections for the direct reactions are given by the average scattering amplitude $\langle f(1 \to 2)\rangle$ obtained by averaging $f(1 \to 2)$ over the energy distribution of the wave packet. The total average cross section is the sum of the direct cross section and the cross section for reactions proceeding through compound nucleus formation,

$$\langle d\sigma(1 \to 2)\rangle = d\sigma_{\mathrm{dir}}(1 \to 2) + d\sigma_{\mathrm{comp}}(1 \to 2) \tag{3F-17}$$

with

$$\begin{aligned} d\sigma_{\mathrm{dir}}(1 \to 2) &= \frac{p_2}{p_1} |\langle f(1 \to 2)\rangle|^2 \, d\Omega \\ d\sigma_{\mathrm{comp}}(1 \to 2) &= \frac{p_2}{p_1} \langle |\Delta f(1 \to 2)|^2\rangle \, d\Omega \end{aligned} \tag{3F-18}$$

The fluctuating part of the scattering amplitude is denoted by $\Delta f \equiv f - \langle f\rangle$. The total average cross section for compound nucleus formation corresponds to the damping of the direct scattering and can be determined from the average amplitude $\langle f\rangle$ by means of the unitarity relation (the optical theorem). This relation, which can be obtained, for example, from Eqs. (1B-31) and (1B-34) and the unitarity condition for the S matrix, gives the total cross section in terms of the imaginary part of the forward elastic scattering amplitude, and yields

$$\begin{aligned} \sigma_{\mathrm{comp}}(1) &= \sum_2 d\sigma_{\mathrm{comp}}(1 \to 2) \\ &= \langle \sigma_{\mathrm{tot}}(1)\rangle - \sigma_{\mathrm{dir}}(1) \\ &= \frac{4\pi\hbar}{p_1} \langle \operatorname{Im} f(1 \to 1)\rangle - \sigma_{\mathrm{dir}}(1) \end{aligned} \tag{3F-19}$$

where the cross sections $\sigma_{\mathrm{comp}}(1)$ and $\sigma_{\mathrm{dir}}(1)$ are obtained by integration over all final channels, 2.

The general form of the average scattering amplitude in the neighborhood of a well-isolated and sharp gross structure resonance can be found by the same procedure as employed for the fine structure resonances, except for the modifications arising from the lack of unitarity of the averaged scattering matrix. Thus, the scattering amplitude $\langle f(1 \to 2)\rangle$ can be expressed as a sum of a nonresonant and a resonant term, as in Eq. (3F-10), and the resonance amplitude has the form (3F-12) with the time reversal relation between amplitudes for formation and decay. However, the total width Γ_r is no longer the sum of the partial widths for the decay into the various open channels for the direct reaction, but receives an additional contribution Γ_c representing the probability for the resonance state to decay by compound nucleus formation,

$$\Gamma_r = \sum_i \Gamma(r \to i) + \Gamma_c \tag{3F-20}$$

The label i refers to the open channels for the direct reaction. (In the analysis of doorway resonances by Feshbach *et al.*, 1967, the width Γ_c is denoted by $\Gamma^{\downarrow}$ while the widths $\Gamma(r \to i)$ to the open channels are labeled $\Gamma_i^{\uparrow}$.)

The lack of unitarity in the scattering matrix, resulting from compound nucleus formation, further implies that the phase of the decay amplitude is no longer related to the phase shift of the nonresonant scattering by Eq. (3F-13a); the difference in phase is associated with the damping of the particle motion in the decay channel.

The total cross section for compound nucleus formation is given by Eq. (3F-19) and may be divided into two parts

$$\sigma_{\text{comp}}(1) = (\sigma_{\text{comp}}(1))_{\text{nr}} + (\sigma_{\text{comp}}(1))_{\text{res}} \tag{3F-21}$$

The first term is the cross section in the absence of the resonance, while the second term gives the contribution from the resonance and includes the effect of interference between the nonresonant and resonant scattering. In deriving the cross sections, it is convenient to write the average scattering amplitude in the form (see Eqs. (3F-10), (3F-12), and (1B-31))

$$\begin{aligned}
\langle f(1 \to 2)\rangle &= \langle f(1 \to 2)\rangle_{\text{nr}} + \langle f(1 \to 2)\rangle_{\text{res}} \\
\langle f(1 \to 2)\rangle_{\text{nr}} &= -i\frac{2\pi\hbar}{(p_1 p_2)^{1/2}}(\langle 2|\langle S\rangle_{\text{nr}}|1\rangle - \delta(1,2)) \\
\langle f(1 \to 2)\rangle_{\text{res}} &= -\frac{2\pi\hbar}{(p_1 p_2)^{1/2}}\sum_{M_r}\frac{g(1 \to r)g(r \to 2)}{E - E_r + \frac{1}{2}i\Gamma_r}
\end{aligned} \tag{3F-22}$$

where $\langle 2|\langle S\rangle_{\text{nr}}|1\rangle$ is the nonresonant part of the S-matrix element. For the resonance part of the cross section for compound nucleus formation, we then obtain from Eq. (3F-19), using also Eqs. (3F-18) and (3F-20),

$$(\sigma_{\text{comp}}(1))_{\text{res}} = \frac{4\pi^2\hbar^2}{p_1^{\,2}}\frac{1}{(E - E_r)^2 + \frac{1}{4}\Gamma_r^{\,2}} \cdot \\
\times \sum_{M_r}\{-|g(1 \to r)|^2(\Gamma_r - \Gamma_c) + [(-i(E - E_r) + \tfrac{1}{2}\Gamma_r)h(1 \to r)g^*(1 \to r) + \text{c.c.}]\} \tag{3F-23}$$

where the amplitude $h(1 \to r)$ is defined by

$$h(1 \to r) \equiv \sum_i \langle i|\langle S\rangle_{\text{nr}}|1\rangle g^*(r \to i) \tag{3F-24}$$

If the nonresonant scattering, describing the motion of the in- and outgoing particles, is not damped by coupling to the compound states, the nonresonant average compound cross section vanishes; moreover, $\langle S\rangle_{\text{nr}}$ is unitary, and the sum over the direct channels, i, in Eq. (3F-24) is a complete sum, giving $h(1 \to r) = g(1 \to r)$ (see Eq. (1B-37)). The resonance cross section (3F-23) is then of the Breit-Wigner form

$$(\sigma_{\text{comp}}(1))_{\text{res}} = \sigma_{\text{comp}}(1) = \frac{4\pi^2\hbar^2}{p_1^{\,2}}\sum_{M_r}\frac{|g(1 \to I_r M_r)|^2\Gamma_c}{(E - E_r)^2 + \frac{1}{4}\Gamma_r^{\,2}} \tag{3F-25}$$

For unpolarized target and projectile, the cross section (3F-25) can also be written (see Eq. (3F-3))

$$\frac{1}{(2s+1)(2I+1)}\sum_{m_s M}\sigma_{\text{comp}}(IM\hat{\mathbf{p}}m_s)=\sum_{lj}\pi\lambda\!\!\!^{-2}\,\frac{(2I_r+1)}{(2s+1)(2I+1)}\,\frac{\Gamma(r\to Ilj)\Gamma_c}{(E-E_r)^2+\frac{1}{4}\Gamma_r^2} \tag{3F-26}$$

(In the helicity representation, the normalization (3F-4) requires an additional factor 2π in the cross sections (3F-23) and (3F-25); see the comment in Sec. 1B-3.)

A damping in the nonresonant scattering occurs, for example, when the incident particle moves in an optical potential with an imaginary part. The amplitudes h and g then differ and we may write

$$h(1\to r)=g(1\to r)b_1\exp\{i\alpha_1\} \tag{3F-27}$$

where b_1 and α_1 are real parameters. (The rotational invariance implies that b_1 and α_1 depend only on the scalar parameters of the entrance channel.) The cross section (3F-23) now takes the form

$$(\sigma_{\text{comp}}(1))_{\text{res}}=\frac{4\pi^2\hbar^2}{p_1^{\,2}}\sum_{M_r}\frac{\Gamma(1\to I_rM_r)(\Gamma_c-\Gamma_r(1-b_1\cos\alpha_1)+2(E-E_r)b_1\sin\alpha_1)}{(E-E_r)^2+\frac{1}{4}\Gamma_r^2} \tag{3F-28}$$

If the phase α_1 differs from 0 (or π), one obtains an asymmetric shape of the resonance cross section. (Such an asymmetry has been considered for the isobaric analog resonances by Robson, 1965.)

3F-2 Resonance Parameters Calculated for Single-Particle Motion

The considerations in the previous section involve no specific assumptions regarding the structure of the resonating system and provide general expressions by means of which the resonance parameters may be extracted from the measured cross sections. Appropriate units for the decay amplitudes for emission of nucleons are the single-particle amplitudes $g_{\text{sp}}(lj)$, which correspond to a situation in which the resonance can be described in terms of motion of a nucleon in the nuclear potential. The ratio of g to g_{sp} characterizes the parentage of the resonance state with respect to the decay channel considered, and is analogous to the parentage factor for bound states (as determined, for example, from nucleon transfer processes; see Appendix 3E).

The present section gives an analysis of resonance effects in potential scattering and provides estimates of the amplitudes g_{sp}. For simplicity, we shall assume a spherical square well potential, which makes possible a simple explicit evaluation of the scattering amplitude. For the actual nuclear potentials, the diffuseness of the surface is of considerable importance (see the estimate on p. 445), and the present model is mainly intended for illustrative purposes. For a quantitative estimate of the single-particle resonance parameters, a numerical integration of the wave equation may be required. (For nonspherical nuclei, the determination of the single-particle units for resonance scattering involves a treatment of the coupling to the rotational motion; see Appendix 5A.)

3F-2a Scattering of spinless neutral particles

We consider first the scattering of a spinless neutral particle. For distances r greater than the range R of the potential, the radial motion for angular momentum l is determined by the equation

$$\left(\frac{d^2}{dr^2} + k^2 - \frac{l(l+1)}{r^2}\right) u_l(r) = 0 \tag{3F-29}$$

with

$$k^2 = \frac{2ME}{\hbar^2} \qquad u_l(r) = r\mathscr{R}_l(r) \tag{3F-30}$$

The regular and irregular solutions to Eq. (3F-29) are denoted by F_l and G_l and can be expressed as

$$\begin{aligned} F_l(r) &= krj_l(kr) \\ G_l(r) &= krn_l(kr) \end{aligned} \tag{3F-31}$$

in terms of the spherical Bessel and Neumann functions.

The general solution for $r > R$ is a linear combination of F_l and G_l, which we can write

$$\begin{aligned} u_l(r) &= \cos\delta_l F_l(r) + \sin\delta_l G_l(r) \\ &\approx \sin\left(kr + \delta_l - l\frac{\pi}{2}\right) \qquad kr \gg l \end{aligned} \tag{3F-32}$$

The phase shifts δ_l determine the scattering amplitude through the usual relation

$$f(\vartheta) = \frac{1}{2ik} \sum_l (\exp\{2i\delta_l\} - 1)(2l+1)P_l(\cos\vartheta) \tag{3F-33}$$

and the scattering cross section is

$$d\sigma = |f(\vartheta)|^2 \, d\Omega \tag{3F-34}$$

The phase shift in Eq. (3F-32) may be determined from the condition that the wave function and its derivative be continuous across the surface $r = R$. Denoting the logarithmic derivative of u_l at $r = R$ by L_l, we have

$$\begin{aligned} L_l &\equiv R\frac{1}{u_l(R)}\left(\frac{du_l}{dr}\right)_{r=R} \\ &= \left(\frac{\cos\delta_l F_l' + \sin\delta_l G_l'}{\cos\delta_l F_l + \sin\delta_l G_l}\right)_{r=R} \end{aligned} \tag{3F-35}$$

with

$$F_l' = R\frac{dF_l}{dr} \qquad G_l' = R\frac{dG_l}{dr} \tag{3F-36}$$

The quantity L_l may be obtained from the solutions of the wave equation for $r < R$, and its properties will be considered below; for the present, we have only to notice that L_l is a function of the total energy E of the scattering system.

The phase shift obtained from Eq. (3F-35) is conveniently written in the form

$$\exp\{2i\delta_l\} = \frac{L_l - \Delta_l + is_l}{L_l - \Delta_l - is_l}\exp\{2i\xi_l\} \tag{3F-37}$$

with the notation

$$\begin{aligned} s_l &= \frac{G_l F_l' - F_l G_l'}{G_l^2 + F_l^2} = kR\frac{1}{G_l^2 + F_l^2} \equiv kRv_l(kR) \\ \Delta_l &= \frac{G_l G_l' + F_l F_l'}{G_l^2 + F_l^2} = -\frac{1}{2}\frac{kR}{v_l}\frac{dv_l}{d(kR)} \\ \exp\{2i\xi_l\} &= \frac{G_l - iF_l}{G_l + iF_l} \end{aligned} \tag{3F-38}$$

where all quantities are evaluated at $r = R$. Explicit expressions for the scattering parameters defined by Eq. (3F-38) are given in Table 3F-1.

l	v_l	Δ_l	ξ_l
0	1	0	$-x$
1	$\dfrac{x^2}{1+x^2}$	$-\dfrac{1}{1+x^2}$	$-x + \frac{1}{2}\sin^{-1}\dfrac{2x}{1+x^2}$
2	$\dfrac{x^4}{9+3x^2+x^4}$	$-\dfrac{18+3x^2}{9+3x^2+x^4}$	$-x + \frac{1}{2}\sin^{-1}\dfrac{18x-6x^3}{9+3x^2+x^4}$
$x \ll l^{1/2}$	$\approx \left[\dfrac{x^l}{(2l-1)!!}\right]^2$	$\approx -l$	$\approx -\dfrac{x}{2l+1}\left[\dfrac{x^l}{(2l-1)!!}\right]^2$

Table 3F-1 Parameters characterizing the scattering of a neutron from a square well potential. The quantities v_l, Δ_l, and ξ_l are defined by Eq. (3F-38). We use the abbreviation $x = kR$.

The quantity v_l gives the transmission through the centrifugal barrier, corresponding to the ratio of the intensities at infinity and at $r = R$, for the outgoing wave

$$u_l^{(+)}(r) = G_l + iF_l \approx \exp\left\{i\left(kr - l\frac{\pi}{2}\right)\right\} \qquad kR \gg l \tag{3F-39}$$

The phase factor ξ_l may be recognized as the phase shift that would describe scattering by an impenetrable sphere ($L_l = \infty$). Thus, the form (3F-37) expresses the total phase shift δ_l as the sum of the smoothly varying part ξ_l, associated with the fact that the wave number suffers an abrupt change at $r = R$, and the additional part depending on the details of the motion for $r < R$, as expressed by L_l.

Resonance effects occur only if the lifetime of the nuclear state is long compared with the time for the particle to cross the nucleus. Such a long-lived state can occur in the present one-particle model only if the centrifugal barrier is large compared to the incident particle energy. In such circumstances, $G_l \gg F_l$, and we have $s_l \ll 1$ and $\xi_l \ll 1$. The total phase shift is therefore small (the centrifugal barrier prevents the particles from coming within the range R), except in the neighborhood of the energy values E_r, for which

$$L_l(E_r) - \Delta_l(E_r) = 0 \tag{3F-40}$$

When this relation is fulfilled, we have $\delta_l \approx \pi/2$, and the contribution to the scattering cross section from this angular momentum channel approaches the maximum value $4\pi(2l+1)k^{-2}$.

If we wish to study the energy variation of the cross section in a small energy interval around the resonance energy E_r, we may expand $L_l - \Delta_l$ in a power series

$$L_l(E) - \Delta_l = -\frac{1}{\gamma}(E - E_r) + \cdots \tag{3F-41}$$

where the expansion coefficient γ may be calculated from a knowledge of L_l and Δ_l,

$$\gamma^{-1} = -\left(\frac{\partial L_l}{\partial E}\right)_{E=E_r} + \left(\frac{\partial \Delta_l}{\partial E}\right)_{E=E_r} \tag{3F-42}$$

Inserting the expansion (3F-41) in Eq. (3F-37), we obtain, to leading order,

$$\begin{aligned}\exp\{2i\delta_l\} &= \exp\{2i\xi_l\}\frac{E - E_r - is_l\gamma}{E - E_r + is_l\gamma} \\ &= \exp\{2i\xi_l\} - \frac{i\Gamma_r}{E - E_r + \frac{1}{2}i\Gamma_r}\exp\{2i\xi_l\}\end{aligned} \tag{3F-43}$$

where

$$\Gamma_r = 2\gamma s_l \tag{3F-44}$$

The scattering amplitude (3F-33) is therefore of the form (3F-10),

$$\begin{aligned}&f(\vartheta) = f_{\text{res}}(\vartheta) + f_{\text{nr}}(\vartheta) \\ &f_{\text{res}} = -\frac{2l+1}{2k}P_l(\cos\vartheta)\frac{\Gamma_r\exp\{2i\xi_l\}}{E - E_r + \frac{1}{2}i\Gamma_r} \\ &f_{\text{nr}} = \frac{2l+1}{2ik}(\exp\{2i\xi_l\} - 1)P_l(\cos\vartheta) + \sum_{l'\neq l}\frac{2l'+1}{2ik}(\exp\{2i\delta_{l'}\} - 1)P_{l'}(\cos\vartheta)\end{aligned} \tag{3F-45}$$

The resonance part is equivalent to the expression (3F-12) with decay amplitudes given by Eq. (3F-3), with

$$g_l = \Gamma_r^{1/2}\exp\{i\xi_l\} \tag{3F-46}$$

It is seen that ξ_l is the phase shift of the nonresonant scattering on which the resonance scattering is superposed. The phase of the decay amplitude (3F-46) is that implied by the general arguments involving unitary and the time reversal invariance of the interaction (see Eq. (3F-13a)).

The resonance width (3F-44) is the product of a factor 2γ depending on the internal structure of the resonance state (a reduced width) and a factor s_l, which represents the transmission through the centrifugal barrier v_l, multiplied by kR (see Eq. (3F-38)). The factor kR is proportional to the outgoing flux.

We now evaluate the logarithmic derivative L_l from the solution of the wave equation in the interior region ($r < R$). If V_0 is the constant potential, the "inside wave number" K is given by

$$K^2 = \frac{2M}{\hbar^2}(E - V_0) \tag{3F-47}$$

and the wave function and its logarithmic derivative at the surface are

$$\begin{aligned} u_l &\propto KRj_l(KR) \\ L_l &= 1 + KR\frac{j_l'(KR)}{j_l(KR)} \end{aligned} \tag{3F-48}$$

The resonance width depends on the derivative of L_l with respect to E. Using the wave equation (3F-29) for u_l and the resonance condition (3F-40), we find

$$\begin{aligned} \left(\frac{\partial L_l}{\partial E}\right)_{E=E_r} &= -\frac{MR^2}{\hbar^2}\left[1 - \frac{l(l+1) - \Delta_l(\Delta_l - 1)}{K^2R^2}\right] \\ &\approx -\frac{MR^2}{\hbar^2} \end{aligned} \tag{3F-49}$$

The last expression is exactly valid for $l = 0$ (in which case $\Delta_l = 0$) and, for $l > 0$, is approximately valid if $kR < l^{1/2}$, since then $\Delta_l \approx -l$ (see Table 3F-1). In a similar manner, we obtain from Eqs. (3F-29) and (3F-38)

$$\frac{\partial \Delta_l}{\partial E} \approx \begin{cases} \dfrac{MR^2}{\hbar^2}\dfrac{2}{2l-1} & l > 0, \quad kR < l^{1/2} \\ 0 & l = 0 \end{cases} \tag{3F-50}$$

From the relations (3F-42), (3F-44), (3F-49), and (3F-50), we finally obtain the single-particle estimate for the width

$$\Gamma_{sp} \approx \begin{cases} \dfrac{2\hbar^2}{MR^2}kRv_l(kR)\dfrac{2l-1}{2l+1} & l > 0, \quad kR < l^{1/2} \\ \dfrac{2\hbar^2}{MR^2}kR & l = 0 \end{cases} \tag{3F-51}$$

3F-2b Semiclassical interpretation of Γ_{sp}

The structure of the single-particle width (3F-51) may be simply understood in terms of the physical effects that determine the particle emission rate in a single-particle model. Quite generally, we expect

$$\Gamma = \frac{\hbar}{\tau}P \tag{3F-52}$$

where τ is the period for the radial motion of the particle inside the potential and P is the barrier penetration factor that gives the magnitude of the flux at infinity for unit flux incident on the nuclear surface from the inside.

We first discuss the emission rate for $l = 0$. The radial period is

$$\tau_{l=0} = \frac{2RM}{\hbar K} \tag{3F-53}$$

and the value of $P_{l=0}$ may be obtained by considering the one-dimensional problem of a particle incident on a potential wall,

$$\begin{aligned} &\varphi = A \exp\{iKx\} + B \exp\{-iKx\} \qquad x < 0, \quad V = V_0 \\ &\varphi = C \exp\{ikx\} \qquad x > 0, \quad V = 0 \\ &B = \frac{K-k}{K+k} A \qquad C = \frac{2K}{K+k} \\ &P_{l=0} = \frac{k}{K}\left|\frac{C}{A}\right|^2 = \frac{4kK}{(K+k)^2} \end{aligned} \tag{3F-54}$$

Thus, the width Γ_{sp} for $l = 0$ has just the value (3F-51), for $k \ll K$.

It should be noted that, in the simple one-body scattering of neutrons with $l = 0$, there are no sharp resonances since, for $kR < 1$, we have $\Gamma_{sp} > E$. This result simply reflects the fact that, in the absence of some restraining barrier or some complexity in the internal motion, the decay time of the resonant state is not longer than the time required for the incident particle to travel a distance equal to the nuclear dimensions. The estimate (3F-51) is still useful, however, since it gives correctly the decay time for the one-particle state.

For $l > 0$, a similar interpretation of Γ_{sp} may be given, but the corresponding factors are slightly more complicated. The classical period of the radial motion may be calculated by integrating over the orbit

$$\begin{aligned} (\tau_l)_{\text{clas}} &= 2\int_{r_0}^{R} \frac{dr}{v_r} = \frac{2M}{\hbar}\int_{r_0}^{R} dr \left(K^2 - \frac{l(l+1)}{r^2}\right)^{-1/2} \\ &= \frac{2MR}{\hbar K}\left(1 - \frac{l(l+1)}{K^2R^2}\right)^{1/2} \end{aligned} \tag{3F-55}$$

The radial velocity is denoted by v_r, and r_0 is the classical turning point, given by $K^2 r_0^2 = l(l+1)$. Actually, the period is somewhat longer than this classical estimate owing to the fact that the particle spends a certain fraction of the time in the classically forbidden barrier region. For the case of a resonant state close to zero energy, we can easily estimate this correction, since the wave function in the barrier region is proportional to r^{-l}. The normalization integral thus becomes

$$\int_0^R dr[Krj_l(Kr)]^2 + [KRj_l(KR)]^2 \int_R^\infty dr \left(\frac{R}{r}\right)^{2l} = \frac{2l+1}{2l-1}\int_0^R dr[Krj_l(Kr)]^2 \tag{3F-56}$$

where we have employed standard expressions for the integral of the Bessel function and the continuity of the wave function at $r = R$,

$$\left(\frac{d}{dr}(Krj_l(Kr))\right)_{r=R} = -lKj_l(KR) \tag{3F-57}$$

The effective period is thus

$$\tau_l = (\tau_l)_{\text{clas}} \frac{2l+1}{2l-1} \tag{3F-58}$$

(The increase in τ corresponds to the contribution to γ resulting from the derivative of Δ_l (see Eqs. (3F-42), (3F-49), and (3F-50).)

It is convenient to consider the barrier penetration P_l as a product of three factors. First, there is the factor P_1 that gives the intensity of the outgoing wave just outside the nuclear surface (in units of the incident intensity just inside the surface). This "mismatch factor" corresponds to the ratio $|C|^2 : |A|^2$ given by Eq. (3F-54) for $l = 0$. For $l \neq 0$, the wave numbers just inside and outside the surface are modified by the centrifugal barrier, and we obtain

$$\begin{aligned} K_{\text{in}} &= \left(K^2 - \frac{l(l+1)}{R^2}\right)^{1/2} \\ K_{\text{out}} &= i\left(\frac{l(l+1)}{R^2} - k^2\right)^{1/2} \approx i\left(\frac{l(l+1)}{R^2}\right)^{1/2} \\ P_1 &= \left|\frac{2K_{\text{in}}}{K_{\text{in}} + K_{\text{out}}}\right|^2 \approx 4\left(1 - \frac{l(l+1)}{K^2R^2}\right) \end{aligned} \tag{3F-59}$$

The next factor, P_2, in the penetration problem is the ratio of the intensity of the wave at infinity to the intensity of the wave just outside the nuclear surface, and equals the transmission factor v_l.

To obtain the ratio of incident to transmitted flux, we must finally multiply by the ratio P_3 of the wave number at infinity, k, to the wave number K_{in} just inside the nuclear surface. Combining the various factors, we thus obtain the estimate

$$P_l = P_1 P_2 P_3 = \frac{4k}{K}\left(1 - \frac{l(l+1)}{K^2R^2}\right)^{1/2} v_l(kR) \tag{3F-60}$$

and this value of P_l, together with the above estimate of τ_l, just yields the expression (3F-51) for the single-particle width.

3F-2c Effect of spin

If we consider the scattering of a particle with spin s, the potential may depend on j as well as on l (spin-orbit force). For each channel lj, however, the radial motion will have exactly the same structure as that discussed above, and we obtain again the one-particle estimate (3F-51) for the single-particle width.

3F-2d Coulomb effects

For a charged incident particle, the above treatment remains valid with only minor changes. The outside solutions F_l and G_l must be replaced by the appropriate wave functions describing motion in a Coulomb field. Thus,

$$\begin{matrix} F_l \\ G_l \end{matrix} \underset{r\to\infty}{\rightarrow} \begin{matrix} \sin \\ \cos \end{matrix} \left\{ kr - l\frac{\pi}{2} - \eta \ln 2kr + \sigma_l \right\} \tag{3F-61}$$

where

$$\eta = \frac{zZe^2}{\hbar v} \tag{3F-62}$$

is the parameter that measures the strength of the Coulomb distortion. The charge numbers of the incident particle and the target nucleus are denoted by z and Z, and the asymptotic velocity is v. The Coulomb phase shift is denoted by σ_l and is given by

$$\exp\{2i\sigma_l\} = \frac{\Gamma(l+1+i\eta)}{\Gamma(l+1-i\eta)} = \frac{(l+i\eta)(l-1+i\eta)\cdots(1+i\eta)}{(l-i\eta)(l-1-i\eta)\cdots(1-i\eta)} \exp\{2i\sigma_0\} \tag{3F-63}$$

The phase shift introduced by Eq. (3F-32) is the additional nuclear phase shift; the total phase shift δ_l, which should be employed in the scattering amplitude (3F-33), is therefore the sum of the nuclear phase shift and the Coulomb phase shift σ_l. Thus, we obtain again the expression (3F-37) where, however, Δ_l and s_l are defined with the regular and irregular Coulomb wave functions replacing the Bessel functions in Eq. (3F-38), and where the potential scattering phase ξ_l includes the Coulomb phase shift

$$\exp\{2i\xi_l\} = \frac{G_l - iF_l}{G_l + iF_l} \exp\{2i\sigma_l\} \tag{3F-64}$$

For $r < R$, the particle moves in a potential consisting of the constant term V_0 and the Coulomb potential depending on the distribution of the nuclear charge. An approximate estimate of the single-particle width may be obtained by assuming constant potential (a Coulomb potential equal to the surface value) and employing the WKB approximation to evaluate the energy derivative of Δ_l. This estimate gives

$$\Gamma_{\mathrm{sp}} \approx \frac{2\hbar^2}{MR^2} kR \frac{V_0}{V_0 + zZe^2/R} v_l(kR, \eta)[1 - ((l+\tfrac{1}{2})^2 + 2kR\eta)^{-1/2}] \tag{3F-65}$$

where v_l is the transmission factor (see (3F-38)) calculated with Coulomb functions. (A collection of formulae and graphical data for evaluating Coulomb penetration factors in the WKB approximation is given by Morrison, 1953.)

3F-2e Isospin dependence of potential

For nuclei with a neutron excess, the nuclear potential involves an isovector component, with the possibility of charge exchange between the nucleon and the nucleus. In the absence of the Coulomb interaction, the eigenstates of scattering would be labeled by the total isospin quantum number T, which can take the values $T_0 \pm 1/2$, where T_0 is the isospin of the target nucleus. However, the Coulomb interaction may imply significant couplings between components in the nuclear motion with $T = T_0 + 1/2$ and $T = T_0 - 1/2$; such couplings are of importance, for example, in the analysis of isobaric analog resonances in proton scattering (see the discussion and the references quoted on pp. 46 ff.).

3F-2f Effect of diffuseness of nuclear surface region

The above estimates of Γ_{sp} have the advantage of simplicity, but suffer from the extreme assumption of a completely sharp nuclear surface. As is well known from the corresponding optical problem, such a surface implies a much greater reflection (and consequently a smaller decay probability) than if the potential goes more gradually to zero. We may obtain an approximate estimate of this effect by treating a modification of the penetration problem defined by Eq. (3F-54), in which we allow the potential to decrease linearly over a distance d.

The solutions in such a region of constant force may be expressed in terms of Bessel functions of order 1/3. For simplicity, we confine ourselves to zero energy and again consider waves incident from the negative x axis,

$$\begin{aligned} &\varphi = A\exp\{iKx\} + B\exp\{-iKx\} && x<0 \quad V=V_0 \\ &\varphi = Cz^{1/2}J_{-1/3}(\tfrac{2}{3}Kdz^{3/2}) && 0<x<d \quad V=zV_0 \quad z=1-\frac{x}{d} \\ &\varphi = D && x>d \quad V=0 \end{aligned} \qquad \text{(3F-66)}$$

By matching the wave functions at $x=0$ and $x=d$, we find

$$\left|\frac{D}{A}\right|^2 = 4[(J_{2/3}(\tfrac{2}{3}Kd))^2 + (J_{-1/3}(\tfrac{2}{3}Kd))^2]^{-1}(\tfrac{1}{3}Kd)^{-2/3}(\Gamma(\tfrac{2}{3}))^{-2} \qquad \text{(3F-67)}$$

This factor is to be compared with the value 4 obtained for $d \to 0$, and the ratio is plotted in Fig. 3F-1. The diffuseness of the nuclear potential is of the order $d \approx 2.5$ fm, which gives $Kd \approx 4$ and thus implies an increase by about a factor 2 in the value of Γ_{sp}. (For estimates of the penetrability corresponding to a Woods-Saxon potential, see, for example, Vogt, 1967.)

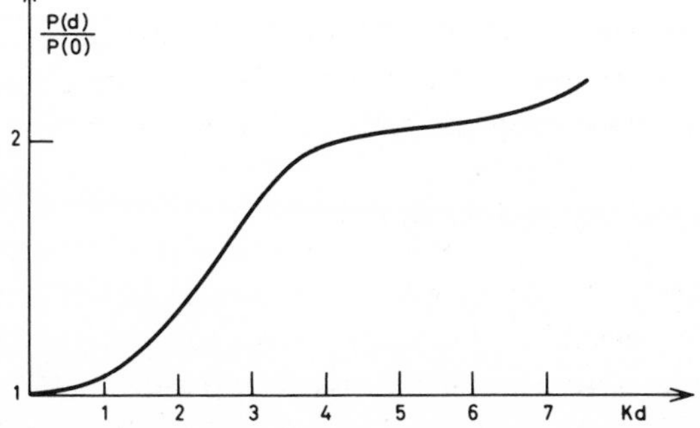

Figure 3F-1 Transmission coefficient for a trapezoidal potential. The figure gives the ratio of the transmission coefficient $P(d)$ for a trapezoidal potential with surface thickness d (see Eqs. (3F-66) and (3F-67)) to that for a step potential ($d=0$, see Eq. (3F-54)). The inside wave number is denoted by K, while the transmitted wave is assumed to have zero energy ($k=0$).

3F-2g Effect of velocity dependence of potential

A velocity dependence of the potential will affect the value of the resonance widths. If we consider the potential as a function of the incident energy, the energy derivative of L_l will be multiplied by $(1 + \partial V_0/\partial E)$ and the width will be reduced by the same factor. The nonlocalities in the potential may also affect the transmission through the surface.

3F-2h Effect of imaginary potential

In the analysis of gross structure resonances, the single-particle units for the resonance parameters refer to particle motion in a complex potential

$$U = V + iW \tag{3F-68}$$

For such a potential, the inside wave number and, hence, the logarithmic derivative L_l to be inserted into the expression (3F-37) for the scattering phase shift δ_l, has an imaginary part. The phase δ_l therefore takes complex values corresponding to the lack of unitarity resulting from the damping of the particle motion in the optical potential.

The general nature of the modifications in the resonance scattering produced by the imaginary potential may be readily seen by considering the leading-order effects associated with small values of W. Denoting by $L_l^{(0)}(E)$ the logarithmic derivative for $W = 0$, we have

$$\begin{aligned} L_l(E) &= L_l^{(0)}(E - iW) \\ &\approx L_l^{(0)}(E) - iW\frac{\partial L_l^{(0)}}{\partial E} \end{aligned} \tag{3F-69}$$

With the resonance parameters E_r and γ defined in terms of $L_l^{(0)}$ (see Eqs. (3F-40) and (3F-41)), we thus obtain from Eq. (3F-37)

$$\exp\{2i\delta_l\} = \exp\{2i\xi_l\} - \frac{i\Gamma_l}{(E - E_r) + \frac{1}{2}i\Gamma_r}\exp\{2i\xi_l\} \tag{3F-70}$$

where

$$\begin{aligned} \Gamma_l &= 2\gamma s_l \\ \Gamma_r &= \Gamma_l + \Gamma_c \\ \Gamma_c &= 2\gamma\frac{\partial L}{\partial E}W \\ &= \begin{cases} -2W & (l = 0) \\ -2\dfrac{2l - 1}{2l + 1}W & (l \neq 0) \end{cases} \end{aligned} \tag{3F-71}$$

The width Γ_l for particle emission is not affected by W, to the order considered, but the total width Γ_r receives an additional contribution Γ_c, which represents the decay of the resonance state caused by the absorption (see Eq. (2-138)). For $l \neq 0$, the reduction of the absorption width corresponds to the fact that the particle spends part of the time in the barrier region, where the potential is real (see Eq. (3F-56)).

The phase of the decay amplitude is not influenced by the absorption since, for the model considered, the nonresonant scattering is that of an impenetrable sphere and therefore not affected by the internal potential.

The reaction cross section associated with the absorption (compound nucleus formation) is

$$(\sigma_l)_{\text{comp}} = \frac{\pi}{k^2}(2l+1)(1-|\exp\{2i\delta_l\}|^2)$$

$$= \frac{\pi}{k^2}(2l+1)\frac{\Gamma_l \Gamma_c}{(E-E_r)^2+\frac{1}{4}\Gamma_r^2} \tag{3F-72}$$

This result is of the form (3F-25), which holds when there is no damping in the non-resonant scattering.

If higher-order effects of W are included, the relations (3F-70) and (3F-72) remain valid, except for the modified values of the parameters E_r, Γ_r, and Γ_l. The rather large imaginary potentials used in the optical model analyses (see, for example, Fig. 2-29) imply values of Γ_c large compared with Γ_l and, under such conditions, there may be little effect of the resonances in the elastic channel (McVoy, 1967a). Provided Γ_c remains small compared with the single-particle level spacing, one may still expect the existence of well-defined metastable states with consequences for other reaction cross sections.

In the proton scattering involving isobaric analog states, the value of Γ_c is determined by the rather weak isospin-violating Coulomb interactions, and one therefore observes sharp resonances with widths much smaller than those associated with compound nucleus formation in the absence of isospin selection rules. (See, for example, the discussion related to Fig. 1-9.)

BIBLIOGRAPHY

The section, figure, or table, where the reference is quoted, is given in brackets. The abbreviation "Ex" refers to sections of illustrative examples. In the case of textbooks and compilations, some of which are quoted extensively, the *loci citati* have been omitted. A cumulative bibliography covering all three volumes will be given in Volume III.

Adler, S. L. (1965), *Phys. Rev.* **140**, B736. [3D-2c]

Ajzenberg-Selove, F., and Lauritsen, T. (1959), *Nuclear Phys.* **11**, 1.

Ajzenberg-Selove, F., and Lauritsen, T. (1968), *Nuclear Phys.* **A114**, 1.

Alburger, D. E., Gallmann, A., Nelson, J. B., Sample, J. T., and Warburton, E. K. (1966), *Phys. Rev.* **148**, 1050. [Fig. 1-7]

Alder, K., and Winther, A. (1966), *Coulomb Excitation*, Academic Press, New York, N.Y.

Alfvén, H. (1965), *Rev. Mod. Phys.* **37**, 652. [2-3b]

Alikhanov, A. I., Galatnikov, Yu. V., Gorodkov, Yu. V., Eliseev, G. P., and Lyubimov, V. A. (1960), *Zhur. Eksp. i Teoret. Fiz.* **38**, 1918; transl. *Soviet Phys. JETP* **11**, 1380. [1-2 Ex]

Aller, L. H. (1961), *The Abundance of Elements*, Wiley (Interscience), New York, N.Y. [Fig. 2-19]

Amati, D. (1964), in *Compt. Rend. Congrès Intern. de Physique Nucléaire*, vol. I, p. 57, ed. P. Gugenberger, C.N.R.S., Paris. [2-5a, 2-5 Ex]

Andersen, B. L., Bondorf, J. P., and Madsen, B. S. (1966), *Phys. Letters* **22**, 651. [3-5b]

Anderson, J. D., and Wong, C. (1961), *Phys. Rev. Letters* **7**, 250. [1-3a]

Anderson, J. D., Wong, C., and McClure, J. W. (1965), *Phys. Rev.* **138**, B615. [2-1f]

Andreev, D. S., Gangrskij, Yu. P., Lemberg, I. Ch., and Nabičvižvili, V. A. (1965), *Izv. Akad. Nauk* **29**, 2231. [Table 3-2]

Arima, A., and Horie, H. (1954), *Progr. Theoret. Phys. (Kyoto)* **12**, 623. [3-3b]

Arndt, R. A., and MacGregor, M. H. (1966), *Phys. Rev.* **141**, 873. [Fig. 2-34]

Asaro, F., and Perlman, I. (1952), *Phys. Rev.* **87**, 393. [Fig. 2-17]

Auerbach, E. H., Dover, C. B., Kerman, A. K., Lemmer, R. H., and Schwarcz, E. H. (1966), *Phys. Rev. Letters* **17**, 1184. [1-3 Ex]

Austern, N. (1963), in *Selected Topics in Nuclear Theory*, p. 17, ed. F. Janouch, Intern. Atomic Energy Agency, Vienna. [3E-1c]

Azhgirey, L. S., Klepikov, N. P., Kumekin, Yu. P., Mescheryakov, M. G., Nurushev, S. B., and Stoletov, G. D. (1963), *Phys. Letters* **6**, 196. [2-5 Ex]

Bahcall, J. N. (1966), *Nuclear Phys.* **75**, 10. [Table 3-5]

Balashov, V. V., and Eramzhyan, R. A. (1967), *Atomic Energy Review* **5**, 3. [3D-3]

Baranger, M. (1967), in *Proc. Intern. Nuclear Physics Conf.*, Gatlinburg, p. 659, ed.-in-chief R. L. Becker, Academic Press, New York, N.Y. [3-2]

Bardin, R. K., Gollon, P. J., Ullman, J. D., and Wu, C. S. (1967), *Phys. Letters* **26B**, 112. [3D-1d]

Barnard, E., Ferguson, A. T. G., McMurray, W. R., and van Heerden, I. J. (1966), *Nuclear Phys.* **80**, 46. [2-1 Ex]

Bartholomew, G. A. (1960), *Nuclear Spectroscopy*, part A, p. 304, ed. F. Ajzenberg-Selove, Academic Press, New York, N.Y. [2-1 Ex]

Batty, C. J., Gilmore, R. S., and Stafford, G. H. (1966), *Nuclear Phys.* **75**, 599. [2-1f]

Baumgartner, E., Conzett, H. E., Shield, E., and Slobodrian, R. J. (1966), *Phys. Rev. Letters* **16**, 105. [2-5a]

Bayman, B. F. (1957), *Groups and their Application to Spectroscopy*, NORDITA Lecture Notes, NORDITA, Copenhagen. See also 2nd edition (1960).

Bayman, B. F. (1966), *Am. J. Phys.* **34**, 216. [1-3a]

Baz', A. I., Gol'danskii, V. I., and Zel'dovich, Ya. B. (1960), *Usp. Fiz., Nauk* **72**, 211; transl. *Soviet Phys. Uspekhi* **3**, 729. [2-3 Ex]

Bearse, R. C., Youngblood, D. H., and Segel, R. E. (1968), *Nuclear Phys.* **A111**, 678. [3-3 Ex]

Becker, J. A., and Wilkinson, D. H. (1964), *Phys. Rev.* **134**, B1200. [Table 3-2]

Beer, G. A., Brix, P., Clerc, H.-G., and Laube, B. (1968), *Phys. Letters* **26**, B506. [3-3 Ex, Table 3-2]

Bég, M. A. B., Lee, B. W., and Pais, A. (1964), *Phys. Rev. Letters* **13**, 514. [3C-4]

Bell, J. S. (1959), *Nuclear Phys.* **12**, 117. [3-1b, 3B-1a]

Belote, T. A., Sperduto, A., and Buechner, W. W. (1965), *Phys. Rev.* **139**, B80. [Table 3-7]

Berggren, T., and Jacob G. (1963), *Nuclear Phys.* **47**, 481. [2-4 Ex]

Bernardini, G. (1966), in *Proc. Intern. School of Physics "Enrico Fermi"*, Course 32, Academic Press, New York, N.Y. [3D-1d]

Bernstein, J., Feinberg, G., and Lee, T. D. (1965), *Phys. Rev.* **139**, B1650. [3C-6a]

Bethe, H. A. (1937), *Rev. Mod. Phys.* **9**, 69. [2-1i]

Bethe, H. A. (1967), in *Proc. Intern. Nuclear Physics Conf.*, Gatlinburg, p. 625, ed.-in-chief R. L. Becker, Academic Press, New York, N.Y. [2-5b]

Bethe, H. A. (1968), in *Proc. Intern. Conf. on Nuclear Structure, J. Phys. Soc. Japan*, **24** Suppl., p. 56. [2-5c]

Bethe, H. A., and Bacher, R. F. (1936), *Rev. Mod. Phys.* **8**, 82. [2-1d, 2-1h]

Biedenharn, L. C., and Brussaard, P. J. (1965), *Coulomb Excitation*, Clarendon Press, Oxford.

Biedenharn, L. C., and van Dam, H. (1965), *Quantum Theory of Angular Momentum*, Academic Press, New York, N.Y.

Bjerregaard, J. H., Hansen, O., Nathan, O., Stock, R., Chapman, R., and Hinds, S. (1967), *Phys. Letters* **24B**, 568. [Fig. 3-2d]

Blatt, J. M., and Weisskopf, V. F. (1952), *Theoretical Nuclear Physics*, Wiley, New York, N.Y.

Blin-Stoyle, R. J. (1960), *Phys. Rev.* **118**, 1605. [1-2 Ex, 1-4a]

Blin-Stoyle, R. J. (1964), in *Selected Topics in Nuclear Spectroscopy*, p. 213, ed. B. J. Verhaar, North-Holland, Amsterdam. [1-3 Ex]

Blin-Stoyle, R. J., and Perks, M. A. (1954), *Proc. Phys. Soc. (London)* **67A**, 885. [3-3b]

Blin-Stoyle, R. J., and Rosina, M. (1965), *Nuclear Phys.* **70**, 321. [3D Ex]

Bloch, C. (1954), *Phys. Rev.* **93**, 1094. [2B-1]

Blomqvist, J., and Wahlborn, S. (1960), *Arkiv Fysik* **16**, 545. [2-4 Ex, 3-3 Ex, Fig. 3-3, Fig. 3-4]

Bodansky, D., Eccles, S. F., Farwell, G. W., Rickey, M. E., and Robinson, P. C. (1959), *Phys. Rev. Letters* **2**, 101. [Fig. 1-4]

Bodansky, D., Braithwaite, W. J., Shreve, D. C., Storm, D. W., and Weitkamp, W. G. (1966), *Phys. Rev. Letters* **17**, 589. [1-2 Ex]

Boerner, H. (1963), *Representations of Groups*, North-Holland, Amsterdam; Wiley, New York, N. Y.

Bohr, A. (1961), in *Lectures in Theoretical Physics*, vol. 3, p. 1, eds. W. E. Britten, B. W. Downs, and J. Downs, Wiley (Interscience), New York, N.Y. [Table 1-1]

Bohr, A., and Mottelson, B. R. (1953), *Mat. Fys. Medd. Dan. Vid. Selsk.* **27**, no. 16. [2D, 3-3a]

Bohr, A., Damgaard, J., and Mottelson, B. R. (1967), in *Nuclear Structure*, p. 1, eds. A. Hossain, Harun-ar-Rashid, and M. Islam, North-Holland, Amsterdam. [Fig. 2-6]

Bohr, N. (1936), *Nature* **137**, 344. [2-1i, 2-1 Ex]

Bohr, N., and Kalckar, F. (1937), *Mat. Fys. Medd. Dan. Vid. Selsk.* **14**, no. 10. [2-1i]

Bohr, N., Peierls, R., and Placzek, G. (1939), *Nature* **144**, 200. [2-1 Ex]

Bollinger, L. M., and Thomas, G. E. (1964), *Phys. Letters* **8**, 45. [2-1] Ex

Bondorf, J. P., Lütken, H., and Jägare, S. (1966), *Phys. Letters* **21**, 185. [1-3 Ex]

Bowen, P. H., Scanlon, J. P., Stafford, G. H., Thresher, J. J., and Hodgson, P. E. (1961), *Nuclear Phys.* **22**, 640. [Fig. 2-29]

Bransden, B. H. (1965), in *Advances in Atomic and Molecular Physics*, vol. 1, p. 85, eds. D. R. Bates and I. Estermann, Academic Press, New York, N.Y. [3E-1c]

Breit, G. (1958), *Rev. Mod. Phys.* **30**, 507. [2-1 Ex, 3C-3]

Breit, G., and Wigner, E. (1936), *Phys. Rev.* **49**, 519. [3F-1b]

Breit, G., Condon, E. U., and Present, R. D. (1936), *Phys. Rev.* **50**, 825. [1-3a, 2-5a]

Breit, G., Hull, M. H., Jr., Lassila, K. E., Pyatt, K. D., Jr., and Ruppel, H. M. (1962), *Phys. Rev.* **128**, 826. [Fig. 2-34, Fig. 2-37]

Brene, N., Veje, L., Roos, M., and Cronström, C. (1966), *Phys. Rev.* **149**, 1288. [3D-2e]

Brentano, P. von, Dawson, W. K., Moore, C. F., Richard, P., Wharton, W., and Wieman, H. (1968), *Phys. Letters* **26B**, 666. [Fig. 3-2f]

Brix, P., and Kopfermann, H. (1949), *Z. Physik* **126**, 344. [2-1 Ex]

Brix, P., and Kopfermann, H. (1958), *Rev. Mod. Phys.* **30**, 517. [Fig. 2-2]

Brown, G. E. (1959), *Rev. Mod. Phys.* **31**, 893. [3F-1b]

Brown, G. E. (1967), *Unified Theory of Nuclear Models*, 2nd edition, North-Holland, Amsterdam.

Brueckner, K. A. (1959), *The Many-Body Problem*, Ecole d'Eté de Physique Théorique, Les Houches, 1958, Wiley, New York. [2-5c]

Brueckner, K. A., Eden, R. J., and Francis, N. C. (1955), *Phys. Rev.* **99**, 76. [3-3a]

Bryan, R. A. (1967), in *Proc. Intern. Nuclear Physics Conf.* Gatlinburg, p. 603, ed.-in-chief R. L. Becker, Academic Press, New York, N.Y. [2-5a]

Bühring, W. (1965), *Nuclear Phys.* **61**, 110. [3D-5]

Bund, G. W., and Wajntal, W. (1963), *Nuovo cimento* **27**, 1019. [2-5b]

Burbidge, E. M., Burbidge, G. R., Fowler, W. A., and Hoyle, F. (1957), *Rev. Mod. Phys.* **29**, 547. [Fig. 2-20, 2-3b, 2-3 Ex]

Burbidge, G. (1962), *Ann. Rev. Nuclear Sci.* **12**, 507. [2-3b, 2-3 Ex]

Burhop, E. H. S. (1967), *Nuclear Phys.* **B1**, 438. [2-1a]

Burnett, D. S., Gatti, R. C., Plasil, F., Price, P. B., Swiatecki, W. J., and Thompson, S. G. (1964), *Phys. Rev.* **134**, B952. [2-1d]

Butler, S. T. (1951), *Proc. Roy. Soc.* (*London*) **A208**, 559. [3E-1a]

Cabibbo, N. (1963), *Phys. Rev. Letters* **10**, 531. [3D-2e]

Calaprice, F. P., Commins, E. D., Gibbs, H. M., Wick, G. L., and Dobson, D. A. (1967), *Phys. Rev. Letters* **18**, 918. [1-2 Ex]

Cameron, A. G. W. (1968), to be published. [Fig. 2-19]

Camp, D. C., and Langer, L. M. (1963), *Phys. Rev.* **129**, 1782. [Table 1-3]

Campbell, E. J., Feshbach, H., Porter, C. E., and Weisskopf, V. F. (1960), *M.I.T. Techn. Rep.* **73**, Cambridge, Mass. [Fig. 2-26]

Carlson, B. C., and Talmi, I. (1954), *Phys. Rev.* **96**, 436. [2-1f]

Cerny, J., and Pehl, R. H. (1964), *Phys. Rev. Letters* **12**, 619. [1-3 Ex]

Cerny, J., Pehl, R. H., Rivet, E., and Harvey, B. G. (1963), *Phys. Letters* **7**, 67. [1-3 Ex]

Chakrabarti, A. (1964), *Ann. Institut Henri Poincaré* **1**, 301. [1A-3a]

Chamberlain, O., Segré, E., Tripp, R. D., Wiegand, C., and Ypsilantis, T. (1957), *Phys. Rev.* **105**, 288. [2-5a]

Chan, L. H., Chen, K. W., Dunning, J. R., Ramsey, N. F., Walker, J. K., and Wilson, R. (1966), *Phys. Rev.* **141**, 1298. [3C-4]

Chen, C. T., and Hurley, F. W. (1966), *Nuclear Data*, Sec. B1-13, p. 1.

Chesler, R. B., and Boehm, F. (1968), *Phys. Rev.* **166**, 1206. [2-1 Ex]

Chilosi, G., Ricci, R. A., Touchard, J., and Wapstra, A. H. (1964), *Nuclear Phys.* **53**, 235. [3-3 Ex]

Chilosi, G., O'Kelley, G. D., and Eichler, E. (1965), *Bull. Am. Phys. Soc.* **10**, 92. [3-4 Ex]

Christensen, C. J., Nielsen, A., Bahnsen, B., Brown, W. K., and Rustad, B. M. (1967), *Phys. Letters* **26B**, 11. [Table 1-1, 3D-3, Table 3-5]

Christensen, J. H., Cronin, J. W., Fitch, V. L., and Turlay, R. (1964), *Phys. Rev. Letters* **13**, 138. [1-2b]

Christensen, P. R., Nielsen, O. B., and Nordby, H. (1963), *Phys. Letters* **4**, 318. [Fig. 3-6]

Church, E. L., and Weneser, J. (1956), *Phys. Rev.* **103**, 1035. [3C-3]

Church, E. L., and Weneser, J. (1960), *Ann. Rev. Nuclear Sci.* **10**, 193. [3C-3]

Clementel, E., and Villi, C. (1955), *Nuovo cimento* **2**, 176. [2-5b]

Cohen, B. L. (1963), *Phys. Rev.* **130**, 227. [3-2 Ex]

Cohen, B. L. (1968), *Phys. Letters* **27B**, 271. [3-2 Ex]

Coleman, S., and Glashow, S. L. (1961), *Phys. Rev. Letters* **6**, 423. [1-3b]

Condon, E. U., and Shortley, G. H. (1935), *The Theory of Atomic Spectra*, Cambridge University Press, London.

Coor, T., Hill, D. A., Hornyak, W. F., Smith, L. W., and Snow, G. (1955), *Phys. Rev.* **98**, 1369. [Fig. 2-3]

Coulon, T. W., Bayman, B. F., and Kashy, E. (1966), *Phys. Rev.* **144**, 941. [Fig. 3-2d]

Craig, R. M., Dore, J. C., Greenlees, G. W., Lilley, J. S., Lowe, J., and Rowe, P. C. (1964), *Nuclear Phys.* **58**, 515. [Fig. 2-28]

Cziffra, P., MacGregor, M. H., Moravcsik, M. J., and Stapp, H. P. (1959), *Phys. Rev.* **114**, 880. [Table 1-1, 2-5a]

Dąbrowski, J., and Sobiczewski, A. (1963), *Phys. Letters* **5**, 87. [Fig. 2-37]

Dalitz, R. H. (1963), in *Proc. Intern. Conf. on Hyperfragments*, St. Cergue, March 1963, CERN Report 64-1, p. 147, CERN, Geneva. [1-3 Ex]

Dalitz, R. H. (1967), in *Proc. 13th Intern. Conf. on High-Energy Physics*, University of California Press, Berkeley, Cal. [Fig. 1-11]

Damgaard, J. (1966), *Nuclear Phys.* **79**, 374. [1-3 Ex]

Damgaard, J., and Winther, A. (1964), *Nuclear Phys.* **54**, 615. [Table 3-6]

Damgaard, J., and Winther, A. (1966), *Phys. Letters* **23**, 345. [3D-4]

Daniel, H., and Schmitt, H. (1965), *Nuclear Phys.* **65**, 481. [1-3 Ex]

Danysz, M., Garbowska, K., Pniewski, J., Pniewski, T., Zakrzewski, J., Fletcher, E. R., Lemonne, J., Renard, P., Sacton, J., Toner, W. T., O'Sullivan, D., Shah, T. P., Thompson, A., Allen, P., Heeran, Sr. M., Montwill, A., Allen, J. E., Beniston, M. J., Davis, D. H., Garbutt, D. A., Bull, V. A., Kumar, R. C., and March, P. V. (1963). *Nuclear Phys.* **49**, 121. [1-3 Ex]

Davis, D. H., Lovell, S. P., Csejthey-Barth, M., Sacton, J., Schorochoff, G., and O'Reilly, M. (1967), *Nuclear Phys.* **B1**, 434. [2-1a]

De Alfaro, V., and Regge, T. (1965), *Potential Scattering*, North-Holland, Amsterdam.

de Boer, J. (1957), in *Progr. in Low Temperature Physics* **1**, 381, ed. C. J. Gorter, North-Holland, Amsterdam. [2-5 Ex]

De Dominicis, C., and Martin, P. C. (1957), *Phys. Rev.* **105**, 1417. [2-5b]

De Forest, T., Jr., and Walecka, J. D. (1966), *Advances in Physics* **15**, 1. [3C-3]

de Groot, S. R., Tolhoek, H. A., and Huiskamp, W. J. (1965), in *Alpha-, Beta-, and Gamma-Ray Spectroscopy*, vol. 2, p. 1199, ed. K. Siegbahn, North-Holland, Amsterdam. [3C-2]

Depommier, P., Duclos, J., Heitze, J., Kleinknecht, K., Rieseberg, H., and Soergel, V. (1968), *Nuclear Phys.* **B4**, 189. [Fig. 1-10]

de-Shalit, A., and Goldhaber, M. (1952), *Phys. Rev.* **92**, 1211. [3-2 Ex]

de-Shalit, A., and Talmi, I. (1963), *Nuclear Shell Theory*, Academic Press, New York, N.Y.

Desjardins, J. S., Rosen, J. L., Havens, W. W., Jr., and Rainwater, J. (1960), *Phys. Rev.* **120**, 2214. [2-1 Ex]

Di Capua, E., Garland, R., Pondrom, L., and Strelzoff, A. (1964), *Phys. Rev.* **133**, B1333. [3D-1d]

Dirac, P. A. M. (1935), *The Principles of Quantum Mechanics*, 2nd edition, Clarendon Press, Oxford.

Dolginov, A. Z. (1961), in *Gamma Luchi*, Chap. 6, p. 524, ed. L. Sliv, Akademia Nauk SSSR, Moscow. [3C-2]

Dragt, A. (1965), *J. Math. Phys.* **6**, 533. [1A-3a]

Drell, S. D., and Walecka, J. D. (1960), *Phys. Rev.* **120**, 1069. [3C-6c]

Dunaitsev, A. F., Petrukhin, V. I., Prokoshkin, Yu. D., and Rykalin, V. I. (1963), *Intern. Conf. on Fundamental Aspects of Weak Interactions*, BNL 837, (C-39), Brookhaven, Upton, N.Y. [Fig. 1-10]

Durand, L. (1964), *Phys. Rev.* **135**, B310. [3D-5]

Dyson, F. J. (1962), *J. Math. Phys.* **3**, 140, 157, 166. [2-1 Ex, 2C-2, 2C-3]

Dyson, F. J. (1962a), *J. Math. Phys.* **3**, 1191. [2C-2]

Dyson, F. J. (1962b), *J. Math. Phys.* **3**, 1199. [1B-2, 2C-2]

Dyson, F. J. (1966), *Symmetry Groups in Nuclear and Particle Physics*, Benjamin, New York, N.Y. [1-3b]

Dyson, F. J., and Mehta, M. L. (1963), *J. Math. Phys.* **4**, 701. [2-1 Ex, 2C-3]

Edmonds, A. R. (1957), *Angular Momentum in Quantum Mechanics*, Princeton University Press, Princeton, N.J.

Ehrman, J. B. (1951), *Phys. Rev.* **81**, 412. [1-3 Ex]

Eichler, J. (1963), *Z. Physik* **171**, 463. [3D-4]

Eichler, J., Tombrello, T. A., and Bahcall, J. N. (1964), *Phys. Letters* **13**, 146. [3D-Ex]

Eisenbud, L., and Wigner, E. P. (1941), *Proc. Nat. Acad. Sci. U.S.* (Wash.) **27**, 281. [1-4]

Ellegaard, C., and Vedelsby, P. (1968), *Phys. Letters* **26B**, 155. [Fig. 3-2f]

Ellegaard, C., Kantele, J., and Vedelsby, P. (1967), *Phys. Letters* **25B**, 512. [3-3c]

Elliott, J. P., and Flowers, B. H. (1957), *Proc. Roy. Soc.* (*London*) **242A**, 57. [1-2 Ex]

Elliott, J. P., Mavromatis, H. A., and Sanderson, E. A. (1967), *Phys. Letters* **24B**, 358. [2-5c]

Elton, L. R. B. (1961), *Nuclear Sizes*, Oxford University Press, Oxford.

Erba, E., Facchini, U., and Saetta-Menichella, E. (1961), *Nuovo cimento* **22**, 1237. [Fig. 2-12]

Ericson, M., and Ericson, T. E. O. (1966), *Ann. Phys.* **36**, 323. [2-4c]

Ericson, T. (1959), *Nuclear Phys.* **11**, 481. [2-1 Ex]

Ericson, T. (1960), *Advances in Physics* **9**, 425. [2B-1]

Ericson, T., and Mayer-Kuckuk, T. (1966), *Ann. Rev. Nuclear Sci.* **16**, 183. [3F-1c]

Erskine, J. R. (1966), *Phys. Rev.* **149**, 854. [Fig. 3-2c]

Erskine, J. R., Marinov, A., and Schiffer, J. P. (1966), *Phys. Rev.* **142**, 633. [3-4 Ex]

Euler, H. (1937), *Z. Physik* **105**, 553. [2-5c]

Evans, H. D. (1950), *Proc. Phys. Soc.* (*London*) **63A**, 575. [Fig. 3-6]

Fano, U. (1961), *Phys. Rev.* **124**, 1866. [2D]

Favro, L. D., and MacDonald, J. F. (1967), *Phys. Rev. Letters* **19**, 1254. [2C-2]

Federman, P., Rubinstein, H. R., and Talmi, I. (1966), *Phys. Letters* **22**, 208. [1-3 Ex]

Fermi, E. (1934), *Z. Physik* **88**, 161. [3D-1b]

Feshbach, H. (1967), in *Proc. Intern. Nuclear Physics Conf.*, Gatlinburg, p. 181, ed.-in-chief R. L. Becker, Academic Press, New York, N.Y. [2-4 Ex]

Feshbach, H., Porter, C. E., and Weisskopf, V. F. (1954), *Phys. Rev.* **96**, 448. [3F-1c]

Feshbach, H., Kerman, A. K., and Lemmer, R. H. (1967), *Ann. Phys.* **41**, 230. [3F-1c]

Feynman, R. P., and Gell-Mann, M. (1958), *Phys. Rev.* **109**, 193. [3D-2c]

Flerov, G. N., Oganeayan, Yu. Ts., Lobanov, Yu. V., Kuznetsov, V. I., Druin, V. A., Perelygin, V. P., Gavrilov, K. A., Tretiakova, S. P., and Plotko, V. M. (1964), *Phys. Letters* **13**, 73. [2-3 Ex]

Foldy, L. L. (1953), *Phys. Rev.* **92**, 178. [3C-4]

Foldy, L. L. (1958), *Rev. Mod. Phys.* **30**, 471. [Table 1-1]

Foldy, L. L., and Walecka, J. (1965), *Phys. Rev.* **140**, B1339. [3D-3]

Fowler, W. A., and Hoyle, F. (1964), *Astrophys. J. Suppl.* **91**. [2-3b, 3D-1d]

Fox, J. D., Moore, C. F., and Robson, D. (1964), *Phys. Rev. Letters* **12**, 198. [1-3 Ex]

Franco, V. (1965), *Phys. Rev.* **140**, B1501. [2-1 Ex]

Frauenfelder, H., and Steffen, R. M. (1965), in *Alpha-, Beta-, and Gamma-Ray Spectroscopy*, vol. 2, p. 997, ed. K. Siegbahn, North-Holland, Amsterdam. [3C-2]

Freeman, J. M., Murray, G., and Burcham, W. E. (1965), *Phys. Letters* **17**, 317. [3D-2c]

Freeman, J. M., Jenkin, J. G., Murray, G., and Burcham, W. E. (1966), *Phys. Rev. Letters* **16**, 959. [Fig. 1-10]

French, J. B. (1964), *Phys. Letters* **13**, 249. [3E-1b]

Frenkel, J. (1936), *Phys. Z. Sowietunion* **9**, 533. [2-1i]

Friedman, F. L., and Weisskopf, V. F. (1955), in *Niels Bohr and the Development of Physics*, p. 134, ed. W. Pauli, Pergamon Press, New York, N.Y. [3F-1c]

Frisch, R., and Stern, O. (1933), *Z. Physik* **85**, 4. [3C-4]

Fujita, J. I. (1962), *Phys. Rev.* **126**, 202. [3D-4]

Fujita, J. I., and Ikeda, K. (1965), *Nuclear Phys.* **67**, 145. [3-4]

Fulbright, H. W., Alford, W. P., Bilaniuk, O. M., Deshpande, V. K., and Verba, J. W. (1965), *Nuclear Phys.* **70**, 553. [1-3 Ex]

Fuller, G. H., and Cohen, V. W. (1965), *Nuclear Moments*, Appendix 1 to *Nuclear Data Sheets*, Oak Ridge Nat. Lab., Oak Ridge, Tenn.

Fulmer, R. H., McCarthy, A. L., Cohen, B. L., and Middleton, R. (1964), *Phys. Rev.* **133**, B955. [Fig. 2-25]

Gamba, A., Malvano, R., and Radicati, L. A. (1952), *Phys. Rev.* **87**, 440. [1-3 Ex]

Garg, J. B., Rainwater, J., Petersen, J. S., and Havens, W. W., Jr. (1964), *Phys. Rev.* **134**, B985. [Fig. 2-9, Fig. 2-10]

Gatto, R. (1967), in *High Energy Physics*, vol. II, p. 1, ed. E. H. S. Burhop, Academic Press, New York, N.Y. [3C-1]

Gaudin, M. (1961), *Nuclear Phys.* **25**, 447. [2C-3]

Gell-Mann, M. (1953), *Phys. Rev.* **92**, 833. [1-3b]

Gell-Mann, M. (1958), *Phys. Rev.* **111**, 362. [3D Ex]

Gell-Mann, M. (1961), *Cal. Inst. Tech. Rep.* CTSL-20, Pasadena, Cal., reproduced in Gell-Mann and Ne'eman (1964). [1-3b]

Gell-Mann, M. (1962), *Phys. Rev.* **125**, 1067. [1-3 Ex]

Gell-Mann, M. (1964), *Phys. Letters* **8**, 214. [1-3b]

Gell-Mann, M., and Berman, S. M. (1959), *Phys. Rev. Letters* **3**, 99. [3D Ex]

Gell-Mann, M., and Ne'eman, Y. (1964), *The Eightfold Way*, Benjamin, New York, N.Y. [1-3b, 1-3 Ex]

Gerholm, T. R., and Pettersson, B. G. (1965), in *Alpha-, Beta-, and Gamma-Ray Spectroscopy*, vol. 2, p. 981, ed. K. Siegbahn, North-Holland, Amsterdam. [3C-3]

Giltinan, D. A., and Thaler, R. M. (1963), *Phys. Rev.* **131**, 805. [2-5a]

Glauber, R. J. (1959), in *Lectures in Theoretical Physics*, vol. 1, eds. W. E. Brittin and L. G. Dunham, Wiley (Interscience), New York, N.Y. [2-5 Ex]

Glendenning, N. K. (1965), *Phys. Rev.* **137**, B102. [3E-2]

Goldberger, M. L., and Watson, K. M. (1964), *Collision Theory*, Wiley, New York, N.Y.

Goldhaber, G. (1967), in *Proc. 13th Intern. Conf. on High-Energy Physics*, University of California Press, Berkeley, Cal. [1-3 Ex]

Goldhaber, M., and Sunyar, A. W. (1951), *Phys. Rev.* **83**, 906. [2-4 Ex]

Goldhaber, M., and Hill, R. D. (1952), *Rev. Mod. Phys.* **24**, 179. [3-2 Ex]

Goldstein, H. (1963), in *Fast Neutron Physics*, Part 2, p. 1525, eds. J. B. Marion and J. L. Fowler, Wiley (Interscience), New York, N.Y. [2-1 Ex]

Gomez, L. C., Walecka, J. D., and Weisskopf, V. F. (1958), *Ann. Phys.* **3**, 241. [2-5b]

Gorodetzky, S., Freeman, R. M., Gallmann, A., and Haas,. F. (1966), *Phys. Rev.* **149**, 801. [Fig. 1-8]

Goshal, S. N. (1950), *Phys. Rev.* **80**, 939. [2-1 Ex]

Gottfried, K. (1963), *Ann. Phys.* **21**, 29. [2-1c]

Green, A. E. S. and Engler, N.A. (1953), *Phys. Rev.* **91**, 40 [Fig. 2-4]

Green, A. E. S., and Sharma, R. D. (1965), *Phys. Rev. Letters* **14**, 380. [2-5a]

Greenlees, G. W., and Pyle, G. J. (1966), *Phys. Rev.* **149**, 836. [2-4 Ex, Table 2-2, Fig. 2-28, Fig. 2-29]

Greenlees, G. W., Pyle, G. J., and Tang, Y. C. (1966), *Phys. Rev. Letters* **17**, 33 [2-4 Ex]

Gustafson, C., Lamm, I. L., Nilsson, B., and Nilsson, S. G. (1967), *Arkiv. Fysik* **36**, 613. [2-3 Ex]

Hahn, B., Ravenhall, D. G., and Hofstadter, R. (1956), *Phys. Rev.* **101**, 1131. [Fig. 2-1]

Halbert, M. L., and Zucker, A. (1961), *Phys. Rev.* **121**, 236. [1-3 Ex]

Halbleib, J. A., Sr., and Sorensen, R. A. (1967), *Nuclear Phys.* **A98**, 542. [3-4a]

Hama, Y., and Hoshizaki, N. (1964), *Compt. Rend. Congrès Intern. de Physique Nucléaire*, Paris 1963, vol. II, p. 195, ed. P. Gugenberger, C.N.R.S., Paris. [2-5 Ex]

Hamada, T., and Johnston, I. D. (1962), *Nuclear Phys.* **34**, 382. [Fig. 2-35]

Hamermesh, M. (1962), *Group Theory and its Application to Physical Problems*, Addison-Wesley, Reading, Mass.

Hamilton, J., and Woolcock, W. S. (1963), *Rev. Mod. Phys.* **35**, 737. [Table 1-1]

Hand, L. N., Miller, D. G., and Wilson, R. (1963), *Rev. Mod. Phys.* **35**, 335. [Table 1-1, 3C-4]

Hansen, P. G., Nielsen, H. L., Wilsky, K., and Cuninghame, J. G. (1967), *Phys. Letters* **24B**, 95. [Table 1-3]

Harari, H., and Rashid, M. A. (1966), *Phys. Rev.* **143**, 1354. [1-3 Ex]

Harchol, M., Jaffe, A. A., Miron, J., Unna, I., and Zioni, Z. (1967), *Nuclear Phys.* **A90**, 459. [2-1f]

Harrison, B. K., Thorne, K. S., Wakano, M., and Wheeler, J. A. (1965), *Gravitation Theory and Gravitational Collapse*, University of Chicago Press, Chicago, Ill. [2-3 Ex]

Haxel, O., Jensen, J. H. D., and Suess, H. E. (1949), *Phys. Rev.* **75**, 1766. [2-2, 2-4a]

Haxel, O., Jensen, J. H. D., and Suess, H. E. (1950), *Z. Physik* **128**, 295. [2-4 Ex]

Hayward, E. (1965), in *Nuclear Structure and Electromagnetic Interactions*, p. 141, ed. N. MacDonald, Oliver and Boyd, Edinburgh. [3C-2]

Heisenberg, W. (1932), *Z. Physik* **77**, 1. [1-3a, 2-5a]

Heitler, W. (1954), *The Quantum Theory of Radiation*, 3rd edition, Clarendon Press, Oxford.

Henley, E. M. (1966), in *Isobaric Spin in Nuclear Physics*, p. 1, eds. J. D. Fox and D. Robson, Academic Press, New York, N.Y. [2-5a]

Henley, E. M., and Jacobsohn, B. A. (1959), *Phys. Rev.* **113**, 225. [1-2c]

Herczeg, P. (1963), *Nuclear Phys.* **48**, 263. [1-4a]

Herman, R., and Hofstadter, R. (1960), *High Energy Electron Scattering Tables*, Stanford University Press, Stanford, Cal. [Fig. 2-1]

Herzberg, G. (1950), *Spectra of Diatomic Molecules*, Van Nostrand, Princeton, N.J.

Hiebert, J. C., Newman, E., and Bassel, R. H. (1967), *Phys. Rev.* **154**, 898. [2-4 Ex]

Hillman, P., Johansson, A., and Tibell, G. (1958), *Phys. Rev.* **110**, 1218. [Fig. 1-6]

Hinds, S., and Middleton, R. (1966), *Nuclear Phys.* **84**, 651. [Fig. 3-2c]

Hinds, S., Middleton, R., Bjerregaard, J. H., Hansen, O., and Nathan, O. (1965), *Phys. Letters* **17**, 302. [Fig. 3-2f]

Hodgson, P. E. (1964), in *Compt. Rend. Congrès Intern. de Physique Nucléaire*, Paris, vol. I, p. 257, ed. P. Gugenberger, C.N.R.S., Paris. [2-4c, 2-4 Ex]

Hofstadter, R. (1957), *Ann. Rev. Nuclear Sci.* **7**, 231. [2-4 Ex]

Hofstadter, R., ed. (1963), *Nuclear and Nucleon Structure*, Benjamin, New York, N.Y. [2-1]

Hoyle, F., and Fowler, W. A. (1963), *Nature* **197**, 533. [2-3b]

Huang, K., and Yang, C. N. (1957), *Phys. Rev.* **105**, 767. [2-5b]

Huffaker, J. N., and Laird, C. E. (1967), *Nuclear Phys.* **A92**, 584. [3D Ex]

Hughes, V. W. (1964), in *Gravitation and Relativity*, Chap. 13, eds. H.-Y. Chiu and W. F. Hoffmann, Benjamin, New York, N.Y. [Table 1-1]

Hull, M. H., Jr., Lassila, K. E., Ruppel, H. M., MacDonald, F. A., and Breit, G. (1962), *Phys. Rev.* **128**, 830. [Fig. 2-34, Fig. 2-37]

Hulthén, L. M., and Sugawara, M. (1957), *Encyclopedia of Physics*, vol. 39, Springer, Berlin. [Fig. 2-36]

Humblet, J. (1967), in *Fundamentals of Nuclear Theory*, eds. A. de-Shalit and C. Villi, Intern. Atomic Energy Agency, Vienna. [3F-1b]

Hund, F. (1937), *Z. Physik* **105**, 202. [1-3a]

Itzykson, C., and Nauenberg, M. (1966), *Rev. Mod. Phys.* **38**, 121. [1C-1, 1C-3, 1C Ex]

Jackson, J. D. (1962), *Classical Electrodynamics*, Wiley, New York, N.Y.

Jackson, J. D., and Blatt, J. M. (1950), *Rev. Mod. Phys.* **22**, 77. [2-5a]

Jacob, G., and Maris, Th. A. J. (1966), *Rev. Mod. Phys.* **38**, 121. [Fig. 2-27]

Jacob, M., and Wick, G. C. (1959), *Ann. Phys.* **7**, 404. [1A-4, 3F-1a]

Jastrow, R. (1950), *Phys. Rev.* **79**, 389. [2-5a]

Jensen, J. H. D., and Mayer, M. G. (1952), *Phys. Rev.* **85**, 1040. [3-3b, 3C-6e]

Jones, K. W., Schiffer, J. P., Lee, L. L., Jr., Marinov, A., and Lerner, J. L. (1966), *Phys. Rev.* **145**, 894. [Fig. 3-2d]

Källén, G. (1967), *Nuclear Phys.* **B1**, 225. [3D-2a]

Karnaukhov, V. A., and Ter-Akopyan, G. M. (1964), *Phys. Letters* **12**, 339. [2-3 Ex]

Kavanagh, R. W. (1964), *Phys. Rev.* **133**, B1504. [3D Ex]

Kazarinov, Yu. M., and Simonov, Yu. N. (1962), *Zhur. Eksp. i Teoret. Fiz.* **43**, 35; transl. *Soviet Phys. JETP* **16**, 24. [Fig. 2-31]

Kelson, I., and Levinson, C. A. (1964), *Phys. Rev.* **134**, B269. [3-2 Ex]

Kemmer, N., Polkinghorne, J. C., and Pursey, D. L. (1959), *Reports on Progr. in Physics* **22**, 368. [1-2c]

Kerman, A. K., McManus, H., and Thaler, R. M. (1959), *Ann. Phys.* **8**, 551. [2-4c, 2-5 Ex]

Kerman, A. K., Svenne, J. P., and Villars, F. M. H. (1966), *Phys. Rev.* **147**, 710. [3-2 Ex]

Kirsten, T., Schaeffer, O. A., Norton, E., and Stoenner, R. W. (1968), *Phys. Rev. Letters* **20**, 1300. [3D-1d]

Kisslinger, L. (1955), *Phys. Rev.* **98**, 761. [2-4c]

Kistner, O. C. (1967), *Phys. Rev. Letters* **19**, 872. [1-2c]

Körner, H. J., Auerbach, K., Braunsfurth, J., and Gerdau, E. (1966), *Nuclear Phys.* **86**, 395. [Table 3-2, Table 3-3]

Kofoed-Hansen, O. (1965), in *Alpha-, Beta-, and Gamma-Ray Spectroscopy*, vol. 2, p. 1517, ed. K. Siegbahn, North-Holland, Amsterdam. [3D-3]

Kohn, W., and Luttinger, J. M. (1965), *Phys. Rev. Letters* **15**, 524. [2-1 Ex]

Kolesov, V. E., Korotkich, V. L., and Malashkina, V. G. (1963), *Izv. Akad. Nauk* **27**, 903. [3-5 Ex]

Konopinski, E. J. (1966), *The Theory of Beta Radioactivity*, Oxford University Press, Oxford.

Konopinski, E. J., and Uhlenbeck, G. E. (1941), *Phys. Rev.* **60**, 308. [Table 3D-1]

Konopinski, E. J., and Rose, M. E. (1965), in *Alpha-, Beta- and Gamma-Ray Spectroscopy*, vol. 2, p. 1327, ed. K. Siegbahn, North-Holland, Amsterdam. [Table 3D-1]

Kopfermann, H. (1958), *Nuclear Moments*, Academic Press, New York.

Kramers, H. A. (1930), *Proc. Koninkl. Ned. Akad. Wetenschap.* **33**, 959. [1-2c]

Kuhn, H. G., and Turner, R. (1962), *Proc. Roy. Soc.* (*London*) **265A**, 39. [2-1 Ex]

Landau, L. (1937), *Physik. Z. Sowjetunion* **11**, 556. [2-1i]

Landau, L. D. (1956), *Zhur. Eksp. i Teoret. Fiz.* **30**, 1058; transl. *Soviet Phys. JETP* **3**, 920. [3-3a]

Landau, L. D. (1958), *Zhur. Eksp. i Teoret. Fiz.* **35**, 97; transl. *Soviet Phys. JETP* **8**, 70. [3-3a]

Lane, A. M. (1962), *Nuclear Phys.* **35**, 676. [2-1g]

Lane, A. M., and Thomas, R. G. (1958), *Rev. Mod. Phys.* **30**, 257. [3F-1b]

Lane, A. M., Thomas, R. G., and Wigner, E. P. (1955), *Phys. Rev.* **98**, 693. [2D]

Lang, J. M. B., and Le Couteur, K. J. (1954), *Proc. Phys. Soc.* (*London*) **67A**, 586. [2B-1]

Lassila, K. E., Hull, M. H., Jr., Ruppel, H. M., MacDonald, F. A., and Breit, G. (1962), *Phys. Rev.* **126**, 881. [Fig. 2-35]

Lauritsen, T., and Ajzenberg-Selove, F. (1961), in *Landolt-Börnstein*, Neue Serie, vol. 1, Springer, Berlin.

Lauritsen, T., and Ajzenberg-Selove, F. (1962), *Nuclear Data Sheets*, The Nuclear Data Group, Oak Ridge Nat. Lab., Oak Ridge, Tenn.

Lauritsen, T., and Ajzenberg-Selove, F. (1966), *Nuclear Phys.* **78**, 10.

Lederer, C. M., Hollander, J. M., and Perlman, I. (1967), *Table of Isotopes*, 6th edition, Wiley, New York, N.Y.

Lee, L. L., Jr., and Schiffer, J. P. (1964), *Phys. Rev.* **136**, B405. [3-5 Ex, 3E-1c]

Lee, L. L., Jr., Schiffer, J. P., Zeidman, B., Satchler, G. R., Drisko, R. M., and Bassel, R. H. (1964), *Phys. Rev.* **136**, B971. [3-5 Ex]

Lee, T. D., and Wu, C. S. (1965), *Ann. Rev. Nuclear Sci.* **15**, 381. [1-2c, 3D-1, 3D-2, 3D-3]

Lee, T. D., and Wu, C. S. (1966), *Ann. Rev. Nuclear Sci.* **16**, 471, 511. [1-2c, 3D-1, 3D-2, 3D-3]

Lee, T. D., and Yang, C. N. (1956), *Phys. Rev.* **104**, 254. [1-2b]

Lemonne, J., Mayeur, C., Sacton, J., Vilain, P., Wilquet, G., Stanley, D., Allen, P., Davis, D. H., Fletcher, E. R., Garbutt, D. A., Shaukat, M. A., Allen, J. E., Bull, V. A., Conway, A. P., and March, P. V. (1965), *Phys. Letters* **18**, 354. [1-3 Ex]

Levinger, J. S. (1960), *Nuclear Photo-Disintegration*, Oxford University Press, Oxford.

Levinger, J. S., and Simmons, L. M. (1961), *Phys. Rev.* **124**, 916. [2-3 Ex]

Levinson, C. A., Lipkin, H. J., and Meshkov, S. (1963), *Phys. Letters* **7**, 81. [1-3b]

Levi-Setti, R. (1964), *Proc. Intern. Conf. on Hyperfragments*, St. Cergue, 1963, CERN Rep. 64-1, ed. W. O. Lock, CERN, Geneva. [Table 1-4]

Lilley, J. S., and Stein, N. (1967), *Phys. Rev. Letters* **19**, 709. [Fig. 3-2f]

Lindgren, I. (1965), in *Alpha-, Beta- and Gamma-Ray Spectroscopy*, vol. 2, p. 1621, ed. K. Siegbahn, North-Holland, Amsterdam.

Lipkin, H. J. (1965), *Lie Groups for Pedestrians*, North-Holland, Amsterdam.

Lipkin, H. J. (1967), in *Proc. Intern. Nuclear Physics Conf.*, Gatlinburg, p. 450, ed.-in-chief R. L. Becker, Academic Press, New York, N.Y. [1-3b]

Listengarten, M. A. (1961), in *Gamma-Luchi*, p. 271, ed. L. A. Sliv, Akad Nauk SSSR,

Moscow. See also Sliv, L. A., and Band, I. M. (1965), in *Alpha-, Beta-, and Gamma-Ray Spectroscopy*, vol. 2, p. 1639, ed. K. Siegbahn, North-Holland, Amsterdam. [3C-3]

Littlewood, D. E. (1950), *The Theory of Group Characters*, Clarendon Press, Oxford.

Lobashov, V. M., Nazarenko, V. A., Saenko, L. F., Smotritsky, L. M., and Kharkevitch, G. I. (1967), *Phys. Letters* **25B**, 104. [Fig. 1-2]

Lomon, E., and Feshbach, H. (1967), *Rev. Mod. Phys.* **39**, 611, [2-5a]

Lynn, J. E. (1968), *The Theory of Neutron Resonance Reactions*, Clarendon Press, Oxford. [Fig. 2-26]

MacDonald, W. M. (1956), *Phys. Rev.* **101**, 271. [2-1 Ex]

Macfarlane, M. H., and French, J. B. (1960), *Rev. Mod. Phys.* **32**, 567. [3E-1b]

MacGregor, M. H., Moravcsik, M. J., and Stapp, H. P. (1959), *Phys. Rev.* **116**, 1248. [Table 1-1]

MacGregor, M. H., Arndt, R. A., and Wright, R. M. (1968), *Phys. Rev.*, in press. [Fig. 2-34]

Macklin, R. L., and Gibbons, J. H. (1965), *Rev. Mod. Phys.* **37**, 166. [2-3b]

Macklin, R. L., and Gibbons, J. H. (1967), *Astrophys. J.* **149**, 577. [2-3b]

Mafethe, M. E., and Hodgson, P. E. (1966), *Proc. Phys. Soc.* (*London*) **87**, 429. [3D Ex]

Majorana, E. (1933), *Z. Physik* **82**, 137. [2-5a]

Malmfors, K. G. (1965), in *Alpha-, Beta-, and Gamma-Ray Spectroscopy*, vol. 2, p. 1281, ed. K. Siegbahn, North-Holland, Amsterdam. [3C-2]

Massey, H. S. W., and Burhop, E. H. S. (1952), *Electronic and Ionic Impact Phenomena*, Oxford University Press, Oxford.

Mattauch, J. H. E., Thiele, W., and Wapstra, A. H. (1965), *Nuclear Phys.* **67**, 1.

Mayer, M. G. (1949), *Phys. Rev.* **75**, 1969. [2-2, 2-4a]

Mayer, M. G. (1950), *Phys. Rev.* **78**, 16. [2-4 Ex]

Mayer, M. G., and Jensen, J. H. D. (1955), *Elementary Theory of Nuclear Shell Structure*, Wiley, New York, N.Y.

Mayeur, C., Sacton, J., Vilain, P., Wilquet, G., Stanley, D., Allen, P., Davis, D. H., Fletcher, E. R., Garbutt, D. A., Shaukat, M. A., Allen, J. E., Bull, V. A., Conway, A. P., and March, P. V. (1965), *Univ. Libre de Bruxelles*, Bulletin No. 24, Presses Acad. Europ., Bruxelles. [Table 1-4]

McVoy, K. W. (1967), in *Fundamentals in Nuclear Theory*, p. 419, Intern. Atomic Energy Agency, Vienna. [3F-1b]

McVoy, K. W. (1967a), *Ann. Phys.* **43**, 91. [2-1 Ex]

Mehta, M. L. (1960), *Nuclear Phys.* **18**, 395. [2C-3]

Mehta, M. L. (1967) *Random Matrices*, Academic Press, New York, N.Y.

Mehta, M. L., and Gaudin, M. (1960), *Nuclear Phys.* **18**, 420. [2C-3]

Meldner, H., Süssmann, G., and Ubrici, W. (1965), *Z. Naturforsch.* **20a**, 1217. [2-4 Ex]

Messiah, A. (1962), *Quantum Mechanics*, North-Holland, Amsterdam.

Meyerhof, W. E., and Tombrello, T. A. (1968), *Nuclear Phys.* **A109**, 1.

Miazawa, H. (1951), *Progr. Theor. Phys.* (*Kyoto*) **6**, 801. [3C-6c]

Michel, F. C. (1964), *Phys. Rev.* **133**, B329. [1-2 Ex]

Migdal, A. B. (1967), *Theory of Finite Fermi Systems and Applications to Atomic Nuclei*, Wiley (Interscience), New York, N.Y.

Miller, P. D., Dress, W. B., Baird, J. K., and Ramsey, N. F. (1967), *Phys. Rev. Letters* **19**, 381. [1-2b]

Mössbauer, R. L. (1965), in *Alpha-, Beta-, and Gamma-Ray Spectroscopy*, vol. 2, p. 1293, ed. K. Siegbahn, North-Holland, Amsterdam. [3C-2]

Moore, C. E. (1949), *Atomic Energy Levels*, Circular 467, vol. 1, p. XL, Nat. Bureau of Standards, Washington, D.C. [Fig. 2-13]

Moravcsik, M. J. (1963), *The Two-Nucleon Interaction*, Clarendon Press, Oxford.

Morpurgo, G. (1958), *Phys. Rev.* **110**, 721. [1-3 Ex]

Morrison, P. (1953), in *Experimental Nuclear Physics*, vol. 2, ed. E. Segré, Wiley, New York, N.Y. [3F-2d]

Moszkowski, S. A. (1965), in *Alpha-, Beta-, and Gamma-Ray Spectroscopy*, vol. 2, p. 863, ed. K. Siegbahn, North-Holland, Amsterdam. [3C-2]

Myers, W. D., and Swiatecki, W. J. (1966), *Nuclear Phys.* **81**, 1. [2-1d, 2-1f, 2-3a, 2-3 Ex]

Nagel, J. G., and Moshinsky, M. (1965), *J. Math. Phys.* **6**, 682. [1C-3b]

Nedzel, V. A. (1954), *Phys. Rev.* **94**, 174. [Fig. 2-3]

Ne'eman, Y. (1961), *Nuclear Phys.* **26**, 222. [1-3b]

Nemirovsky, P. E., and Adamachuk, Yu. V. (1962), *Nuclear Phys.* **39**, 551. [2-1 Ex]

Neutron Cross Sections (1964), Sigma Center, Brookhaven Nat. Lab., BNL 325, Suppl. 2, Brookhaven, N.Y.

Newman, E., Hiebert, J. C., and Zeidman, B. (1966), *Phys. Rev. Letters* **16**, 28. [Fig. 3-2d]

Newson, H. W. (1966), in *Nuclear Structure Studies with Neutrons*, p. 195, eds. N. de Mevergies *et al.*, North-Holland, Amsterdam. [2-4 Ex]

Nishijima, K. (1954), *Progr. Theor. Phys.* (*Kyoto*) **12**, 107. [1-3b]

Nordheim, L. A. (1951), *Rev. Mod. Phys.* **23**, 322. [2-4 Ex]

Nozières, P. (1964), *Theory of Interacting Fermi Systems*, Benjamin, New York, N.Y. [2-5c]

Nuclear Data Sheets, Nuclear Data Group, Oak Ridge Nat. Lab., Oak Ridge, Tenn.

Oehme, R. (1963), in *Strong Interactions and High Energy Physics*, ed. R. G. Moorhouse, Oliver and Boyd, Edinburgh and London. [1-2a]

Okubo, S. (1962), *Progr. Theor. Phys.* (*Kyoto*) **27**, 949. [1-3 Ex]

Osborne, R. K., and Foldy, L. L. (1950), *Phys. Rev.* **79**, 795. [3C-6a]

Pauly, H., and Toennies, J. P. (1965), in *Advances in Atomic and Molecular Physics*, vol. 1, p. 195, eds. D. R. Bates and I. Estermann, Academic Press, New York, N.Y. [2-1 Ex]

Perey, F., and Buck, B. (1962), *Nuclear Phys.* **32**, 353. [2-4c]

Perey, F. G., and Schiffer, J. P. (1966), *Phys. Rev. Letters* **17**, 324. [2-1 Ex]

Peterson, J. M. (1962), *Phys. Rev.* **125**, 955. [Fig. 2-3]

Pniewsky, J., and Danysz, M. (1962), *Phys. Letters* **1**, 142. [1-3 Ex]

Pontecorvo, B., and Smorodinski, Y. (1961), *Zhur. Eksp. i Teoret. Fiz.* **41**, 239; transl. *Soviet Phys. JETP* **14**, 173. [3D-1d]

Porter, C. E., and Thomas, R. G. (1956), *Phys. Rev.* **104**, 483. [2-1 Ex]

Porter, C. E., and Rosenzweig, N. (1960), *Ann. Acad. Sci. Finland*, **A6**, no. 44. [2C-1]

Prowse, D. J. (1966), *Phys. Rev. Letters* **17**, 782. [1-3 Ex]

Racah, G. (1942), *Phys. Rev.* **62**, 438. [3-1b]

Racah, G. (1951), *Group Theory and Spectroscopy*, Lecture Notes, Inst. for Advanced Study, Princeton, N.J.

Rainwater, J. (1950), *Phys. Rev.* **79**, 432. [3-3a]

Ramsey, N. F. (1956), *Molecular Beams*, Clarendon Press, Oxford.

Raynal, J. (1967), *Nuclear Phys.* **A97**, 572. [3A-2]

Reid, R. V. Jr. (1968), *Ann. Phys.* (to be published). [2-5 Ex]

Reines, F., Cowan, C. L., and Goldhaber, M. (1954), *Phys. Rev.* **96**, 1157. [Table 1-1]

Reines, F., Cowan, C. L., and Kruse, H. W. (1957), *Phys. Rev.* **109**, 609. [Table 1-1]

Ricci, R. A., Girgis, R. K., and van Lieshout, R. (1960), *Nuclear Phys.* **21**, 177. [Table 1-3]

Richard, P., Moore, C. F., Becker, J. A., and Fox, J. D. (1966), *Phys. Rev.* **145**, 971. [Fig. 1-9, Table 1-2]

Ridley, B. W., and Turner, J. F. (1964), *Nuclear Phys.* **58**, 497. [Fig. 2-28]

Robson, D. (1965), *Phys. Rev.* **137**, B535. [1-3 Ex]

Rojo, O., and Simmons, L. M. (1962), *Phys. Rev.* **125**, 273. [2-5a]

Rood, H. P. C. (1966), *Nuovo cimento*, Suppl. Ser. *1*, **4**, 185. [3D-3]

Roos, P. G., and Wall, N. S. (1965), *Phys. Rev.* **140**, B1237. [Fig. 2-29]

Rose, M. E. (1955), *Multipole Fields*, Wiley, New York, N.Y.

Rose, M. E. (1957), *Elementary Theory of Angular Momentum*, Wiley, New York, N.Y.

Rose, M. E. (1965), in *Alpha-, Beta-, and Gamma-Ray Spectroscopy*, vol. **2**, p. 887, ed. K. Siegbahn, North-Holland, Amsterdam. [3C-3]

Rosen, L., Beery, J. G., Goldhaber, A. S., and Auerbach, E. H. (1965), *Ann. Phys.* **34**, 96. [2-4 Ex, Fig. 2-29]

Rosenblum, S., and Valadares, M. (1952), *Compt. rend.* **235**, 711. [Fig. 2-17]

Rosenfeld, A. H., Barbaro-Galtieri, A., Podolsky, W. J., Price, L. R., Soding, P., Wohl, C. G., Roos, M., and Willis, W. J. (1967), *Rev. Mod. Phys.* **39**, 1.

Rosenfeld, L. (1948), *Nuclear Forces*, North-Holland, Amsterdam.

Rosenzweig, N. (1963), in *Statistical Physics*, Brandeis Summer Institute, vol. 3, p. 91, ed. K. W. Ford, Benjamin, New York, N.Y. [2C-1]

Rosenzweig, N., and Porter, C. E. (1960), *Phys. Rev.* **120**, 1968. [2C-3]

Rosenzweig, N., Monahan, J. E., and Mehta, M. L. (1968), *Nuclear Phys.* **A109**, 437. [2C-2]

Ross, A. A., Lawson, R. D., and Mark, H. (1956), *Phys. Rev.* **104**, 401. [2-4 Ex]

Rutherford, E., Chadwick, J., and Ellis, C. D. (1930), *Radiations from Radioactive Substances*, Cambridge University Press, Cambridge.

Sachs, R. G. (1948), *Phys. Rev.* **74**, 433. [3C-6d]

Sachs, R. G. (1953), *Nuclear Theory*, Addison-Wesley, Reading, Mass.

Salisbury, S. R., and Richards, H. T. (1962), *Phys. Rev.* **126**, 2147. [Table 3-8]

Salling, P. (1965), *Phys. Letters* **17**, 139. [Table 3-2]

Scharff-Goldhaber, G. (1952), *Physica* **18**, 1105. [Fig. 2-17]

Scharff-Goldhaber, G. (1953), *Phys. Rev.* **90**, 587. [Fig. 2-17]

Schneid, E. J., Prakash, A., and Cohen, B. L. (1967), *Phys. Rev.* **156**, 1316. [Table 1-2]

Schopper, H. F. (1966), *Weak Interactions and Nuclear Beta Decay*, North-Holland, Amsterdam.

Schwinger, J. (1950), *Phys. Rev.* **78**, 135. [2-5a]

Seeger, P. A., Fowler, W. A., and Clayton, D. D. (1965), *Astrophys. J. Suppl.* **97**, 121. [2-3b]

Segel, R. E., Olness, J. W., and Sprenkel, E. L. (1961), *Phys. Rev.* **123**, 1382. [Fig. 1-1]

Segel, R. E., Olness, J. W., and Sprenkel, E. L. (1961a), *Phil. Mag.* **6**, 163. [Fig. 1-1]

Segel, R. E., Singh, P. P., Allas, R. G., and Hanna, S. S. (1963), *Phys. Rev. Letters* **10**, 345. [Fig. 3-2b]

Shapiro, I. S., and Estulin, I. V. (1956), *Zhur. Eksp. i Teoret. Fiz.* **30**, 579; transl. *Soviet Phys. JETP* **3**, 626. [Table 1-1]

Shaw, G. L. (1959), *Ann. Phys.* **8**, 509. [2-5b]

Shirley, D. A. (1964), *Rev. Mod. Phys.* **36**, 339. [3C-3]

Shull, C. G., and Nathans, R. (1967), *Phys. Rev. Letters* **19**, 384. [1-2b]

Siegbahn, K., ed. (1965), *Alpha-, Beta-, and Gamma-Ray Spectroscopy*, North-Holland, Amsterdam.

Siegert, A. J. F. (1937), *Phys. Rev.* **52**, 787. [3C-6c]

Silverberg, L. (1962), *Arkiv Fysik* **20**, 341. [3-2 Ex]

Silverberg, L. (1964), *Nuclear Phys.* **60**, 483. [3-2 Ex]

Singh, P. P., Segel, R. E., Siemssen, R. H., Baker, S., and Blaugrund, A. E. (1967), *Phys. Rev.* **158**, 1063. [Table 3-2]

Slater, J. C. (1929), *Phys. Rev.* **34**, 1293. [2-1h]

Sliv, L. A., and Kharitonov, Yu. I. (1965), *Phys. Letters* **16**, 176. [2-1 Ex]

Sood, P. C., and Green, A. E. S. (1957), *Nuclear Phys.* **5**, 274. [2-1f]

Sorensen, R. (1966), *Phys. Letters* **21**, 333. [2-1 Ex]

Sosnovsky, A. N., Spivak, P. E., Prokofiev, Yu. A., Kutikov, I. E., and Dobrinin, Yu. P. (1959), *Nuclear Phys.* **10**, 395. [Table 1-1]

Spruch, L. (1950), *Phys. Rev.* **80**, 372. [3C-6d]

Stähelin, P., and Preiswerk, P. (1951), *Helv. Phys. Acta* **24**, 623. [Fig. 2-17]

Stahl, R. H., and Ramsey, N. F. (1954), *Phys. Rev.* **96**, 1310. [Fig. 2-31]

Stanford, C. P., Stephenson, T. E., and Bernstein, S. (1954), *Phys. Rev.* **96**, 983. [Table 1-1]

Stanford Conference on Nuclear Sizes and Density Distributions (1958), *Rev. Mod. Phys.* **30**, 412. [2-1a]

Stapp, H. P., Ypsilantis, T. J., and Metropolis, N. (1957), *Phys. Rev.* **105**, 302. [2-5a, 2-5 Ex]

Stech, B., and Schülke, L. (1964), *Z. Physik* **179**, 314. [3D-3]

Streater, R. F., and Wightman, A. S. (1964), *PCT, Spin and Statistics, and all that*, Benjamin, New York, N.Y. [1-2c]

Strömgren, B. (1968), *NORDITA Lectures*, NORDITA, Copenhagen. [2-3b]

Stroke, H. H., Blin-Stoyle, R. J., and Jaccarino, V. (1961), *Phys. Rev.* **123**, 1326. [3C-3]

Strominger, D., Hollander, J. M., and Seaborg, G. T. (1958), *Rev. Mod. Phys.* **30**, 585.

Strutinski, V. M. (1958), unpublished lectures, The Niels Bohr Institute, Copenhagen. [2B-1]

Strutinski, V. M. (1967), *Arkiv Fysik* **36**, 629. [2-3 Ex]

Suess, H. E., and Urey, H. C. (1956), *Rev. Mod. Phys.* **28**, 53. [Fig. 2-19]

Sugimoto, K., Mizobuchi, A., Nakai, K., and Matuda, K. (1965), *Phys. Letters* **18**, 38. [Table 3-3]

Swift, A., and Elton, L. R. B. (1966), *Phys. Rev. Letters* **17**, 484. [2-1 Ex]

Tabakin, F. (1964), *Ann. Phys.* **30**, 51. [2-5 Ex]

Taketani, M., and articles by Iwadare, J., Otsuki, S., Tamagaki, R., Machida, S., Toyoda, T., Watari, W., Nishijima, K., Nakamura, S., and Sasaki, S. (1956), *Progr. Theoret. Phys.* (*Kyoto*), Suppl. **3**. [2-5a]

Tamagaki, R. (1967), *Rev. Mod. Phys.* **39**, 629. [2-5a]

Tamura, T. (1966), *Phys. Letters* **22**, 644. [1-3 Ex]

Tanaka, S. (1960), *J. Phys. Soc. Japan* **15**, 2159. [2-1 Ex]

Terasawa, T. (1960), *Prog. Theoret. Phys. (Kyoto)* **23**, 87. [2-5b]

Thomas, R. G. (1952), *Phys. Rev.* **88**, 1109. [1-3 Ex]

Thouless, D. J. (1961), *The Quantum Mechanics of Many-Body Systems*, Academic Press, New York, N.Y.

Trainer, L. E. H. (1952), *Phys. Rev.* **85**, 962. [1-3 Ex]

Tsukada, K., Tanaka, S., Maruyama, M., and Tomita, Y. (1966), *Nuclear Phys.* **78**, 369. [2-1 Ex, Fig. 2-11]

Turner, J. F., Ridley, B. W., Cavanagh, P. E., Gard, G. A., and Hardacre, A. G. (1964), *Nuclear Phys.* **58**, 509. [Fig. 2-28]

Tyrén, H., Kullander, S., Sundberg, O., Ramachandran, R., Isacsson, P., and Berggren, T. (1966), *Nuclear Phys.* **79**, 321. [Fig. 2-27]

Uher, R. A., and Sorensen, R. A. (1966), *Nuclear Phys.* **86**, 1. [2-1 Ex]

Urey, H. C. (1964), *Rev. Geophysics* **2**, 1. [Fig. 2-19]

Van Oostrum, K. J., Hofstadter, R., Nöldeke, G. K., Yearian, M. R., Clark, B. C., Herman, R., and Ravenhall, D. G. (1966), *Phys. Rev. Letters* **16**, 528. [2-1 Ex]

Veltman, M. (1966), *Phys. Rev. Letters* **17**, 553. [3D-4]

Villars, F. (1947), *Helv. Phys. Acta* **20**, 476. [3-3b]

Vogt, E. (1967), in *Proc. Intern. Nuclear Physics Conf.*, Gatlinburg, p. 748, ed.-in-chief R. L. Becker, Academic Press, New York, N.Y. [3F-2f)

Wahlborn, S. (1965), *Phys. Rev.* **138**, B530. [1-2 Ex]

Wapstra, A. H. (1953), *Arkiv Fysik* **6**, 263. [Table 3-6]

Warburton, E. K., Parker, P. D., and Donovan, P. F. (1965), *Phys. Letters* **19**, 397. [3-2 Ex]

Way, K., and Hurley, F. W. (1966), *Nuclear Data* **A1**, 473.

Weidenmüller, H. A. (1960), *Nuclear Phys.* **21**, 397. [3D Ex]

Weinberg, S. (1958), *Phys. Rev.* **112**, 1375. [3D-2b]

Weinberg, S. (1962), *Phys. Rev.* **128**, 1457. [3D-1d]

Weinberg, S. (1962a), *Nuovo cimento* **25**, 15. [3D-1d]

Weisberger, W. I. (1965), *Phys. Rev. Letters* **14**, 1047. [3D-2c]

Weisskopf, V. F. (1937), *Phys. Rev.* **52**, 295. [2-1i, 2-1 Ex]

Weisskopf, V. F. (1957), *Nuclear Phys.* **3**, 423. [2-1g]

Weizsäcker, von, C. F. (1935), *Z. Physik* **96**, 431. [2-1d]

Wheatley, J. C. (1966), in *Quantum Fluids*, p. 183, ed. D. F. Brewer, North-Holland, Amsterdam. [2-5b]

Wheeler, J. A. (1955), in *Niels Bohr and the Development of Physics*, ed. W. Pauli, Pergamon Press, London. [2-3a, 2-3 Ex]

Wheeler, J. A. (1964), in *Gravitation and Relativity*, Chap. 10, eds. H.-Y. Chiu and W. F. Hoffmann, Benjamin, New York, N.Y. [2-3 Ex]

Wigner, E. P. (1937), *Phys. Rev.* **51**, 106. [1-3a]

Wigner, E. P. (1939), *Phys. Rev.* **56**, 519. [3-4a]

Wigner, E. P. (1958), *Ann. Math.* **67**, 325; see also *ibid.* **62**, 548 (1955) and **65**, 203 (1957). [2C-1]

Wigner, E. P. (1959), *Group Theory and its Applications to the Quantum Mechanics of Atomic Spectra*, Academic Press, New York, N.Y.

Wilets, L., Hill, D. L., and Ford, K. W. (1953), *Phys. Rev.* **91**, 1488. [3C-3]

Wilkinson, D. H., and Mafethe, M. E. (1966), *Nuclear Phys.* **85**, 97. [1-3 Ex]

Wilmore, D., and Hodgson, P. E. (1964), *Nuclear Phys.* **55**, 673. [2-4c]

Wilson, R. (1963), *The Nucleon-Nucleon Interaction*, Wiley (Interscience), New York, N.Y.

Winner, D. R., and Drisko, R. M. (1965), *Techn. Rep., Univ. of Pittsburgh*, Sarah Mellon Scaife Rad. Lab., Pittsburgh, Pa. [Fig. 2-29]

Winther, A. (1962), *On the Theory of Nuclear Beta-Decay*, Munksgaard, Copenhagen. [3D-3]

Witsch, von W., Richter, A., and von Brentano, P. (1967), *Phys. Rev. Letters* **19**, 524. [1-2 Ex]

Wood, R. W., Borchers, R. R., and Barschall, H. H. (1965), *Nuclear Phys.* **71**, 529. [2-1 Ex]

Wu, C. S. (1964), *Rev. Mod. Phys.* **36**, 618. [3D-Ex]

Wu, C. S. (1967), in *Proc. Intern. Nuclear Physics Conf.*, Gatlinburg, p. 409, ed.-in-chief R. L. Becker, Academic Press, New York, N.Y. [2-1 Ex, 3C-3]

Wu, C. S. (1968), in *Proc. Intern. Symposium on the Physics of One or Two Electron Atoms*, Arnold Sommerfeld Centennial Memorial Meeting (to be published). [2-1 Ex]

Wu, C. S., and Moszkowski, S. A. (1966), *Beta Decay*, Wiley (Interscience), New York, N.Y.

Wu, C. S., Ambler, E. Hayward, R. W., Hoppes, D. D., and Hudson, R. F. (1957), *Phys. Rev.* **105**, 1413. [1-2b, 1-2 Ex]

Wyatt, P. J., Wills, J. G., and Green, A. E. S. (1960), *Phys. Rev.* **119**, 1031. [2-4c, 2-4 Ex]

Yamanouchi, T. (1937), *Proc. Phys.-Math. Soc. Japan* **19**, 436. [1C-1c]

Yennie, D. R., Ravenhall, D. G., and Wilson, R. N. (1954), *Phys. Rev.* **95**, 500. [Fig. 2-1]

Youngblood, D. H., Aldridge, J. P., and Class, C. M. (1965), *Phys. Letters* **18**, 291. [Table 3-2]

Yule, H. P. (1967), *Nuclear Phys.* **A94**, 442. [Table 3-4]

Zeldes, N., Grill, A., and Simievic, A. (1967), *Mat. Fys. Skr. Dan. Vid. Selsk.* **3**, no. 5. [2-1d, 2-1 Ex, Fig. 2-5]

Zweig, A. (1964), *CERN Reports TH-401* and *TH-412*, CERN, Geneva; see also *Proc. Intern. School of Physics "Ettore Majorana"*, ed. A. Zichichi, Academic Press, New York, N.Y. (1965). [1-3b]

Zyryanova, L. N. (1963), *Once-Forbidden Beta-Transitions*, Pergamon Press, New York, N.Y.

INDEX

References to individual nuclei are collected at the end of the index

NUCLEI